The Catholic Directory for Scotland

THE REDEEMER

The

Catholic Directory
for Scotland
2000

Year of the Great Jubilee

172ND ANNUAL PUBLICATION

BY AUTHORITY OF THE ARCHBISHOPS AND
BISHOPS OF SCOTLAND

GLASGOW: JOHN S. BURNS & SONS

First Published 1829

Published by the Editor from the College Press at Aquhorties, 1829, and from the College Press at Blairs, 1830; and subsequently from Edinburgh, 1831-1834; Dundee, 1835-1848; Aberdeen, 1849-1859; Edinburgh, 1860-1890; and Aberdeen, 1890-1905.

Published by Sands & Co., Edinburgh and Glasgow, 1906-1936

First Published by John S. Burns and Sons, Glasgow, 1937

© John S. Burns and Sons, 2000

ISBN 0 946356 94 7

ISSN 0306-5677

PRINTED IN SCOTLAND BY
JOHN S. BURNS & SONS
25 FINLAS STREET, GLASGOW G22 5DS

CONTENTS

The Clergy of Scotland

Notes

Postal addresses: Users of the *Directory* are reminded that in Scotland the names of the historic counties no longer form part of postal addresses. It is to be noted also that the names of the local authority areas are not part of postal addresses unless they are the names of post towns. In Dumfries and Galloway, however, and in Highland it has been felt appropriate in some cases, because of the very size of the local authority areas, to give a closer indication of the locations in which the parishes are to be found. In this issue, a start has been made in following the recommendation of the Royal Mail that the names of post towns should be shown in capital letters.

Vigil-Mass — this term donates a Mass fulfilling the Sunday or Holy Day obligation and celebrated the previous evening. All other Sunday or Holy Day Mass times are for the day itself.

⚕	—the church/chapel has a loop aerial for hearing aid users.
♿	—the church/chapel has easy access for wheel-chair users.
Ⓐ	—the church/chapel has easy access for wheel-chair users and adapted toilet facilities for disabled people.

Catholic Schools. The printing without brackets of the name of a local authority school in a parish entry indicates that the school is situated within the parish. The printing of the name of a local authority primary school within brackets indicates that the parish, at least in part, falls within the official catchment area of the school even though the school is situated outwith the parish.

Statistics. For a few years, the statistics of the various parishes in the country were presented in a more comprehensive manner. Unfortunately, it appeared that this was not as acceptable as had been hoped. Specifically it had not been realised by many that the figures for the estimated Catholic populations of the parishes were being included in the general table of statistics instead of with each parish as had been the practice up till then. It was therefore decided for last year to return to a more traditional manner of publishing the statistics. In particular the figures for the estimated Catholic populations were returned to the individual parish entries, where they will be found after the published details of the Masses and other Services, and before other information concerning the particular parish. In cases where no up-to-date figure has been provided the most recent figure available has been printed, identified as such by the printing of an asterisk (*).

INDEX OF PLACES

* In Cities and large towns with districts identifiable by name (however arrived at), the parishes are generally listed alphabetically both by their dedication and by the district in which they are situated.

LITURGICAL CALENDAR
FOR 2000
YEAR OF THE GREAT JUBILEE

DECEMBER 1999

24 Friday	Christmas Eve. Opening of the Great Jubilee.
25 SATURDAY	*CHRISTMAS DAY. Holy Day of Obligation.*
26 SUNDAY	*THE HOLY FAMILY.*
27 Monday	St. John, Apostle and Evangelist.
28 Tuesday	The Holy Innocents, MM.
29 Wednesday	Of the Octave of Christmas, optional collect of St. Thomas Becket, B.M.
30 Thursday	Of the Octave of Christmas.
31 Friday	Of the Octave of Christmas, optional collect of St. Silvester I, Pope.

JANUARY 2000

1	Saturday	Octave Day of Christmas. Solemnity of Mary, Mother of God.
2	**SUNDAY**	*THE EPIPHANY.*
3	Monday	Weekday.
4	Tuesday	Weekday.
5	Wednesday	Weekday.
6	Thursday	Weekday.
7	Friday	Weekday. or St. Raymond of Peñafort, Pr.
8	Saturday	Weekday. (Aberdeen: Weekday or St. Nathalan, B.)
9	**SUNDAY**	*THE BAPTISM OF OUR LORD.*
10	Monday	Weekday (First week "of the year").
11	Tuesday	Weekday
12	Wednesday	Weekday.
13	Thursday	St. Kentigern, B.
14	Friday	Weekday.
15	Saturday	Weekday, or Our Lady
16	**SUNDAY**	*SECOND SUNDAY "OF THE YEAR".*
17	Monday	St. Antony, Ab.
18	Tuesday	Weekday.
19	Wednesday	Weekday. (Dunkeld: St. Faolan, B.)
20	Thursday	Weekday, or St. Fabian, Pope, M., or St.Sebastian, M.
21	Friday	St. Agnes, Virg., M.
22	Saturday	Weekday, or St. Vincent, Deacon, M., or Our Lady.
23	**SUNDAY**	*THIRD SUNDAY "OF THE YEAR".*
24	Monday	St. Francis de Sales, B.D.
25	Tuesday	The Conversion of St. Paul, Apostle
26	Wednesday	SS. Timothy and Titus, BB.
27	Thursday	Weekday, or St. Angela Merici, Virg.
28	Friday	St. Thomas Aquinas, Pr.D.
29	Saturday	Weekday, or Our Lady.
30	**SUNDAY**	*FOURTH SUNDAY "OF THE YEAR".*
31	Monday	St. John Bosco, Pr.

FEBRUARY

1	Tuesday	Weekday.
2	Wednesday	The Presention of Our Lord. Blessing and Procession of the Candles.
3	Thursday	Weekday, or St. Blaise, B.M., or St. Ansgar, B.
4	Friday	Weekday.
5	Saturday	St. Agatha, Virg., M.

6	**SUNDAY**	***FIFTH SUNDAY "OF THE YEAR".***
7	Monday	Weekday.
8	Tuesday	Weekday, or St. Jerome Emilian, Pr.
9	Wednesday	Weekday.
10	Thursday	St. Scholastica, Virg.,
11	Friday	Weekday, or Our Lady of Lourdes.
12	Saturday	Weekday, or Our Lady.

13	**SUNDAY**	***SIXTH SUNDAY "OF THE YEAR".***
14	Monday	SS. Cyril, monk, and Methodius, B., Co-Patrons of Europe.
15	Tuesday	Weekday
16	Wednesday	Weekday.
17	Thursday	Weekday, or the Seven Holy Founders of the Servite Order. (Argyll and The Isles: St. Finan, B.)
18	Friday	Weekday. (Argyll and The Isles: St. Colman, B.)
19	Saturday	Weekday, or Our Lady.

20	**SUNDAY**	***SEVENTH SUNDAY "OF THE YEAR".***
21	Monday	Weekday, or St. Peter Damian, B.D.
22	Tuesday	The Chair of St. Peter, Apostle.
23	Wednesday	St. Polycarp, B.M.
24	Thursday	Weekday.
25	Friday	Weekday.
26	Saturday	Weekday, or Our Lady. (Dunkeld: Anniversary of the Episcopal Ordination of Bishop Vincent Logan, 1981).

27	**SUNDAY**	***EIGHTH SUNDAY "OF THE YEAR".***
28	Monday	Weekday..
29	Tuesday	Weekday.

MARCH

1	Wednesday	Weekday.
2	Thursday	Weekday.
3	Friday	Weekday.
4	Saturday	Weekday, or St. Casimir, or Our Lady.

5	**SUNDAY**	***NINTH SUNDAY "OF THE YEAR'.***
		(Galloway: Anniversary of the death of Bishop Joseph McGee, 1983)
6	Monday	Weekday.
7	Tuesday	SS. Perpetua and Felicity, MM.
8	Wednesday	Ash Wednesday. ***Fast and Abstinence.*** ***Easter Duty Period begins.***
9	Thursday	Weekday, optional collect of St. Frances of Rome, religious.
10	Friday	St. John Ogilvie, Pr.M.
11	Saturday	Weekday. (Argyll and The Isles: optional collect of St. Constantine, M.).

12	**SUNDAY**	***FIRST SUNDAY IN LENT.***
13	Monday	Weekday.
14	Tuesday	Weekday.
15	Wednesday	Weekday.
16	Thursday	Weekday.
17	Friday	St. Patrick, B.
18	Saturday	Weekday, optional collect of St. Cyril of Jerusalem, B.D.

19	**SUNDAY**	***SECOND SUNDAY IN LENT.***
20	Monday	St. Joseph, Husband of Our Lady (from 19th).
21	Tuesday	Weekday.
22	Wednesday	Weekday.
23	Thursday	Weekday, optional collect of St. Turibius of Mogrovejo, B.
24	Friday	Weekday. (Argyll and The Isles: Anniversary of the death of Bishop Colin MacPherson, 1990)
25	Saturday	The Annunciation of Our Lord. (Glasgow: Anniversary of the death of Archbishop James Donald Scanlan, 1976).

26	**SUNDAY**	***THIRD SUNDAY IN LENT.***
27	Monday	Weekday.
28	Tuesday	Weekday.
29	Wednesday	Weekday. (Paisley: Anniversary of the death of Bishop James Black, 1968)
30	Thursday	Weekday.
31	Friday	Weekday.

APRIL

1	Saturday	Weekday. (Aberdeen: Optional collect of St. Gilbert, B.)

2	**SUNDAY**	*FOURTH SUNDAY IN LENT.*
3	Monday	Weekday.
4	Tuesday	Weekday, optional collect of St. Isidore, B.D.
5	Wednesday	Weekday, optional collect of St. Vincent Ferrer, Pr.
6	Thursday	Weekday.
7	Friday	Weekday, optional collect of St. John Baptist de la Salle, Pr..
8	Saturday	Weekday.

9	**SUNDAY**	*FIFTH SUNDAY IN LENT.*
10	Monday	Weekday.
11	Tuesday	Weekday, optional collect of St. Stanislaus, B.M.
12	Wednesday	Weekday.
13	Thursday	Weekday, optional collect of St. Martin I, Pope, M.
14	Friday	Weekday.
15	Saturday	Weekday.

16	**SUNDAY**	*PALM SUNDAY. Blessing and Procession of Palms.*
17	Monday	Monday in Holy Week.
18	Tuesday	Tuesday in Holy Week.
19	Wednesday	Wednesday in Holy Week.
20	Thursday	Maundy Thursday. Easter Triduum begins with Evening Mass of the Lord's Supper. Watching at the Place of Repose.
21	Friday	Good Friday. Afternoon Liturgy of the Passion. *Fast and Abstinence.*
22	Saturday	Holy Saturday. Vigil Mass of Easter after nightfall.

23	**SUNDAY**	*EASTER SUNDAY.*
24	Monday	Easter Monday.
25	Tuesday	Easter Tuesday.
26	Wednesday	Easter Wednesday.
27	Thursday	Easter Thursday
28	Friday	Easter Friday*
29	Saturday	Easter Saturday.

30	**SUNDAY**	*SECOND SUNDAY OF EASTER ("LOW SUNDAY").*

*St. Catherine of Siena has now been proclaimed a Co-Patroness of Europe. Her Feast cannot be celebrated this year since the date falls in Easter Week.

MAY

1	Monday	Weekday, or St. Joseph the Worker. (St. Andrews and Edinburgh:Cathedral: Dedication of the Church, from 18th April.) (Glasgow: Cathedral: Dedication of the Church, from 28th April).
2	Tuesday	St. Athanasius, B.D.
3	Wednesday	SS. Philip and James, Apostles. (Aberdeen: Anniversary of the Episcopal Ordination of Bishop Mario J. Conti, 1977).
4	Thursday	Weekday.
5	Friday	Weekday.
6	Saturday	Weekday.

7	**SUNDAY**	***THIRD SUNDAY OF EASTER.***
8	Monday	Weekday.
9	Tuesday	Weekday.
10	Wednesday	Weekday.
11	Thursday	Weekday.
12	Friday	Weekday, or SS. Nereus and Achilleus, MM., or St. Pancras, M.
13	Saturday	Weekday.

14	**SUNDAY**	***FOURTH SUNDAY OF EASTER.***
		(Paisley: Anniversary of the Episcopal Ordination of Bishop John Aloysius Mone, 1984).
15	Monday	Weekday.
16	Tuesday	Weekday.
17	Wednesday	Weekday.
18	Thursday	Weekday, or St. John I, Pope, M.
19	Friday	Weekday.
20	Saturday	Weekday, or St. Bernardine of Siena, Pr.

21	**SUNDAY**	***FIFTH SUNDAY OF EASTER.***
22	Monday	Weekday.
23	Tuesday	Weekday.
24	Wednesday	Weekday.
25	Thursday	Weekday, or St. Bede the Venerable, Pr.D., or St Gregory VII, Pope, or St. Mary Magdalene dei Pazzi, Virg.
26	Friday	St. Philip Neri, Pr.
27	Saturday	Weekday, or St. Augustine of Canterbury, B.

28	**SUNDAY**	***SIXTH SUNDAY OF EASTER.***
29	Monday	Weekday. (Aberdeen: Anniversary of the death of Bishop Michael Foylan, 1976).
30	Tuesday	Weekday.
31	Wednesday	The Visitation of our Lady. (Motherwell: Anniversary of the Episcopal Ordination of Bishop Joseph Devine, 1977).

JUNE

1	**THURSDAY**	*THE ASCENSION OF OUR LORD. Holy Day of Obligation.*
2	Friday	Weekday or SS. Marcellinus and Peter, MM.
3	Saturday	SS. Charles Lwanga and Companions, MM.

4	**SUNDAY**	*SEVENTH SUNDAY OF EASTER.*
5	Monday	St. Boniface, B.M.
6	Tuesday	Weekday, or St. Norbert, B.
7	Wednesday	Weekday.
8	Thursday	Weekday.
9	Friday	St. Columba, Ab. (Galloway: Anniversary of the Episcopal Ordination of Bishop Maurice Taylor, 1981).
10	Saturday	Weekday.

11	**SUNDAY**	*PENTECOST or WHITSUNDAY.*
12	Monday	Weekday (Tenth week "of the year").
13	Tuesday	St. Anthony of Padua, Pr.D.
14	Wednesday	Weekday.
15	Thursday	Weekday.
16	Friday	Weekday.
17	Saturday	Weekday, or Our Lady.

18	**SUNDAY**	*TRINITY SUNDAY, Easter Duty Period ends.*
19	Monday	Weekday (Eleventh week "of the year"), or St. Romuald, Ab..
20	Tuesday	Weekday.
21	Wednesday	St. Aloysius, Gonzaga, religious.
22	Thursday	Weekday, or St. Paulinus of Nola, B., or SS. John Fisher, B., and Thomas More, MM.
23	Friday	Weekday.
24	Saturday	The Birthday of St. John the Baptist.

25	**SUNDAY**	*CORPUS CHRISTI.*
26	Monday	Weekday (Twelfth week "of the year").
27	Tuesday	Weekday, or St. Cyril of Alexandria, B.D.
28	Wednesday	St. Irenaeus, B.M.
29	**THURSDAY**	*SS. PETER and PAUL, Apostles. Holy Day of Obligation.*
30	Friday	The Sacred Heart of Jesus.

JULY

1	Saturday	The Immaculate Heart of Mary.

2	**SUNDAY**	***THIRTEENTH SUNDAY "OF THE YEAR".***
3	Monday	St. Thomas, Apostle.
4	Tuesday	Weekday, or St. Elizabeth of Portugal.
5	Wednesday	Weekday, or St. Antony Mary Zaccaria, Pr.
6	Thursday	Weekday, or St. Maria Goretti, Virg., M.
7	Friday	Weekday.
8	Saturday	Weekday, or Our Lady.

9	**SUNDAY**	***FOURTEENTH SUNDAY "OF THE YEAR".***
		(Aberdeen City, Our Lady of Aberdeen).
10	Monday	Weekday.
11	Tuesday	St. Benedict, Ab., Patron of Europe.
12	Wednesday	Weekday.
		(Aberdeen, Argyll and The Isles, St. Drostan, Ab.)
13	Thursday	Weekday, or St. Henry.
14	Friday	Weekday, or St. Camillus de Lellis, Pr.
15	Saturday	St Bonaventure, B.D.

16	**SUNDAY**	***FIFTEENTH SUNDAY "OF THE YEAR".***
17	Monday	Weekday.
18	Tuesday	Weekday.
19	Wednesday	Weekday.
		(St. Andrews and Edinburgh: Anniversary of the death of Cardinal Gordon Joseph Gray, 1993.)
20	Thursday	Weekday.
21	Friday	Weekday, or St. Laurence of Brindisi, Pr.D.
22	Saturday	St. Mary Magdalene.

23	**SUNDAY**	***SIXTEENTH SUNDAY "OF THE YEAR".****
24	Monday	Weekday.
25	Tuesday	St. James, Apostle.
26	Wednesday	SS. Joachim and Anne, Parents of Our Lady.
27	Thursday	Weekday.
28	Friday	Weekday.
29	Saturday	St. Martha.

30	**SUNDAY**	***SEVENTEENTH SUNDAY "OF THE YEAR".***
31	Monday	St. Ignatius Loyola, Pr.

*St. Bridget of Sweden has now been proclaimed a Co-Patroness of Europe. Her Feast cannot be celebrated this year, since the date falls on a Sunday.

AUGUST

1	Tuesday	St. Alphonsus Liguori, B.D.
2	Wednesday	Weekday, or St. Eusebius of Vercelli, B., or St. Peter Julian Eynard, Pr.
3	Thursday	Weekday.
4	Friday	St. John Vianney, Pr.
5	Saturday	Weekday, or Dedication of the Basilica of St. Mary Major. (St. Andrews and Edinburgh: Anniversary of the Episcopal Ordination of Archbishop Keith Patrick O'Brien, 1985).

6	**SUNDAY**	***THE TRANSFIGURATION OF OUR LORD.*** (Anniversary of the death of Pope Paul VI, 1978.)
7	Monday	Weekday (Eighteenth week "of the year"), or SS. Sixtus II, Pope, and Companions, MM. or St. Cajetan, Pr.
8	Tuesday	St. Dominic, Pr.
9	Wednesday	St. Teresa Benedicta of the Cross, Virg., M., Co-Patroness of Europe. (Argyll and The Isles: St. Oswald, M.)
10	Thursday	St. Laurence, deacon, M.
11	Friday	St. Clare, Virg.
12	Saturday	Weekday, or Our Lady. (Argyll and The Isles, Dunkeld: St. Blaan, B.)

13	**SUNDAY**	***NINETEENTH SUNDAY "OF THE YEAR".***
14	Monday	St. Maximilian Kolbe, Pr.M.
15	**TUESDAY**	***THE ASSUMPTION OF OUR LADY.*** *Holy Day of Obligation..*
16	Wednesday	Weekday, or St. Stephen of Hungary.
17	Thursday	Weekday.
18	Friday	Weekday.
19	Saturday	Weekday, or St. John Eudes, Pr., or Our Lady

20	**SUNDAY**	***TWENTIETH SUNDAY "OF THE YEAR".***
21	Monday	St. Pius X, Pope.
22	Tuesday	Our Lady the Queen.
23	Wednesday	Weekday, or St. Rose of Lima, Virg.
24	Thursday	St. Bartholomew, Apostle.
25	Friday	Weekday, or St. Louis, or St. Joseph of Calasanz, Pr.
26	Saturday	St. Ninian, B.

27	**SUNDAY**	***TWENTY-FIRST SUNDAY "OF THE YEAR".***
28	Monday	St. Augustine, B.D.
29	Tuesday	The Martyrdom of St. John the Baptist.
30	Wednesday	Weekday.
31	Thursday	Weekday. (Argyll and The Isles: St. Aidan, B.)

SEPTEMBER

1	Friday	Weekday.
		(St. Andrews and Edinburgh: St. Giles, Ab.)
2	Saturday	Weekday, or Our Lady.

3	**SUNDAY**	***TWENTY-SECOND SUNDAY "OF THE YEAR".***
4	Monday	Weekday.
		(St. Andrews and Edinburgh: St. Cuthbert, B.)
5	Tuesday	Weekday.
6	Wednesday	Weekday.
7	Thursday	Weekday.
		(Glasgow: Dedication of the Church, in consecrated churches only.)
8	Friday	The Birthday of Our Lady.
9	Saturday	Weekday, or St. Peter Claver, Pr., or Our Lady.

10	**SUNDAY**	***TWENTY-THIRD SUNDAY "OF THE YEAR".***
11	Monday	Weekday.
12	Tuesday	Weckday.
13	Wednesday	St. John Chrysostom, B.D.
14	Thursday	The Exaltation of the Cross.
15	Friday.	Our Lady of Sorrows.
		(Paisley: St. Mirin, B.)
16	Saturday	SS. Cornelius, Pope, and Cyprian, B., MM.

17	**SUNDAY**	***TWENTY-FOURTH SUNDAY "OF THE YEAR".***
18	Monday	Weekday.
19	Tuesday	Weekday, or St. Januarius, B.M.
20	Wednesday	SS. Andrew Kim Taegon, Pr., Paul Chong Hasang and Companions, MM.
21	Thursday	St. Matthew, Apostle and Evangelist.
22	Friday	Weekday.
23	Saturday	Weekday, or Our Lady.
		(Argyll and The Isles: St. Adamnan, Ab.)

24	**SUNDAY**	***TWENTY-FIFTH SUNDAY "OF THE YEAR".***
25	Monday	Weekday.
26	Tuesday	Weekday, or SS. Cosmas and Damian, MM.
27	Wednesday	St. Vincent de Paul, Pr.
28	Thursday	Weekday, or St. Wenceslaus, M., or SS. Laurence Ruiz and Companions, MM.
		(Galloway: Dedication of the Cathedral).
		(Anniversary of the death of Pope John Paul I, 1978).
29	Friday	SS. Michael, Gabriel and Raphael, Archangels.
30	Saturday	St. Jerome, Pr.D.

OCTOBER

1	**SUNDAY**	***TWENTY-SIXTH SUNDAY "OF THE YEAR".***
2	Monday	The Holy Guardian Angels.
3	Tuesday	Weekday
4	Wednesday	St. Francis of Assisi.
5	Thursday	Weekday. (Aberdeen: Dedication of the Cathedral).
6	Friday	Weekday, or St. Bruno, Pr.
7	Saturday	Our Lady of the Rosary.

8	**SUNDAY**	***TWENTY-SEVENTH SUNDAY "OF THE YEAR".***
9	Monday	Weekday, or SS. Denis, B., and Companions, MM., or St. John Leonardi, Pr.
10	Tuesday	Weekday.
11	Wednesday	Weekday.
12	Thursday	Weekday. (Argyll and The Isles: St. Kenneth, Ab.)
13	Friday	Weekday.
14	Saturday	Weekday, or St. Callistus I, Pope, M., or Our Lady.

15	**SUNDAY**	***TWENTY-EIGHTH SUNDAY "OF THE YEAR".***
16	Monday	Weekday, or St. Hedwig, religious, or St. Margaret Mary Alacoque, Virg.
17	Tuesday	St. Ignatius of Antioch, B.M.
18	Wednesday	St. Luke, Evangelist. (Dunkeld: Anniversary of the death of Bishop William Andrew Hart, 1992).
19	Thursday	Weekday, or SS. John de Brébeuf, Pr., and Companions, MM., or St. Paul of the Cross, Pr.
20	Friday	Weekday.
21	Saturday	Weekday, or Our Lady

22	**SUNDAY**	***TWENTY-NINTH SUNDAY "OF THE YEAR".*** (Anniversary of the Solemn Installation of Pope John Paul II, 1978.)
23	Monday	Weekday, or St. John of Capestrano, Pr.
24	Tuesday	Weekday, or St. Antony Mary Claret, B.
25	Wednesday	Weekday.
26	Thursday	Weekday.
27	Friday	Weekday.
28	Saturday	SS. Simon and Jude, Apostles.

29	**SUNDAY**	***THIRTIETH SUNDAY "OF THE YEAR".***
30	Monday	Weekday.
31	Tuesday	Weekday.

NOVEMBER

1 WEDNESDAY *ALL SAINTS. Holy Day of Obligation.*
2 Thursday   All Souls.
3 Friday   Weekday or St. Martin de Porres, religious.
4 Saturday   St. Charles Borromeo, B.

5 SUNDAY   *THIRTY-FIRST SUNDAY "OF THE YEAR".*
6 Monday   Weekday.
7 Tuesday   Weekday.
8 Wednesday   Bl. John Duns Scotus, Pr.
9 Thursday   Dedication of the Lateran Basilica.
10 Friday   St. Leo the Great, Pope, D.
11 Saturday   St. Martin of Tours, B.

12 SUNDAY   *THIRTY-SECOND SUNDAY "OF THE YEAR".*
13 Monday   Weekday.
                 (Aberdeen: St. Machar, B.)
14 Tuesday   Weekday.
15 Wednesday   Weekday, or St. Albert the Great, B.D.
16 Thursday   St. Margaret, Queen, Patroness of Scotland.
17 Friday   St. Elizabeth of Hungary, religious.
18 Saturday   Weekday, or Dedication of the Basilicas of SS.
                 Peter and Paul, Apostles, or Our Lady.
                 (Aberdeen: or St. Fergus, B.)

19 SUNDAY   *THIRTY-THIRD SUNDAY "OF THE YEAR".*
20 Monday   Weekday.
21 Tuesday   The Presentation of Our Lady.
22 Wednesday   St. Cecilia, Virg., M.
23 Thursday   Weekday, or St. Clement I, Pope M., or St.
                 Columbanus, Ab.
24 Friday   SS. Andrew Dung-Lac, Pr. and Companions, MM.
25 Saturday   Weekday, or Our Lady.

26 SUNDAY   *CHRIST THE KING.*
27 Monday   Weekday (Thirty-fourth or last week "of the year").
                 (Dunkeld: St. Fergus, B.)
                 (Paisley: Dedication of the Cathedral.)
28 Tuesday   Weekday.
29 Wednesday   Weekday.
30 Thursday   St. Andrew, Apostle, Patron of Scotland.
                 (Glasgow: Anniversary of the Episcopal
                 Ordination of Cardinal Thomas Joseph Winning,
                 1971.)

DECEMBER

1	Friday	Weekday.
2	Saturday	Weekday, or Our Lady.

3	**SUNDAY**	***FIRST SUNDAY OF ADVENT.***
4	Monday	Weekday, or St. John of Damascus, Pr.D.
5	Tuesday	Weekday.
6	Wednesday	Weekday, or St. Nicholas, B. (Argyll and The Isles: Anniversary of the Episcopal Ordination of Bishop Ian Murray, 1999.) (Motherwell: Anniversary of the death of Bishop Francis Thomson, 1987)
7	Thursday	St. Ambrose, B.D.
8	Friday	The Immaculate Conception of Our Lady.
9	Saturday	Weekday.

10	**SUNDAY**	***SECOND SUNDAY OF ADVENT.***
11	Monday	Weekday, or St. Damasus 1, Pope.
12	Tuesday	Weekday, or St. Jane Frances de Chantal, religious.
13	Wednesday	St. Lucy, Virg., M.
14	Thursday	St. John of the Cross, Pr.D. (Motherwell: Dedication of the Cathedral.)
15	Friday	Weekday. (Motherwell: St. John of the Cross, Pr.D. from 14th.)
16	Saturday	Weekday.

17	**SUNDAY**	***THIRD SUNDAY OF ADVENT.***
18	Monday	Weekday.
19	Tuesday	Weekday.
20	Wednesday	Weekday.
21	Thursday	Weekday, optional collect of St. Peter Canisius, Pr.D.
22	Friday	Weekday.
23	Saturday	Weekday, optional collect of St. John of Kety, Pr.

24	**SUNDAY**	***FOURTH SUNDAY OF ADVENT.***
25	**MONDAY**	***CHRISTMAS DAY. Holy Day of Obligation.***
26	Tuesday	St. Stephen, the First Martyr.
27	Wednesday	St. John, Apostle and Evangelist.
28	Thursday	The Holy Innocents, MM.
29	Friday	Of the Octave of Christmas, optional collect of St. Thomas Becket, B.M.
30	Saturday	Of the Octave of Christmas.

31	**SUNDAY**	***THE HOLY FAMILY.*** Last day of the Twentieth Century AD. and of the Second Christian Millennium.

JANUARY 2001

1	Monday	Octave Day of Christmas. Solemnity of Mary, Mother of God.
		First day of the Twenty-first Century A.D. and of the Third Christian Millennium.
2	Tuesday	SS. Basil the Great and Gregory Nazianzen, B.D.
3	Wednesday	Weekday.
4	Thursday	Weekday.
5	Friday	Weekday.
6	Saturday	Weekday.
		Close of the Great Jubilee.
7	**SUNDAY**	***THE EPIPHANY.***
8	Monday	The Baptism of Our Lord.
9	Tuesday	Weekday (First week "of the year").
10	Wednesday	Weekday.
11	Thursday	Weekday
12	Friday	Weekday.
13	Saturday	St. Kentigern, B.
14	**SUNDAY**	***SECOND SUNDAY "OF THE YEAR".***
15	Monday	Weekday.
16	Tuesday	Weekday.
17	Wednesday	Weekday.
18	Thursday	Weekday.
19	Friday	Weekday.
		(Dunkeld: St. Faolan, B.)
20	Saturday	Weekday, or St. Fabian, Pope, M., or St.Sebastian, M.,or Our Lady.
21	**SUNDAY**	***THIRD SUNDAY "OF THE YEAR".***
22	Monday	Weekday, or St. Vincent, deacon, M.
23	Tuesday	Weekday.
24	Wednesday	St. Francis de Sales, B.D.
25	Thursday	The Conversion of St. Paul, Apostle
26	Friday	SS. Timothy and Titus, BB.
27	Saturday	Weekday, or St. Angela Merici, Virg. or Our Lady.
28	**SUNDAY**	***FOURTH SUNDAY "OF THE YEAR".***
29	Monday	Weekday.
30	Tuesday	Weekday.
31	Wednesday	St. John Bosco, Pr.

FEBRUARY

1	Thursday	Weekday.
2	Friday	The Presention of Our Lord.
		Blessing and Procession of the Candles.
3	Saturday	Weekday, or St. Blaise, B.M., or St. Ansgar, B.,or Our Lady.
4	**SUNDAY**	*FIFTH SUNDAY "OF THE YEAR".*
5	Monday	St. Agatha, Virg., M.
6	Tuesday	SS. Paul Miki and Companions, MM.
7	Wednesday	Weekday.
8	Thursday	Weekday, or St. Jerome Emilian, Pr.
9	Friday	Weekday.
10	Saturday	St. Scholastica, Virg.
11	**SUNDAY**	*SIXTH SUNDAY "OF THE YEAR".*
12	Monday	Weekday.
13	Tuesday	Weekday.
14	Wednesday	SS. Cyril, monk, and Methodius, B., Patrons of Europe.
15	Thursday	Weekday
16	Friday	Weekday.
17	Saturday	Weekday, or the Seven Holy Founders of the Servite Order, or Our Lady.
		(Argyll and The Isles: St. Finan, B.)
18	**SUNDAY**	*SEVENTH SUNDAY "OF THE YEAR".*
19	Monday	Weekday.
20	Tuesday	Weekday.
21	Wednesday	Weekday, or St. Peter Damian, B.D.
22	Thursday	The Chair of St. Peter, Apostle.
23	Friday	St. Polycarp, B.M.
24	Saturday	Weekday, or Our Lady.
25	**SUNDAY**	*EIGHTH SUNDAY "OF THE YEAR".*
26	Monday	Weekday.
		(Dunkeld: Anniversary of the Episcopal Ordination of Bishop Vincent Logan, 1981).
27	Tuesday	Weekday.
28	Wednesday	Ash Wednesday. *Fast and Abstinence.*
		Easter Duty Period begins.

THE POPE
AND THE
COLLEGE OF CARDINALS

HIS HOLINESS
POPE JOHN PAUL II
BISHOP OF ROME
VICAR OF JESUS CHRIST

SUCCESSOR OF ST. PETER, PRINCE OF THE APOSTLES,
SUPREME PONTIFF OF THE UNIVERSAL CHURCH,
PATRIARCH OF THE WEST, PRIMATE OF ITALY,
ARCHBISHOP AND METROPOLITAN OF THE ROMAN
PROVINCE,
SOVEREIGN OF THE TEMPORAL DOMINIONS OF
HOLY ROMAN CHURCH,
SERVANT OF THE SERVANTS OF GOD

His Holiness, Pope John Paul II (Karol Wojtyla) was born at
Wadowice, in the archdiocese of Cracow, on 18th May, 1920;
ordained priest on 1st November, 1946, ordained titular bishop of
Ombi on 28th September, 1958; promoted to the archbishopric of
Cracow on 13th January, 1964; created cardinal priest of the title
S. Cesareo in Palatio on 26th June, 1967; elected Pope on 16th
October, 1978; inaugurated on 22nd October, 1978.

THE COLLEGE OF CARDINALS

Cardinal Bishops and Patriarchs

Bernardin Gantin, Bishop of Ostia and Palestrina, created Cardinal in 1977.

Paolo Bertoli, Bishop of Frascati, created Cardinal in 1969.

Roger Etchegaray, Bishop of Porto and Santa Rufina, created Cardinal in 1979.

Josef Ratzinger, Bishop of Velletri, created Cardinal in 1977.

Angelo Sodano, Bishop of Albano, created Cardinal in 1991.

Lucas Moreira Neves, Bishop of Sabina and Poggio Mirteto, created Cardinal in 1988.

Nasrallah Pierre Sfeir, Patriarch of Antioch of the Maronites, created Cardinal in 1994.

Cardinal Priests

Franziskus Konig, created Cardinal in 1958.

Paul Zoungrana, created Cardinal in 1965.

Corrado Ursi, created Cardinal in 1967.

Silvio Oddi, Cardinal *in Curia*, created Cardinal in 1969.

Paul Gouyon, created Cardinal in 1969.

Stephen Kim Sou Hwan, created Cardinal in 1969.

Eugenio de Araujo Sales, Archbishop of Rio de Janeiro, created Cardinal in 1969.

Johann Willebrands, Cardinal *in Curia*, created Cardinal in 1969.

Pietro Palazzini, Cardinal *in Curia*, created Cardinal in 1973.

Luis Aponte Martinez, created Cardinal in 1973.

Raul Francisco Primatesta, created Cardinal in 1973.

Salvatore Pappalardo, created Cardinal in 1973.

Marcelo Gonzales Martin, created Cardinal in 1973.

Maurice Otunga, Archbishop of Nairobi, created Cardinal in 1973.

Paulo Evaristo Arns, created Cardinal in 1973.

Pio Taofinu'u, Archbishop of Samoa-Apia, created Cardinal in 1973.

Opilio Rossi, Cardinal *in Curia*, created Cardinal in 1976.

Giuseppe Maria Sensi, Cardinal *in Curia*, created Cardinal in 1976.

Juan Carlos Aramburu, created Cardinal in 1976.

Corrado Bafile, Cardinal *in Curia*, created Cardinal in 1976.

Hyacinthe Thiandoum, Archbishop of Dakar, created Cardinal in 1976.

Jaime Sin, Archbishop of Manila, created Cardinal in 1976.

William Wakefield Baum, Cardinal *in Curia*, created Cardinal in 1976.

Aloisio Lorscheider, Archbishop of Aparecida, created Cardinal in 1976.

Giuseppe Caprio, Cardinal *in Curia*, created Cardinal in 1979.

Marco Cè, Patriarch of Venice, created Cardinal in 1979.

Eghano Righi-Lambertini, Cardinal *in Curia*, created Cardinal in 1979.

Ernesto Corripio Ahumada, created Cardinal in 1979.

Gerald Emmett Carter, created Cardinal in 1979.

Franciszek Macharski, Archbishop of Cracow, created Cardinal in 1979.

Ignatius Gong Pin-Mei, Archbishop of Shanghai, created Cardinal in 1979.

Aurelio Sabattani, Cardinal *in Curia*, created Cardinal in 1983.

Franjo Kuharic, Archbishop of Zagreb, created Cardinal in 1983.

Giuseppe Casoria, Cardinal *in Curia*, created Cardinal in 1983.

Michael Michai Kitbunchu, Archbishop of Bangkok, created Cardinal in 1983.

Alexandre do Nascimento, Archbishop of Luanda, created Cardinal in 1983.

Alfonso Lopez Trujillo, Cardinal *in Curia*, created Cardinal in 1983.

Godfried Danneels, Archbishop of Malines-Bruxelles, created Cardinal in 1983.

Thomas Stafford Williams, Archbishop of Wellington, created Cardinal in 1983.

Carlo Maria Martini, Archbishop of Milan, created Cardinal in 1983.

Jean Marie Lustiger, Archbishop of Paris, created Cardinal in 1983.

Jozef Glemp, Archbishop of Gniezno and Warsaw, created Cardinal in 1983.

Joachim Meisner, Archbishop of Cologne, created Cardinal in 1983.

Simon Lourdusamy, Cardinal *in Curia*, created Cardinal in 1985.

Francis Arinze, Cardinal *in Curia*, created Cardinal in 1985.

Juan Francisco Fresno Larrain, created Cardinal in 1985.

Antonio Innocenti, Cardinal *in Curia*, Created Cardinal in 1985.

Miguel Obando Bravo, Archbishop of Managua, created Cardinal in 1985.

Augustin Mayer, Cardinal *in Curia*, created Cardinal in 1985.

Angel Suquia Goicoechea, created Cardinal in 1985.

Ricardo Vidal, Archbishop of Cebu, created Cardinal in 1985.

Henryk Roman Gulbinowicz, Archbishop of Wroclaw, created Cardinal in 1985.

Paulos Tzadua, Archbishop of Addis Ababa, created Cardinal in 1985.
Jozef Tomko, Cardinal *in Curia*, created Cardinal in 1985.
Myroslav Ivan Lubacvsky, Archbishop of Leopoli of the Ukrainians, created Cardinal in 1985.
Andrzej Maria Deskur, Cardinal *in Curia*, created Cardinal in 1985.
Paul Poupard, Cardinal *in Curia*, created Cardinal in 1985.
Albert Vachon, created Cardinal in 1985.
Rosalio Castillo Lara, created Cardinal in 1985.
Friedrich Wetter, Archbishop of Munich and Frisingen, created Cardinal in 1985.
Silvano Piovanelli, Archbishop of Florence, created Cardinal in 1985.
Adrianus Simonis, Archbishop of Utrecht, created Cardinal in 1985.
Edouard Gagnon, Cardinal *in Curia*, created Cardinal in 1985.
Alfons Stickler, Cardinal *in Curia*, created Cardinal in 1985.
Bernard Law, Archbishop of Boston, created Cardinal in 1985.
John O'Connor, Archbishop of New York, created Cardinal in 1985.
Giacomo Biffi, Archbishop of Bologna, created Cardinal in 1985.
Anthony Padiyara, Archbishop of Ernakulam, created Cardinal in 1988.
Jose Freire Falcao, Archbishop of Brasilia, created Cardinal in 1988.
Michele Giordano, Archbishop of Naples, created Cardinal in 1988.
Alexandre Jose Maria dos Santos, Archbishop of Maputo, created Cardinal in 1988.
Giovanni Canestri, created Cardinal in 1988.
Simon Ignatius Pimenta, created Cardinal in 1988.
Edward Bede Clancy, Archbishop of Sydney, created Cardinal in 1988.
James Aloysius Hickey, Archbishop of Washington, created Cardinal in 1988.
Edmund Casimir Szoka, Cardinal *in Curia*, created Cardinal in 1988.
Laszlo Paskai, Archbishop of Esztergom, created Cardinal in 1988.
Christian Wiyghan Tumi, Archbishop of Garoua, created Cardinal in 1988.
Hans Hermann Groer, created Cardinal in 1988.
Vincentas Sladkevicius, created Cardinal in 1988.
Jean Margeot, Bishop of Port-Louis, created Cardinal in 1988.
John Baptist Wu Cheng-Chung, Bishop of Hong-Kong, created Cardinal in 1988.
Eduardo Martinez Somalo, Cardinal *in Curia*, created Cardinal in 1988.
Achille Silvestrini, Cardinal *in Curia*, created Cardinal in 1988.
Angelo Felici, Cardinal *in Curia*, created Cardinal in 1988.
Antonio Maria Javierre Ortas, Cardinal *in Curia*, created Cardinal in 1988
Alexandru Todea, created Cardinal in 1991.
Frédéric Etsou-Nzabi-Bamungwabi, Archbishop of Kinshasa, created Cardinal in 1991.

Nicolas de Jesus Lopez Rodriguez, Archbishop of Santo Domingo, created Cardinal in 1991.

Roger Michael Mahony, Archbishop of Los Angeles, created Cardinal in 1991.

Anthony Joseph Bevilacqua, Archbishop of Philadelphia, created Cardinal in 1991.

Giovanni Saldarini, created Cardinal in 1991.

Cahal Brendan Daly, created Cardinal in 1991.

Camillo Ruini, Cardinal *in Curia*, created Cardinal in 1991.

Jan Chryzostom Korec, Bishop of Nitra, created Cardinal in 1991.

Henri Schwery, Bishop of Sion, created Cardinal in 1991.

Georg Maximilian Sterzinsky, Bishop of Berlin, created Cardinal in 1991.

Miloslav Vlk, Archbishop of Prague, created Cardinal in 1994.

Peter Seiichi Shirayanga, Archbishop of Tokyo, created Cardinal in 1994.

Thomas Joseph Winning, Archbishop of Glasgow, created Cardinal in 1994.

Adolfo Antonio Suarez Rivera, Archbishop of Monterrey, created Cardinal in 1994.

Jaime Lucas Ortega y Alamino, Archbishop of San Cristobal de Habana, created Cardinal in 1994.

Julius Ruyadi Darmaatmadja, Archbishop of Jakarta, created Cardinal in 1994.

Pierre Eyt, Archbishop of Bordeaux, created Cardinal in 1994.

Emmanuel Wamala, Archbishop of Kampala, created Cardinal in 1994.

William Henry Keeler, Archbishop of Baltimore, created Cardinal in 1994.

Augusto Vargas Alzamora, created Cardinal in 1994.

Jean-Claude Turcotte, Archbishop of Montreal, created Cardinal in 1994.

Ricardo Maria Carles Gordo, Archbishop of Barcelona, created Cardinal in 1994.

Adam Joseph Maida, Archbishop of Detroit, created Cardinal in 1994.

Vinko Puljic, Archbishop of Vrhbosna, Sarajevo, created Cardinal in 1994.

Armand Gaetan Razafindratandra, Archbishop of Antananarivo, created Cardinal in 1994.

Paul Joseph Pham Dinh Tung, Archbishop of Ha Nôi, created Cardinal in 1994.

Juan Sandoval Iniguez, Archbishop of Guadalajara, created Cardinal in 1994.

Bernardino Echeverria Ruiz, Archbishop Emeritus of Guayaquil and Apostolic Administrator of Ibarra, created Cardinal in 1994.

Kazimierz Swiatek, Archbishop of Minsk-Mohilev, created Cardinal in 1994.

Ersilio Tonini, Archbishop Emeritus of Ravenna-Cervia, created Cardinal in 1994.

Salvatore De Giorgi, Archbishop of Palermo, created Cardinal in 1998.

Serafim Fernandes de Araujo, Archbishop of Belo Horizonte, created Cardinal in 1998.

Antonio Maria Rouco Varela, Archbishop of Madrid, created Cardinal in 1998.

Aloysius Matthew Ambrozic, Archbishop of Toronto, created Cardinal in 1998.

Dionigi Tettamanzi, Archbishop of Genoa, created Cardinal in 1998.

Polycarp Pengo, Archbishop of Dar-es-Salaam, created Cardinal in 1998.

Christoph Schönborn, Archbishop of Vienna, created Cardinal in 1998.

Norberto Rivera Carrera, Archbishop of Mexico City, created Cardinal in 1998.

Francis Eugene George, Archbishop of Chicago, created Cardinal in 1998.

Paul Shan Kuo-Hsi, Archbishop of Kaohsiung, created Cardinal in 1998.

Adam Kozlowiecki, titular Archbishop of Potenza Picena, created Cardinal in 1998.

Cardinal Deacons

Pio Laghi, Cardinal *in Curia*, created Cardinal in 1991.

Edward Idris Cassidy, Cardinal *in Curia*, created Cardinal in 1991.

Jose Sanchez, Cardinal *in Curia*, created Cardinal in 1991.

Virgilio Noe, Cardinal *in Curia*, created Cardinal in 1991.

Fiorenzo Angelini, Cardinal *in Curia*, created Cardinal in 1991.

Luigi Poggi, Cardinal *in Curia*, created Cardinal in 1994.

Vincenzo Fagiolo, Cardinal *in Curia*, created Cardinal in 1994.

Carlo Furno, Cardinal *in Curia*, created Cardinal in 1994.

Jan Pieter Schotte, Cardinal *in Curia*, created Cardinal in 1994.

Gilberto Agustoni, Cardinal *in Curia*, created Cardinal in 1994.

Jorge Arturo Medina Estevez, Cardinal *in Curia*, created Cardinal in 1998.

Dario Castillón Hoyos, Cardinal *in Curia*, created Cardinal in 1998.

Lorenzo Antonetti, Cardinal *in Curia*, created Cardinal in 1998.

James Francis Stafford, Cardinal *in Curia*, created Cardinal in 1998.

Giovanni Cheli, Cardinal *in Curia*, created Cardinal in 1998.

Francesco Colasuonno, Cardinal *in Curia*, created Cardinal in 1998.

Dino Monduzzi, Cardinal *in Curia*, created Cardinal in 1998.

THE APOSTOLIC NUNCIATURE

Apostolic Delegation to Scotland, 1868-9, 1912-14; Apostolic Delegation to Great Britain, Malta, Gibraltar, and Bermuda, 21 November 1938; Apostolic Nunciature to Great Britain (and papal representation to Gibraltar), 17 January 1982.

His Excellency the Apostolic Nuncio
His Excellency Archbishop Pablo Puente

Born in Colindres (Spain) 16.6.1931

Studied at the Pontifical University of Comillas obtaining the Licence in Philosophy and Theology.

Ordained Priest 2.4.1956 for the Diocese of Santander

Studied Canon Law at the Pontifical Gregorian University obtaining the Doctorate

Entered the Diplomatic Service of the Holy See in 1962

Service in: Paraguay, Santo Domingo, Kenya and Tanzania; Secretariat of State 1969-1973, Lebanon, Yugoslavia.

Apostolic Nuncio in Indonesia 18 March 1980

Consecrated Titular Archbishop of Macri 25 May 1980

Apostolic Nuncio in Senegal, Mali, Cape Verde Islands, Mauritania and Guinea-Bissau 15 March 1986

Since 1989 Apostolic Nuncio in Lebanon, in Kuwait and Delegate to Arabian Peninsula

Apostolic Nuncio to Great Britain since 1997

Counsellor: Monsignor Jean-Marie Speich
Private Secretary: Mgr. Peter Grant
Address: 54 Parkside, LONDON SW19 5NE
Tel: 0181-946 1410; Fax: 0181-947 2494*
Telegraphic Address: (Overseas) Nuntius, London SW19

Apostolic Delegates:
Archbishop (later Cardinal) William Godfrey (1938-1954)
Archbishop Gerald Patrick O'Hara (1954-1963)
Archbisop Hyginus Cardinale (1963-1969)
Archbisop Domenico Enrici (1969-1973)
Archbishop Bruno Bernard Heim (1973-1982)

Apostolic Nuncios
Archbishop Bruno Bernard Heim (1982-1985)
Archbishop Luigi Barbarito (1986-1997)

*From Easter Sunday, the dialling code will be 020-8

THE CHURCH IN SCOTLAND

THE HIERARCHY OF SCOTLAND

I
FROM THE EXTINCTION OF THE HIERARCHY
IN 1603 TO ITS RESTORATION IN 1878

The ancient hierarchy ended with the death of James Beaton, archbishop of Glasgow, at Paris on 24th April, 1603, aged 86.
On 13th October 1653 a Prefecture Apostolic for Scotland was established by the Congregation de Propaganda Fide.

PREFECTS APOSTOLIC
1. WILLIAM BALLANTINE: born 1618; convert from presbyterianism; priest, Rome, 3rd December 1645; prefect, 13th October 1653; died Elgin, 2nd September 1661.

2. ALEXANDER WINCHESTER: born Garmouth, Moray, c. 1625; priest, Rome, 21st May 1656; prefect, 12th June 1662; resigned July 1697; died Banff, 14th January 1708.

THE VICARS APOSTOLIC OF SCOTLAND
I: 1694-1727
On 16th March 1694 a Vicariate Apostolic for Scotland was established under a titular bishop.
1. **Thomas Nicolson:** born at Birkenbog, Banffshire, c. 1645; convert from episcopalianism; priest, Padua, 9th March 1686; nominated titular bishop of Peristasis, 7th September 1694, and consecrated at Paris, 27th February 1695; died Preshome, 12th October 1718.

This list has been compiled from James Darragh: *The Catholic Hierarchy of Scotland — a biographical list, 1653-1985* (Glasgow: John S. Burns, 1986); and the history of the mediaeval dioceses from D.E.R. Watt: *Fasti ecclesiae Scoticanae medii aevi ad annum 1638* (Scottish Record Society, n.s. 1, 1969) and Ian B. Cowan and David E. Easson: *Medieval religious houses — Scotland* (2nd edn. 1976).

2. **James Gordon:** born Glastirum, Enzie, Banffshire, 31st January 1665; priest, Paris [?1692]; nominated titular bishop of Nicopolis and coadjutor vicar apostolic, 21st August 1705, and consecrated at Montefiascone, Italy, 11th April 1706; succeeded 12th October 1718; translated to Lowland District, 23rd July 1727.

3. **John Wallace:** baptised Arbroath, 8th April 1654; convert from episcopalianism; priest, Preshome, 3rd April 1708; nominated titular bishop of Cyrrhus and coadjutor vicar apostolic, 30th April 1720, and consecrated at Edinburgh, 21st September 1720; died Edinburgh, 30th June 1733.

II: 1727-1827

On 23rd July 1727 Scotland was divided into two vicariates, the Lowland and Highland Districts.

Lowland District

James Gordon, translated 23rd July 1727; died Thornhill, Perthshire, 18th February 1746.

4. **Alexander Smith:** born Fochabers, Moray, "about Peter's Day", 1684; priest, Preshome, 19th April 1712; nominated titular bishop of Mosynopolis and coadjutor vicar apostolic, 19th September 1735, and consecrated at Edinburgh, 2nd November 1735; succeeded, 18th February 1746; died Edinburgh, 21st August 1767.

5. **James Grant:** born Wester Boggs, Enzie, Banffshire, July 1706; priest, Rome, 4th April 1733; nominated titular bishop of Sinitis and coadjutor vicar apostolic, 21st February 1755, and consecrated at Edinburgh, 13th November 1755; succeeded, 21st August 1767; died Aberdeen, 3rd December 1778.

6. **George Hay:** born Edinburgh, 24th August 1729; convert from episcopalianism; priest, Rome, 2nd April 1758; nominated titular bishop of Daulia and coadjutor vicar apostolic, 5th October 1768, and consecrated at Scalan, 21st May 1769; succeeded, 3rd December 1778; resigned, 24th August 1805; died Aquhorties, 15th October 1811

7. **John Geddes:** born Mains of Corridoun, Enzie, Banffshire, 29th August 1735; priest, Rome, 18th March 1759; nominated titular bishop of Marocco and coadjutor vicar apostolic, 30th September 1779, and consecrated at Madrid, 30th November 1780; retired, on grounds of ill-health, 26th October 1793; died Aberdeen, 11th February 1799.

8. **Alexander Cameron:** born Braemar, Aberdeenshire, 28th July 1747; priest, Rome, 2nd February 1772; nominated titular bishop of Maximianopolis in Palaestina and coadjutor vicar apostolic, 19th September 1797, and consecrated at Madrid, 28th October 1798; succeeded, 24th August 1805; resigned, 20th August 1825; died Edinburgh, 7th February 1828.

9. **Alexander Paterson:** born at Pathhead, Enzie, Banffshire, March 1766; priest, Douai, France [?1791]; nominated titular bishop of Cybistra and coadjutor vicar apostolic, 14th May 1816, and consecrated at Paisley, 18th August 1816; succeeded, 20th August 1825; translated to Eastern District, 13th February 1827.

Highland District

Alexander John Grant was nominated titular bishop of Sura, 16th September 1727, and first vicar apostolic, Highland District, 19th September 1727, but died before consecration.

10. **Hugh MacDonald:** born Morar, Inverness-shire, 2nd February 1699; priest, Scalan, 18th September 1725; nominated titular bishop of Diana and vicar apostolic, Highland District, 12th February 1731, and consecrated at Edinburgh, 18th October 1731; died in Glen Garry, 12th March 1773.

11. **John MacDonald:** born Ardnamurchan, Argyllshire, 1727; priest, Rome, 1st April 1752; nominated titular bishop of Tiberiopolis and coadjutor vicar apostolic, 25th February 1761, and consecrated at Preshome, 27th September 1761; succeeded, 12th March 1773; died Knoydart, 9th May 1779.

12. **Alexander MacDonald:** born Bornish, South Uist, 1736; priest, Rome, 10th August 1764; nominated titular bishop of Polemonium and vicar apostolic, 30th September 1779, and consecrated at Scalan, 12th March 1780; died Samalaman, 9th September 1791.

13. **John Chisholm:** born in Strath Glass, Inverness-shire, September 1752; priest, Douai, France, April 1777; nominated titular bishop of Oreus and vicar apostolic, 8th November 1791, and consecrated at Edinburgh, 12th February 1792; died on Lismore, 8th July 1814.

14. **Aeneas Chisholm:** born in Strath Glass, Inverness-shire, 1759; priest, [? Valladolid], 1783; nominated titular bishop of Diocaesarea and coadjutor vicar apostolic, 11th May 1804, and consecrated on Lismore, 15th September 1805; succeeded, 8th July 1814; died on Lismore, 31st July 1818.

15. **Ranald MacDonald:** born at Edinburgh, 1756; priest, Douai, France [?1780]; nominated titular bishop of Arindela and vicar apostolic, 27th August 1819, and consecrated at Edinburgh, 25th February 1820; translated to Western District, 13th February 1827.

III: 1827-1878
On 13th February 1827 Scotland was divided into three Vicariates, the Eastern, the Western and the Northern.

Eastern District
Alexander Paterson, translated 13th February 1827; died Dundee, 30th October 1831.

Andrew Scott, coadjutor vicar apostolic, Western District, apostolic administrator, 24th December 1831.

16. **Andrew Carruthers:** born Drumillan Miln, New Abbey, Kirkcudbrightshire, baptised 8th February 1770; priest, Aberdeen, 25th March 1795; nominated titular bishop of Ceramus and vicar apostolic, 28th September 1832, and consecrated at Edinburgh, 13th January 1833; died Dundee, 24th May 1852.
17. **James Gillis:** born Montreal, Canada, 7th April 1802; priest, Aquhorties, 9th June 1827; nominated titular bishop of Limyra and coadjutor vicar apostolic, 28th July 1837, and consecrated at Edinburgh, 22nd July 1838; succeeded, 24th May 1852; died Edinburgh, 24th February 1864.
18. **John Menzies Strain:** born Edinburgh, 8th December 1810; priest, Rome, 9th June 1833; nominated titular bishop of Abila Lysaniae and vicar apostolic, 2nd September 1864, and consecrated at Rome, 25th September 1864; translated to archdiocese of St. Andrews and Edinburgh, 15th March 1878.

Western District

Ranald MacDonald: translated 13th February 1827; died Fort William, 20th September 1832.
19. **Andrew Scott:** born Chapelford, Enzie, Banffshire, 15th February 1772; priest, Aberdeen, 25th March 1795; nominated titular bishop of Erythrae and coadjutor vicar apostolic, 13th February 1827, and consecrated at Glasgow, 21st September 1828; succeeded, 20th September 1832; resigned, 15th October 1845; died Greenock, 4th December 1846.

20. **John Murdoch:** born Wellsheads, Enzie, Banffshire, baptised 9th October 1796, priest, [?Valladolid], 19th March 1821; nominated titular bishop of Castabala and coadjutor vicar apostolic, 4th June 1833, and consecrated at Glasgow, 20th October 1833; succeeded, 15th October 1845; died Glasgow, 15th December 1865.

21. ALEXANDER SMITH: born Newbigging, Clochan, Banffshire, baptised 26th January 1813; priest, Glasgow, 2nd February 1836; nominated titular bishop of Paros and coadjutor vicar apostolic, 6th July 1847, and consecrated at Glasgow, 3rd October 1847; died Glasgow, 15th June 1861 without succeeding.

22. **John Gray:** born Buckie, Banffshire, 16th June 1817; priest, Rome, 1st May 1841; nominated titular bishop of Ipsus and coadjutor vicar apostolic, 6th May 1862, and consecrated at Glasgow, 19th October 1862; succeeded, 15th December 1865; resigned, 4th March 1869; died Rothesay, 14th January 1872.

23. JAMES LYNCH, C.M.: born Dublin, Ireland, baptised 23rd January 1807; priest, Maynooth, Ireland, 18th June 1833; nominated titular bishop of Arcadiopolis in Asia and coadjutor vicar apostolic 31st August 1866 and consecrated at Paris, 4th November 1866; translated to Kildare and Leighlin, Ireland, as coadjutor, 13th April 1869; succeeded, 5th March 1888; died Blackrock, Co. Dublin, 19th December 1896.

    George Errington (1804-1886), titular archbishop of Trabezus, elected apostolic delegate in Scotland, 27th January 1868, but declined appointment, 12th August 1868.

24. **Charles Petre Eyre:** born York, England, 7th November 1817; priest, Rome, 19th March 1842; nominated apostolic delegate in Scotland and titular archbishop of Anazarbus, 11th December 1868, and consecrated at Rome, 31st January 1869; apostolic administrator, Western District 16th April 1869; translated to archdiocese of Glasgow, 15th March 1878.

Northern District

25. **James Kyle:** born Edinburgh, 22nd September 1788; priest, Aquhorties, 21st March 1812; nominated titular bishop of Germanicia and vicar apostolic, 13th February 1827, and consecrated at Aberdeen, 28th September 1828; died Preshome, 23rd February 1869.

26. **John MacDonald:** born in Strath Glass Inverness-shire, 2nd July 1818 priest, Preshome, 4th November 1841; nominated titular bishop of Nicopolis and coadjutor vicar apostolic, 11th December 1868, but (James Kyle having died the previous day) was consecrated as vicar apostolic at Aberdeen, 24th February 1869; translated to diocese of Aberdeen, 15th March 1878.

II
FROM THE RESTORATION OF THE HIERARCHY IN 1878 TO THE PRESENT DAY

The Apostolic Letter *Ex supremo* of Leo XIII, 4th March 1878, divided Scotland into the Province of St. Andrews and Edinburgh with a Metropolitan See and four Suffragan Sees of Aberdeen, Argyll and The Isles, Dunkeld, and Galloway, and the Archdiocese of Glasgow directly subject to the Holy See. The Apostolic Constitutions *Maxime interest* and *Dominici gregis* of Pius XII, 25th May 1947, erected the Archdiocese of Glasgow into a Province, with a Metropolitan See and two Suffragan Sees of Motherwell and Paisley.

A pamphlet entitled *Diocesan Map of Scotland*, showing maps of each of the dioceses of Scotland, was published by *The Mercat Cross* in 1953.

THE PROVINCE OF ST. ANDREWS AND EDINBURGH

The Province of St. Andrews and Edinburgh consists of the Archdiocese of St. Andrews and Edinburgh and the four Suffragan Sees of Aberdeen, Argyll and The Isles, Dunkeld, and Galloway.

ARCHDIOCESE OF ST. ANDREWS AND EDINBURGH

Comprising: the City of Edinburgh; Scottish Borders, East Lothian; Midlothian; West Lothian; Falkirk; Stirling (except the parishes of Callander & Aberfoyle & Doune & Killin and Dunblane); Fife (except the parishes of Cupar & Auchtermuchty; High Valleyfield & Kincardine-on-Forth; and Newport-on-Tay & Leuchars & Tayport); in East Dunbartonshire, the parishes of Lennoxtown, Milton of Campsie and Torrance; in North Lanarkshire, the parish of Kilsyth.

The bishops associated with Kinrimund, St. Andrews, had assumed ecclesiastical primacy in Scotland from Dunkeld by the beginning of the tenth century. The last of the Celtic bishops died in 1093; the line of the medieval bishops began in 1109 but the Church and the bishopric were not securely established until 1144. The independence of the Scottish Church from the metropolitan claims of the archbishops of York was established by Celestine III with the Bull Cum universi, *13th March 1192. St. Andrews was erected a Metropolitan See by Sixtus IV, 14th August 1472. The See was vacant from the execution at Stirling on 6th April 1571 of John Hamilton (1547-1571) until the restoration of the hierarchy in 1878.*

I. *ARCHBISHOPS*

1. **John Menzies Strain:** born Edinburgh, 8th December 1810; priest, Rome 9th June 1833; nominated titular bishop of Abila Lysaniae and vicar apostolic, Eastern District, 2nd September 1864, and consecrated at Rome, 25th September 1864; translated to archdiocese of St. Andrews and Edinburgh, 15th March 1878; died Edinburgh, 2nd July 1883.

2. **William Smith:** born Edinburgh, 3rd July 1819; priest, Rome, 15th April 1843; nominated archbishop of St. Andrews and Edinburgh, 2nd October 1885, and consecrated at Edinburgh, 28th October 1885; died Edinburgh, 16th March 1892.

3. **Angus MacDonald:** born Borrodale, Inverness-shire, 18th September 1844; priest, Ushaw, Co. Durham, 7th July 1872; nominated bishop of Argyll and The Isles, 22nd March 1878, and consecrated at Glasgow, 23rd May 1878; translated to St. Andrews and Edinburgh, 15th July 1892, died Edinburgh, 29th April 1900.

4. **James Smith:** born Edinburgh, 18th October 1841; priest, Rome, 31st March 1866; nominated bishop of Dunkeld, 14th August 1890, and consecrated at Dundee, 28th October 1890, translated to St. Andrews and Edinburgh, 30th August 1900; died Edinburgh, 25th November 1928.

5. **Andrew Thomas** *(in religion* **Joseph) McDonald, O.S.B:** born Fort William, 12th February 1871; priest, Fort Augustus, 9th August 1896; elected abbot of the Abbey of St. Benedict, Fort Augustus, 27th August 1919; nominated archbishop of St. Andrews and Edinburgh 19th July 1929, and consecrated at Edinburgh, 24th September 1929; died Edinburgh, 22nd May 1950.

6. **Gordon Gray:** born Leith, 10th August 1910; priest, Edinburgh, 15th June 1935; nominated archbishop of St. Andrews and Edinburgh, 20th June 1951, and consecrated at Edinburgh, 21st September 1951; created cardinal priest, 28th April 1969; retired 30th May 1985; died Edinburgh, 19th July 1993.

7. **Keith Michael Patrick O'Brien:** born Ballycastle, Co. Antrim, Ireland, 17th March 1938; priest, Edinburgh, 3rd April 1965; nominated archbishop of St. Andrews and Edinburgh, 30th May 1985, and ordained at Edinburgh, 5th August 1985.

II. *AUXILIARY BISHOPS*

1. HENRY GREY GRAHAM: born Maxton, Roxburghshire 8th March 1874; convert from presbyterianism; priest, Rome, 22nd December 1906; nominated titular bishop of Tipasa in Numidia (and auxiliary bishop), 30th August 1917, and consecrated at Edinburgh, 16th November 1917; returned to archdiocese of Glasgow as parish priest, Holy Cross, Glasgow, 1930; died Glasgow, 5th December 1959.

2. JAMES MONAGHAN: born Bathgate, West Lothian, 11th July 1914; priest, Edinburgh, 11th June 1940; nominated titular bishop of Cell Ausaille (and auxiliary bishop), 24th April 1970, and ordained at Edinburgh, 23rd May 1970; retired as auxiliary bishop 13th July, 1989; died Edinburgh, 3rd June 1994.

3. KEVIN LAWRENCE RAFFERTY: born Garvagh, Co. Derry, Ireland, 24th June 1933; priest, Kilkenny, Ireland, for Archdiocese of St. Andrews and Edinburgh, 22nd June 1957; nominated titular bishop of Ausuaga (and auxiliary bishop), 19th June 1990, and ordained at Edinburgh, 15th August 1990; died Livingston, 19th April 1996.

DIOCESE OF ABERDEEN

Comprising: the City of Aberdeen; Aberdeenshire; Highland (except the parish of Kingussie, the former district of Lochaber and the Isle of Skye); Moray; Orkney Islands; Shetland Islands.

The early twelfth century ecclesiastical centre at Mortlach, Banffshire, is traditionally the original site of the bishopric of Aberdeen. Certainly it did not originate at Aberdeen but was transferred there by David I under its fourth bishop, Nechtan, before 1131x1132. It became a suffragan of St. Andrews in 1472. It was vacant from the death of William Gordon (1546-1577) until the restoration of the hierarchy in 1878.

BISHOPS

1. **John MacDonald:** born in Strath Glass, Inverness-shire, 2nd July 1818; priest, Preshome, 4th November 1841; nominated titular bishop of Nicopolis and coadjutor vicar apostolic, Northern District, 11th December 1868, but (James Kyle having died the previous day) was consecrated as vicar apostolic at Aberdeen, 24th February 1869; translated to diocese of Aberdeen, 15th March 1878; died Aberdeen, 4th February 1889.

2. **Colin Crant:** born in Glen Gairn, Aberdeenshire, 3rd February 1832; priest, Blairs, 22nd December 1855; nominated bishop of Aberdeen, 16th July 1889, and consecrated at Aberdeen, 13th August 1889; died six weeks later at Aberdeen, 26th September 1889.

3. **Hugh MacDonald, C.Ss.R.:** born Borrodale, Inverness-shire, 7th November 1841; priest, Ushaw, Co. Durham, 21st September 1867; professed Redemptorist noviciate, Liverpool, 15th October 1871; provincial, 1884-1890; nominated bishop of Aberdeen, 14th August 1890 and consecrated at Aberdeen, 23rd October 1890; died Edinburgh, 29th May 1898.

4. **Aeneas Chisholm:** born Inverness, 26th June 1836; priest, Rome, 15th May 1859; nominated bishop of Aberdeen, 7th January 1899, and consecrated at Aberdeen, 24th February 1899; died Edinburgh, 13th January 1918.

5. **George Henry Bennett:** born St. John, Antigua, West Indies 24th June 1875; priest, Rome, 9th April 1898; nominated bishop of Aberdeen 18th June 1918, and consecrated at Aberdeen, 1st August 1918; died Aberdeen, 25th December 1946.

6. **John Alexander Matheson:** born Tomintoul, Banffshire, 28th April 1901; priest, Rome, 7th March 1925; nominated bishop of Aberdeen, 2nd August 1947, and consecrated at Aberdeen, 24th September 1947; died Aberdeen, 5th July 1950.

7. **Frank Raymond Walsh, W.F.:** born Cirencester, Gloucestershire, England, 15th September 1901; priest, Rome, 7th March 1925; professed White Fathers' noviciate, Algeria, 9th September 1931; nominated bishop of Aberdeen, 20th June 1951, and consecrated at Aberdeen, 12th September 1951; resigned 22nd July 1963, and translated to titular See of Birta, 12 September 1963; resigned titular See of Birta, 7th December 1970; died Grantham, Lincolnshire, England, 27th October 1974.

8. **Michael Foylan:** born Shettleston, Lanarkshire, 29th June 1907; priest, Kinnoull, 5th July 1931, nominated bishop of Aberdeen, 8th December 1964, and consecrated at Aberdeen, 25th March 1965; died Aberdeen, 28th May 1976.

9. **Mario Giuseppe Conti:** born Elgin, Moray, 20th March 1934; priest Rome, 26th October 1958; nominated bishop of Aberdeen, 28th February 1977, and ordained at Aberdeen, 3rd May 1977.

DIOCESE OF ARGYLL AND THE ISLES

Comprising: Argyll and Bute (except the parishes of Cardross, Helensburgh, Garelochhead and Rosneath); in North Ayrshire, the Isle of Arran; Western Isles; in Highland, the parish of Kingussie, the former district of Lochaber and the Isle of Skye.

Argyll was founded 1183x1189 by a division of the diocese of Dunkeld. It was located at Lismore c. 1225. It became a suffragan of St. Andrews in 1472 and of Glasgow in 1492. In 1553 James Hamilton was appointed bishop but he conformed to the reformed Church after 1560 and the See was vacant until the restoration of the hierarchy in 1878.

The See of The Isles was originally conjoined with Man (or Sodor). The medieval bishops from x1079 recognised the metropolitan authority of York until 1153 when Rome made them subject to Trondheim, Norway, but this was only nominal after 1349. Man and The Isles were separated from 1387. The Isles became a suffragan of St. Andrews in 1472. It was vacant from the translation of Alexander Gordon (1553-1558) until the restoration of the hierarchy in 1878.

BISHOPS

1. **Angus MacDonald:** born Borrodale, Inverness-shire, 18th September 1844; priest, Ushaw, Co. Durham, 7th July 1872; nominated bishop of Argyll and The Isles, 22nd March 1878, and consecrated at Glasgow, 23rd May 1878; translated to St. Andrews and Edinburgh, 15th July 1892.

2. **George Smith:** born Cuttlebrae, Enzie, Banffshire, 24th January 1840; priest, Paris, 17th December 1864; nominated bishop of Argyll and The Isles, 31st December 1892, and consecrated at Oban, 25th April 1893 died Oban, 18th January 1918.

3. **Donald Martin:** born Salen, Acharacle, Argyllshire, 6th October 1873; priest, Oban, 23rd September 1905; nominated bishop of Argyll and The Isles, 2nd April 1919, and consecrated at Oban, 11th June 1919; died Oban, 6th December 1938.

4. **Donald Campbell:** born Bohuntine, Inverness-shire, 8th December 1894; priest, Rome, 3rd April 1920; nominated bishop of Argyll and The Isles, 5th October 1939, and consecrated at Oban, 14th December 1939; translated to Glasgow, 6th January 1945.

5. **Kenneth Grant:** born Fort William, 18th March 1900; priest, Glasgow 24th April 1927; nominated bishop of Argyll and The Isles, 15th December 1945, and consecrated at Oban, 27th February 1946; died Glasgow, 7th September 1959.

6. **Stephen McGill, P.S.S.:** born Glasgow, 4th January 1912; priest, Glasgow 29th June 1936; priest of St. Sulpice, July 1937; nominated bishop of Argyll and The Isles, 4th April 1960, and consecrated at Oban, 22nd June 1960; translated to Paisley, 25th July 1968.

7. **Colin Aloysius Macpherson:** born Lochboisdale, South Uist, 5th August 1917; priest, Rome, 23rd March 1940; nominated bishop of Argyll and The Isles, 2nd December 1968, and ordained at Oban, 6th February 1969; died Oban, 24th March, 1990.

8. **Roderick Wright:** born Glasgow, 28th June 1941; priest, Glasgow, 29th June 1964; incardinated, diocese of Argyll and The Isles, 1974; nominated bishop of Argyll and The Isles, 11th December, 1990, and ordained at Oban, 15th January, 1991; resigned, 19th September, 1996.

9. **Ian Murray:** born Lennoxtown, 15th December 1932; priest, Valladolid,17th March 1956; nominated bishop of Argyll and The Isles, 3rd November 1999, and ordained at Oban, 7th December 1999

DIOCESE OF DUNKELD

Comprising: the City of Dundee; Angus; Clackmannan; Perthshire and Kinross; in Fife, the parishes of Cupar & Auchtermuchty, High Valleyfield & Kincardine-on-Forth, and Newport-on-Tay & Leuchars & Tayport; in Stirling, the parishes of Callander & Aberfoyle & Doune & Killin, and Dunblane.

The See of Dunkeld existed before the ninth century and had become the administrative centre of the Scottish Church by 849. The See was revived by Alexander I and the line of medieval bishops runs from c1114xc1120. It became a suffragan of St. Andrews in 1472 and of Glasgow in 1492. The See became vacant during the episcopate of Robert Crichton (1547; deprived at the reformation but lived until 1585) and it remained so until the restoration of the hierarchy in 1878.

I. *BISHOPS*

1. **George Rigg:** born Croghmore, Kirkpatrick Irongray, Kirkcudbrightshire, 19th July 1814; priest, Valladolid, 25th July 1838; nominated bishop of Dunkeld, 22nd March 1878, and consecrated at Rome, 26th May 1878; died Perth, 18th January 1887.

2. **James Smith:** born at Edinburgh, 18th October 1841; priest, Rome, 31st March 1866; nominated bishop of Dunkeld, 14th August 1890, and consecrated at Dundee, 28th October 1890, translated to St. Andrews and Edinburgh, 30th August 1900.

3. **Angus Macfarlane:** born Spean Bridge, Inverness-shire, 10th January 1843; priest, Rome, 26th April 1868; nominated bishop of Dunkeld, 21st February 1901, and consecrated at Dundee, 1st May 1901; died Dundee, 24th September 1912.

4. **Robert Fraser:** born Kennethmont, Aberdeenshire, 10th August 1858; priest, Rome, 13th August 1882; nominated bishop of Dunkeld, 14th May 1913, and consecrated at Rome, 25th May 1913; died ten months later at Dundee, 28th March 1914.

5. **John Toner:** born Glasgow, 14th March 1857; priest, Palencia, Spain, 25th March 1882; nominated bishop of Dunkeld, 8th September 1914, and consecrated at Dundee, 15th October 1914; died Dundee, 31st May 1949.

6. **James Donald Scanlan:** born Glasgow, 24th January 1899; priest, Westminster, 29th June 1929; nominated titular bishop of Cyme and coadjutor bishop of Dunkeld, 27th April 1946, and consecrated at Dundee, 20th June 1946; succeeded to Dunkeld, 31st May 1949; translated to Motherwell, 23rd May 1955.

7. **William Andrew Hart:** born Dumbarton, 9th September 1904; priest, Valladolid, 25th May 1929; nominated bishop of Dunkeld, 27th May 1955, and consecrated at Dundee, 21st September 1955; resigned 26th January 1981; died Dundee, 18th October 1992.

8. **Vincent Paul Logan:** born Bathgate, West Lothian, 30th June 1941; priest, Edinburgh, 14th March 1964; nominated bishop of Dunkeld, 26th January 1981, and ordained at Dundee, 26th February 1981.

II. *COADJUTOR BISHOPS*

1. JAMES MAGUIRE: born Loanhead, Midlothian, 29th August 1882; priest, Edinburgh, 22nd July 1906; nominated titular bishop of Ilium and coadjutor bishop of Dunkeld, 5th October 1939, and consecrated at Dundee, 30th November 1939; died without succeeding at Dundee, 10th October 1944.
2. JAMES DONALD SCANLAN: consecrated titular bishop of Cyme and coadjutor bishop of Dunkeld, 20th June 1946; succeeded 31st May 1949 (see entry (6) above).

DIOCESE OF GALLOWAY

Comprising: East Ayrshire; North Ayrshire (except the Isle of Arran); South Ayrshire; and Dumfries and Galloway.

The See of Whithorn is associated from the late fourth century with St. Ninian but it is possible that a Christian community existed there before his arrival. There was a continuous succession of bishops in the eighth century. The See was revived c. 1128 and recognised the metropolitan authority of York until 1355. It became a suffragan of St. Andrews in 1472 and of Glasgow in 1492. The See was, in effect, vacant from the death of Andrew Durie (1541-1558) since his successor, Alexander Gordon, conformed at the reformation in 1560, and it remained vacant until the restoration of the hierarchy in 1878.

I. *BISHOPS*

1. **John McLachlan:** born at Glasgow, 7th September 1826; priest, Rome, 16th March 1850; nominated bishop of Galloway, 22nd March 1878, and consecrated at Glasgow, 23rd May 1878; died Dumfries, 16th January 1893.
2. **William Turner:** born Aberdeen, 12th December 1844; priest, Rome, 26th April 1868; nominated bishop of Galloway, 16th June 1893, and consecrated at Dumfries, 25th July 1893; died Dumfries, 19th January 1914.
3. **James William McCarthy:** born at Newcastle-on-Tyne, England, 30th January 1853; priest, Glasgow, 4th May 1879; nominated bishop of Galloway, 25th May 1914, and consecrated at Dumfries, 9th June 1914; died Dumfries, 24th December 1943.

4. **William Henry Mellon:** born Edinburgh, 6th January 1877; priest, Rome, 29th March 1902, nominated titular bishop of Daulia and coadjutor bishop of Galloway, 21st August 1935, and consecrated at Edinburgh, 28th October 1935; succeeded to Galloway, 24th December 1943; died Dumfries, 2nd February 1952.
5. **Joseph Michael McGee:** born Monzievaird and Strowan, Perthshire, 13th December 1904; priest, Valladolid, 25th May 1929; nominated bishop of Galloway, 19th July 1952, and consecrated at Dumfries, 11th November 1952; resigned, 4th April 1981; died Prestwick, 5th March 1983.
6. **Maurice Taylor:** born Hamilton, Lanarkshire, 5th May 1926; priest, Rome, 2nd July 1950; nominated bishop of Galloway, 4th April 1981, ordained at Coodham, Kilmarnock, Ayrshire, 9th June 1981.

II. *COADJUTOR BISHOP*

1. WILLIAM HENRY MELLON: consecrated titular bishop of Daulia and coadjutor bishop of Galloway, 28th October 1935; succeeded 24th December 1943 (see entry (4) above).

THE PROVINCE OF GLASGOW

The Province of Glasgow was re-erected in 1947 by the Apostolic Constitution Dominici gregis *and consists of the Archdiocese of Glasgow and the two Suffragan Sees of Motherwell and Paisley.*

ARCHDIOCESE OF GLASGOW

Comprising: the City of Glasgow (except the parishes of St. Benedict and St. Clare, Easterhouse; Baillieston; and Craigend & Garthamlock); East Dunbartonshire (except the parishes of Lennoxtown, Milton of Campsie and Torrance); West Dunbartonshire; in Argyll and Bute, the parishes of Cardross, Garelochhead, Helensburgh and Rosneath, in East Renfrewshire, the part of the parish of Thornliebank lying outside the City of Glasgow; in North Lanarkshire, the parishes of Condorrat, Cumbernauld and Croy and the area of Auchinloch.

The episcopal church associated with St. Kentigern in the sixth century was in the Kingdom of Strathclyde. He built a church at Glasgow, and one at Hoddam, Dumfriesshire, where for a time he placed his See. The See of Glasgow was revived by Earl David (David I) c. 1114x1118. It was designated by Pope Alexander III "the special daughter of the Roman See": 30th April 1175, and confirmed in this honour, 30th July 1176. It became a suffragan of St. Andrews in 1472 but was itself erected a metropolitan See by Innocent VIII, 9th January 1492. It was vacant from the death in Paris on 24th April 1603 of James Beaton (1551-1603) until the restoration of the hierarchy in 1878.

I. *ARCHBISHOPS*

1. **Charles Petre Eyre:** born York, England, 7th November 1817; priest Rome, 19th March 1842; nominated apostolic delegate in Scotland and titular archbishop of Anazarbus, 11th December 1868, and consecrated at Rome, 31st January 1869; apostolic administrator, Western District, 16th April 1869; translated to archdiocese of Glasgow, 15th March 1878; died Glasgow, 27th March 1902.

2. **John Maguire:** born Glasgow 8th September 1851; priest, Rome, 27th March 1875; nominated titular bishop of Trocmades (and auxiliary bishop), 6th April 1894, and consecrated at Glasgow, 11th June 1894; translated to Glasgow, 4th August 1902; died Glasgow, 14th October 1920.

3. **Donald Mackintosh:** born Glasnacardoch, Inverness-shire, 10th October 1877; priest, Rome, 1st November 1900; nominated archbishop of Glasgow, 24th February 1922, and consecrated at Rome, 21st May 1922; died Bearsden, 8th December 1943.

4. **Donald Campbell:** born at Bohuntine, Inverness-shire, 8th December 1894; priest, Rome, 3rd April 1920; nominated bishop of Argyll and The Isles, 5th October 1939, and consecrated at Oban, 14th December 1939; translated to Glasgow, 6th January 1945; died Lourdes, France, 22nd July 1963.

5. **James Donald Scanlan:** born Glasgow, 24th January 1899; priest, Westminster, 29th June 1929; nominated titular bishop of Cyme and coadjutor bishop of Dunkeld, 27th April 1946, and consecrated at Dundee, 20th June 1946; succeeded to Dunkeld, 31st May 1949; translated to Motherwell, 23rd May 1955; translated to Glasgow, 29th January 1964; resigned, 23rd April 1974; died London, 25th March 1976.

6. **Thomas Joseph Winning:** born Wishaw, Lanarkshire, 3rd June 1925; priest, Rome, 18th December 1948; nominated titular bishop of Louth (and auxiliary bishop), 22nd October 1971, and ordained at Glasgow, 30th November 1971; translated to Glasgow, 23rd April 1974; created cardinal priest, 26th November 1994.

II. *COADJUTOR ARCHBISHOP*

1. DONALD MACKINTOSH: born Bohuntine, Inverness-shire, 24th December 1844; priest, Blairs, 31st May 1871; nominated titular archbishop of Chersonesus in Zechia and coadjutor archbishop of Glasgow, 11th June 1912, and consecrated at Glasgow, 2nd July 1912; died without succeeding at Glasgow, 8th October 1919.

III. *AUXILIARY BISHOPS*

1. JOHN MAGUIRE: consecrated titular bishop of Trocmades (and auxiliary bishop), 11th June 1894; translated to Glasgow, 4th August 1902 (see entry (2) above).
2. JAMES WARD: born Dumbarton, 4th September 1905; priest, Glasgow, 29th June 1929; nominated titular bishop of Sita (and auxiliary bishop), 2nd July 1960, and consecrated at Glasgow, 21st September 1960; died Glasgow, 21st October 1973.
3. THOMAS JOSEPH WINNING: ordained titular bishop of Louth (and auxiliary bishop), 30th November 1971; translated to Glasgow, 23rd April 1974 (see entry (6) above).
4. CHARLES McDONALD RENFREW: born Glasgow, 21st June 1929; priest, Rome, 4th April 1953; nominated titular bishop of Abula (and auxiliary bishop), 5th May 1977, and ordained at Glasgow, 31st May 1977; died Glasgow, 27th February 1992.
5. JOSEPH DEVINE: born Glasgow, 7th August 1937; priest, Glasgow, 29th June 1960; nominated titular bishop of Voli (and auxiliary bishop), 5th May 1977, and ordained at Glasgow, 31st May 1977; translated to Motherwell, 13th May 1983.
6. JOHN ALOYSIUS MONE: born Glasgow, 22nd June 1929; priest, Glasgow, 12th June 1952; nominated titular bishop of Abercorn (and auxiliary bishop), 24th April 1984, and ordained at Glasgow, 14th May 1984; translated to Paisley, 8th March 1988.

DIOCESE OF MOTHERWELL

Comprising: in the City of Glasgow, the parishes of St. Benedict and St. Clare, Easterhouse, Baillieston; and Craigend & Garthamlock; North Lanarkshire (except the parishes of Kilsyth, Condorrat, Croy and Cumbernauld and the area of Auchinloch); and South Lanarkshire.

The Diocese of Motherwell was erected as a Suffragan See of the Archdiocese of Glasgow by the Apostolic Constitution Maxime interest *of the 25th May 1947.*

BISHOPS

1. **Edward Wilson Douglas:** born Glasgow, 27th August 1901; priest, Glasgow, 1st May 1924; nominated bishop of Motherwell, 7th February 1948, and consecrated at Motherwell, 21st April 1948; resigned and translated to titular See of Botrys, 9th February 1954; died Glasgow, 12th June 1967.

2. **James Donald Scanlan**: born Glasgow, 24th January 1899; priest, Westminster, 29th June 1929; nominated titular bishop of Cyme and coadjutor bishop of Dunkeld, 27th April 1946, and consecrated at Dundee, 20th June 1946; succeeded to Dunkeld, 31st May 1949; translated to Motherwell, 23rd May 1955; translated to Glasgow, 29th January 1964.

3. **Francis Thomson:** born Edinburgh, 15th May 1917; priest, Edinburgh 15th June 1946; nominated bishop of Motherwell, 8th December 1964, and consecrated at Motherwell, 24th February 1965; resigned, 14th December 1982; died Glasgow, 6th December, 1987.

4. **Joseph Devine:** born Glasgow, 7th August 1937; priest, Glasgow, 29th June 1960; nominated titular bishop of Voli (and auxiliary bishop of Glasgow), 5th May 1977, and ordained at Glasgow, 31st May 1977; translated to Motherwell, 13th May 1983.

DIOCESE OF PAISLEY

Comprising: East Renfrewshire (except the part of the parish of Thornliebank lying outside the City of Glasgow); Inverclyde; and Renfrewshire.

The Diocese of Paisley was erected as a Suffragan See of the Archdiocese of Glasgow by the Apostolic Constitution Maxime interest *of the 25th May 1947.*

BISHOPS

1. **James Black:** born Glasgow, 25th June 1894; priest, Glasgow, 27th June 1920; nominated bishop of Paisley, 28th February 1948, and consecrated at Paisley, 14th April 1948; died Kilmacolm, 29th March 1968.

2. **Stephen McGill, P.S.S.:** born Glasgow, 4th January 1912; priest, Glasgow, 29th June 1936; nominated bishop of Argyll and The Isles, 4th April 1960, and consecrated at Oban, 22nd June 1960; translated to Paisley, 25th July 1968; retired 30th March 1988.

3. **John Aloysius Mone:** born Glasgow, 22nd June 1929; priest, Glasgow 12th June 1952; nominated titular bishop of Abercorn (and auxiliary bishop of Glasgow), 24th April 1984, and ordained at Glasgow, 14th May 1984; translated to Paisley, 8th March 1988.

BISHOPS' CONFERENCE OF SCOTLAND

President: His Eminence
Cardinal Thomas J. Winning,
K.C.H.S., S.T.L., D.C.L., D.D., F.E.I.S.,
Archbishop of Glasgow.

Episcopal Secretary: The Right Reverend Maurice Taylor,
S.T.D.,
Bishop of Galloway.

General Secretary: The Very Reverend
Monsignor Henry Docherty,
Ph.L., S.T.L., M.Litt., F.S.A.Scot., S.Int.S.S.
General Secretariat,
64 Aitken Street,
AIRDRIE ML6 6LT
Tel.: Airdrie (01236) 764061.
Fax: (01236) 762489.
E-mail: GenSec@BpsConfScot.com

Press and Media
Relations Officer: The Right Reverend Monsignor
Thomas A. Connelly.

Media Office: 5 St. Vincent Place, GLASGOW G1 2DH
Tel.: 0141-221 1168.
Fax: 0141-204 2458.
Home Tel./Fax: 0141-641 2244.
E-mail: Scotbishopsconference
@compuserve.com
or 101613.1627@compuserve.com
Internet:
http://www.stac.ac.uk/CMO/.

The Bishops' Conference of Scotland is the permanently constituted assembly of the Bishops of Scotland. To promote its work the Conference establishes various agencies, the most important of which are termed Commissions. Priests other than bishops, religious and lay people are included in the membership of these agencies. The agencies have an advisory function in relation to the Conference; each, according to its remit, may also have an executive function; and, between meetings of the Conference, an agency may respond to an immediate problem by taking decisions or issuing a statement in its own name.

THE COMMISSIONS

It is the common function of all the Commissions to advise the Bishops' Conference and to promote development within the area of concern of the remit given to each. The Conference appoints a Bishop President and all members of each Commission. Members of secretariats, committees etc. which assist the work of a Commission are not necessarily members of the Commission itself.

Christian Doctrine and Unity

This Commission comprises a Doctrine Section and a Unity Section, the latter being an extension of the former and including other priests, religious and laity who have had wide experience in ecumenical affairs. The remit of the Commission includes Catholic Doctrine, Moral Theology and Canon Law; ecumenical relations with other Christian Churches and dialogue with those of other faiths and with unbelievers.

President:	The Right Reverend Mario J. Conti, K.C.H.S., Ph.L., S.T.L., D.D., F.R.S.E., Bishop of Aberdeen.
Secretary:	The Very Reverend Monsignor Henry Docherty, General Secretariat, 64 Aitken Street, AIRDRIE ML6 6LT. Tel.: Airdrie (01236) 764061. Fax: (01236) 762489. E-mail: GenSec@BpsConfScot.com

Communications

The mission of the Church through the various modern means of communication — the printed word, radio, television, films, etc.; the organization of study days and training courses to educate communicators and recipients on the most beneficial use of the media.

President:	The Right Reverend Joseph Devine,Ph.D., Bishop of Motherwell.
Vice-President:	The Right Reverend Monsignor Thomas A. Connelly.
Chairman:	Professor Thomas Carbery, O.B.E.
Executive Secretary:	Mr. Michael Morris.

Offices of the Commission:	Catholic Media Office, 5 St. Vincent Place, GLASGOW G1 2DH. Tel.: 0141-221 1168 Fax: 0141-204 2458 E-mail: Scotsbishopsconference @compuserve.com or 101613.1627@compuserve.com Internet: http://www.stac.ac.uk/CMO/.

COMMITTEES: 1. NEWS MEDIA AND NEW TECHNOLOGY
Convener: Mr. Christopher Dempsey.

2. RELIGIOUS BROADCASTING
Convener: Mr. Ronald Convery, M.A. (Hons).

Education
All matters pertaining to education.

President: His Eminence
Cardinal Thomas J. Winning,
Archbishop of Glasgow.
Chairman: Mr. Brian Bonnar, LL.B.
Vice-Chairman: Miss Susan McCormick, M.A.
Field Officer: Mr. John Oates, M.Λ., B.A.
Secretary: Mr. Leo Duffy, J.P., M.A.
Offices of the Commission:

St. Andrew's Campus,
University of Glasgow,
Duntocher Road,
Bearsden,
GLASGOW G61 4QA.
Tel.: 0141-943 0494.

Heritage
The preservation of our Scottish Catholic Heritage at home and abroad.

President: The Right Reverend Mario J. Conti,
Bishop of Aberdeen.
Secretary: Dr. Mary McHugh, B.A., M.Litt., Ph.D.,
LL.B., F.S.A.Scot.
c/o Archdiocese of Glasgow,
196 Clyde Street, GLASGOW G1 4JY.
Tel.: 0141-226 5898.
Fax: 0141-225 2600.

SCOTTISH CATHOLIC ARCHIVES
The custody, preservation and cataloguing of all Scottish Catholic Archives in the ownership of the Bishops' Conference.

Keeper of the Archives and Administrator of Columba House:	Dr. Christine Johnson, Ph.D., Columba House, 16 Drummond Place, EDINBURGH EH3 6PL. Tel.: 0131-556 3661.

Justice and Peace
Social justice and human rights at both national and international levels.

President:	The Right Reverend John A. Mone, Bishop of Paisley.
Secretary:	Mrs. Maryanne Ure.
Offices of the Commission:	65 Bath Street, GLASGOW G2 2BX. Tel./Fax: 0141-333 0238.

Liturgy
The liturgy of the Church, including its music.

President:	The Right Reverend Maurice Taylor, Bishop of Galloway.
Secretary:	The Reverend Peter M. Gallacher, Ph.B., S.T.L., S.L.L. Christ the King, 220 Carmunnock Road, GLASGOW G44 5AP. Tel.: 0141-637 2882.

COMMITTEE FOR CHURCH MUSIC

Acting Secretary:	The Right Reverend Monsignor Patrick G. Fitzpatrick, L.R.A.M., B.Mus.Sac., L.C.G., B.Mus.Hons., S.T.L., D.C.E., St. Leo's, 5 Beech Avenue, GLASGOW G41 5BY. Tel.: 0141-427 0293

Social Care
All matters concerning child welfare, the socially deprived in all areas, the aged, etc.; the co-ordination of the activities of Catholic organizations working in these fields. The Commission is responsible for the SECRETARIAT FOR THE PASTORAL CARE OF MIGRANT WORKERS AND TOURISTS, which fosters interest in the pastoral care of seafarers, migrant oil workers, tourists, and other people on the move, and directs those engaged in this work.

President: The Right Reverend John A. Mone
Bishop of Paisley.

National Co-ordinator: Mr. David McCann.

SECRETARIAT FOR THE PASTORAL CARE OF MIGRANT WORKERS AND
TOURISTS

Offices of the
Commission and
Secretariat:
1/2, 15c Hill Street,
GLASGOW G3 6RE
Tel./Fax: 0141-572 0115.

APOSTLESHIP OF THE SEA

National Director: Mr. Leo Gilbert,
Stella Maris, 937 Dumbarton Road,
GLASGOW G14 9UF
Tel.: 0141-339 6657.

Priestly Formation
The preparation and selection of candidates for the Seminary; developments in
seminary training; the continuing formation of priests.

President: The Right Reverend Vincent Logan,
Bishop of Dunkeld.
Secretary: The Reverend Gerard Livingstone.
Offices of the
Commission:
National Vocations Office,
2 Chesters Road, Bearsden,
GLASGOW G61 4AG.
Tel./Fax: 0141-774 7651.

Vocations
The promotion and fostering of vocations to all forms of consecrated life—
priest, deacon, religious, missionary and member of secular institute.

President: The Most Reverend
Keith Patrick O'Brien,
K.M., K.C.H.S., B.Sc., Dip.Ed.
Archbishop of St. Andrews
and Edinburgh.
National
Vocations Directors:
The Reverend Stephen Connolly
The Reverend Michael Bagan.
Offices of the
Commission:
National Vocations Office,
2 Chesters Road, Bearsden,
GLASGOW G61 4AG.
Tel./Fax: 0141-943 1995.

The Lay Faithful

President: The Most Reverend
Keith Patrick O'Brien,
Archbishop of St. Andrews
and Edinburgh.

SECRETARIAT FOR THE LAITY

Secretary: Mr. John Coultas,
K.C.H.S., D.H.E., M.I.L.A.M., J.P.,
72 Etive Crescent, Bishopbriggs,
GLASGOW G64 1EY
Tel.: 0141-772 2274.

SECRETARIAT FOR YOUNG PEOPLE

Secretary: Mr. John Coultas,
72 Etive Crescent,
Bishopbriggs,
GLASGOW G64 1EY.
Tel.: 0141-772 2274.

Mission

President: The Right Reverend Joseph Devine,
Bishop of Motherwell.

Secretary: The Reverend Joseph Coyle, S.T.D.
St. Joseph's, Faifley,
CLYDEBANK G81 5EZ.
Tel.: Duntocher (01389) 872236.

Ex Officio: The Right Reverend Monsignor
Daniel Foley,
6 Wilkieston Road, Ratho,
NEWBRIDGE EH28 8RH.
Tel./Fax: 0131-333 1051.

OTHER AGENCIES OF THE BISHOPS' CONFERENCE

The President or other person in charge of each of these agencies is appointed by the Bishops' Conference. Other members are elected or appointed in different ways according to the needs of each agency.

Scottish Catholic International Aid Fund

S.C.I.A.F. is the official Third World Agency of the Catholic Church in Scotland. It supports relief and development projects overseas and runs a Lenten Campaign and an education programme in Catholic schools and parishes to raise our awareness as Christians of our obligations to the poor.

President:	The Right Reverend John A. Mone, Bishop of Paisley.
Chairman:	Vacant.
Executive Director:	Mr. Paul Chitnis, B.A.
Offices of the Fund:	19 Park Circus, GLASGOW G3 6BE. Tel.: 0141-354 5555. Fax: 0141-354 5533. E-mail: SCIAF@SCIAF.ORG.UK WWWSCIAF.ORG.UK

Tribunal

The Scottish Catholic Tribunal deals with requests for the dissolution of the bond of marriage and declarations of nullity.

President:	The Reverend Gerard Tartaglia, Ph.B., S.T.B., J.C.L.
Tribunal Offices:	22 Woodrow Road, GLASGOW G41 5PN. Tel.: 0141-427 3036. Fax: 0141-427 7715.

Jubilee 2000 National Committee

President:	The Right Reverend Vincent Logan, Bishop of Dunkeld.
Secretary:	Miss Rena McVey.
Office:	Jubilee 2000 Office, General Secretariat, 64 Aitken Street, AIRDRIE ML6 6LT. Tel.: 01236-760085. Fax: 01236-760050.

REPRESENTATIVES OF THE BISHOPS' CONFERENCE

Council of European Bishops' Conferences (C.C.E.E.)
Member for Scotland: His Eminence
Cardinal Thomas J. Winning,
Archbishop of Glasgow.

**Commission of Bishops' Conferences of the European Community
(C.O.M.E.C.E)**
Member for Scotland: The Right Reverend John A. Mone,
Bishop of Paisley.

Missio-Scotland
(Pontifical Mission Societies)

Directly responsible to the Congregation for the Evangelisation of Peoples

President: The Right Reverend Monsignor
Daniel Foley,
6 Wilkieston Road,
Ratho,
NEWBRIDGE EH28 8RH.
Tel:/Fax: 0131-333 1051.

1. SOCIETY FOR THE PROPAGATION OF THE FAITH
Secretary: The Reverend Joseph Coyle,
St. Joseph's, Faifley,
CLYDEBANK G81 5EZ.
Tel.: Duntocher (01389) 872236.

2. SOCIETY OF ST. PETER APOSTLE
Secretary: The Reverend John Futers,
Corpus Christi,
16 Dunvegan Avenue,
Portlethen, ABERDEEN AB12 4QF.
Tel.: 01224-780256.

3. SOCIETY FOR MISSIONARY CHILDREN
Secretary: Vacant.

4. PONTIFICAL MISSIONARY UNION
Secretary: The Reverend Leo Glancy,
Christ the King,
Bowhouse Road,
GRANGEMOUTH FK3 0HB.
Tel.: 01324-484974.

Catholic Bishops' Joint Committee on Bio-ethics

The Committee was set up jointly by the three Bishops' Conferences of Great Britain and Ireland. It is made up of two bishops from each conference and a number of priests and lay people with expertise in the fields of moral theology, bio-ethics, medicine, law and clinical practice. It advises the bishops and, through Working Parties, produces publications giving a Catholic perspective on current bio-ethical topics.

Chairman:	His Eminence Cardinal Thomas J.Winning Archbishop of Glasgow.
Secretary:	The Reverend Paul G. Murray, B.Sc., Ph.B., S.T.L. 196 Clyde Street, GLASGOW G41 4JY Tel.: 0141-225 2605. Fax:0141-225 2600. E-mail:cathcthic@aol.com

Joint Commission of Bishops and Conference of Religious in Scotland

This commission consists of two members of the Bishops' Conference and four members of the Conference of Religious in Scotland, and is a forum for mutual counsel, liaison and communication on matters of mutual concern at both national and diocesan levels.

Chairperson:	The Right Reverend Vincent Logan, Bishop of Dunkeld.
Bishop Members:	The Right Reverend Vincent Logan, Bishop of Dunkeld. The Right Reverend Maurice Taylor, Bishop of Galloway.
C.R.S. Members:	Secretary : Sister Margaret Healy, C.S.J.P. Sr. Teresa Naughton, L.S.U., Reverend Ian Wilson, O.S.A. Brother Lewis Dorrian, F.M.S.
Official Address:	C.R.S. Secretariat, Carmelite Monastery,, 29 Mansionhouse Road, GLASGOW G41 3DN. Tel./Fax: 0141-649 6535.

CATHOLIC MEMBERS OF ACTS (ACTION OF CHURCHES TOGETHER IN SCOTLAND) AND CTBI (CHURCHES TOGETHER IN BRITAIN AND IRELAND).

Except in the case of eventual election by ACTS or CTBI (indicated by an asterisk), the following appointments have been made by the Bishops" Conference of Scotland.

ACTS:

CONVENER OF CENTRAL COUNCIL:
Sister Maire Gallagher, C.B.E., S.N.D.*

CENTRAL COUNCIL:
The Right Reverend Mario J. Conti, Bishop of Aberdeen;
The Right Rev. Joseph Devine, Bishop of Motherwell
The Very Reverend Mgr. Henry Docherty,
Sister Maire Gallagher, S.N.D.,
Dr. Robert Corrins, Mrs. Irene Patton
Mr. John Coultas, Mr. Scott MacKenzie.

(8 members)

COMMISSION FOR THEOLOGY AND UNITY:
The Reverend James Quinn, S.J.
The Reverend John H. Fitzsimmons
The Reverend Philip Kerr.

COMMISSION ON JUSTICE, PEACE, SOCIAL AND MORAL ISSUES:
Mr. Timothy Duffy, Mr. David McCann.

COMMISSION ON MISSION, EVANGELISM AND EDUCATION:
Sister Maire Gallagher, S.N.D., Mr. John Oates, Miss Patricia Lockhart.

COMMITTEE ON LOCAL AND REGIONAL ECUMENISM:
Mr. John Cairns, Mr. Gordon McCormack

COMMITTEE ON COMMUNICATIONS:
The Right Reverend Monsignor Thomas A. Connelly* *(ex officio)*, Mr. Tom Cooney.

YOUTH ACTION:
Mr.Chris Docherty.

NEWS's (NETWORK OF ECUMENICAL WOMEN IN SCOTLAND):
Mrs. Maryanne Ure, Mrs. Irene Patton.

SCOTTISH CHURCHES HOUSE COMMITTEE:
Mr. John Coultas.

FINANCE COMMITTEE:
   Mr. James Butterly.

CTBI:

PRESIDENCY:
   The Right Reverend Mario J. Conti, Bishop of Aberdeen*.

STEERING COMMITTEE:
   The Very Reverend Monsignor Henry Docherty*.

CHURCH REPRESENTATIVES MEETING:
   The Right Reverend Mario J. Conti, Bishop of Aberdeen;
   The Very Reverend Mgr. Henry Docherty*.

ASSEMBLY:
   The Right Reverend Mario J. Conti, Bishop of Aberdeen
   The Right Reverend Joseph Devine, Bishop of Motherwell.
   The Very Reverend Mgr. Henry Docherty,
   Sister Maire Gallagher, S.N.D.,
   Dr. Robert Corrins, Mrs. Irene Patton
   Mr. John Coultas, Mr. Scott MacKenzie.
   (All the above are also on the Central Council of ACTS)
   Mr, James Butterly, Mr. Paul Chitnis (S.C.I.A.F.),
   Mr. Tom Cooney, The Reverend John H. Fitzsimmons,
   Miss Patricia Lockhart, Mr. David McCann,
   Mr. Gordon McCormack, Prof. B.J. McGettrick,
   Mr. John Oates, Miss Maryanne Ure, Mrs. Isa Wilson.
                                          (19 members)

INTER-FAITH AND RACIAL JUSTICE AGENCIES

CAIRS (Churches' Agency for Inter-Faith relations):
Secretary: Sister Isabel Smyth, S.N.D.,
326 West Princes Street,
GLASGOW G4 9HA.
Tel.: 0141-339 8174.

SCARJ (Scottish Churches' Agency for Racial Justice):
Secretary: Mrs. Cecilia Boccorh, 65 Bath Street,
GLASGOW G2 2BX
Tel.: 0141-333 9020
Fax: 0141-333 0238.

CONFERENCE OF RELIGIOUS
IN SCOTLAND

President:	Sister Teresa Naughton, L.S.U.
Vice-President:	Brother Lewis Dorrian, F.M.S.
General Secretary:	Sister Margaret Healy, C.S.J.P.
	C.R.S. Secretariat,
	Carmelite Monastery,
	29 Mansionhouse Road,
	GLASGOW G41 3DN
	Tel./Fax: 0141-649 6535.

Archdiocese of
St. Andrews and Edinburgh

CRUX SPES UNICA

Archbishop and Metropolitan
Most Reverend Keith Patrick O'Brien
K.M., K.C.H.S., B.Sc., Dip.Ed.

Born at Ballycastle, Co. Antrim, Ireland, 17th March 1938, educated St. Patrick's High School, Dumbarton, and Holy Cross Academy, Edinburgh; University of Edinburgh (B.Sc., 1959; Dip.Ed., 1966); St. Andrew's College Drygrange, Roxburghshire; ordained priest at Edinburgh, 3rd April 1965, assistant priest, Holy Cross, Edinburgh, 1965-66; St. Bride, Cowdenbeath, 1966-71; St. Patrick, Kilsyth, 1972-75; St. Mary, Bathgate, 1975-78; spiritual director, St. Andrew's College, Drygrange; 1978-80 rector, St. Mary's College, Blairs, 1980-85; nominated archbishop of St. Andrews and Edinburgh, 30th May 1985, and ordained by Gordon Gray, cardinal priest and archbishop emeritus of St. Andrews and Edinburgh, at Edinburgh, 5th August 1985; Sovereign Military Order of Malta: Grand Cross conventual chaplain, 1985; founded Gillis College, Edinburgh, 7th September 1986. Gillis College was closed as the Diocesan Seminary and the students transferred to the new National Major Seminary in September 1993. Equestrian Order of the Holy Sepulchre of Jerusalem: Knight Commander with Star 1991. Apostolic Administrator of the Diocese of Argyll and The Isles, 1996-99.

Residence: Archbishop's House, 42 Greenhill Gardens, EDINBURGH EH 10 4BJ .☎ 0131-447 3337. Fax: 0131-447 0816.
E-mail:archkp@lineone.net
archbishopedin.free-online.co.uk
   Secretary: Miss Norah Magennis.

VICARS-GENERAL

Right Rev. Mgr. Anthony Canon McNally,
St. Columba's, 9 Upper Gray Street, EDINBURGH EH9 ISN.
☎ 0131-667 1605.

Right. Rev. Mgr. Alistair Lawson, B.A.,
St Mary's & St Columba's,
9 Livery Street, BATHGATE EH48 4HS.
☎ 01506-655766

ADMINISTRATION
Address: Diocesan Offices, Gillis Centre
113 Whitehouse Loan, EDINBURGH EH9 1BB
☎ 0131-452 8244; Fax: 0131-452 9153
Archdiocesan Website: edinburghdiocese.free-online.co.uk
Chancery Office: e-mail: stanedchancery@lineone.net
Finance Office: e-mail: stanedfinance@lineone.net

Moderator of the Curia
Right Rev. Mgr Anthony Canon McNally, V.G.

Chancellor
Rev: Francis Kerr

Vice Chancellor
Rev. Nicholas Hodgson Ph.B., S.T.L., J.C.L.

Diocesan Secretary
Rev. Jeremy Bath, S.T.B.

Registrar for Deceased Clergy
Rev. Jeremy Bath, S.T.B.

Chancery Secretary
Mrs. Molly Wade

Finance
Right Rev. Mgr. A. L. Duffy (Treasurer)
Mr. George Lavery (Accountant)

Buildings and Fabric
Secretary — Vacant
Mr Alan McGregor (Buildings Officer)
Miss Anna Kulwicka (Buildings Secretary)

RELIGIOUS EDUCATION
Address: Gillis Centre, 113 Whitehouse Loan,
EDINBURGH EH9 1BB
Tel: 0131-447 0986 Fax: 0131-446 0370

Director & Episcopal Vicar for Education
Rev. James G. Tracey

Archdiocesan Adviser — School Staffing
Miss Teresa Gourlay, M.A.

Primary R.E. Adviser
Sr. Monica McDonald, D.C.E.

Secondary R.E.Adviser
Mr. Jeffrey Bagnall, B.D., M.Phil.(Theology)

Chaplaincy Co-ordinator
Sr. Ann-Marie McLaughlin, O.S.F.

Director of S.P.R.E.D.
Sr. Cecilia Dowd, D.C., Dip. S.W., Dip Rel.Educ.

Miss Veronica Laidlaw — School Board Liaison & Support & Special Schools
    Adviser
Mrs. May Fitzgerald — Primary School Support — City of Edinburgh
Mrs. Freda Sanlan — Primary School Support — West Lothian
Mrs. Kay Gilfillan — Primary School Support — Fife
Mrs. Joyce McLeod — Office Secretary

Representatives on Local Authority Education Committees
(Contact phone number for representatives-R.E.Office. Tel/Fax 0131-447 0986)

City of Edinburgh Council	Mr. George McLafferty
East Lothian Council	Mr. Tom O'Malley
West Lothian Council	Mr. Robert Birrell
Midlothian Council	Mr. James Linn
Fife Council	Mrs. Brigitte Sweeney
Falkirk Council	Mr. John Oates
Stirling Council	Mr. Hilary Moraes
Scottish Borders Council	Mrs. Margaret Mullen

PASTORAL CO-ORDINATION
Address: Gillis Centre, 113 Whitehouse Loan
EDINBURGH EH9 1BB
☎ 0131-447 9943

Pastoral Co-ordinator
Rev. Charles Barclay, Dip. R.E.

Pastoral Development Officer
Sr. Claire Wardhaugh, R.S.C.J.

ONGOING PRIESTLY FORMATION

Rev. Hugh White, St. Matthew's, 36 Carnethie Street,
ROSEWELL EH24 9AT ☎ 0131-440 2150

GILLIS CENTRE
Address: 115 Whitehouse Loan
EDINBURGH EH9 1BB
☎/Fax: 0131-447 2807

Centre Manager
Mrs. Anthea Donaghue
(For all bookings of rooms and conference facilities including St. Margaret's Chapel)

Chairman of Gillis Management Committee
Rev. Francis Kerr

AGENCIES AT GILLIS CENTRE

Child Protection Officer:	☎ 0131-557 5878
Communications:	☎ 0131-440 3360.
Covenant Centre:	☎ 0131-452 8234.
HOPE:	☎ 0131-447 7165
Justice and Peace:	☎ 0131-452 8559.
Library:	☎ 0131-447 1992.
Formation for Ministry —**Limex**	☎ 0131-452 8794/228 1900.
Mount Vernon Management Committee:	☎ 0131-452 8244 (Ext 36)
Natural Family Planning:	☎ 0131-447 5915.
Pastoral Co-ordinator's Office:	☎ 0131-447 9943
R.E. Office:	☎ 0131-447 0986
Scottish Catholic Marriage Care:	☎ 0131-452 8240.
Social Care Commission:	☎ 0131-452 8794.
St. Andrew's Children's Society:	☎ 0131-452 8248.
Youth Service:	☎ 0131-452 8247.

ADVISORS TO THE ARCHBISHOP
Episcopal Vicars

Episcopal Vicar for Mission Awareness:
Rev. Leo Glancy, Christ the King, Bowhouse Road,
GRANGEMOUTH FK3 0HB. ☎ *01324-484974*

Episcopal Vicar for Justice and Peace:
Rev. Gerard Hand, S.T.L., St. Patrick's, 30 Low Craigends, Kilsyth,
GLASGOW G65 0PF. ☎ *0123-822136*

Episcopal Vicar for Education:
Rev. James Tracey, Holy Cross, 11 Bangholm Loan,
EDINBURGH EH5 3AH. ☎ *0131-552 3957.*

Episcopal Vicar for Liturgy:
Rev. Michael Regan, B.A., M.Litt., M.Th., Scotus College,
2 Chesters Road, Bearsden, GLASGOW G61 4AG. ☎ *0141-942 8384.*

Episcopal Vicars for Religious:
Very Rev. Francis Conway, O.F.M. St. Teresa of Lisieux,
120 Niddrie Mains Road,Craigmillar, EDINBURGH. ☎ *0131-661 2185.*
Sr. Helen McLaughlin, R.S.C.J., House of Prayer, 8 Nile Grove,
EDINBURGH EH10 4RF. ☎ *0131-447 1772.*
Episcopal Vicar for Ecumenism:
Rev. Philip Kerr, Ph.L, S.T.L., St. Francis Xavier's, 1 Hope Street, FALKIRK FK1
5AT. ☎ *(01324) 623567.*

Episcopal Vicar for Social Care:
Rev. Jock J. Dalrymple, S.T.L., St. Mary's Presbytery,
35 North Street, Leslie, GLENROTHES KY6 3DJ. ☎ *01592-741963.*
Project Worker: Mrs. Maureen McEvoy, Gillis Centre, 113 Whitehouse Loan,
EDINBURGH EH9 1BB. ☎ *0131-452 8794.*

College of Consultors

Right Rev. Mgr Anthony Canon McNally, V.G.,
Right Rev. Mgr Alistair Lawson, BA., V.G.,
Very Rev. James Canon Rae,
Rev. Jeremy Bath, S.T.B
Rev. David Gemmell, M.Th.
Rev. Kenneth Owens, B.Sc, Ph.B., S.T.L *(Secretary)*

Assembly of Priests

His Grace The Archbishop *(President)*
Rev. Kenneth Owens, B.Sc., Ph.B., S.T.L. *(Secretary)*

Trustees:

Most Rev. Keith Patrick O'Brien, Archbishop of St. Andrews & Edinburgh
Right Rev. Mgr. Anthony Canon McNally - Senior V.G.
Rev. Francis Kerr - Chancellor

ARCHDIOCESAN COMMITTEES

Finance Committe:
(Chairman) Vacant; Right Rev. Mgr. Anthony L. Duffy *(Secretary)* ;Rev. Thomas
McNulty; Mr. Harry McCann; Mr. George Lavery..

Fabric and Planning Committee:
Right Rev. Mgr. Alastair Lawson,B.A., V.G. *(Chairman)*; Mr. Donald
MacDonald; Mr. Gerard McCue; Mr. Ian McPherson.

The Secretaries Committee:
Most Rev. Keith Patrick O'Brien; Right Rev. Mgr. Anthony L. Duffy; Rev.
David Barr.

Director of Vocations:
Rev. Michael Bagan
St. Margaret of Scotland
Drip Road, STIRLING
FK9 4UA
☎/Fax: (01786) 474883

Mount Vernon Management Committee:
Right Rev. Mgr. Anthony Canon McNally, V.G. *(Chairman)*
Mr. Gerald Farmer C.A. *(Secretary)*
Sir Thomas Farmer, C.B.E., K.C.S.G. *(Member)*

Cemetery Address: 49 Mount Vernon Road
                        EDINBURGH EH16 6JG
                        ☎ 0131-664 3064

ARCHDIOCESAN YOUTH SERVICE
Address: Gillis Centre, 113 Whitehouse Loan,
EDINBURGH EH9 1BB
☎ 0131-452 8247 (Office) 041 071 3049 (Mobile)
0131-452 9153 (Fax)

1. ARCHDIOCESAN YOUTH SERVICE OFFICES
Contact: Ms Rhona E. Hutchison.

Providing training and support services to young people and youth leaders:

* Assistance in Setting up a Youth Group
* Youth Exchange - Grants
* World Youth Day - Rome 2000
* Child Protection Guidelines & Training
* Training for Youth Leaders
* Diocesan and National Youth Contacts
* Networking
* Information & Resources

2. ARCHDIOCESAN YOUTH FORMATION GROUP
Most Rev. Keith Patrick O'Brien; Rev. David Gemmell; Rev. James Smith; Ms. Rhona Hutchison; Rev. John Cudlipp; Mr. Mike Knox; Mrs. Anne Johnstone.

3. REGIONAL YOUTH FORMATION GROUPS

CENTRAL
Miss Noeleen Breen, 27 Greenacre Place, Bannockburn, STIRLING FK7 8PA
☎ 01786-812505

EDINBURGH
Mr. Mike Knox, 5 Sandford Gardens, EDINBURGH EH15 1LP ☎ 131-468 4040

FIFE
Vacant.

WEST LOTHIAN
Mrs. Anne Johnstone, 44 Kirk Road, BATHGATE EH48 1BP. ☎01506-634397
Rev. James Smith, St Joseph's, 49 Raeburn Crescent, Whitburn, BATHGATE EH47 8HQ. ☎01501-740348

EAST/MID LOTHIAN
Ms. Rhona Hutchison, Archdiocesan Youth Service, Gillis Centre, 113 Whitehouse Loan, EDINBURGH EH9 1BB. ☎ 0131-452 8247

4. YOUTH FOR LOURDES
Mr. Patrick Barry, 36 Bartongate Avenue, EDINBURGH EH4 8BG. ☎ 0131-538 1170

5. S.C.I.A.F.
  Miss Miriam McHardy, SCIAF, 19 Park Circus, GLASGOW G3 6BE
     ☎ 0141-354 5555

6. SALESIAN VOLUNTEERS & YOUTH PROJECTS
  Rev. Peter Johnson, 631 Ferry Road, EDINBURGH EH4 2TT. ☎ 0131-315
  2571.

CATHEDRAL CHAPTER
(Erected, 23rd December, 1885.)

Provost:	Very Reverend Thomas Hanlon
Canons:	Right Rev. Mgr. Anthony McNally, V.G.
	(Canon Theologian)
	Very Rev. Patrick Rourke
	Very Rev. James Rae *(Secretary)*
	Very Rev. Michael McCullagh
	Very Rev. Michael J. Cassidy
	(Canon Penitentiary)
	Very Rev. Philip Doherty
	Very Rev. John McAllister
	Very Rev. Liam Healy
	Very Rev. Brian Byrne
	Very Rev. Alexander Bremner
	Very Rev. John Urquhart
	Very Rev. Stephen Judge
Honorary Canons:	Right Rev. Ian Murray,
	Bishop of Argyll and The Isles
	Right Rev. Mgr. Patrick J. Grady,
	Prot.Ap., B.A.
	Very Rev. Michael O'Connor
	Very Rev. Hugh Gordon
	Very Rev. John McNay
	Very Rev. William Anthony
	Very Rev. Lawrence Glancey, Ph.L., M.A.
	Very Rev. Peter Gallacher, M.A., Dip. Ed.
	Very Rev. Richard Somers, B.A.
	Very Rev. Daniel J. Boyle, M.A.
	Very Rev. John Rogerson
	Very Rev. Eamon O'Brien

DEANERIES.

1. St. Thomas of Aquin: Cathedral; Holy Cross; Sacred Heart; St. Albert the Great; St. Columba's; St. Joseph's House; St. Mark; St Patrick; St. Peter; Polish Community; Ukranian Community.

Dean—Rev. Alexander Mitchell
Secretary - Vacant.

2. Holy Rood: St. Catherine of Alexandria; St. Gregory the Great; St. John the Evangelist;, St. John Vianney; St. Mary Magdalene; St. Mary, Star of the Sea; SS Ninian & Triduana; St. Teresa of Lisieux.

Dean—Rev. Kenneth Owens
Secretary - Rev. Michael Sloan

3. St. Augustine: St. Andrew; St. Cuthbert; St. John Ogilvie; St. John the Baptist; St. Joseph; St. Kentigern; St. Margaret; St. Margaret Mary; St. Paul; Currie; Ratho; South Queensferry.

Dean—Right Rev. Mgr. Anthony Duffy
Secretary - Rev. Nicholas Hodgson

4.. St. Andrew: Aberdour; Bowhill; Burntisland; Falkland; St. Mary, Mother of God Glenrothes; St. Paul, Glenrothes; Our Lady of Perpetual Succour, Kirkcaldy; St. Pius X , Kirkcaldy; Leven; Methil; Pittenweem & Craill; Kennoway; St. Andrews.

Dean—Rev. Brian M. Halloran.
Secretary - Rev. Aidan Cannon

5. St. Cuthbert: Duns & Eyemouth; Galashiels; Gattonside; Hawick; Innerleithen; Jedburgh; Kelso; Peebles; Selkirk & Melrose & Earlston.

Dean—Rev. John Creanor.
Secretary - Rev. John Robinson

6. St. David: Bonnyrigg & Rosewell; North Berwick; Dalkeith; Dunbar; Gorebridge; Haddington; Loanhead; Musselburgh; Newbattle; North Berwick; Nunraw; Pathhead; Penicuik; Tranent; Prestonpans; St. Joseph's Hospital; Tranent.

Dean—Rev. Patrick Boylan
Secretary - Rev. John McInnes

7. St. Margaret: Ballingry; Cowdenbeath; Our Lady of Lourdes Dunfermline; St. Margaret, Dunfermline; Inverkeithing; Kelty, Lochgelly; Lochore; Oakley; Rosyth; H.M.S. Cochrane, Rosyth.

Dean—Rev. David Barr.
Secretary - Rev. Daniel Doherty

8. St. Mary: Addiewell; Armadale; Bathgate; Blackburn; Broxburn; East Calder; Fauldhouse; Linlithgow; Stoneyburn; St. Andrew, Livingston; St. Peter, Livingston, St. Philip Livingston; West Calder, Whitburn; Winchburgh.

Dean—Rev. Allan Chambers
Secretary - Rev . James Peat

9. St Mungo; Bo'ness; Bonnybridge; St. Francis Xavier, Falkirk; St. Mary of the Angels, Falkirk; Christ the King, Grangemouth; Sacred Heart, Grangemouth; Larbert; Polmont; Slamanan; Polish Community,

Dean—Very Rev. John Canon Urquhart
Secretary - Rev. Simon Hughes

10. St. Ninian; Banknock; Bannockburn; Blanefield; Buchlyvie; Cowie; Denny; Kilsyth; Lennoxtown; Milton of Campsie; Holy Spirit, Stirling; St. Margaret of Scotland, Stirling; St. Mary, Stirling; Torrance.

Dean:—Vacant.
Secretary - Rev. Gerard Hand

CITY OF EDINBURGH

(Corresponding to the former County of the City of Edinburgh.)

ST. MARY'S CATHEDRAL (1814, 1896) Broughton St.

Rev. David Gemmell, M.Th., *Administrator* (1978)
Rev. John Cudlipp, B.D. (1997)
Rev. Andrzey Kozminski, S.A.C. (1988)

POSTAL ADDRESS: Cathedral House, 61 York Place, EDINBURGH EH1 3JD.
☎ 0131-556 1798/0027; Fax: 0131-556 4281.

E-mail:Stmaryscathedral@bt.internet.com

Website: http://www.btinternet.com/~stmaryscathedral/st_marys/
Sunday Masses: Vigil-Mass, 6 p.m.; 7.30, 9.30, 11.30 a.m., 7.30 p.m. Holy
Days of Obligation, Masses: Vigil-Mass 6 p.m.; 7.30, 9.30 a.m., 12.45, 7.30
p.m. Confessions: Saturday, 10.30 to 11.30 a.m., 1.15 to 2, 5 to 5.45p.m.
Estimated Catholic population: 1,300.

ORATORY OF ST. ANNE, 9 RANDOLPH PLACE (1931), SERVED FROM THE
CATHEDRAL. SERVICES AS ANNOUNCED.
CONVENT OF THE SACRED HEART, 11 EYRE PLACE, EDINBURGHEH3 5ES.
☎0131-558 1629.
MISSIONARIES OF CHARITY, 18 HOPETOUN CRESCENT, EDINBURGH EH7 4AY.
☎0131-556 5444
VICTORIA MANOR NURSING HOME ATTENDED FROM THE CATHEDRAL
ST. MARY'S PRIMARY SCHOOL[1].

ST. ALBERT THE GREAT (established 1931, Parish erected 1971), Catholic Chaplaincy: University of Edinburgh and Edinburgh College of Art; George Square.

Very Rev. Euan Marley, O.P., M.A., *Prior, Parish Priest* (1994)
Rev. Bede Bailey, O.P. (1941)
Rev. Fergus Kerr, O.P., M.A., S.T.M., D.D. (1962)
Rev. Anthony Axe, O.P., B.A., M.A. (1982)
Rev. Richard Conrad, O.P., S.T.L., M.A., Ph.D. (1985)
Rev. Thomas Kearns, O.P., *Chaplain* (1991)
Bro. John Martin McGowan, O.P.

POSTAL ADDRESS: Blackfriars, 25 George Square, EDINBURGH EH8 9LD.
☎ 0131-650 0900; Fax.: 0131 650 0902.
E-mail: stdoms@globalnet.co.uk

Sunday Masses: 9, 10, 11 a.m., 12 noon; 7.15 p.m. (in University term
only). Evening Prayer, 5.40 p.m.Holy Days of Obligation, Masses: 12.15,
5.15 p.m. Confessions: at call.

ST. ANDREW, Ravelston (1900, 1901), Belford Road. (United with St. Margaret, Davidson's Mains, 1989)

Very Rev. Stephen Canon Judge, B.D., M.Th. (1958)

Postal address: St. Margaret's, 149 Main Street, Davidson's Mains, EDINBURGH EH4 5AQ. ☎ 0131-336 1083.

Sunday Mass: 9.30 a.m. Holy Days of Obligation, Masses: 9.30 a.m., 7.30 p.m.
Estimated Catholic population: 600.

LYNEDOCH NURSING HOME, MURRAYFIELD NURSING HOME, TOWER NURSING HOME AND STRACHAN HOUSE (KIRKCARE) ATTENDED FROM ST. MARGARET'S.

ST. ANDREW, UKRAINIAN CATHOLIC CHURCH OF OUR LADY OF POCHAEV AND, Dalmeny Street (1947, 1965)—page 407.

ST. ANNE'S ORATORY (1931), 9 Randolph Place, served from the Cathedral.

Services as announced.

ST. CATHERINE OF ALEXANDRIA, Gracemount (1947, 1958), Gracemount Drive.

Rev. Michael Fallon (1977)
Sr. Mary Steedman, R.S.M.

POSTAL ADDRESS: St. Catherine's, 2 Captains Row, EDINBURGH EH16 6QP.
☎ 0131-664 1596.
E-mail:mikefallon@zoom.co.uk

Sunday Masses: Vigil-Mass, 6.30 p.m.; 10.30 a.m. Holy Days of Obligation, Masses: Vigil-Mass 7.30 p.m., 10 a.m., 7.30 p.m. Confessions: Saturday, 5.30 to 6.15 p.m.
Estimated Catholic population: 1,000.

SOUTHFIELD HOSPITAL, BALM WELL HOUSE, FAIRMILE MARIE CURIE CENTRE, GUTHRIE COURT AND LIBERTON GARDENS AND PRINCESS MARGARET ROSE ORTHOPAEDIC HOSPITAL, ATTENDED FROM ST. CATHERINE'S.
ST. CATHERINE'S PRIMARY SCHOOL.

ST. COLUMBA, Newington (1889), Upper Gray Street.

Right Rev. Mgr. Anthony Canon McNally, V.G. (1955)

POSTAL ADDRESS: St. Columba's, 9 Upper Gray Street, EDINBURGH EH9
1SN. ☎ 0131-667 1605.

Sunday Masses: 11 a.m., 6.30 p.m. Holy Days of Obligation, Masses: 9.30
a.m., 7.30 p.m. Confessions: Saturday, 10.30 to 11 a.m., 6 to 6.30 p.m.
Estimated Catholic population: 1,000.

HELPERS OF THE HOLY SOULS, 47 MAYFIELD ROAD, EDINBURGH EH9 2NQ.
☎0131-668 2202.
ROYAL BLIND SCHOOL, CRAIGMILLAR PARK, AND ROYAL HOSPITAL FOR SICK
CHILDREN, SCIENNES ROAD, ATTENDED FROM ST. COLUMBA'S.

ST. CUTHBERT, Slateford (1889, 1896), Slateford Road.

Right Rev. Mgr. Anthony L. Duffy (1973)

POSTAL ADDRESS: St. Cuthbert's, 104 Slateford Road, EDINBURGH EH14 1PT.
☎ 0131-443 1317 (or, during Diocesan Office hours, 0131-452 8244.)

Sunday Masses: Vigil-Mass, 6 p.m.; 10 a.m. Evening Service: as
announced. Holy Days of Obligation, Masses: 9.30 a.m., 7.30 p.m.
Confessions: Saturday, after 10 a.m. Mass; at other times by appointment.
Estimated Catholic population: 1,050.

ST. CUTHBERT'S PRIMARY SCHOOL.

ST. GREGORY THE GREAT, The Inch (1972), Walter Scott Avenue.

Rev. Kenneth J. Owens, B.Sc., Ph.B., S.T.L., M.P.S. (1989)
Rev. William McGeady (1997)

POSTAL ADDRESS: St. Gregory the Great, 19 Ellangowan Terrace,
EDINBURGH EH16 5TD. ☎ 0131-664 4349.

Sunday Mass: 9.30 a.m. Holy Days of Obligation, Masses:10 a.m.,
6 p.m. Confessions: Saturday, after 10 a.m. Mass; on request.
Estimated Catholic population: 1,000.

LIBERTON HOSPITAL ATTENDED FROM ST. GREGORY'S.
(ST. JOHN VIANNEY'S PRIMARY SCHOOL.)

HERIOT-WATT UNIVERSITY—See Riccarton page 116.

HOLY CROSS, Trinity (1922, 1925). Bangholm Loan, Ferry Road.

Rev. James G. Tracey (1988)

POSTAL ADDRESS: Holy Cross, 11 Bangholm Loan, EDINBURGH EH5 3AH. ☎/Fax: 0131-552 3957.

E-mail: j.tracey@talk21.com

Sunday Masses: Vigil-Mass, 6.30 p.m.; l0 a.m. Holy Days of Obligation, Masses: 9.30 a.m., in school; 7 p.m. Confessions: anytime, on request. Estimated Catholic population: 1,050.   ✎ ♿

FOCOLARE COMMUNITY, 14 SUMMERSIDE PLACE, EDINBURGH EH6 4NZ. ☎ 0131-554 6976.
ST. COLUMBA'S HOSPICE, BONNINGTON NURSING HOME, BRAEBURN HOUSE NURSING HOME, EILDON LODGE NURSING HOME, TRINITY LODGE NURSING HOME, ABBEYFIELD HOUSES (Inverlieth Row and Laverockbank Terrace),VIEWPOINT HOUSING (Inverleith Terrace and Lennox House) AND LEONARD CHESHIRE FOUNDATION ATTENDED FROM HOLY CROSS.
HOLY CROSS PRIMARY SCHOOL.

ST. JOHN THE BAPTIST, Corstorphine (1938, 1963), St. Ninian's Road.

Rev. Charles Barclay (1961)

POSTAL ADDRESS: St. John the Baptist, 37 St. Ninian's Road, EDINBURGH EH12 8AL. ☎ 0131-334 1693; Fax: 0131-334 9441.
E-mail: charles.barclay@virgin.net.

Sunday Masses: Vigil-Mass, 6 p.m.; 10 a.m. Evening Service: as announced. Holy Days of Obligation, Masses: 9.30 a.m., 7.30 p.m. Confessions: Saturday, 9.30 to 10.00 a.m.; on request.   ✎ Ⓐ
Estimated Catholic population: 1,010.

QUEEN MARGARET UNIVERSITY COLLEGE, CORSTORPHINE HOSPITAL AND MURRAYFIELD HOSPITAL, BELGRAVE LODGE NURSING HOME, CORSTORPHINE NURSING HOME, PENTLAND HOME, TOR NURSING HOME, KIRK CARE SHELTERED HOUSING COMPLEX, MURRAY COTTAGES,SAUNDERS COURT, STRUAN LODGE, CLAYPOT PARK AND THE CEDARS ATTENDED FROM ST. JOHN'S.
ST. AUGUSTINE'S HIGH SCHOOL, (FOX COVERT R.C. PRIMARY SCHOOL).

ST. JOHN THE EVANGELIST Portobello (1835, 1906), Brighton Place.

Very Rev. James Canon Rae (1951)

POSTAL ADDRESS: St. John's, 3 Sandford Gardens, EDINBURGH EH15 1LP. ☎ 0131-669 5447.

Sunday Masses: Vigil-Mass, 6.30 p.m.; 10 a.m., 6.30 p.m. Holy Days of Obligation, Masses:10 a.m., 7 p.m. Confessions: Saturday, 10.30 a.m.
Estimated Catholic population: 1,900. 🎗 ♿

CONVENT OF THE SACRED HEART, 16/18 WESTBANK PLACE, SEAVIEW GATE, EDINBURGH EH15 IUD. ☎0131-669 5403; FAX: 0131-669 7973.
WORD INCARNATE COMMUNITY, LINDISFARNE HOUSE, 5 SANDFORD GARDENS, EDINBURGH EH15 ILP ☎ 0131-669 7973.
ST. JOHN'S PRIMARY SCHOOL; HOLY ROOD HIGH SCHOOL.

ST. JOHN OGILVIE, Wester Hailes (1970, 1978), Murrayburn Drive.

Rev. Michael O'Connor, O.M.I. (1973)

POSTAL ADDRESS: St. John Ogilvie's, 159 Sighthill Drive, EDINBURGH EH11 4PY. ☎ 0131-453 5035.
Sunday Masses: Vigil-Mass, 6.30 p.m.; 9, 11 a.m. Holy Days of Obligation
Masses: 9.15 a.m., 7.30 p.m. Confessions: Saturday, 7.15 p.m.
Estimated Catholic population: 1,800. Ⓐ

URSULINES OF JESUS, 19 SIGHTHILL CRESCENT, EDINBURGH EH11 4QE. ☎ 0131-453 6265.
MILESTONE HOUSE ATTENDED FROM ST. JOHN OGILVIE'S.
(ST. JOSEPH'S PRIMARY SCHOOL, Broomhouse; ST. AUGUSTINE'S HIGH SCHOOL, Broomhall)).

ST. JOHN VIANNEY, Gilmerton (1952), Fernieside Gardens.

Rev. Kenneth J. Owens, B.Sc., Ph.B., S.T.L., M.P.S. (1989)
Rev. William McGeady (1997)

POSTAL ADDRESS: St. John Vianney's, 40 Fernieside Gardens, Gilmerton, EDINBURGH EH17 7HN. ☎ 0131-658 1793/664 4349; Fax:0131-658 1793.
E-mail:K.Owens@btinternet.com
Sunday Masses:10,30 a.m. Evening Service as announced. Holy Days of Obligation, Masses: 10 a.m., 7.30 p.m. Confessions: on request.
Estimated Catholic population: 800. 🎗 Ⓐ

CONVENT OF THE SACRED HEART, 51 FERNIEHILL ROAD, GILMERTON, EDINBURGH EH17 7BL. ☎0131-664 7188.
CONVENT OF THE GOOD SHEPHERD, 449 GILMERTON ROAD, EDINBURGH EH17 7JG. ☎0131-664 3463.
ST. BARNABAS' SHELTERED HOME, CRAIGOUR HOME, GILMERTON NURSING HOME AND MURRAY HOME SERVED FROM ST. JOHN VIANNEY'S.
(ST. JOHN VIANNEY PRIMARY SCHOOL).

ST. JOSEPH, Sighthill (1953, 1950), Broomhouse Street North.

Rev. John Reid, O.S.A., S.T.L., B.A. (1970)
Rev. Benedict Beary, O.S.A., (1976)
Rev. Laurence Brasill, O.S.A., S.T.L., M.A. (1966)

POSTAL ADDRESS: St. Joseph's, 20A Broomhouse Place North, EDINBURGH EH11 3UE. ☎ 0131-443 3777. Fax.: 0131-443 9290

Sunday Masses: 8.30 a.m., 11 a.m. Holy Days of Obligation, Masses: 9.30 a.m. (school), 12.30, 7 p.m. Confessions:any time on request
Estimated Catholic population: 1,000.   Ⓐ

H.M.PRISON EDINBURGH ATTENDED FROM ST. JOSEPH'S (MASS, 9 A.M. SATURDAY).
FORD'S ROAD RESIDENTIAL HOME ATTENDED FROM ST. JOSEPH'S.
ST. JOSEPH'S PRIMARY SCHOOL.

ST. KENTIGERN, Barnton (1966), Parkgrove Avenue.

Rev. Nicholas C. Hodgson, Ph.B., S.T.L., J.C.L. (1990)

POSTAL ADDRESS: St. Kentigern's, 26 Parkgrove Avenue, EDINBURGH EH4 7QR. ☎ 0131-336 4984.

Sunday Masses: 9, 11 a.m. Holy Days of Obligation, Masses: Vigil Mass, 7.30 p.m., 9.15 a.m. Confessions: after weekday Mass.
Estimated Catholic population: 2,000.   ♫ ♿

BALFOUR COURT, CLERMISTON HOUSE, STUART COURT AND THE MARGARET BLACKWOOD HOUSING ASSOCIATION ATTENDED FROM ST. KENTIGERN'S.
FOX COVERT R.C.PRIMARY SCHOOL.

ST. MARGARET, Davidson's Mains, (1958, 1953), Main Street. (United with St. Andrew, Ravelston, 1989).

Very Rev. Stephen Canon Judge, B.D., M.Th. (1958)

POSTAL ADDRESS: St. Margaret's, 149 Main Street, Davidson's Mains, EDINBURGH EH4 5AQ. ☎ 0131-336 1083.

Sunday Masses: Vigil-Mass, 6.15 p.m, 11.30 a.m. Holy Days of Obligation Masses: Vigil-Mass, 7 p.m.; 9.30 a.m. Confessions: as announced. Estimated Catholic population: 440.   🎗 Ⓐ

ST. JOHN RESPITE HOME, LYNEDOCH NURSING HOME, MURRAYFIELD NURSING HOME, TOWER NURSING HOME, SILVERLEA RESPITE HOME AND STRACHAN HOUSE ATTENDED FROM ST. MARGARET'S.
(FOX COVERT R.C.PRIMARY SCHOOL.)

ST. MARGARET MARY, Granton (1939), Boswall Parkway.

Very Rev. Michael J. Canon Cassidy (1954)
Sr. Rose Swan *(Parish Sister,*☎ 0131-552 7482)

POSTAL ADDRESS: St. Margaret Mary's, 87 Boswall Parkway, EDINBURGH EH5 2JQ. ☎ 0131-552 4782.   🎗 Ⓐ

Sunday Masses: Vigil-Mass, 5.30 p.m.; 10.30 a.m. Evening Service: as announced. Holy Days of Obligation, Masses: Vigil-Mass, 7.30 p.m.; 10 a.m., 7.30 p.m. Confessions: Saturday, after 10.30 a.m. Mass, after Vigil-Mass; on request.
Estimated Catholic population: 1,000.

FRANCISCAN SISTERS OF THE IMMACULATE CONCEPTION, QUEEN MARGARET'S FRANCISCAN HOUSE, 87A BOSWALL PARKWAY, EDINBURGH EH5 2JQ. ☎ 0131-552 7482).
CHESHIRE HOMES, EAGLE LODGE, FERRYFIELD HOUSE AND ASHBROOK CENTRE ATTENDED FROM ST. MARGARET MARY'S.
(ST. DAVID'S PRIMARY SCHOOL, HOLY CROSS PRIMARY SCHOOL).

ST. MARK, Oxgangs (1961, 1962), Oxgangs Avenue.

Rev. Alexander J. Mitchell (1968)

POSTAL ADDRESS: St. Mark's Presbytery, Oxgangs Avenue, EDINBURGH EH13 9HX. ☎ 0131-441 3915.

Sunday Masses: 9, 11 a.m., 6 p.m. Holy Days of Obligation, Masses: 9 a.m. 7.30 p.m. Confessions: Saturday, 6 to 7 p.m.; on request.
Estimated Catholic population: 2,500.   🎗 ♿

NAPIER UNIVERSITY SERVED FROM ST. MARK'S.
PRIMARY SCHOOL.

ST. MARY MAGDALENE, Bingham and Magdalene, Portobello (1961, 1966), Bingham Avenue.

Rev. Thomas Hennessy (1959)

POSTAL ADDRESS: 16 Milton Crescent, EDINBURGH EH15 3PF. ☎ 0131-669 3611.

Sunday Mass: 10 a.m. Evening Service: as announced. Holy Days of Obligation, Masses: 10 a.m., 7 p.m. Confessions: Saturday, after morning Mass; by request.
Estimated Catholic population: 360.

Ⓐ

KIRKCARE SHELTERED HOUSING COMPLEX, JEWEL HOUSE OLD PERSONS' HOME AND SOUTHPARK RETIREMENT HOME ATTENDED FROM ST. MARY MAGDALENE'S.
(ST. JOHN'S PRIMARY SCHOOL, Portobello.)

ST. MARY, STAR OF THE SEA, Leith (1847, 1852), Constitution Street.

Very Rev. Malachy Sheehan, O.M.I., *Superior* (1957)
Rev. Terence Williams-Keogh, O.M.I. (1977)

POSTAL ADDRESS: St. Mary, Star of the Sea, 106 Constitution Street, Leith, EDINBURGH EH6 6AW. ☎ 0131-554 2482; 0131-467 7449; Fax: 0131-553 1660.

Sunday Masses: Vigil-Mass, 6 p.m.; 10, 11.30 a.m. Evening Service, First Sunday, 5.30 p.m. (Catholic Men's Society, Procession and Benediction of the Blessed Sacrament). Holy Days of Obligation, Masses: Vigil-Mass, 7.30 p.m.; 8 a.m., 12.15 p.m. Confessions: Saturday, 10.30 to 11.30 a.m., 5.30 to 5.50 p.m., after Vigil-Mass.
Estimated Catholic population: 2,000.

Ⓢ Ⓐ

HOLY FAMILY CONVENT, 10 JOHN'S PLACE, LEITH, EDINBURGH EH6 7EL. ☎ 0131-554 6585.
LEITH HOSPITAL, CLAREMONT, FERRYLEA AND PORT HAVEN NURSING HOMES, L'ARCHE COMMUNITY, DONALDSON COURT, GORDON COURT, MANDERSON COURT AND ST. NICHOLAS COURT SHELTERED HOUSING ATTENDED FROM ST. MARY'S.
ST. MARY'S PRIMARY SCHOOL, (HOLY CROSS PRIMARY SCHOOL).

SS. NINIAN AND TRIDUANA, Restalrig (1906, 1932), Marionville Road.

Rev. Michael Sloan (1974)

POSTAL ADDRESS: St. Ninian's, 232 Marionville Road, EDINBURGH EH7 6BE. ☎ 0131-661 2867.

E-mail:ninians@dircon.co.uk
Sunday Masses: Vigil-Mass, 5 p.m.; 10.15 a.m. Holy Days of Obligation, Masses: Vigil-Mass, 7.30 p.m.; 10 a.m. Confessions: on request.
Estimated Catholic population: 2,000.

EASTERN CENERAL HOSPITAL AND ELSIE INGLIS NURSING HOME ATTENDED FROM ST. NINIAN'S.
ST. NINIAN'S PRIMARY SCHOOL.

ST. PATRICK (1834; built 1771 as an Episcopalian church, re-opened as a Catholic church, 1856), Cowgate.

Very Rev. Godfrey Tortolano, O.F.M., *Guardian and Parish Priest* (1960)
Rev. Stephen McGrath, O.F.M., *Vicar* (1960)
Rev. Bartholomew Timoney, O.F.M., L.R.A.M., A.R.C.M. (1955)
Rev. Con O'Connell, O.F.M. (1955)
Rev. Alberic Torrens, O.F.M. (1956)
Sister Patricia Fallon, D.C., *Parish Sister*

POSTAL ADDRESS: Franciscan Friary, 5 South Gray's Close, 40 High Street, EDINBURGH EH1 1TQ. ☎ 0131-556 1973; Fax.: 0131-557 4650
E-mail:stpatricks@btinternet.com

Sunday Masses: Vigil-Mass, 5 p.m.; 9, 11 a.m., 4.30 p.m. Holy Days of Obligation, Masses: Vigil-Mass, 6 p.m.; 8 a.m., 12.30 p.m. Confessions: Saturday, 11.30 a.m. to 12.30 p.m.; Monday to Friday, 12 noon to 12.15 p.m.
Estimated Catholic population: 700.
The Registers of the former Parish of St Francis, Lothian Street, are preserved in St Patrick's.

JERICHO BENEDICTINE HOSTEL, OLD ST. FRANCIS', 53 LOTHIAN STREET, EDINBURGH EH1 1HB. ☎0131-225 8230.
CITY MORTUARY ATTENDED FROM ST. PATRICK'S.

ST. PAUL, Muirhouse (1969, 1971), Muirhouse Avenue.
Parish Staff: Very Rev. Christopher Heaps, S.D.B. (1990)
Sr. Maureen Dunn, D.C.
Hospital Chaplaincy: Rev. Peter Dooley, S.D.B. (1961)

Youth Co-ordinator:
Rev. Peter Johnson, S.D.B., C.Q. S.W. (1993)

In Community:
Rev. James Maher, S.D.B. (1945)
Rev. Terence Lavery, S.D.B. (1958)

POSTAL ADDRESS: St. Paul's, 4 Muirhouse Avenue, Edinburgh EH4 4UB.
☎ 0131-332 3320; Fax: 0131-539 5687.
E-mail:sdb_edinburgh@msn.com

Sunday Masses: 9.15, 11.15 a.m. Holy Days of Obligation, Masses: 10 a.m.,
7 p.m. Confessions: Saturday, 10.30 to 11 a.m.; on request.
Estimated Catholic population: 1,000.

DAUGHTERS OF CHARITY OF ST. VINCENT DE PAUL, ST. VINCENT'S CONVENT, 629
FERRY ROAD, EDINBURGH EH4 2TT. ☎0131-315 2059.
ROYAL VICTORIA HOSPITAL, WESTERN GENERAL HOSPITAL, CRAIGROYSTON
COMMUNITY HIGH SCHOOL AND SILVERLEA OLD FOLK'S HOME ATTENDED FROM
ST. PAUL'S.
ST. DAVID 'S PRIMARY SCHOOL.

ST. PETER, Morningside (1906, 1907), Falcon Avenue.

Rev. Francis Kerr (1970)

POSTAL ADDRESS: St. Peter's, 77 Falcon Avenue, Morningside, EDINBURGH
EH10 4AN. ☎ 0131-447 2502.

Sunday Masses: 9, 11 a.m., 5.30 p.m. Holy Days of Obligation, Masses: 9.30
a.m., 6.30 p.m. Confessions: Saturday, 11.15 to 11.45 a.m., 6.30 to 7 p.m.;
by request at presbytery.
Estimated Catholic population: 1,200.

CONVENT OF THE SACRED HEART, HOUSE OF PRAYER, 8 NILE GROVE, EDINBURGH
EH10 4RF. ☎0131-447 1772 (ADMINISTRATION)/0990 (COMMUNITY).
LITTLE COMPANY OF MARY, MARIAN HOUSE, 7 OSWALD ROAD, EDINBURGH EH9
2HE. ☎0131-667 0148. (SERVED FROM ST. PATRICK'S).
ST. MARGARET'S CONVENT (URSULINES OF JESUS), 88 STRATHEARN ROAD,
EDINBURGH EH9 4AQ. ☎0131-447 2278. (SERVED BY CANON ROGERSON).
ABBEYFIELD HOUSES, (BRAID AVENUE, CANAAN LANE, COLINTON ROAD, GRANGE
LOAN, GREENHILL PLACE, POLWARTH TERRACE); VIEWPOINT HOUSING
(KILRAVOCK, ST. RAPHAEL'S, CUNNINGHAME HOUSE, MORNINGSIDE DRIVE); THE
ELMS, MORLICH HOUSE, OAKLANDS, PITSLIGO HOUSE, STRATHEARN HOUSE,
SUNNYSIDE, (RETIRED PEOPLE'S HOMES); ASHFIELD, ASHLEY COURT, BRAIDVIEW,
CHURCH HILL, CHAMBERLAIN, CLUNY LODGE, COLINTON,DUNVEGAN, THE
HERMITAGE, MORNINGSIDE (NURSING HOMES); THE ROYAL BLIND ASYLUM HOME
AND SCHOOL; GARVALD HOUSE COMMUNITY, RESIDENTIAL ACCOMMODATION FOR

PEOPLE WITH SPECIAL NEEDS: 4 GREENHILL TERRACE, 162 CRAIGLEA DRIVE, 38 GREENHILL GARDENS, 65 MORNINGSIDE DRIVE AND 35 & 37 MORNINGSIDE PARK, ALL ATTENDED FROM ST. PETER'S.

THE ROYAL EDINBURGH HOSPITAL: MASSES: WEDNESDAY, 3 P.M., THIRD SATURDAY OF THE MONTH, 2.30 P.M. CHAPLAINS. REV. FRANCIS KERR (ST. PETER'S), SISTER PATRICIA FOGARTY (ST. MARGARET'S CONVENT).

ASTLEY-AINSLIE HOSPITAL: CHAPLAINS: REV FRANCIS KERR, (ST PETER'S); MRS. SHEILA DUFFY (☎0131-447 8671).

ST. PETER'S PRIMARY SCHOOL.

THE SACRED HEART OF JESUS, Lauriston(1859, 1860), Lauriston Street.

Very Rev. Jack Mahoney, S.J., *Superior* (1962)

Parish Staff: Rev. Peter Randall, S.J., *Parish Priest (1997)*

Sr. Annunciata Glancy, R.S.M.
Sr. Anne Haugh, L.C.M.

Hospital Chaplain: To be notified
Also in Residence:
Rev. Isaias Gerard Capaldi, S.J. (1939)
Rev. John McQuade, S.J. (1950)
Rev. James O'Neill, S.J. (1946)
Rev. James Quinn, S.J. (1950)
Rev. Joseph Senespleda, S.J. (1958)

POSTAL ADDRESS: Sacred Heart, 28 Lauriston Street, EDINBURGH EH3 9DJ. ☎ (*Parish*) 0131-229 9821; (*Community*) 0131-229 9104.; Fax: 0131-228 5142.

E-mail: sacdheart@aol.com

Sunday Masses: Vigil-Mass, 6.30 p.m.; 7.45, 10, 11.15 a.m., 8 p.m. Evening Service as announced. Holy Days of Obligation, Masses: Vigil-Mass, 5.45 p.m.; 7.45, 10 a.m., 12.30, 5.45 p.m. Confessions: Daily, 12 noon to 12.25 p.m.; Saturday, 1 to 2 p.m., 5 to 6.20 p.m. Exposition of the Blessed Sacrament, Saturday 5 to 6.15 p.m.

Estimated Catholic population: 800.

ST. CATHARINE'S CONVENT OF MERCY, 4 LAURISTON GARDENS, EDINBURGH EH3 9HH. ☎ 0131-229 2659. SERVED FROM SACRED HEART.

ST. JOSEPH'S HOUSE (LITTLE SISTERS OF THE POOR), 43 GILMORE PLACE, EDINBURGH EH3 9NG. ☎0131-229 5672. CHAPLAIN: VERY REV. HUGH CANON GORDON (1937). ☎ 0131-228 9084

THE ROYAL INFIRMARY, THE ROYAL MATERNITY (SIMPSON MEMORIAL) HOSPITAL, CHALMERS HOSPITAL AND EYE PAVILION. CHAPLAIN: ATTENDED FROM SACRED HEART. ☎ 0131-229 9104

ST. THOMAS OF AQUIN'S SECONDARY SCHOOL; (ST. CUTHBERT'S PRIMARY SCHOOL, Slateford; ST. PETER'S PRIMARY SCHOOL, Morningside).

ST. TERESA OF LISIEUX, Craigmillar (1938, 1962), Niddrie Mains Road.

Very Rev. Robert Francis Conway, O.F.M., C.Q.S.W.,
Guardian and Parish Priest (1965)
Rev. Desmond McGuire, O.F.M., *Vicar* (1948)
Rev. Reginald Clancy, O.F.M., B.A.(Hons.) (1955)
Rev. George Brown, O.F.M., M.A. (1958)
Sr. Frances Sugrue, S.M.G, Dip. Theol.,*Parish Sister.*

POSTAL ADDRESS: Franciscan Friary, 120 Niddrie Mains Road, Craigmillar, EDINBURGH EH16 4EG. ☎ 0131-661 2185; Fax:0131-652 0601.

Sunday Masses: Vigil Mass, 6 p.m.; 10.30 a.m. Evening Service: as announced. Holy Days of Obligation, Masses: 6.55, 9.30 a.m., 7 p.m. Confessions: Saturday, 5.30 p.m.; at call.
Estimated Catholic population: 600.   **Ⓐ**

POOR SERVANTS OF THE MOTHER OF GOD, 11/3-4, WAUCHOPE ROAD, EDINBURGH EH16 4PT. ☎0131-661 2296.
CONVENT OF THE LITTLE SISTERS OF THE ASSUMPTION, 2/1 WAUCHOPE ROAD, EDINBURGH EH16 4PU. ☎0131-467 3615.
THE THISTLE FOUNDATION ATTENDED FROM ST. TERESA'S.
ST. FRANCIS PRIMARY SCHOOL; HOLY ROOD HIGH SCHOOL.

GILLIS CENTRE, Marchmont (1993, Chapel opened as Convent Chapel, 1835), Whitehouse Loan. (Former Archdiocesan Major Seminary, 1986).

Rev. Francis Kerr, *Administrator* (1970)
Mrs. Anthea Donaghue, *Centre Manager*

POSTAL ADDRESS: Gillis Centre, 115 Whitehouse Loan, EDIINBURGH EH9 7BB. ☎ 0131-447 2807.

ST. MARGARET'S CONVENT (URSULINES OF JESUS), 88 STRATHEARN ROAD, EDINBURGH EH9 4AQ. ☎ 0131-447 2278. CHAPLAINCY SERVICE PROVIDED BY VERY REV. JOHN CANON ROGERSON.

PARISHES OUTSIDE THE CITY OF EDINBURGH

(The name given last before the name of the Church is the Local Authority).

ABERDOUR, Fife. Served from Burntisland.

ADDIEWELL, West Lothian, St. Thomas, (1913, 1923). Blackburn Road. (Linked with Our Lady and St. Bridget, West Calder, 1998).

Rev. Allan T. Chambers (1980)

POSTAL ADDRESS: St. Mary's, 4 West Road, WEST CALDER EH55 8EF. ☎ & Fax: West Calder (01506)871240.

Sunday Mass: 10.15 a.m. Holy Days of Obligation, Masses as announced locally. Confessions: Saturday, 9.30 a.m.
Estimated Catholic population: 500

ST. THOMAS' PRIMARY SCHOOL.

ARMADALE, West Lothian, The Sacred Heart and St. Anthony (1928, 1974), Wotherspoon Crescent.

Very Rev. Brian P. Canon Byrne (1956)

POSTAL ADDRESS: Sacred Heart and St. Anthony's, 2A Wotherspoon Crescent, Armadale, BATHGATE EH48 2JD. ☎ Armadale (01501) 730261.

Sunday Masses: Vigil-Mass, 6.30 p.m.; 10 a.m. Holy Days of Obligation, Masses: 9 a.m., 7 p.m. Confessions: after each Saturday Mass.
Estimated Catholic population: 1,000.

TIPPETHILL HOSPITAL, COLINSHIEL OLD PEOPLE'S HOME AND OCHILVIEW COURT (SHELTERED HOUSING) ATTENDED FROM ARMADALE.
ST. ANTHONY'S PRIMARY SCHOOL.

AVONBRIDGE, Falkirk, served from Falkirk, St. Francis Xavier's.

AYTON, Berwickshire. Served from Duns.

BALERNO, City of Edinburgh, St. Joseph (1885), Main Street, served from Currie.

Sunday Mass: Vigil-Mass, 6 p.m. Holy Days of Obligation, Mass: 7 p.m. Confessions: by appointment.

ASHLEY GRANGE NURSING HOME SERVED FROM CURRIE.

BALFRON, Stirling, St. Anthony (1867) Dunmore Street. Served from Buchlyvie.

Sunday Mass: 11.30 a.m. Holy Days of Obligation, Mass as announced locally.

BALLINGRY, Fife, St. Bernard (1961, 1959), Hill Road. (United with St. Kenneth, Lochore, 1987 and St. Patrick, Lochgelly, 1995).

Rev. Stuart F. Gray, B.D. (1995)

POSTAL ADDRESS: The Presbytery, Main Street, Glencraig, LOCHGELLY KY5 8AL. ☎ Lochgelly (01592) 860225; Fax: 01592- 861849.
E-mail: Parishoffice@saintlytrio.demon.co.uk

Sunday Masses: Vigil-Mass, 6 p.m.(Ballingry); 10 a.m. (Lochore); 12 noon (Lochgelly). Holy Days of Obligation,Masses: Vigil-Mass, 7 p.m. (Lochore); 9 a.m. (Lochgelly); 10.45 a.m. (Ballingry). Confessions: Saturday, after Vigil-Mass.
Estimated Catholic population: 400.

ST. KENNETH'S PRIMARY SCHOOL.

BANKNOCK, Falkirk, St. Luke's (1969, 1974), Garngrew Road, Haggs.

Rev. Robert Hendrie, Ph.L., S.T.L.(1962)

POSTAL ADDRESS: St. Luke's, Garngrew Road, Haggs, Banknock, BONNYBRIDGE FK4 1HP. ☎/Fax.: Banknock (01324) 840368.
E-mail: slubank@aol.com
Sunday Masses: 10.45 a.m., 6 p.m. Holy Days of Obligation, Masses: 9.30 a.m., 7 p.m. Confessions: Saturday, 6 to 6.45 p.m.
Estimated Catholic popuation: 870.

BANKVIEW NURSING HOME ATTENDED FROM ST. LUKE'S.

BANNOCKBURN, Stirling, Our Lady and St. Ninian (1898, 1927), Quakerfield.

Rev. Patrick Burke, M.Th., S.T.D. (1991)
Sr. Vincent Larkin, D.W. *(Pastoral Assistant)*

POSTAL ADDRESS: Catholic Presbytery, 52 Quakerfield, Bannockburn, STIRLING FK7 8HZ. ☎ /Fax: Bannockburn (01786) 812249.
Sunday Masses: Vigil-Mass, 6.30 p.m.; 12 noon. Holy Days of Obligation Masses: Vigil-Mass, 7 p.m.;11 a.m.Confessions: Friday, after 9.30 a.m. Mass; Saturday 5.30 to 6.15 p.m; by appointment. Exposition of the Blessed Sacrament, Wednesday, 6 to 6.55 p.m.
Estimated Catholic population: 1,500.

BANNOCKBURN HOSPITAL, FAIRVIEW NURSING HOME AND WILLIAM SIMPSON HOME, Plean, ATTENDED FROM ST. NINIAN'S.
ST. MARY'S PRIMARY SCHOOL.

BATHGATE, West Lothian, St. Columba, Kirkton (1978), Marina Road, Boghall (Parish of The Immaculate Conception).

Resident Priest: Rev. George Suszko, S.A.C. (1989)

POSTAL ADDRESS: St. Columba's, 143 Marina Road, Boghall, BATHGATE EH48 1SZ. ☎ Bathgate (01506)653955.
Sunday Mass: 10.30 a.m. Holy Days of Obligation, Mass as arranged.

BATHGATE, West Lothian, The Immaculate Conception (1858, 1908), Livery Street.

Right Rev. Mgr. Alistair Lawson, B.A., V.G. (1966)
Sister Ethna O'Connell, *Parish Sister.*
Sister Nancy Raftery, *Parish Sister.*

POSTAL ADDRESS: St. Mary's, 9 Livery Street BATHGATE EH48 4HS. ☎ Bathgate (01506) 655766. Fax: 01506-631233
E-mail: alistairlawson@lineone.net
Website: http//www.stmarcol.fsnet.co.uk/

Sunday Masses: Vigil-Mass, 6.30 p.m.; 9, 11.30 a.m. Holy Days of Obligation, Masses: Vigil-Mass, 7 p.m.; 9.30 a.m. Confessions: Saturday, after morning Mass, 5 to 6 p.m.
Estimated Catholic population: 3,200.
The Registers of the St. Columba's, Boghall (1978 to 1989), are preserved in St Mary's.

MISSIONARY SISTERS OF THE HOLY ROSARY, 20 KIRK ROAD, BATHGATE EH48 1BN. ☎BATHGATE (01506) 653268.
MEADOWVALE NURSING HOME ATTENDED FROM ST. MARY'S.
ST. MARY'S PRIMARY SCHOOL, ST. COLUMBA'S PRIMARY SCHOOL.

BLACKBURN, West Lothian, Our Lady of Lourdes (1905, 1961), Bathgate Road.(Linked with Our Lady's, Stoneyburn, 1998)

Rev. James A. MacDonald (1989)

POSTAL ADDRESS: Our Lady of Lourdes, 30 Bathgate Road, Blackburn, BATHGATE EH47 7LF. ☎ Bathgate (01506) 652957.

Sunday Masses: Vigil-Mass, 6.30 p.m. 10.30 a.m. Evening Service: as announced. Holy Days of Obligation, Masses as announced. Confessions: Saturday, after 10 a.m. Mass, 5.30 to 6 p.m.
Estimated Catholic population: 1,200.

ALMONDVALE OLD PEOPLE'S HOME AND REDMILL NURSING HOME ATTENDED FROM OUR LADY OF LOURDES.
OUR LADY OF LOURDES PRIMARY SCHOOL, ST. KENTIGERN'S ACADEMY.

BLANEFIELD, Stirling, St. Kessog (1964, 1893), Campsie Dene Road.

Rev. Albert J. Gardner (1970)

POSTAL ADDRESS: St. Kessog's, 4 Campsie Dene Road, Blanefield, GLASGOW G63 9BN. ☎ Blanefield (01360) 770300.

Sunday Mass: 11 a.m. Holy Days of Obligation, Masses:10 a.m., 7 p.m. Confessions: Sunday, 10.15 to 10.45 a.m.
Estimated Catholic population: 300.

LENNOX CASTLE HOSPITAL, Lennoxtown, CLEDDANS NURSING HOME, Blanefield, AND DALNAIR HOUSE, Croftamie, ATTENDED FROM ST. KESSOG'S. DRYMEN SERVED FROM BLANEFIELD.

BO'NESS, Falkirk, St. Mary of the Assumption (1889, 1990), Dean Road.

Rev. Andrew A. Forrest (1959)

POSTAL ADDRESS: St. Mary's Presbytery, Linlithgow Road, BO'NESS EH51 0DP. ☎ Bo'ness (01506) 822339.

Sunday Masses: Vigil-Mass, 6 p.m.; 10.30 a.m. Holy Days of Obligation, Masses: 10 a.m., 7.30 p.m. Confessions: Saturday, after morning Mass, 5.15 to 5.50 p.m.
Estimated Catholic population: 650.

BO'NESS HOSPITAL, ROSYTH HOUSE WOODLANDS HOME AND GRANGE NURSING HOME ATTENDED FROM ST. MARY OF THE ASSUMPTION.
ST. MARY'S PRIMARY SCHOOL.

BONNYBRIDGE, Falkirk, St. Joseph (1910, 1925), Broomhill Road.

Rev. Daniel Boyd, L.C.L. (1961)

POSTAL ADDRESS: St. Joseph's, 30 Broomhill Road, BONNYBRIDGE FK4 2AN.
☎ Bonnybridge (01324) 812417.

Sunday Masses: Vigil-Mass, 6.45 p.m., 11 a.m. Evening Service: as announced. Holy Days of Obligation, Masses: 9.30 a.m., 7 p.m. Confessions: Tuesday, 7.30 p.m.; Saturday, 10.30 a.m.; 7.30 p.m.
Estimated Catholic population: 950.   ⛨ ⛨

BONNYBRIDGE HOSPITAL AND WHEATLANDS HOME ATTENDED FROM ST. JOSEPH'S.
ST. JOSEPH'S PRIMARY SCHOOL.

BONNYRIGG, Midlothian, Our Lady of Consolation (1952, 1957), Hawthornden Avenue. (United with St. Matthew, Rosewell, 1990).

Rev. Hugh White, S.T.L., L.S.S. (1963)
Sr. Rose Harding

POSTAL ADDRESS: St. Matthew's, 36 Carnethie Street, ROSEWELL EH24 9AT.
☎/Fax: 0131-440 2150.
E-mail:hughw@clara.net

Sunday Masses: Vigil-Mass, 6 p.m. 11.30 a.m. Evening Service, as announced. Holy Days of Obligation, Masses as announced locally. Confessions and Night Prayer: Monday, after evening Mass; Confessions, Saturday, after morning Mass.
Estimated Catholic population: (with Rosewell) 1,300.   ⛨

NAZARETH HOUSE, 13 HILLHEAD, BONNYRIGG EH19 2JF ☎0131-663 7191.
CHAPLAIN: REV. JOSEPH WALSH, M.H.M. (1949). ☎0131-654 2513. SUNDAY
MASS: 9.30 A.M. HOLY DAYS OF OBLIGATION, MASS: 9.30 A.M.
CONVENT OF THE SACRED HEART, 28 CAMPVIEW ROAD, BONNYRIGG EH19 3EZ.
☎0131-663 0845.
LASSWADE SERVED FROM BONNYRIGG.
ST. MARY'S PRIMARY SCHOOL.

BOWHILL, Fife, St. Ninian (1920, 1932), Derran Drive. (United with St. Pius X, Kirkcaldy, 1995).

Rev. Christopher Heenan, B.D. (1995)

POSTAL ADDRESS: St. Pius Presbytery, Brodick Road,KIRKCALDY KY2 6EY.
☎ Kirkcaldy (01592) 261901; Fax: 01592-269951.
E-mail: sarto10@aol.com.
Sunday Mass: 12 noon. Holy Days of Obligation, Mass: 10 a.m.
Confessions, on request.
Estimated Catholic population: 750.   ⛨

SUNNYBRAES AND BARROGIL NURSING HOMES ATTENDED FROM ST. PIUS X
ST NINIAN'S PRIMARY SCHOOL.

BROXBURN, West Lothian, SS. John Cantius and Nicholas (1862, 1881), West Main Street.

Rev. James Peat, B.D. (1996)

POSTAL ADDRESS: SS. John Cantius and Nicholas, 34 West Main Street, BROXBURN EH52 5RJ. ☎ Broxburn (01506) 852040.
E-mail: jimpeat@broxburn57.freeserve.co.uk

Sunday Masses: Vigil-Mass, 6.30 p.m.; 9, 11.40 a.m., Holy Days of Obligation, Masses: Vigil-Mass, 7 p.m., 10 a.m. Confessions: Saturday, 9.15 to 9.50 a.m., 5.15 to 6.15 p.m.
Estimated Catholic population: 2,000.

BANGOUR VILLAGE HOSPITAL, BINNY HOUSE (SUE RYDER HOME), GOSHEN HOUSE, MIDDLETON HALL NURSING HOME, STRATHBROCK LODGE AND WESTFIELD HOME ATTENDED FROM BROXBURN.
ST. NICHOLAS' PRIMARY SCHOOL.

BUCHLYVIE, Stirling, St. Patrick's Missionary Society (Kiltegan Fathers), (1965).

Very Rev. Niall Martin, *Superior* (1977)
Rev. Sean O'Dowd, B.A. (1963)
Rev. Seamus Reihill, B.A. (1956)
Rev. Seamus Whelan, B.A. (1961)

POSTAL ADDRESS: St. Patrick's, Buchlyvie, STIRLING FK8 3PB. ☎ Buchlyvie (01360) 850274; Fax: 01360-850552.
E-mail:Stpatsbuch@aol.com.

Sunday Mass: 10 a.m.

BURNTISLAND, Fife, St. Joseph (1930, 1974), Cowdenbeath Road.

Rev. Daniel P. Doherty (1998)

POSTAL ADDRESS: St. Joseph's, East Toll, Cowdenbeath Road, BURNTISLAND KY3 0LJ. ☎ Burntisland (01592) 872207.

Sunday Masses: Vigil-Mass, 6.30 p.m.; 9, 10.30 a.m. Holy Days of Obligation, Masses: Vigil-Mass, 7 p.m.; 10.30 a.m. Confessions: before Mass; on request.
Estimated Catholic population: 500.

ABERDOUR and KINGHORN served from Burntisland.
(ST. MARIE'S PRIMARY SCHOOL, Kirkcaldy).

COLDSTREAM, Scottish Borders. Served from Kelso.

Sunday Mass: 9.15 a.m. in St. Mary's Episcopal Church, Lennel Road.
Confessions, on request, before Mass.

COWDENBEATH, Fife, Our Lady and St. Bride (1902, 1922), Stenhouse Street.

Very Rev. Philip Canon Doherty (1955)

POSTAL ADDRESS: Our Lady and St. Bride's, 74 Stenhouse Street,
COWDENBEATH KY4 9DD. ☎ Cowdenbeath (01383) 510549.

Sunday Masses: 10.30 a.m., 5.30 p.m. Holy Days of Obligation, Masses: 10
a.m., 7 p.m. Confessions: Saturday, after Mass, 6 to 6.30 p.m.
Estimated Catholic population: 902.

ABBOTSFORD NURSING HOME, CRAIGIE HOUSE NURSING HOME AND VALLEY
HOUSE NURSING HOME ATTENDED FROM OUR LADY AND ST. BRIDE'S.
ST. BRIDE'S PRIMARY SCHOOL.

COWIE, Stirling, The Sacred Heart (1915, 1937), Bannockburn Road.

Rev. Patrick Burke, M.Th., S.T.D. (1991)
Sr. Mary Lewis, D.W. *(Pastoral Assistant)*

POSTAL ADDRESS: Catholic Presbytery, 52 Quakerfield, Bannockburn,
STIRLING FK7 8HZ. ☎/Fax: Bannockburn (01786) 812249.

Sunday Mass: 10.30 a.m. Holy Days of Obligation, Mass: 9 30 a.m.
Confessions: Saturday, after Mass; Sunday, 9.45 to 10.15 a.m.
Estimated Catholic population: 500.

DAUGHTERS OF WISDOM, SACRED HEART, BANNOCKBURN ROAD, COWIE,
STIRLING FK7 7BG. ☎BANNOCKBURN (01786) 813466; FAX: (01786) 480414.
ST. MARGARET'S PRIMARY SCHOOL.

CRAIL, Fife, Most Holy Trinity (1942), Westgate North. Served from Pittenweem.

Sunday Mass: 10.05 a.m. Holy Days of Obligation, Mass: 10.05 a.m.

CURRIE, City of Edinburgh, Our Lady, Mother of the Church (1885, 1966), Curriehill Road.

Rev. Stephen A. Gilhooley (1990)

POSTAL ADDRESS: Our Lady's, 222 Lanark Road West, CURRIE EH14 5NW.
☎/Fax: 0131-449 2372.
E-mail: strevegilhooley@virgin.net
Sunday Mass: 11.30 a.m. Holy Days of Obligation, Mass: 10 a.m.
Confessions: by appointment.
Estimated Catholic population: 975*.

ASHLEY GRANGE NURSING HOME ATTENDED FROM OUR LADY'S.
BALERNO AND RATHO SERVED FROM CURRIE.
(ST. CUTHBERT'S PRIMARY SCHOOL, Slateford).

DALKEITH, Midlothian, St. David (1854), Eskbank Road.

Very Rev. Liam Canon Healy (1956)

POSTAL ADDRESS: St. David's, 41 Eskbank Road, DALKEITH EH22 3BH.
☎ 0131-663 4286.

Sunday Masses: Vigil-Mass, 6 p.m.; 10.30 a.m. Evening Service, 4 p.m.
when announced. Holy Days of Obligation Masses: 10.30 a.m., 7.30 p.m.
Confessions: Saturdays, 11 a.m. to 12 noon, 5 to 5.50 p.m.
Estimated Catholic population: 900.

CONVENT OF THE SACRED HEART, "ROSEHILL", PARK ROAD, ESKBANK, DALKEITH
EH22 3DH. ☎0131-660 6602.
ARCHVIEW NURSING HOME, WESTFIELD PARK HOME AND WHITEHILL NURSING
HOME, ATTENDED FROM ST. DAVID'S .
ST. DAVID'S PRIMARY SCHOOL, ST. DAVID'S SECONDARY SCHOOL.

DALKEITH, Midlothian, St. Luke and St. Anne, Mayfield (1948, 1971), Stone Place. (United with St. Margaret, Gorebridge, 1992).

Rev. John E. McInnes, B.D. (1996)

POSTAL ADDRESS: St. Luke's, 2A Stone Place, Mayfield, DALKEITH EH22
5PG. ☎ 0131-663 1476.

Sunday Masses: 11.30 a.m., 6 p.m. Holy Days of Obligation, Masses as
announced. Confessions: Wednesday, 7 to 8 p.m., during Exosition of the
Blessed Sacrament; by appointment .
Estimated Catholic population: 950.

The Registers of the former Parish of St Anne, Newtongrange (closed 1971), are preserved in St.Luke and St, Anne's.

CONVENT OF RELIGIOUS OF JESUS AND MARY, HEBRON, STONE PLACE, MAYFIELD, DALKEITH EH22 5PG. ☎0131-660 3862.
NEWBATTLE LODGE AND DARAG SHELTERED HOUSING (Mayfield) AND ST. ANNE'S SHELTERED HOUSING (Newtongrange) ATTENDED FROM ST. LUKE'S.
ST. LUKE'S PRIMARY SCHOOL.

DENNY, Falkirk, St. Alexander (1890, 1933), Stirling Street.
Rev. Ryszard Holuka, S.T.L., M.A. (1974)

POSTAL ADDRESS: St. Alexander's, 100 Stirling Street, DENNY FK6 6DL. ☎ Falkirk (01324) 823310; Hall, Falkirk (01324) 825372; Fax: 01324-822836;
E.mail:113157.1643@compuserve.com

Sunday Masses: Vigil-Mass, 6 p.m.; 9.30 a.m., 12 noon. Holy Days of Obligation, Masses: 6.45, 9.30a.m., 12.30, 7.30p.m. Confessions: Saturday 10.30 a.m. to 12 noon, 5 to 5.30 p.m.
Estimated Catholic population: 3,000.

STRATHCARRON HOSPICE ATTENDED FROM ST. ALEXANDER'S.
ST. PATRICK'S PRIMARY SCHOOL.

DRYMEN, Stirling. Served from Blanefield.
Sunday Mass, first Sunday in May to last Sunday in October: 5 p.m. in Church of Scotland Hall (opposite car park, Aberfoyle Road).

DUNBAR, East Lothian, Our Lady of the Waves (1877), Westgate.
Rev. Peter Kelly, Dip.Theol., Dip.Phil./Arts (1998)

POSTAL ADDRESS: Our Lady of the Waves, Westgate, DUNBAR EH42 1JL ☎ Dunbar (01368) 862701.
Sunday Masses: Vigil-Mass, 6.30 p.m.; 10.30 a.m.; (July and August) 5 p.m. Evening Service (first Sunday of the month), 4.45 p.m. Holy Days of Obligation, Masses: 9.30 a.m., 7 p.m. Confessions: Saturday, 5.45 to 6.15 p.m.; Sunday, 9.45 to 10.15 a.m.
Estimated Catholic population: 500.

BELHAVEN HOSPITAL, EMMAUS RESIDENTIAL HOME, LAMMERMUIR HOUSE RESIDENTIAL HOME AND ST. ANDREW'S HOUSE RESIDENTIAL HOME, DUNBAR, ATTENDED FROM DUNBAR.

DUNFERMLINE, Fife, St. Margaret (1846, 1896), East Port.

Rev. David M. Barr (1972)

POSTAL ADDRESS: St. Margaret's, 4 Viewfield Terrace, DUNFERMLINE KY12 7HZ. ☎/Fax: Dunfermline (01383) 625611.
E-mail:Dunfermline@saint.margarets.ourfamily.com
Website:www.saint.margarets.ourfamily.com
Sunday Masses: Vigil-Mass, 6.30 p.m.; 9, 11 a.m. Holy Days of Obligation, Masses: Vigil-Mass 7.30p.m.; 10 a.m. Confessions: Saturday, 10.45 a.m. to 12 noon.
Estimated Catholic population: 2,000.

DAUGHTERS OF CHARITY OF ST. VINCENT DE PAUL, ST. MARY'S CONVENT, 4 ARTHUR STREET, DUNFERMLINE KY12 0PR. ☎ DUNFERMLINE (01383) 722474 SERVED FROM ST. MARGARET'S.
QUEEN MARGARET HOSPITAL, CAMERON LODGE, LEYS PARK NURSING HOME, FORREST HOUSE, MATTHEW FYFFE HOME, JEAN MACKIE HOME AND JOHN DOUGLAS HOME ATTENDED FROM ST. MARGARET'S.
ST. MARGARET'S PRIMARY SCHOOL, ST. COLUMBA'S HIGH SCHOOL.

DUNFERMLINE, Fife, Our Lady of Lourdes (1964, 1957), Aberdour Road.

Rev. Thomas Mullen (1977)

POSTAL ADDRESS: Our Lady of Lourdes Presbytery, 67 Aberdour Road, DUNFERMLINE KY11 4QZ. Tel.: Dunfermline (01383) 722202.

Sunday Masses: 10.30 a.m., 5 p.m. Holy Days of Obligation, Masses: as announced. Confessions: Wednesday, 7.30 p.m.; Saturday, 10.30 a.m.
Estimated Catholic population: 1,200.

DUNS, Scottish Borders, Our Lady Immaculate and St. Margaret (1880, 1883), Bridgend.

Rev. David John Henry (1962)

POSTAL ADDRESS: Our Lady and St. Margaret's, 48 Bridgend, DUNS TD11 3EX. ☎ Duns (01361) 883714.

Sunday Masses: Vigil-Mass, 6 p.m.; 9 a.m. Evening Service: as announced. Holy Days of Obligation, Masses: 8 a.m., 7 p.m. Confessions: Saturday, 5.30 to 5.50 p.m.; on request.
Estimated Catholic population: 250.

KNOLL HOSPITAL, Duns, SALT GREENS, Eyemouth, AND SUE RYDER HOME, Marchmont, ATTENDED FROM DUNS.
EYEMOUTH SERVED FROM DUNS.

DYSART, Fife, Carmelite Convent, Hot Pot Wynd. Served from Kirkcaldy, Our Lady of Perpetual Succour ("St. Marie's").

Sunday Mass: 9 a.m. Holy Days of Obligation, Mass: 11.15 a.m.

EARLSTON: Scottish Borders, St. Cuthbert's Chapel Hall, Westfield Road. Served from Galashiels and Selkirk.

Sunday : Vigil-Mass, 7.30 p.m.Weekday Eucharistic Service, Thursday, 11.30 a.m.

St. Andrew's Nursing Home, Drygrange, attended from Selkirk.

EAST CALDER, West Lothian, St. Theresa (1893, 1933), Main Street.

Rev. Thomas W. Flynn, R.G.N. (1976)

Postal address: St. Theresa's, Kilronan Park, 41 Main Street, East Calder, Livingston EH53 0ES. ☎/Fax.: Mid-Calder (01506) 880918.

E-mail:Theresas41@aol.com

Sunday Masses: Vigil-Mass: 6 p.m.; 10.30 a.m. Evening Service: 4 p.m. as announced. Holy Days of Obligation, Masses: 9 a.m., 7 p.m. Confessions: After daily Mass; Saturday, after Vigil-Mass; any time on request. Estimated Catholic population: 500.   🎵 Ⓐ

Linburn (Training Centre for Blind), attended from East Calder. St. Paul's Primary School.

EYEMOUTH, Scottish Borders, St. Andrew(1961), Station Road. Served from Duns.

Sunday Mass: 11 a.m. Evening Service: as announced. Holy Days of Obligation, Mass: Vigil-Mass, previous evening, 7 p.m. Confessions: before Mass; on request.

FALKIRK, St. Francis Xavier (1839, 1961), Hope Street. (United with St. Mary, Slamannan, 1989).

Rev. Philip J. Kerr, Ph.B., S.T.L. (1979)
Rev. Simon Hughes, B.Mus.(Hons.), B.D. (1995)
Rev. Zbigniew Sarelo (1976)

POSTAL ADDRESS: St. Francis Xavier's, 1 Hope Street, Falkirk FK1 5AT.
☎ Falkirk (01324) 623567; Fax: 01324-617145.
E-mail:stfxfalkirk@netscapeonline.co.uk

All Masses, etc., in St. Francis Xavier's unless otherwise stated. Sunday Masses: Vigil-Mass, 7 p.m.; 8.30 (Carmel), 9, 10.30 a.m., 12 noon, 1 p.m. (Polish), 7 p.m. Evening Service: 4.45 p.m. (Carmel). Holy Days of Obligation, Masses: 7, 8.30 (Carmel), 9, 10.30 a.m., 7.30 p.m. Confessions: Thursday, 7 to 7.30 p.m.; Saturday, 10.30 to 11.15 a.m., 6.15 to 7.00 p.m.
Estimated Catholic population: 4,100.

Polish Priest: Rev. Anthony Debkowski (1969), Garfield, Comely Place, Falkirk FK1 1QQ. ☎ Falkirk (01324) 621902.

CARMELITE CONVENT, 3 ARNOTHILL, FALKIRK FKI 5RZ. ☎ FALKIRK (01324) 623352. SERVED FROM ST. FRANCIS XAVIER'S. MASS ON SUNDAYS AND HOLY DAYS OF OBLIGATION: 8.30 A.M.
SISTERS OF ST. MARTHA OF PERIGUEUX, ST. MARTHA'S CONVENT, 25 WELLSIDE PLACE, FALKIRK FKI 5RL. ☎FALKIRK (01324) 628121.
ROYAL INFIRMARY, BURNBRAE HOME, ERIDEN NURSING HOME, GRAHAMSTON HOUSE, NORWOOD HOME AND SUMMERFORD HOME, Falkirk, AND BLACKFAULDS NURSING HOME, Avonbridge, ATTENDED FROM ST. FRANCIS XAVIER'S.
ST. ANDREW'S PRIMARY SCHOOL, ST. FRANCIS XAVIER'S PRIMARY SCHOOL, ST MUNGO'S HIGH SCHOOL.

FALKIRK, St. Mary of the Angels, Camelon (1923, 1960), Glasgow Road.

Rev. Michael Purcell, Ph.L. (Lovan.), M.A. (Lovan.),
Ph.D. (Edin.) (1981)

POSTAL ADDRESS: St. Mary of the Angels, Glasgow Road, Camelon, FALKIRK FK1 4HJ. ☎ /Fax:Falkirk (01324) 621038.
E-mail: M.Purcell@ed.ac.uk

Sunday Masses: Vigil-Mass, 6.30p.m.; 10.30a.m. Evening Service as announced. Holy Days of Obligation, Mass: 7.30 p.m. Confessions: Saturday, 5.30 p.m.
Estimated Catholic population: 700.

DORRATOR COURT SHELTERED HOUSING, "TAYAVALLA" FAMILY SUPPORT SERVICE, FALKIRK GRAMPIAN NURSING HOME, WELLSIDE NURSING HOME AND ROSVAIL SPECIAL SCHOOL ATTENDED FROM ST. MARY OF THE ANGELS.
(ST. FRANCIS XAVIER'S PRIMARY SCHOOL)

FALKLAND, Fife, Chapel Royal (1901; built 1512; re-opened 1934). Served from Leven.

Sunday Mass: 10.15 a.m. Holy Days of Obligation, Mass: Vigil-Mass, 6 p.m. Confessions:as announced.

FAULDHOUSE, West Lothian, St. John the Baptist (1865, 1873), Main Street.

Rev. John Agnew (1961)

POSTAL ADDRESS: St. John's, 115 Main Street, Fauldhouse, BATHGATE EH47 9BJ. ☎ Fauldhouse (01501) 770225.
Sunday Masses: Vigil-Mass, 6.30 p.m.; 9.30, 11.30 a.m. Holy Days of Obligation, Masses: 9 a.m., 7 p.m. Confessions: Tuesday and Saturday, after Mass.
Estimated Catholic population: 875.

BIELD OLD PEOPLE'S HOME AND CROFTHEAD NURSING HOME ATTENDED FROM ST. JOHN'S.
ST. JOHN'S NURSERY AND PRIMARY SCHOOLS.

GALASHIELS, Scottish Borders, Our Lady and St. Andrew (1852, 1858), Market Street.

Rev. John Creanor (1965)

POSTAL ADDRESS: Catholic Presbytery, Market Street, GALASHIELS TD1 1BY. ☎ Galashiels (01896) 752328.

Sunday Masses: Vigil-Mass, 6 p.m.; 11 a.m. Holy Days of Obligation, Masses: 10 a.m. (normally in Primary School), 7.30 p.m. Confessions: Saturday, after 10 a.m. Mass, 5.30 p.m. to start of Vigil-Mass.
Estimated Catholic population: 750.

BORDERS GENERAL HOSPITAL; SCOTTISH COLLEGE OF TEXTILES, Galashiels, DINGLETON HOSPITAL, Melrose, AND HERIOT-WATT UNIVERSITY ATTENDED FROM GALASHIELS.
EARLSTON SERVED FROM GALASHIELS.
ST. MARGARET'S PRIMARY SCHOOL.

GATTONSIDE, The Borders, St. Aidan's Chapel (Brothers of Charity) (1955, 1963).

Chaplain: Rev. Andrzej Kaim, S.A.C.

POSTAL ADDRESS: St. Aidan's, Gattonside, MELROSE TD6 9NW. ☎ Melrose (01896) 822159.

Sunday Mass, 11 a.m. Holy Days of Obligation, Mass, 5 p.m.

GLENROTHES, Fife, St. Mary, Mother of God, Leslie (1966), Leslie High Street.

Rev. Jock J. Dalrymple, M.A., S.T.L. (1986)
Sr. Bridget McCann, S.N.D., *Parish Sister.*

POSTAL ADDRESS: St. Mary's Presbytery, 35 North Street, Leslie, GLENROTHES KY6 3DJ. ☎ Glenrothes (01592) 741963; Fax: (01592) 744781.

Sunday Mass:9.30 a.m. Confessions: alternate Saturdays, 10.30 to 11 a.m. Estimated Catholic population: 2,000.

BULFARG HOME, SOUTH PARKS HOME, WEST PARK HOME ATTENDED FROM ST. MARY'S .
(ST. PAUL'S PRIMARY SCHOOL).

GLENROTHES, Fife, St. Paul (1958), Warout Road.

Rev. Jock J. Dalrymple, M.A., S.T.L. (1986)
Sr. Anne Doherty, S.N.D., *Parish Sister.*
Sr. Jennifer Smith, S.N.D., *Parish Sister.*

POSTAL ADDRESS: St.Paul's Presbytery, Warout Road, GLENROTHES KY7 4ER. ☎ Glenrothes (01592) 752543.

Sunday Masses: 11.30 a.m., 6.30 p.m. Confessions: alternate Saturdays, 10.30 to 11 a.m.
Estimated Catholic population: 2,000.

SISTERS OF NOTRE DAME DE NAMUR, CONVENT OF NOTRE DAME, 196 COLLISTON AVENUE, GLENROTHES KY7 4BW. ☎GLENROTHES (01592) 772453. CHESHIRE HOME, ABBOTSFORD HOME AND ALAN McCLURE HOME, ATTENDED FROM ST. PAUL'S.
ST. PAUL'S PRIMARY SCHOOL.

GOREBRIDGE, Midlothian, St. Margaret (1952, 1904), Lady Brae. (United with St. Luke and St. Anne, Mayfield, Dalkeith,1992).

Rev. John E. McInnes, B.D. (1996)

POSTAL ADDRESS: St. Luke's, 2A Stone Place, Mayfield, DALKEITH EH22 5PG. ☎ 0131-663 1476.

Sunday Mass: 10 a.m. Holy Days of Obligation, Masses as announced. Confessions: by appointment; Saturday, after 10 a.m. Mass.
Estimated Catholic population: 450.

ST. ANDREW'S PRIMARY SCHOOL.

GRANGEMOUTH, Falkirk, Christ the King (1970, 1975), Bowhouse Road.

Rev. Leo Glancy (1963)

POSTAL ADDRESS: Christ the King, Bowhouse Road, GRANGEMOUTH FK3 0HB. ☎ Grangemouth (01324) 484974; Fax: 01324-665303
E-mail: leoctr@aol.com.

Sunday Masses: 11 a.m. Holy Days of Obligation Masses: 9.30 a.m., 7.30 p.m. Confessions: Saturday, after 10 a.m. Mass, 6.30 to 7.30 p.m, during Exposition of the Blessed Sacrament.
Estimated Catholic population: 1,100.

CUNNINGHAM HOUSE (OLD PEOPLE'S HOME) ATTENDED FROM CHRIST THE KING
SACRED HEART PRIMARY SCHOOL.

GRANGEMOUTH, Falkirk, Sacred Heart (1901, 1927), Drummond Place.

Rev. Joseph McMahon, B.A. (1960)

POSTAL ADDRESS: Sacred Heart, 1 Drummond Place, GRANGEMOUTH FK3 9JA. ☎ /Fax: Grangemouth (01324) 482253.

E-mail: consitor@aol.com

Sunday Mass: 9.30 a.m. Evening Service: as announced. Holy Days of Obligation, Masses: 10 a.m., 7 p.m. Confessions: Saturday, after Mass to 11 a.m., 6 to 6.30 p.m; on request.
Estimated Catholic population: 725.

(SACRED HEART PRIMARY SCHOOL.)

HADDINGTON, East Lothian, St. Mary (1853, 1862) Poldrate.

Very Rev. James Canon Friel (1956)

POSTAL ADDRESS: St. Mary's, Poldrate, HADDINGTON EH41 4DA. ☎ Haddington (01620) 822138.

Sunday Masses: Vigil-Mass, 6 p.m.; 10 a.m. Evening Service: 4 p.m. (as announced). Holy Days of Obligation, Masses: 9.30 a.m., 7.30 p.m. Confessions: Saturday, 9.15 to 9.45 a.m., 5 to 5.45 p.m.
Estimated Catholic population: 700.

ROODLANDS GENERAL HOSPITAL, AND HERDMANFLATT HOSPITAL ATTENDED FROM HADDINGTON.
ST. MARY'S PRIMARY SCHOOL.

HAWICK, Scottish Borders, SS. Mary and David (1843, 1844), Buccleuch Street.

Rev. George Rodgers (1969)

POSTAL ADDRESS: SS. Mary and David, 15 Buccleuch Street, HAWICK TD9 0HH. ☎ Hawick (01450) 372037.

Sunday Masses: Vigil-Mass, 6.30 p.m.; 11.15 a.m. Holy Days of Obligation, Masses: Vigil-Mass, 7 p.m.; 10 a.m. Confessions: on request.
Estimated Catholic population: 750.

SISTERS OF ST. AUGUSTINE OF THE MERCY OF JESUS, ST. ANDREW'S CONVENT, STIRCHES, HAWICK TD9 7NS. ☎HAWICK (01450) 372360. SERVED FROM ST. MARY'S. SUNDAY MASS AS ANNOUNCED
ST. MARGARET'S NURSING HOME, COTTAGE HOSPITAL AND DEANFIELD RESIDENTIAL HOME , ATTENDED FROM ST. MARY'S.
ST. MARGARET'S PRIMARY SCHOOL.

INNERLEITHEN, Scottish Borders, St. James (1881), High Street. Served from Peebles.

Rev. John G. Robinson (1972)

POSTAL ADDRESS: St. Joseph's, 17 Rosetta Road, PEEBLES EH45 8JU. ☎ Peebles (01721) 720865.

Sunday Mass: 11.15 a.m. Evening Service as announced.Holy Days of Obligation, Mass: 7p.m. Confessions: on request.
Estimated Catholic population: 150

ST. RONAN'S HOUSE, ATTENDED FROM PEEBLES.
(HALYRUDE PRIMARY SCHOOL, PEEBLES)

INVERKEITHING, Fife, St. Peter-in-Chains (1979, 1977), Hope Street.

Very Rev. John Canon McAllister (1955)

POSTAL ADDRESS: St. Peter-in-Chains, 28 Hope Street, INVERKEITHING KY11 ILW. ☎/Fax.: Inverkeithing (01383) 413195.
E-mail: John.Mac@btinternet.com

Sunday Masses: Vigil-Mass, 6 p.m.; 9.45, 11.45 a.m. Evening Service: as announced. Holy Days of Obligation, Masses: 11 a.m., 7.15 p.m. Confessions: Thursday and Saturday, after Mass.
Estimated Catholic population: 1,200.

HENDERSON HOUSE NURSING HOME, Dalgety Bay, ATTENDED FROM ST. PETER-IN-CHAINS.
(ST. JOHN'S PRIMARY SCHOOL, ROSYTH).

JEDBURGH, Scottish Borders, The Immaculate Conception (1855, 1937), Old Bongate.

Rev. John A. Morrison (1990)

POSTAL ADDRESS: Immaculate Conception, 2 Old Bongate, JEDBURGH TD8 6DR. ☎/Fax: Jedburgh (01835) 862426.

Sunday Masses: Vigil-Mass, 5.30 p.m.; 11 a.m. Holy Days of Obligation, Masses: 10 a.m., 7 p.m. Confessions: Saturday, 10.30 to 11 a.m.,4.30 to 5 p.m.
Estimated Catholic population: 300.

SISTERS OF MARIE REPARATRICE, ST. MARGARET'S, 55 BONGATE, JEDBURGH TD8 6DT. ☎JEDBURGH (01835) 862305. SERVED FROM ST. MARY'S.
SISTER MARGARET COTTAGE HOSPITAL, CASTLEGATE, AND MILLFIELD OLD PEOPLE'S HOME, ATTENDED FROM ST. MARY'S.

KELSO, Scottish Borders, The Immaculate Conception (commonly known as 'St. Mary's') (1854, 1858), Bowmont Street.

Rev. Joseph Portelli (1974)

POSTAL ADDRESS: St. Mary's, Bowmont Street, KELSO TD5 7DZ. ☎ Kelso (01573) 224725.

Sunday Masses: Vigil-Mass, 7 p.m.; 10.30 a.m. Evening Service, as announced. Holy Days of Obligation, Masses: 10 a.m., 7 p.m. Confessions: Saturday, 6.15 to 6.45 p.m.
Estimated Catholic population: 350.

COLDSTREAM SERVED FROM KELSO.
GROVE HOUSE, QUEEN'S HOUSE, KELSO HOSPITAL, AND BOWMONT STREET HOUSE FOR THOSE WITH LEARNING DIFFICULTIES, Kelso, COTTAGE HOSPITAL AND LENNEL HOUSE, Lennel, ALL ATTENDED FROM ST. MARY'S.

KELTY, Fife, St. Joseph (1913, 1922), Cocklaw Street. (United with St. John & St. Columba, Rosyth, 1993).

Rev. John Scally, B.D. (1993)

POSTAL ADDRESS: St. John and St. Columba's, 137 Admiralty Road, Rosyth, DUNFERMLINE KYll 2QL. ☎/Fax: Inverkeithing (01383) 412084.

Sunday Mass: 9.30 a.m. Holy Days of Obligation, Mass: 9.30 a.m. Confessions: before or after Mass, or by appointment.
Estimated Catholic population: 700.

LYNEBANK HOSPITAL, DUNFERMLINE, ATTENDED FROM ST. JOHN & ST. COLUMBA'S.
ST. JOSEPH'S PRIMARY SCHOOL.

KENNOWAY, Fife, St. Giles (1959, 1958), Langside Crescent. (United with St. Peter, Leven, 1989).

Rev. Joseph McIntyre (1976)

POSTAL ADDRESS: St. Peter's, 9 Forman Road, LEVEN KY8 4HH. Tel: Leven (01333) 425627.

Sunday Mass: 11.30 a.m. Holy Days of Obligation, Vigil-Mass, 7 p.m.; 10.30 a.m. Confessions: after Masses.
Estimated Catholic population: 300.

ST. AGATHA'S PRIMARY SCHOOL, Leven.

KILSYTH, North Lanarkshire, St. Patrick (1860, 1965), Low Craigends.

Rev. Gerard R. Hand, S.T.L. (1973)
Sr. Angela, O.S.F. *Pastoral Assistant.*

POSTAL ADDRESS: St. Patrick's, 30 Low Craigends, Kilsyth, GLASGOW G65 0PF. ☎ Kilsyth (01236) 822136; Fax: 01236-827087.

Sunday Masses: Vigil-Mass, 6.30 p.m.; 9.30 a.m., 12 noon. Holy Days of Obligation, Masses: 10 a.m., 7.30 p.m. Confessions: Wednesday, after 10 a.m. Mass; Saturday, after 10 a.m. Mass, 5.30 to 6.15 p.m.
Estimated Catholic population: 3.000.

FRANCISCAN SISTERS OF THE IMMACULATE CONCEPTION, ST. ANDREW'S CONVENT 32 LOW CRAIGENDS, KILSYTH, GLASGOW G65 0PF. ☎KILSYTH (01236) 823927. VICTORIA MEMORIAL COTTAGE HOSPITAL, BURNGREEN LODGE AND CRAIG EN GOYNE NURSING HOME ATTENDED FROM ST. PATRICK'S.
ST. PATRICK'S PRIMARY SCHOOL.

KINGHORN, Fife. Served from Burntisland.

Sunday Mass: 9 a.m. in St. Peter's and St. Mary's Episcopal Church, David the First Street, Kinghorn.

KIRKCALDY, Fife, Our Lady of Perpetual Succour ("St. Marie's") (1865, 1901, 1975), Dunnikier Road.

Rev. Patrick Clarke (1962)
POSTAL ADDRESS: St. Marie's, Whytebank, 101 Dunnikier Road, KIRKCALDY KY2 5AP. ☎ Kirkcaldy (01592) 592111; Fax: 01592-597410.
E-mail: saint.maries@cableinet.co.uk

Sunday Masses: Vigil-Mass, 6.30 p.m.; 9 (Carmel), 11 a.m. Holy Days of Obligation, Masses: Vigil-Mass, 7.30 p.m.; 10, 11.15 (Carmel) a.m. Confessions: Saturday, after 10 a.m. Mass; on request.
Estimated Catholic population: 1,700.

CARMELITE MONASTERY OF ST TERESA OF THE CHILD JESUS, HOT POT WYND, DYSART, KIRKCALDY KY1 2TF. ☎KIRKCALDY (01592) 651430; FAX: 01592-651753. E-MAIL: DYSCARMEL@ENTERPRISE.NET
SERVED FROM ST. MARIE'S, KIRKCALDY.

CROSS AND PASSION CONVENT, 28 BEVERIDGE ROAD, KIRKCALDY KY1 1UY. ☎KIRKCALDY (01592) 266339.

FORTH PARK MATERNITY HOSPITAL, FORTH PARK GERIATRIC HOSPITAL, VICTORIA ACUTE HOSPITAL, WHYTEMAN'S BRAE PSYCHO/GERIATRIC HOSPITAL, VICTORIA HOSPICE; ABBEYFIELD HOME, ABBOTSFORD HOME, ADAM HOUSE, GOWRIE HOUSE, MARCHBANK, METHVEN HOME, MORNINGSIDE HOME, RAITH GATES HOME, STATION COURT HOME, WILBY HOUSE (Kirkcaldy) AND CAMILLA HOME (Auchtertool) ATTENDED FROM ST. MARIE'S.

ST. MARIE'S PRIMARY SCHOOL; ST. ANDREW'S SECONDARY SCHOOL.

KIRKCALDY Fife, St. Pius X (1964, 1956), Brodick Road, Templehall. (United with St. Ninian, Bowhill, 1995).

Rev. Christopher Heenan, B.D. (1995)

POSTAL ADDRESS: St. Pius' Presbytery, Brodick Road, KIRKCALDY KY2 6EY. ☎ Kirkcaldy (01592) 261901; Fax: 01592-269951.
E-mail:sarto10@aol.com.

Sunday Masses: 10 a.m., 6 p.m. Holy Days of Obligation, Mass: 7 p.m.
Confessions: Saturday, 6.30 to 7 p.m.
Estimated Catholic population: 1,200.   🔯 Ⓐ

APPIN HOME AND CHAPEL LEVEL NURSING HOME ATTENDED FROM ST. PIUS X.
(ST MARIE'S PRIMARY SCHOOL)

LARBERT, Falkirk, Our Lady of Lourdes and St. Bernadette (1933, 1935), Main Street.

Very Rev. John Canon Urquhart (1959)

POSTAL ADDRESS: St. Bernadette's, 323 Main Street, LARBERT FK5 4EU. ☎ Larbert (01324) 553250; Fax:01324-555971.

Sunday Masses: 11.30 a.m., 6.30 p.m. Holy Days of Obligation, Masses: 9.30a.m., 7.30p.m. Confessions: Saturday, after Morning Mass; Thursday, 6.30 to 7p.m.
Estimated Catholic population: 1,200.   🔯 Ⓐ

BELLSDYKE HOSPITAL, ROYAL SCOTTISH NATIONAL HOSPITALS, TORWOODHALL, AIRTHREY CARE AND CARRONDALE NURSING HOMES ATTENDED FROM LARBERT.
(ST FRANCIS XAVIER'S PRIMARY SCHOOL Falkirk)

LASSWADE, Midlothian. (Parish of Our Lady of Consolation, Bonnyrigg).Nazareth House, 13 Hillhead, Bonnyrigg.

Sunday Mass: 9.30 a.m. Holy Days of Obligation, Mass: 9.30 a.m.

LENNOXTOWN, East Dunbartonshire, St. Machan (1831, 1846), Chapel Street.

Rev. William Conway, S.T.L., L.S.S. (1968)

POSTAL ADDRESS: St. Machan's, Chapel Street, Lennoxtown, GLASGOW G66 7DE. ☎ Lennoxtown (01360) 310276.

Sunday Masses: Vigil-Mass, 5.30 p.m.; 11.30 a.m. Holy Days of Obligation Masses: 10 a.m., 7.30 p.m. Confessions: Saturday, after 10 a.m. Mass, after Vigil-Mass; at request.
Estimated Catholic population: 1,800.   Ⓐ

SECULAR INSTITUTE OF THE SCHOENSTATT SISTERS OF MARY, SCHOENSTATT, CLACHAN OF CAMPSIE, LENNOXTOWN, GLASGOW G65 7AG. ☎LENNOXTOWN (01360) 312718; FAX: 01360-312291.
WHITEFIELD LODGE NURSING HOME ATTENDED FROM ST. MACHAN'S.
ST. MACHAN'S PRIMARY SCHOOL.

LESLIE, see GLENROTHES, St. Mary, page 101.

LEVEN, Fife, St. Peter, (1977), Durie Street. (United with St. Giles, Kennoway, 1989).

Rev. Joseph McIntyre (1976)

POSTAL ADDRESS: St. Peter's, 9 Forman Road, LEVEN KY8 4HH. ☎ Leven (01333) 425627.

Sunday Masses: Vigil Mass, 6 p.m.; 9 a.m. Holy Days of Obligation, Masses: 9.30 a.m., 7p.m. Confessions: Saturday, after Vigil-Mass.

Estimated Catholic population: 400.

LEVEN BEACH NURSING HOME, PARKDALE HOME, AND SCOONIE HOUSE NURSING HOME, Leven, AND LOMOND VALE NURSING HOME, Falkland, ATTENDED FROM ST. PETER'S.
ST. AGATHA'S PRIMARY SCHOOL; (ST. COLUMBA'S PRIMARY SCHOOL, CUPAR).

LINLITHGOW, West Lothian, St. Michael (1850, 1893), Blackness Road.

Rev. James Ferrari (1960)

Postal address: St. Michael's, 53 Blackness Road, LINLITHGOW EH49 7JA. ☎ Linlithgow (01506) 842145.

Sunday Masses: 9, 11.30 a.m., 4.30 p.m. Holy Days of Obligation, Masses: 10 a.m., 7 p.m. Confessions: Saturday, 10.30 to 11 a.m., 6.30 to 7 p.m. Estimated Catholic population: 1,500.   🟦 Ⓐ

"LAETARE" CATHOLIC YOUTH INTERNATIONAL HOLIDAY HOSTEL, LAETARE, 53 BLACKNESS ROAD, LINLITHGOW EH49 7JA.☎LINLITHGOW (01506) 842214.
ST. MICHAEL'S HOSPITAL AND CLARENDON OLD PEOPLE'S HOME ATTENDED FROM ST. MICHAEL'S.
ST. JOSEPH'S PRIMARY SCHOOL.

LIVINGSTON, West Lothian, St. Andrew (1966, 1970), Victoria Street, Craigshill.

Rev. Gordon J. Muchall, LL.B., N.P. (1992)
Sister Maureen Delaney, *(Parish Sister)*
Anna-Maria Diamond *(Parish Pastoral Assistant)*

POSTAL ADDRESS: St. Andrew's, 126 Victoria Street, Craigshill, LIVINGSTON EH54 5BJ. ☎ Livingston (01506) 432141.
E-mail:St.Andrews_wlothian@lineone.net
Sunday Masses: Vigil-Mass, 6.30 p.m.; 9.30 a.m. (except July and August; in St. Paul's, Ladywell), 11 a.m. (in St. Andrew's). Holy Days of Obligation, Masses: Vigil-Mass, 7.30 p.m.; 10 a.m. Confessions: Saturday, after Masses; on request.
Estimated Catholic population: 3,000.

ST. PAUL'S ECUMENICAL CHURCH, CEDAR BANK, LADYWELL: SUNDAY MASS, 9.30 A.M. (EXCEPT JULY AND AUGUST)   Ⓐ
ST. JOHN'S HOSPITAL, HOWDEN. CHAPLAIN: REV. GORDON J. MUCHALL, ST. ANDREW'S (FIRST FRIDAY MASS, 5 P.M.).
CRAIGENGAR HOUSE AND HANOVER HOUSE, LIVINGSTON, ATTENDED FROM ST. ANDREW'S.
ST. ANDREW'S PRIMARY SCHOOL; ST. MARGARET'S ACADEMY.

LIVINGSTON, West Lothian, St. Peter, Carmondean (1982, 1983), Carmondean Centre Road.

Rev. Gerard Prior (1990)
Sr. Carmel *(Parish Sister* ☎ 01506-413727)
Hugh Mair *(Parish Assistant;* ☎ 01506-493164)
George Fleming *(Pastoral Assistant to Hospital)*

POSTAL ADDRESS: St. Peter's, 9 Carmondean Centre, LIVINGSTON EH54 8PT.
☎ Livingston (01506) 438787.

Sunday Masses: 9.30, 11.30 a.m., 5.30 p.m. Holy Days of Obligation,
Masses: 9.30 a.m., 7.30 p.m. Confessions: Saturday, 10.30 to 11.30 a.m.
Estimated Catholic population: 2000.

NETHER DECHMONT COTTAGES, PEACOCK NURSING HOME, PENTLANDVIEW
COURT AND RESTONDEAN ATTENDED FROM ST. PETER'S.
ST. JOHN OGILVIE'S PRIMARY SCHOOL.

LIVINGSTON, West Lothian, St. Philip, Dedridge (1984), The Lanthorn Community Centre, Kenilworth Rise.

Rev. Andrew Davie , B.D. (1996)

POSTAL ADDRESS: St. Philip's, 83 Kenilworth Rise, Dedridge, LIVINGSTON
EH54 6JL. ☎/Fax: Livingston (01506) 414453.

Sunday Masses: 9.30 a.m., 12.15 p.m.. Holy Days of Obligation, Masses:
Vigil-Mass, 7 p.m.; 9.30 a.m. (in primary school). Confessions: on request
before and after every Mass.
Estimated Catholic population: 1,900.

SISTERS OF THE HOLY FAMILY OF BORDEAUX, 32 PEVERIL RISE, DEDRIDGE,
LIVIGSTON EH54 6NU. ☎LIVINGSTON (01506) 414453.
LIVINGSTON NURSING HOME, WOODLANDS NURSING HOME AND LIMECROFT
RESIDENTIAL HOME ATTENDED FROM ST. PHILIP'S.
ST NINIAN'S PRIMARY SCHOOL.

LOANHEAD, Midlothian, St. Margaret (1881, 1878), Clerk Street.

Rev. Patrick Boylan, L.S.S. (1977)

POSTAL ADDRESS: St. Margaret's, 16 Clerk Street, LOANHEAD EH20 9DR.
☎/Fax: 0131-440 0412.

Sunday Masses: 9.20, 11.30 a.m. Holy Days of Obligation, Masses: 9 a.m.
7.30 p.m. Confession, Saturday, 9.20 to 9.50; by arrangement.
Estimated Catholic population: 750.

LOANHEAD HOSPITAL, KILBRECK, MAYBURN HOUSE, PINE VILLA AND THORNLEA, Loanhead; DRUMMOND GRANGE, Lasswade; WOODFIELD PARK, Bilston; ALL ATTENDED FROM LOANHEAD.
COMMUNITY OF THE TRANSFIGURATION (ECUMENICAL COMMUNITY), Roslin.
ST. MARGARET'S PRIMARY SCHOOL.

LOCHGELLY, Fife, St. Patrick (1877, 1953), Station Road. (United with St. Kenneth, Lochore, 1987 and St. Bernard, Ballingry, 1995).

Rev. Stuart F. Gray, B.D. (1995)

POSTAL ADDRESS: The Presbytery, Main Street, Glencraig, LOCHGELLY KY5 8AL. ☎ Lochgelly (01592) 860225; Fax: 01592-861849..
E-mail: Parishoffice@saintlytrio.demon.co.uk

Sunday Masses: Vigil-Mass, 6 p.m.(Ballingry); 10 a.m. (Lochore); 12 noon (Lochgelly). Holy Days of Obligation,Masses: Vigil-Mass, 7 p.m. (Lochore); 9 a.m. (Lochgelly); 10.45 a.m. (Ballingry). Confessions: Friday, 7 to 7.30 p.m.
Estimated Catholic population: 750.

JENNY GRAY HOUSE AND MOSSVIEW HOUSE ATTENDED FROM ST. PATRICK.
ST. PATRICK'S PRIMARY SCHOOL.

LOCHORE, Fife, St. Kenneth (1913, 1924), Main Street, Glencraig. (United with St. Bernard, Ballingry, 1987; St. Patrick, Lochgelly, 1995).

Rev. Stuart F. Gray, B.D.(1995)

POSTAL ADDRESS: The Presbytery, Main Street, Glencraig, LOCHGELLY KY5 8AL. ☎ Lochgelly (01592) 860225; Fax:01592-861849.
E-mail: Parishoffice@saintlytrio.demon.co.uk.

Sunday Masses: Vigil-Mass, 6 p.m.(Ballingry); 10 a.m. (Lochore); 12 noon (Lochgelly). Holy Days of Obligation,Masses: Vigil-Mass, 7 p.m. (Lochore); 9 a.m. (Lochgelly); 10.45 a.m. (Ballingry). Confessions: Saturday, 10.30 to 11 a.m.
Estimated Catholic population: 500.

GRAHAM COURT SHELTERED HOUSING.
ST. KENNETH'S PRIMARY SCHOOL.

MARCHMONT, Scottish Borders, St. Joan of Arc. Served from Duns.

Services as announced.

MELROSE, Scottish Borders, St. Cuthbert's, (1985; built in 1866 as a United Presbyterian Church.) High Cross Avenue.

Rev. John Creanor (1965)

POSTAL ADDRESS: Catholic Presbytery, Market Street, GALASHIELS TD1 lBY. ☎ Galashiels (01896) 752328.

Sunday Mass: 9.30 a.m. Holy Days of Obligation, Mass: 6.30 p.m.
Estimated Catholic population: 150　　　　　　　　　　　　　　🅰

BORDERS GENERAL HOSPITAL AND DINGLETON HOSPITAL, Melrose, ATTENDED FROM GALASHIELS.

METHIL, Fife, St. Agatha (1903, 1923), Methil Brae.

Rev. P. Aidan Cannon (1973)

POSTAL ADDRESS: St. Agatha's, 160 Methil Brae, Methil, LEVEN KY8 3LU. ☎/Fax.: Leven (01333) 423803.

Sunday Masses: Vigil-Mass, 5 p.m.; 10 a.m. Holy Days of Obligation, Masses: Vigil-Mass, 7.30 p.m.:, 9.30 a.m.Confessions: Tuesday to Saturday, 9 to 9.25 a.m.; Saturday, 4.30 to 4.55., 6 to 6.30 p.m. Exposition of the Blessed Sacrament, every day, 7 to 9 a.m.
Estimated Catholic population:1,500.　　　　　　　　　　🌀 🅰

CAMERON HOSPITAL, RANDOLPH WEMYSS MEMORIAL HOSPITAL, AND METHILHAVEN OLD FOLK'S HOME,Methil, AND BIELD SHELTERED HOUSING, Buckhaven, ATTENDED FROM ST. AGATHA'S.
(ST. AGATHA'S PRIMARY SCHOOL, Leven.)

MILTON OF CAMPSIE, East Dunbartonshire, St. Paul (1972, 1982), Birdston Road.

Rev. James Boyle (1968)

POSTAL ADDRESS: St. Paul's, 16 Birdston Road, Milton of Campsie, GLASGOW G66 8BU. ☎ Lennoxtown (01360) 310355.

Sunday Masses: 9.30 a.m., 4.30 p.m. Holy Days of Obligation, Masses: 9.30 a.m., 7.30 p.m. Confessions: Saturday, 6.30 to 7.30 p.m.
Estimated Catholic population:1,000.　　　　　　　　　　　　♿

BIRDSTON NURSING HOME ATENDED FROM ST. PAUL'S.
(ST. MACHAN'S PRIMARY SCHOOL, Lennoxtown)

MUSSELBURGH, East Lothian, Our Lady of Loretto and St. Michael (1889, 1905), Newbigging.

Rev. Joseph McMullan (1965)

POSTAL ADDRESS: Priest's House, 17 Newbigging, MUSSELBURGH EH21 7AJ. ☎ 0131-665 2137.

Sunday Masses: Vigil-Mass, 6 p.m. 9, 10.15 a.m. (Convent),11.30 a.m. Holy Days of Obligation, Masses: 9.15 a.m.,10.15 a.m. (Convent), 7.30 p.m. Confessions: Saturday, 10.30 to 11.30 a.m., 7 p.m. Estimated Catholic population: 1,890.

SISTERS OF CHARITY OF ST. PAUL THE APOSTLE, ST. ANNE'S CONVENT, WINDSOR GARDENS, MUSSELBURGH EH21 7LP. ☎0131-665 5591 (CONVENT); 0131-665 6653 (GUESTS),. ATTENDED FROM ST. MICHAEL'S. (SUNDAY MASS, 10.15 A.M.). DAUGHTERS OF CHRAITY OF ST. VINCENT DE PAUL,GLENESK, 6 DELTA PLACE, INVERESK, MUSSELBURGH EH21 7TP. ☎0131-653 2345. EDENHALL CENERAL HOSPITAL, CARBERRY NURSING HOME,ESKGREEN OLD PEOPLE'S HOME, GREENFIELD PARK RESIDENTIAL HOME AND MAXWELL COURT ATTENDED FROM ST. MICHAEL'S. LORETTO R.C.PRIMARY SCHOOL.

NEWBATTLE, Midlothian, St. Luke and St. Anne (1948, 1971)—see Dalkeith, St. Luke and St. Anne.

NEWTONGRANGE. See Dalkeith, St. Luke and St. Anne.

NORTH BERWICK, East Lothian, Our Lady, Star of the Sea (1870, 1879), Law Road.

Right Rev. Mgr. John C. Barry, D.C.L., M.A. (1944)

POSTAL ADDRESS: Our Lady, Star of the Sea, 9 Law Road, NORTH BERWICK EH39 4PN. ☎ North Berwick (01620) 892195.

Sunday Masses: Vigil-Mass, 7 p.m.; 9, 11 a.m. Holy Days of Obligation, Masses: 10 a.m., 7.30 p.m. Confessions: Saturday, 6 to 6.45 p.m. and on request. Estimated Catholic population: 430.

(Ramp in Church; Facilities in Hall)

EDINGTON HOSPITAL, ABBEY NURSING HOME, COPPER BEECH NURSING HOME, REDCROFT HOME, FIDRA NURSING HOME, North Berwick, THE POPLARS, Aberlady, ALL ATTENDED FROM NORTH BERWICK.

NUNRAW, East Lothian, Sancta Maria Abbey, Nunraw, Garvald, Haddington. Cistercians of the Strict Observance (1946, 1969).

Right Rev. Dom Donald McGlynn, O.C.R., S.T.L, *Abbot* (1959)
Rev. Michael Sherry, O.C.R. (1934)
Rev. Stephen Murphy, O.C.R. (1950)
Rev. Hugh Randolph, O.C.R. (1958)
Rev. Raymond Jaconelli, O.C.R., *Guest Master* (1958)
Rev. Luke McNally, O.C.R. (1959)
Rev. Thomas Hood, O.C.R. (1962)
Rev. Leonard Norman, O.C.R., B.Sc. (1965)
Rev. Mark Caira, O.C.R. (1973)
Rev. Martin Troubridge-Warren, O.C.R. (1978)

POSTAL ADDRESS: Sancta Maria Abbey, Nunraw, HADDINGTON EH41 4LW.
Tel. (Abbey) Garvald (01620) 830223; (Guest House) Garvald (01620) 830228; Fax: (01620) 830304.
E-mail: domdonald@iname.com
Internet: http.members.xcom/Nunraw/abbey.htm

Sunday Mass: 11 a.m. (Sung Mass). Vespers and Benediction, 4 p.m. Exposition of the Blessed Sacrament, second Sunday of every month, 1 to 4.30 p.m. Compline, 7.30 p.m. Holy Days of Obligation, Mass: 11 a.m. (Sung Mass). Guest House, Mass daily, 8.30 a.m. Confessions: at call.

OAKLEY, Fife, The Holy Name (1857, 1958), Station Road.

Rev. Michael Carey (1951)

POSTAL ADDRESS: Shrub Cottage, Station Road, Oakley, DUNFERMLINE KY12 9NW. ☎ New Oakley (01383) 850335.

Sunday Masses: Vigil-Mass, 6.30 p.m.; 10.15 a.m. Evening Service: as announced. Holy Days of Obligation, Masses: Vigil-Mass, 7.30 p.m.; 10 a.m., 11 a.m. in school. Confessions: Saturday, 10.30 to 11 a.m.; before and after all weekday Masses: any time on request.
Estimated Catholic population: 600.

BANDRUM NURSING HOME (Saline), ATTENDED FROM HOLY NAME.
HOLY NAME PRIMARY SCHOOL.

ORMISTON, East Lothian. Served from Tranent.

PATHHEAD, Midlothian, St. Mary (1872), Main Street.

Rev. Andrew Monaghan, M.Th. (1964)

POSTAL ADDRESS: St. Mary's, 48 Main Street, PATHHEAD EH37 5QB. ☎ Ford (01875) 320266.

Sunday Mass: 9.30a.m. Holy Days of Obligation, Masses as announced. Confessions as announced..
Estimated Catholic population: 70.   Ⓐ

(ST. DAVID'S PRIMARY SCHOOL, Dalkeith)

PEEBLES, Scottish Borders, St. Joseph (1850, 1858), Rosetta Road.

Rev. John G. Robinson (1972)

POSTAL ADDRESS: St. Joseph's, 17 Rosetta Road, PEEBLES EH45 8JU. ☎ Peebles (01721) 720865.
E-mail:frjrobinson@lineone.net

Sunday Masses: Vigil-Mass, 6 p.m.; 9.15 a.m. Holy Days of Obligation. Masses: Vigil-Mass, 7 p.m.; 9.30 a.m. Confessions: Saturday, 5.15 to 5.45 p.m.   Ⓢ Ⓐ
Estimated Catholic population: 400.

HAY LODGE HOSPITAL, PEEBLES NURSING HOME AND DUNWHINNY LODGE RESIDENTIAL HOME, Peebles, AND CASTLECRAIG CLINIC, Blyth Bridge, ATTEND-ED FROM ST. JOSEPH'S.
INNERLEITHEN AND TRAQUAIR SERVED FROM PEEBLES.
HALYRUDE PRIMARY SCHOOL.

PENICUIK, Midlothian, The Sacred Heart (1882), John Street.

Rev. Thomas McNulty (1956)

POSTAL ADDRESS: Sacred Heart, 56 John Street, PENICUIK EH26 8HL. ☎ Penicuik (01968) 673709.

Sunday Masses: Vigil-Mass, 6 p.m.; 10.30 a.m. Holy Days of Obligation, Masses: 9.15 a.m., 7 p.m. Confessions: Saturday: 10.30 a.m., during Holy Hour at 5p.m.
Estimated Catholic population: 950.   Ⓢ Ⓐ

SCOTTISH INFANTRY DEPOT, Glencorse, Milton Bridge, AND BROOMLEE RESIDENTIAL SCHOOL, West Linton, ATTENDED FROM PENICUIK.
SACRED HEART PRIMARY SCHOOL.

PITTENWEEM, Fife, Christ the King (1953, 1935), Milton Place.

Rev. William G. Brennan (1962)

POSTAL ADDRESS: Catholic Church, 1A Milton Place, Pittenweem, ANSTRUTHER KY10 2LR. ☎ Anstruther (01333) 311262.

Sunday Masses: Vigil-Mass (June, July, August), 5.15 p.m.; 12 noon. Evening Service: as announced. Holy Days of Obligation, Mass: 7.15 p.m. Confessions: Saturday, after morning Mass; on request.
Estimated Catholic population: 150.   Ⓐ

LADY WALK HOUSE, Anstruther, AND ST. MARGARET'S RESIDENTIAL HOME, Elie, ATTENDED FROM CHRIST THE KING.
CRAIL SERVED FROM PITTENWEEM.
(GREYFRIARS PRIMARY SCHOOL, St. Andrews).

POLMONT, Falkirk, St. Anthony (1913, 1985), Rumford.

Very Rev. Thomas Provost Hanlon, L.S.S., S.T.L., Ph.L. (1952)

POSTAL ADDRESS: St. Anthony's Presbytery, Rumford, FALKIRK FK2 0SB. ☎ Polmont (01324) 715650.

Sunday Masses: 11 a.m., 4.30 p.m. Holy Days of Obligation, Masses: 9.30 a.m., 7.30 p.m. Confessions: Saturday, after 11 a.m. Mass, 6.30 to 7.15 p.m.; on request.
Estimated Catholic population: 1,100.   ⚡ ♿

IVYBANK HOME, OAKBANK HOME AND ST. MARGARET'S HOME (Polmont), SUMMERDALE HOME (Brightons), HAINING HOME (Maddiston), WALLACEVIEW HOME (Redding Muirhead), AND BARLESTONE PARK HOME (West Quarter), ATTENDED FROM ST. ANTHONY'S.
(ST ANDREW'S PRIMARY SCHOOL, Falkirk)

PRESTONPANS, East Lothian, St. Gabriel (1932, 1966).

Very Rev. Frank Keevins, C.P., *Parish Priest, Superior* (1983)
Rev. Hugh McAvoy, C.P. (1980)
Bro. Martin Denny, C.P., *Parish Assistant.*

POSTAL ADDRESS: St. Gabriel's, West Loan, PRESTONPANS EH32 9JX. ☎ Prestonpans (01875) 810052; Fax: (01875) 814974.

Sunday Masses:Vigil-Mass, 6 p.m., in St. James' Oratory, Wallyford; 9, 11 a.m., 6 p.m. Holy Days of Obligation, Masses: 9 a.m., 7.30 p.m.; also 6 p.m. in St. James' Oratory, Wallyford. Confessions: Saturday, 10.30 to 11.30 a.m., 7 to 7.30 p.m.
Estimated Catholic population: 2,000.   ⚡ Ⓐ

ADAMWOOD, COCKENZIE HOUSE, DRUMMHOR AND LEVENHALL NURSINGHOMES SERVED FROM ST. GABRIEL'S.
WALLYFORD SERVED FROM PRESTONPANS.
ST. GABRIEL'S PRIMARY SCHOOL, (LORETTO PRIMARY SCHOOL, Musselburgh)

RATHO, City of Edinburgh, St. Mary (1883), Wilkieston Road. Served from Currie.

Sunday Mass: 9.30 a.m. Holy Days of Obligation, Mass: Vigil-Mass, 7 p.m. Confessions: by appointment.

TREFOIL RESIDENTIAL SCHOOL FOR HANDICAPPED CHILDREN ATTENDED FROM CURRIE.

RICCARTON, City of Edinburgh, Chaplaincy Centre, Heriot-Watt University (1977). Served from St. Joseph's, Sighthill, Edinburgh.

Rev. John Reid, O.S.A., *Chaplain* (1970)

POSTAL ADDRESS: St. Joseph's, 20A Broomhouse Place North, EDINBURGH EH11 3UE Tel: 0131-443 3777;Fax: 0131-443 9290.

Sunday Vigil-Mass, 6 p.m., during Academic Year only.

ROSEWELL, Midlothian, St. Matthew (1889, 1923), Carnethie Street. (United with Our Lady of Consolation, Bonnyrigg, 1990).

Rev. Hugh White, S.T.L., L.S.S. (1963)

Postal address: St. Matthew's, 36 Carnethie Street, ROSEWELL EH24 9AT. Tel. & Fax: 0131-440 2150.
E-mail:hughw@clara.net
Sunday Mass: 9.30 a.m. Evening service: as announced. Holy Days of Obligation, Masses as announced locally. Confessions and Night Prayer: Friday, after evening Mass.
Estimated Catholic population: (with Bonnyrigg) 1,300.   [A]

ROSSLYNLEE PSYCHIATRIC HOSPITAL. SERVED FROM ST. JOSEPH'S.
ST. MATTHEW'S PRIMARY SCHOOL.

ROSYTH, St. John and St. Columba, (1913, 1926), Crossroads, and SS. Peter and Paul(1991), Castle Road. (United with St. Joseph, Kelty, 1993).

Rev. John Scally, B.D. (1993)

POSTAL ADDRESS: St. John and St. Columba's, 137 Admiralty Road, Rosyth, DUNFERMLINE KYI1 2QL. ☎/Fax: Inverkeithing (01383) 412084.

Sunday Masses: Vigil-Mass, 6 p.m. (SS. Peter and Paul); 11 a.m. (St. John and St. Columba). Holy Days of Obligation, Vigil-Mass: 7 p.m. (St. John and St. Columba); 7 p.m. (SS. Peter and Paul), 7 p.m. Confessions:Before and after Mass; by appointment.
Estimated Catholic population: 1,500.

H.M.S. CALEDONIA SERVED FROM ROSYTH.
ST. JOHN'S PRIMARY SCHOOL.

ST. ANDREWS, Fife, St. James (1884, 1910), The Scores.

Rev. Brian M. Halloran, B.D., M.Phil., Ph.D. (1959)
POSTAL ADDRESS: St. James', 17 The Scores, ST. ANDREWS KY16 9AR. ☎ St. Andrews (01334) 472856.
E-mail: bmh4@st.andrews.ac.uk

Sunday Masses: Vigil-Mass (July and August only), 7.30 p.m.; 9, 11 a.m., 4 p.m. Holy Days of Obligation, Masses: 10 a.m., 7.30 p.m. Confessions: Saturday, after 9.30 a.m. Mass, 6 to 7 p.m.
Estimated Catholic population: 600.

CHAPLAINCY FOR UNIVERSITY CATHOLICS (1964), CANMORE, 24 THE SCORES, ST. ANDREWS KY16 9AS. ☎ST. ANDREWS (01334) 472179.

The Registers of the Chaplaincy for University Catholics from 1970 to 1987 are preserved in St. James'.

MEMORIAL COTTAGE HOSPITAL, St. Andrews, SERVED FROM ST. JAMES'
GREYFRIARS PRIMARY SCHOOL.

SELKIRK, Scottish Borders, Our Lady and St. Joseph
(1866, 1879), High Street. (Parish of Galashiels)

Rev. Duncan MacFarlane, *Permanent Deacon* (1992)
Rev. George Rodgers P.P. (*Hawick*)

POSTAL ADDRESS: The Old Schoolhouse, 103 High Street, SELKIRK TD7 4JX.
☎ Selkirk (01750) 21779.

Sunday Mass: 9.30 a.m. Evening Service: Holy Hour, 3 p.m. Holy Days of
Obligation; Vigil-Mass, 7 p.m. Confessions as announced.
Estimated Catholic population: 300.

EARLSTON SERVED FROM SELKIRK.
BORDERS GENERAL HOSPITAL (NON-EMERGENCY COVER),
DRYGRANGE NURSING HOME, RIVERSIDE NURSING HOME, THORNFIELD OLD
PEOPLE'S HOME AND 'THE BIELD' SHELTERED HOUSING COMPLEX ATTENDED
FROM SELKIRK.
ST. JOSEPH'S PRIMARY SCHOOL.

SLAMANNAN, Falkirk, St. Mary (1885, 1960), Bank Street.
(United with St. Francis Xavier, Falkirk, 1989).

Rev. Philip J. Kerr, Ph.B., S.T.L. (1979)
Rev. Simon Hughes, B.Mus.(Hons.), B.D. (1995)

POSTAL ADDRESS: St. Francis Xavier's, 1 Hope Street, FALKIRK FK1 5AT.
☎ Falkirk (01324) 623567.
E-mail:IMU647655@aol.com
Sunday Mass: 11 a.m. Holy Days of Obligation: Vigil-Mass, 7.30 p.m.

SOUTH QUEENSFERRY, City of Edinburgh, St. Margaret
(1887, 1934), Loch Road. (United with St. Philomena,
Winchburgh, 1994).

Rev. Paul Capaldi (1980)

POSTAL ADDRESS: Hope View, Loch Road, SOUTH QUEENSFERRY EH30 9LS.
☎/Fax: 0131-331 1007.

Sunday Masses: Vigil Mass, 5 p.m.; 9.30 a.m. Holy Days of Obligation,
Masses as announced locally. Confessions as announced.
Estimated Catholic population: 1,400.

ST. MARGARET'S PRIMARY SCHOOL.

STIRLING, Holy Spirit (1964), McGrigor Road.

Very Rev. Alexander Canon Bremner, L.C.L. (1957)

POSTAL ADDRESS: Holy Spirit, 1 McGrigor Road, St. Ninians, STIRLING FK7 9BL. ☎ Stirling (01786) 474277.

Sunday Masses: 10 a.m., 5.30 p.m. Holy Days of Obligation, Masses: 10 a.m., 7.30 p.m. Confessions: Saturday, 9.30 to 10 a.m., 6 to 7 p.m. Estimated Catholic population: 1,100.

MARGARET BLACKWOOD H. & A. COMPLEX ATTENDED FROM HOLY SPIRIT. ST. MODAN'S HIGH SCHOOL.

STIRLING, St. Margaret of Scotland, Raploch (1954, 1994), Drip Road.

Rev. Michael Bagan (1978)

POSTAL ADDRESS: St. Margaret of Scotland, Drip Road, STIRLING FK9 4UA. ☎/Fax: Stirling (01786) 474883.
E-mail:113466.2422@compuserve.com.

Sunday Masses: 11 a.m., 6.30 p.m. Holy Days of Obligation, Masses: 10 a.m., 7.30 p.m. Confessions: after daily Mass; by arrangement. Estimated Catholic population: 800.

KILDEAN HOSPITAL AND FORTHBANK NURSING HOME ATTENDED FROM ST. MARGARET'S.
ST. MARY'S PRIMARY SCHOOL, Kildean.

STIRLING, St. Mary (1838, 1905), Upper Bridge Street

Rev. Loreto Tabone (1974)
Marist Sisters, *Pastoral Assistants*
Also in Residence: Rev. Brian G. Gowans *(Scottish Prison Service)*(1985)

POSTAL ADDRESS: St. Mary's, 15 Upper Bridge Street, STIRLING FK8 lES. ☎ Stirling (01786) 473749.

Sunday Masses: Vigil-Mass, 6.15p.m.; 11.30a.m. Holy Days of Obligation, Masses: 8, 10 a.m., 7.30 p.m. Confessions: Saturday, 10.30 to 11.30 a.m., 5 to 6 p.m.
Estimated Catholic population: 2,500.

MARIST SISTERS, 19 PRINCES STREET, STIRLING FK8 IHQ. ☎STIRLING (01786) 475168.

STIRLING ROYAL INFIRMARY, ABBEYFIELD SOCIETY (2), ALLAN HOUSE, BEECH GARDENS, LAURENCECROFT, WELLGREEN AND WESTERLANDS NURSING/RESIDENTIAL HOMES, Stirling, ABBEYFIELD SOCIETY, ALLAN LODGE, Drumpark, AND VIEWFORTH NURSING HOME, Bridge of Allan, ATTENDED FROM ST. MARY'S.

(**ST. MARY'S PRIMARY SCHOOL, Kildean; ST. MARY'S PRIMARY SCHOOL, Bannockburn.**)

STIRLING, CHAPLAINCY FOR CATHOLICS AT THE UNIVERSITY OF (1970).

Rev. Patrick Burke, M.Th., S.T.D. (1991)

POSTAL ADDRESSES: St. Francis Xavier's, 1 Hope Street, FALKIRK FK1 5AT. ☎ 01324-623567;
Chaplaincy, University of Stirling, STIRLING FK9 4LA. ☎ Stirling (01786) 467164.
E-mail: chapl@stir.ac.uk
Sunday Mass in Chaplaincy Area: 7 p.m. during term; out of term, as announced. Holy Days of Obligation, Mass: 1.15 p.m., during term.
Confessions: by appointment.

STONEYBURN, West Lothian, Church of Our Lady (1953, 1951), Burnbrae Road. (Linked with Our Lady of Lourdes, Blackburn, 1998).

Rev. James A. MacDonald (1989)

POSTAL ADDRESS: Our Lady's, 8 Burnbrae Road, Stoneyburn, BATHGATE EH47 8DF.☎ Bathgate (01506)652957.

Sunday Mass: 9 a.m. Holy Days of Obligation, Masses as announced locally. Confessions: as announced.
Estimated Catholic population: 700.

OUR LADY'S PRIMARY SCHOOL.

TORRANCE, East Dunbartonshire, St. Dominic (1981, 1903), School Road.

Rev. James Boyle (1968)

POSTAL ADDRESS: St. Paul's, 16 Birdston Road, Milton of Campsie, GLASGOW G66 8BU. ☎ Lennoxtown (01360) 310355.

Sunday Masses: Vigil-Mass, 6.30 p.m.; 11 a.m. Holy Days of Obligation, Masses: Vigil-Mass, 7.30 p.m.; 11 a.m. Confessions: Saturday, after Vigil-Mass to 7.30 p.m.
Estimated Catholic population: 300.

(ST. MACHAN'S PRIMARY SCHOOL, Lennoxtown).

TRANENT, East Lothian, St. Martin of Tours (1891, 1969), High Street.

Rev. Jeremy C. Bath, S.T.B. (1993)

POSTAL ADDRESS: St. Martin's, High Street, TRANENT EH33 1HJ. ☎ /Fax:Tranent (01875) 610232.

Sunday Masses: Vigil-Mass, 6 p.m.; 10.30 a.m. Holy Days of Obligation, Masses: 9 a.m., 7.30 p.m. Confessions: Saturday, 5.15 p.m. and after Vigil-Mass.
Estimated Catholic population: 1,000.

ORMISTON SERVED FROM TRANENT.
TRANENT NURSING HOME ATTENDED FROM ST. MARTIN'S.
FA'SIDE LODGE, AND TYNEHOLM HOUSE AND TYNEHOLM STABLES NURSING HOME, SERVED FROM ST. MARTIN'S.
ST. MARTIN OF TOURS PRIMARY SCHOOL.

TRAQUAIR HOUSE, Scottish Borders, Domestic Oratory. Served from Peebles.

Mass, last Wednesday of the month, April to September, 7 p.m., and as announced.

WALLYFORD, East Lothian, St. James. Served from Prestonpans.

Masses in St. James' Oratory, 14 Salters Road: Sunday, Vigil-Mass, 6 p.m.; Holy Days of Obligation, 6 p.m.

WEST CALDER, West Lothian, Our Lady and St. Bridget (1877), West End.

Rev. Allan T. Chambers (1980)

POSTAL ADDRESS: St. Mary's, 4 West End, WEST CALDER EH55 8EF. ☎ /Fax.: West Calder (01506) 871240.
E-mail: allan@talk21.com

Sunday Masses: Vigil-Mass, 5.15 p.m.; 9,ʹ 11.30 a.m. Holy Days of Obligation, Masses: 10 a.m. (in St. Mary's School, Polbeth, during term), 7.30 p.m. Confessions: Saturday, 4.50 to 5.10 p.m.; Wednesday, 7 to 7.30 p.m., during Holy Hour, 6.30 to 7.30 p.m.
Estimated Catholic population: 1,000.   **A**

GOWANLEA AND STUART COURT SHELTERED HOUSING ATTENDED FROM ST. MARY'S. ST. MARY'S PRIMARY SCHOOL.

WHITBURN, West Lothian, St. Joseph (1953, 1979), Raeburn Crescent.

Rev. James Smith (1989)

POSTAL ADDRESS: St. Joseph's, 49 Raeburn Crescent, Whitburn, BATHGATE EH47 8HQ. ☎/Fax: Whitburn (01501) 740348.

Sunday Masses: Vigil-Mass, 5 p.m.; 10 a.m. Holy Days of Obligation, Masses: 10 a..m., 7.30 p.m. Confessions: Saturday, 4.15 to 4.55 p.m.; by apointment.
Estimated Catholic population: 760.   **A**

WHITDALE HOME AND WEAVER COURT ATTENDED FROM ST. JOSEPH'S. ST. JOSEPH'S PRIMARY SCHOOL.

WINCHBURGH, West Lothian, St. Philomena (1903, 1925), Niddry Road. (United with St. Margaret's, South Queensferry, 1994).

Rev. Paul Capaldi (1980)

POSTAL ADDRESS: Hope View, Loch Road, SOUTH QUEENSFERRY EH30 9LS. ☎ 0131-331 1007.

In residence:

Rev. Thomas Rhatigan, M.A. (1947) *(Retired).*

POSTAL ADDRESS: St. Philomena's, Niddry Road, Winchburgh, BROXBURN EH52 6RY. ☎ Winchburgh(01506) 891310.

Sunday Masses: Vigil Mass, 6 p.m., 11.30 a.m. Holy Days of Obligation: Masses as announced. Confessions as announced.
Estimated Catholic population: 500.

HOLY FAMILY PRIMARY SCHOOL.

RETIRED PRIESTS OF THE ARCHDIOCESE

Very Rev. William Canon Anthony, 3 Craigs Terrace, Rumford, FALKIRK FK2 OSD. ☎ (01324) 717058

Rev. Kenneth Batchelor, Flat 32, 18 Lauder Road, EDINBURGH EH9 2EL. ☎ 0131-667 9265.

Very Rev. Daniel J. Canon Boyle, M.A., 12 Green Road, KINROSS KY13 7TP☎ (01577)862608.

Right Rev. Mgr. James K., Brennan, Kilcready, Mullinavat, Waterford, IRELAND.

Rev. Gordon R. Brown, M.A., Ph.L., 77A Falcon Avenue, EDINBURGH EH10 4AN. ☎ 0131-447 0545.

Rev. John Callaghan, 23A Calder Court, Braehead, STIRLING FK7 7QU.☎ (01786) 465731.

Rev Matthew Donoghue, Nazareth House, 13 Hillhead,BONNYRIGG EH19 2JF.☎ 0131-663 4252.

Right Rev. Mgr. Daniel Foley, 6 Wilkieston Road, Ratho, NEWBRIDGE EH28 8RH. Tel. 0131-333 1051.

Very Rev. Peter Canon Gallacher, M.A., 45 Gilmore Place, EDINBURGH EH3 9NG. ☎ 0131-229 5672.

Very Rev. Lawrence A. Canon Glancey, Ph.L., M.A., St. Andrew's, 77 Belford Road, EDINBURGH EH4 3DS. ☎ 0131-332 6925.

Very Rev. Hugh F. Canon Gordon, 45 Gilmore Place, EDINBURGH EH3 9NG. Tel. 0131-228 9084.

Right Rev. Mgr. Patrick J. Canon Grady, Prot. Ap., B.A., 47 Gilmore Place, EDINBURGH EH4 9NG. ☎ 0131-221 1646.

Rev. Douglas Hutton, St. Andrew's, 77 Belford Road, EDINBURGH EH4 3DS. ☎ 0131-332 2958.

Rev. Patrick Kelly, 2 Durham Terrace, Newmills, DUNFERMLINE KY12 8SZ

Very Rev. Michael C. Canon McCullagh, St. Anne's Convent, Windsor Gardens, MUSSELBURGH EH21 7LP. ☎ 0131-653 2725.

Rev. Patrick J. McFadden, 16 Townparks. Convoy, Lifford, Co. Donegal, IRELAND .

Rev. John J. McHugh, Crinken Lane, Shankill, Co. Dublin, IRELAND.

Rev. James A. McMahon, M.A.,45 Gilmore Place, EDINBURGH EH3 9NG. Tel. 0131 -229 5171.

Right Rev. Mgr. John J. McMeel, Mulraney, Brighton Road, CUPAR KY15 5DH.

Very Rev. John Canon McNay, 31 Station Road, Oakley, DUNFERMLINE KY12 9RJ. ☎ New Oakley (01383) 852372.

Rev. Michael McNulty, Sligo Road, West End, Bundoran, Co. Donegal, IRELAND.

Very Rev. Eamonn Canon O'Brien, St. Andrew's, 77 Belford Road, EDINBURGH EH4 3DS. ☎ 0131-343 1217.

Very Rev. Michael Canon O'Connor, General Hospital, Skibbereen, Co. Cork, IRELAND.

Rev. Thomas Rhatigan, St. Philomena's, Niddry Road, Winchburgh, BROXBURN EH52 6RY. ☎ Winchburgh (01506) 391310.

Rev. Benedict Robinson, Jericho House, 14 Shankland Road, GREENOCK PA15 2NE

Very Rev. John Canon Rogerson, The Hermitage, 115 Whitehouse Loan, EDINBURGH EH9 1BB. ☎ 0131-447 9740.

Very Rev. Patrick J. Canon Rourke, Climber Hall, Kells, Co. Meath, IRELAND.

Right Rev. Mgr. Daniel Simpson, The Hermitage, 115 Whitehouse Loan, EDINBURGH EH91BB. ☎ 0131-447 6210.

Very Rev. Richard Canon Somers, Carrigetna, Kilmoganny, Co. Kilkenny, IRELAND .

Right Rev. Mgr. John Tweedie, Flat 50, 25 Springbank Gardens, FALKIRK FK2 7DF. ☎ Falkirk (01324) 839928.

Rev. James B. Walsh, Sancta Maria, Ballyness, Falcarragh, Letterkenny, Co. Donegal, IRELAND.

Rev. Francis Welsh, c/o Whyte, 241 Muiryhall Street, COATBRIDGE ML5 3NR

CO-ORDINATING SCHOOL CHAPLAINS

Holy Rood High, Edinburgh	Rev. Michael Fallon.
St. Augustine's, Edinburgh	Vacant.
St. Thomas of Aquin's, Edinburgh	Rev. John Cudlipp.
St. Margaret's, Livingston	Rev. Gerard Prior.
St. Kentigern's, Blackburn	Rev. Alex Davie.
St. David's, Dalkeith	Rev. Jeremy Bath
St. Columba's, Dunfermline	Rev. Stuart F. Gray.
St. Mungo's, Falkirk	Rev. Leo Glancy.
St. Andrew's, Kirkcaldy	Rev. Christopher Heenan.
St. Modan's, Stirling	Rev. Michael Bagan.

UNIVERSITY CHAPLAINS

Edinburgh University	Rev. Thomas Kearns, O.P
St. Andrews University	Rev. Brian Halloran.
Heriot-Watt University	Rev. John Reid, O.S.A.
Stirling University	Rev. Patrick Burke.
Napier University	Rev. Alexander Mitchell.

COLLEGE CHAPLAINCY

Jewel and Esk Valley College
  (incorporaing former Moray House College of Education

Edinburgh College of Art	Rev. Thomas Kearns, O.P
Queen Margaret College	Rev. Charles Barclay.

HOSPITALS IN THE ARCHDIOCESE

City of Edinburgh	Parish Contact No.
The Royal Infirmary	To be notified
(including Simpson Memorial	
& Chalmers Hospital.)	
Royal Victoria Hospital	St. Paul's
Western General Hospital	☎ 0131-332 3320
Southfield Hospital	St. Catherine's
Fairmile Nursing Home	☎ 0131-664 1596
Princess Margaret Rose Hospital	

Royal Hospital for Sick Children	St. Columba's ☎ 0131-667 1605
Liberton Hospital	St. Gregory's ☎ 0131-664 4349
Gogarburn Hospital Murrayfield Hospital and Corstorphine Hospital	St. John the Baptist's ☎ 0131-334 1693
City Hospital Milestone House	St. Mark's ☎ 0131-441 3915
Leith Hospital	St. Mary's, Leith ☎ 0131-554 2482
Eastern General Hospital	St. Ninian's ☎ 0131-661 2867
Royal Edinburgh Hospital, West House Astley Ainslie Hospital	St. Peter's ☎ 0131-447 2502
St. Columba's Hospice	Holy Cross ☎ 0131-552 3957

The Lothians

Tippethill Hospital	Sacred Heart and St. Anthony, Armadale ☎ Armadale (01501) 730261
Bo'ness Hospital	St. Mary of the Assumption, Bo'ness ☎ Bo'ness (01506) 822339
Bangour Village Hospital	SS. John Cantius & Nicholas, Broxburn ☎ Broxburn (01506) 852040
Belhaven Hospital	Our Lady of the Waves, Dunbar ☎ Dunbar (01368) 862701

Roodlands Hospital	St. Mary's, Haddington
Herdmanflatt Hospital	☎ (01620) 822138.
St. John's Hospital	St. Andrew's Livingston
	☎ Livingston (01506) 432141
St. Michael's Hospital	St. Michael's, Linlithgow
	☎ Linlithgow (01506) 842145
Loanhead Hospital	St. Margaret's, Loanhead
	☎ 0131-440 0412
Edenhall Gen. Hospital	Our Lady of Loretto & St. Michael,
	Musselburgh
	☎ 0131-665 2137
Rosslynlee Mental Hosp.	St. Matthew's, Rosewell
	☎ 0131-440 2150
Edington Cottage Hospital	Our Lady, Star of the Sea,
	North Berwick
	☎ North Berwick (01620)
	892195

Stirlingshire

Bannockburn Hospital	Our Lady & St. Ninian's,
	Bannockburn
	☎ Bannockburn (01786)
	812249
Bonnybridge Hospital	St. Joseph.s, Bonnybridge
	☎ Bonnybridge (01324)
	812417
Falkirk Royal Infirmary	St. Francis Xavier's, Falkirk
	☎ Falkirk (01324) 623567
Kilsyth & District Cottage Hospital	St. Patrick's Kilsyth
	☎ Kilsyth (01236) 822136
Birdston Hospital	St. Paul's, Milton of Campsie
	☎ Lennoxtown (01360)
	310355

Kildean Hospital

St. Margaret's, Stirling
☎ Stirling (01786) 474883

Bellsdyke Hospital
Royal Scottish National Hospitals

Our Lady of Lourdes
& St. Bernadette, Larbert
☎ Larbert (01324) 553250

Stirling Royal Infirmary
King's Park Hospital

St. Mary's, Stirling
☎ Stirling (01786) 473749

Lennox Castle Hospital

St. Kessog's, Blanefield
☎ Blanefield (01360) 770300.

Strathcarron Hospice

St. Alexander's, Denny
☎ (01324) 823310.

Fife

Forth Park Hospital, Kirkcaldy
Victoria Hospital, Victoria Hospice
Whyteman's Brae Hospital

St. Marie's, Kirkcaldy
☎ Kirkcaldy (01592)592111.

Queen Margaret Hospital

St. Margaret's, Dunfermline
☎ Dunfermline (01383)
625611.

Glenrothes Hospital

St. Mary's, Leslie, Glenrothes
☎ Glenrothes (01592) 741963.

Lynebank Hospital

St. John's and St. Columba's,
Rosyth
☎ Inverkeithing (01383)
412084

Cameron Hospital
Randolph Wemyss Memorial
  Hospital

St. Agatha's, Methil
☎ Leven (01333) 423803

Memorial Cottage Hospital

St. James', St. Andrews
☎ St. Andrews (01334)
472856

Scottish Borders

Knoll Hospital	Our Lady and St. Margaret's, Duns
	☎ Duns (01361) 883714
Cottage Hospital (Hawick)	SS. Mary & David, Hawick
Haig Maternity Hosp.	☎ Hawick (01450) 372037
Sister Margaret Cottage Hospital	Immaculate Conception
	Jedburgh
	☎ (02835) 862426.
Cottage Hospital (Kelso)	St. Mary's, Kelso
Inch Hospital	☎ Kelso (01573) 224725
Cottage Hospital (Coldstream)	
Dingleton Hospital	Our Lady and St. Andrew, Galashiels
Borders General Hospital	☎ Galashiels (01896)752328.
Hay Lodge Hospital	St. Joseph's, Peebles
	☎ Peebles (01721) 720865.

INSTITUTES OF CONSECRATED LIFE
AND
SOCIETIES OF APOSTOLIC LIFE

MEN

AUGUSTINIANS (1986)
(1995) St. Joseph's, 20A Broomhouse Place North, EDINBURGH EH11 3UE. ☎
0131-443 3777; Fax.: 0131-443 9290

CISTERCIANS (1946)
Sancta Maria Abbey, Nunraw, HADDINGTON EH41 4LW
☎ Garvald (01620) 830223.; Fax: 01620-830304
E-mail:domdonald@iname.com
Internet:http.members.xoom.Nunraw/abbey/htm

DOMINICANS (1931)
University Chaplaincy for Catholic Students, Blackfriars, 25 George Square,
EDINBURGH EH8 9LD. ☎ 0131-650 0900; Fax; 0131-650 0902.
E-mail: stdoms@globalnet.co.uk

FRANCISCANS (1926)
St. Patrick's, 5 South Gray's Close, 40 High Street, EDINBURGH EH1 1TQ.
☎ 0131-556 1973; Fax: 0131-557 4650.
E-mail:stpatricks@btinternet.com

St. Teresa's, 120 Niddrie Mains Road, Craigmillar, EDINBURGH EH16 4EG.
☎ 0131-661 2185;Fax: 0131-652 0601.

JESUITS (1859)
The Sacred Heart, 28 Lauriston Street, EDINBURGH EH3 9DJ.
☎ 0131-229 9821 (Parish), 0131-229 9104 (Community); Fax: 0131-228 5142.
E-mail: sacdheart@aol.com

OBLATES OF MARY IMMACULATE (1859)
St. Mary, Star of the Sea, 106 Constitution Street, Leith, EDINBURGH EH6
6AW. ☎ 0131-554 2482 or 0131-467 7449; Fax: 0131-553 1660.

(1980) St. John Ogilvie, 159 Sighthill Drive, Wester Hailes, EDINBURGH EH11
4PY. ☎ 0131-453 5035.

PASSIONISTS (1932)
St. Gabriel's, West Loan, PRESTONPANS EH32 9JX.
☎ Prestonpans (01875) 810052; Fax: 01875-814974.

ST. PATRICK'S MISSIONARY SOCIETY (1965)
St. Patrick's, Buchlyvie, STIRLING FK8 3PB. ☎ Buchlyvie (01360) 850274;
Fax: 01360-850552.E-mail: stpatsbuch@aol.com

SALESIANS (1950)
(1984) St. Paul's, 4 Muirhouse Avenue, EDINBURGH EH4 4UB.
☎ 0131-332 3320; Fax.: 0131-539 5687.
E-mail: sdb_edinburgh@msn.com

BROTHERS OF CHARITY (1944)
(1955) St. Aidan's, Gattonside, MELROSETD6 9NW.
☎ Melrose (01896) 822226.
Chaplain: Rev. Andrzej Kaim, S.A.C.

JERICHO BENEDICTINES (1989)
53 Lothian Street, EDINBURGH EH1 1HB. ☎ 0131-225 8230.

WOMEN

CONGREGATION OF THE MOST HOLY CROSS AND PASSION (1907)
(1976) Cross and Passion Convent, 28 Beveridge Road, KIRKCALDY KY1 1UY.
☎ Kirkcaldy (01592) 266339.

CONGREGATION OF OUR LADY OF CHARITY OF THE GOOD SHEPHERD (1921)
(1977) Convent of the Good Shepherd, Broomlands, 449 Gilmerton Road,
EDINBURGH EH17 7JG ☎ 0131-664 3463

DAUGHTERS OF CHARITY OF ST. VINCENT DE PAUL (1898)
(1991) St. Mary's Convent, 4 Arthur Street, DUNFERMLINE KY12 0PR. ☎
Dunfermline (01383) 722474.

(1971) St. Vincent's, 629 Ferry Road, EDINBURGH EH4 2TT.
☎ 0131-315 2059.

(1999) "Glenesk", 6 Delta Place, Inveresk, MUSSELBURGH EH21 7TP.
☎ 0131-653 2345.

DAUGHTERS OF WISDOM (1960)
(1996)Sacred Heart, Bannockburn Road, Cowie, STIRLING FK7 7BG.
☎ Bannockburn (01786) 813466; Fax: 01786-480414.

DISCALCED CARMELITES (1925)

(1931) Carmelite Monastery of St. Teresa of the Child Jesus, Dysart,
KIRKCALDY KY1 2TF. ☎ Kirkcaldy (01592) 651430; Fax: (01592) 651753.
E-mail: dyscarmel@enterprise.net

(1931) Carmelite Monastery of the Immaculate Conception, 3 Arnothill,
FALKIRK FK1 5RZ. ☎ Falkirk (01324) 623352

FRANCISCANS OF THE IMMACULATE CONCEPTION (1973)

St. Andrew's Convent, 32 Low Craigends, Kilsyth, GLASGOW G65 OPF.
☎ Kilsyth (01236) 823927.

(1999) Franciscan Sisters, Queen Margaret's House, 87A Boswall Parkway,
EDINBURGH EH5 2JQ.☎ 0131-552 7482.

HELPERS OF THE HOLY SOULS (1903)

(1989) Helpers' Convent, 47 Mayfield Road, EDINBURGH EH9 2NQ.
☎ 0131-668 2202.

LITTLE COMPANY OF MARY (1916)

Marian House, 7 Oswald Road, EDINBURGH EH9 2HE.
☎ 0131-667 0148.

LITTLE SISTERS OF THE ASSUMPTION (1946)

(1977) Little Sisters of the Assumption,2/2 Wauchope Road, EDINBURGH
EH16 4PU. ☎ 0131-467 3615.

LITTLE SISTERS OF THE POOR (1863)

St. Joseph's House, 43 Gilmore Place, EDINBURGH EH3 9NG.
☎ 0131-229 5672; Fax.: 0131-228 5470.
Chaplain: Very Rev. Hugh Canon Gordon (1937), 47 Gilmore Place,
EDINBURGH EH3 9NG. ☎ 0131-228 9084.

MARIST SISTERS (1974)

Marist Sisters, 19 Princes Street, STIRLING FK8 IHQ. ☎ Stirling (01786)
475168.

MISSIONARIES OF CHARITY (1983)

(1993) 18 Hopetoun Crescent, EDINBURGH EH7 4AY. ☎ 0131-556 5444.

MISSIONARY SISTERS OF OUR LADY OF THE
HOLY ROSARY (1973)

Holy Rosary Sisters, 20 Kirk Road, BATHGATE EH48 IBN.
☎ Bathgate (01506) 653268.

POOR CLARES (1895)
(1992) Mount Alvernia, 2 Humbie Mains, HUMBIE EH36 5PW.
☎/Fax: (01875) 833627. E-mail:humbie.pcs@aol.com

POOR SERVANTS OF THE MOTHER OF GOD (1949)
(1992) The Poor Servants of the Mother of God, 11/3-4 Wauchope Road,
EDINBURGH EH16 4PT. ☎ 0131-661 2296.

THE POOR SISTERS OF NAZARETH (1931)
Nazareth House, 13 Hillhead, BONNYRIGG EH79 2JF.
☎ 0131-663 7191; (Residents: 0131-663 4252).
Fax: 0131-663 0979.
Chaplain: Rev. Joseph Walsh, M.H.M. (1949) ☎ 0131-654 2513.

RELIGIOUS OF JESUS AND MARY (1974)
(1978) Convent of the Religious of Jesus and Mary, Hebron, Stone Place,
Mayfield, DALKEITH EH22 5NR. ☎ 0131-660 3862.

SECULAR INSTITUTE OF THE SCHOENSTATT SISTERS OF MARY (1989)
Schoenstatt, The Clachan, Campsie Glen, GLASGOW G66 7AB.
☎ Lennoxtown (01360) 312718; Fax: 01360-312291.

SISTERS OF CHARITY OF ST. PAUL THE APOSTLE (1870)
St. Anne's Convent, Windsor Gardens, MUSSELBURGH EH21 7LP.
☎ 0131-665 1062 (Convent); 0131-665 6653 (Guests).

SISTERS OF ST. MARTHA OF PERIGUEUX (1971)
St. Martha's Convent, 25 Wellside Place, FALKIRK FK1 5RL.
☎ Falkirk (01324) 628121.

SISTERS OF THE HOLY FAMILY OF BORDEAUX (1854)
(1854) Holy Family Convent, 10 John's Place, Leith, EDINBURGH EH6 7EL.
☎ 0131-554 6585.

(1976) Holy Family Convent, 32 Peveril Rise, Dedridge West, LIVINGSTON,
EH54 6NU. ☎ Livingston (01506) 413727.

SISTERS OF ST. AUGUSTINE OF THE MERCY OF JESUS (1926)
St. Andrew's Convent, Stirches, HAWICK TD9 7NS.
☎ Hawick (01450) 372360; Fax: 01450-377801.

SISTERS OF MARIE REPARATRICE (1904)
(1995) St. Margaret's, 55 Bongate, JEDBURGH TD8 6DT.
☎ Jedburgh (01835) 862305.

SISTERS OF MERCY (1858)
St. Catharine's Convent of Mercy, 4 Lauriston Gardens, EDINBURGH
EH3 9HH. ☎ 0131-229 2659.

SISTERS OF NOTRE DAME DE NAMUR (1972)
Convent of Notre Dame, 196/197 Colliston Avenue, Pitteuchar, GLENROTHES
KY7 4PW. ☎ Glenrothes (01592) 772453. E-mail:jk.smith@virgin.net

SOCIETY OF THE SACRED HEART (1918)
(1980) Convent of the Sacred Heart, 51 Ferniehill Road, Gilmerton,
EDINBURGH EH17 7BL. ☎ 0131-664 7188; Fax: 0131-664 7188.

(1985) Convent of the Sacred Heart, House of Prayer, 8 Nile Grove,
EDINBURGH EH10 4RF. ☎ 0131-447 0990 (Community)/1772
(Administration); Fax: 0131-446 9122.

(1986) Convent of the Sacred Heart, 11 Eyre Place, EDINBURGH EH3 5ES.
☎ 0131-558 1629.

(1990) Convent of the Sacred Heart, 16/18 Westbank Place, Seaview Gate,
Portobello, EDINBURGH EH15 IUD. ☎ 0131-669 5403; Fax: 0131-669 7973
Sr Monica MacDonald. Sr Ethel Lamont
(1985) Convent of the Sacred Heart, "Rosehill", 27 Park Road, Eskbank,
DALKEITH EH22 3DH. ☎ 0131-660 6602; Fax: 0131 654 1011.
(1999) Convent of the Sacred Heart, 28 Campview Road, BONNYRIGG EH19
3EZ. ☎ 0131-663 0845.

URSULINES OF JESUS (1834)
(1957, 1986) St. Margaret's Convent, 88 Strathearn Road,
EDINBURGH EH9 2AQ. ☎ 0131-447 2278.
Chaplain: Very Rev. John Canon Rogerson(1947), The Hermitage, Gillis
Centre 115 Whitehouse Loan, EDINBURGH EH9 1BB. ☎ 0131-447 9740.

(1986) St. Angela's Convent, 19 Sighthill Crescent, Wester Hailes, EDINBURGH
EH11 4QE. ☎ 0131-453 6265; Fax: 0131-453 4062.

Diocese of Aberdeen

TOGETHER IN CHRIST

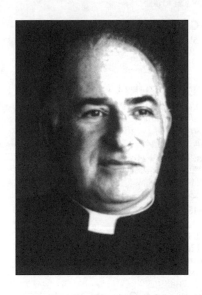

Bishop of Aberdeen
Right Rev. Mario Joseph Conti,
K.C.H.S., Ph.L., S.T.L, D.D., F.R.S.E.

Born at Elgin, Moray, 20th March 1934; educated at St. Marie's Convent,
Elgin, Springfield School, Elgin, St. Mary's College, Blairs, Scots College,
Rome (Ph.L. (1955), S.T.L. (1959), Gregorian University, Rome);
ordained priest at Rome, 26th October 1958; assistant priest, St. Mary's
Cathedral, Aberdeen 1959-62, parish priest, Wick 1962-67, Thurso,
1967-77, nominated bishop of Aberdeen, 28th February 1977, and
ordained by Gordon Gray, cardinal archbishop of St. Andrews and
Edinburgh, at Aberdeen, 3rd May 1977, commendatore nell' Ordine al
Merito della Repubblica Italiana, 1981, honorary D.D. (University of
Aberdeen), 1989, Equestrian Order of the Holy Sepulchre of Jerusalem,
Knight Commander, 1989, Chaplain *ad honorem* to the Sovereign Military
Order of St. John of Jerusalem, Rhodes and Malta, 1991; Principal
Chaplain to the British Association of the Order of Malta, 1995; Fellow of
the Royal Society of Edinburgh.

Residence: Bishop's House, 3 Queen's Cross, ABERDEEN AB15 4XU.
☎ Aberdeen (01224) 319154; Fax: 01224-325570.
Secretary: Mrs. Irene Melling.

VICAR-GENERAL

Right Rev. Mgr. John Provost Copland, St. Thomas', Chapel Street,
KEITH AB5 3AL. ☎ Keith (01542) 882352.

THE DIOCESAN CURIA

"The Diocesan Curia is composed of those institutions and persons who assist the Bishop in governing the entire diocese, especially in directing pastoral action, in providing for the administration of the diocese, and in exercising judicial power." (Code of Canon Law, Canon 469)

Curial Address: Bishop's House,
3 Queen's Cross, ABERDEEN AB15 1XU
☎ 01224-319154.
Fax: 01224-325570.

I. ADMINISTRATION

Procurator: Rev. Andrew Mann,
B.A., S.T.B., Dip. Comm.,
Sacred Heart,
15 Grampian Road, Torry,
ABERDEEN AB11 8ED.
☎ 01224-878489.

Treasurer: Very Rev. Robert A. Canon McDonald,
St. Mary's, Huntly Street,
INVERNESS IV3 5VR.
☎ Inverness (01463) 233519.

Chancellor: Rev. Deacon John Woodside,
Bishop's House,
3 Queen's Cross, ABERDEEN AB15 1XU.
☎ 01224-319154/869424.
Fax: 01224-325570/869424.

Master of Ceremonies: Very Rev. Charles T. Canon Stanley,
Our Lady of Aberdeen,
70 Cairngorm Crescent,
Kincorth, ABERDEEN AB12 5BR.
☎ 01224-876704.

II. ORGANS OF CONSULTATION

College of Consultors: Right Rev. Mgr. John Provost Copland, V.G.
Very Rev. Bernard Canon MacDonald;
Very Rev. Robert Canon McDonald;
Very Rev. Peter A. Canon Moran;
Very Rev. William Canon Anderson;
Very Rev. Alistair M. Canon Doyle.

Liaison Committee: (Diocesan Pastoral Council):	*Ex officio:* V.G.; Deans; Pastoral Planning Officer; Vocations Officer; Communications Officer; Chairman of Priests' Council; Secretary of Priests' Council; Chairperson of Diocesan Conference of Religious; Diocesan Youth Co-ordinator; Representatives of Education Committee Church Representatives. *Elected:* Lay members of Deanery Pastoral Councils (4)

Priests' Council: *Chairman,* Rev. Christopher Brannan, *Secretary,* Rev. Stuart P. Chalmers, S.T.L., St. Mary's, Bridgefield, STONEHAVEN AB39 2JE. ☎ Stonehaven (01569) 762433.

Conference of Religious: *Chairperson,* Sr. Ethel Lamont, R.S.C.J. (Aberdeen). *Secretary,* Sr. Eileen McKernan, F.M.M., 9 Gordon Grove, ELLON AB41 9AS. ☎ 01358-722388. *Treasurer:* Sr. Mary Oliver, Sister of Mercy (Elgin).

Finance Committee: *ex officio:* Bishop; Vicar General; Deans. *Procurator,* Rev. Andrew Mann, B.A., S.T.B., Dip. Comm. *Treasurer,* Very Rev. Robert Canon McDonald; Rev. Deacon Brian Kilkerr, K.C.H.S.,A.B.I.I.B.A.; Mr. Patrick Mitchell, LL.B.; Mr. Bernard Murphy; Mr. Anthony Ward; Mr. Peter Macdonald. *Secretary,* Mrs. Joyce Simpson, LL.B., *Company address* (Endowment Trust of R.C. Diocese of Aberdeen): Messrs. Craigens, Advocates, 13 Bon-Accord Crescent, ABERDEEN AB11 6NN. ☎ 01224-588295/6.

III. PASTORAL AND CATECHETICAL: THE OGILVIE CENTRE

Communications Officer: Mr. Tom Cooney.
Pastoral Planning Officer: Rev. Andrew Mann, S.T.B.
Catechetical Officer: Rev. Dr. Colin Stewart, Ph.B., S.T.B., Dip.Ed., M.Ed., Ph.D.
Adult Formation: 16 Huntly Street, ABERDEEN AB10 1SH ☎/Fax: 01224-645401.

IV. CATHOLIC EDUCATION

Representatives on Local Authority Education Committees

Aberdeen:	Mr. Mario Vicca, LL.B.
Aberdeenshire:	Very Rev. Peter A. Canon Moran, Ph.L., S.T.L., M.A., L.T.C.L. 116 North Street, INVERURIE AB51 4TL.
Moray:	Mrs. Roma Hossack, 46 Gordon Street, New Elgin, ELGIN IV30 3EP.
Highland:	cf. Argyll and The Isles.

Supervisor for Religious Education in Catholic Schools: Mrs. Sarah Reid, 19 Gladstone Place, ABERDEEN AB10 6UX
☎ Aberdeen (01224) 322719.

V. FAMILY AND MARRIAGE SUPPORT— CATHOLIC MARRIAGE CARE

Aberdeen: *Chairman:* Mr. John Everett.
Secretary: Mrs. Kay Cooney.
Margaret House,
132 Huntly Street,
ABERDEEN AB10 1SU.
Appointments: ☎ 01224-643174.

Inverness: Rev. Deacon Jacques Cooke, C.Eng.
M.I.Chem.E.,
42 Kenneth Street,
INVERNESS IV3 5DH.
Appointments: ☎ 01463-230670.

Natural Family Planning: *Contact:* Catholic Marriage Care, Aberdeen.

VI. VOCATIONAL PROMOTION AND FORMATION

Vocations Officer: Rev. Edward Traynor,
St. Peter's,
BUCKIE AB56 1QN.
☎ 01542-832196.

Junior Vocations Promoter: Vacant.

For Permanent Diaconate: Rev. Deacon John Futers,
Corpus Christi,
16 Dunvegan Avenue,
Portlethen, ABERDEEN AB12 4NE.
☎ 01224-780256.

VII. YOUTH FORMATION
ST. MICHAEL'S CENTRE, TOMINTOUL
Director: Rev. Dr. Colin Stewart, Ph.B., S.T.B.
Dip.Ed., M.Ed., Ph.D.,
St. Michael's, Main Street, Tomintoul,
BALLINDALLOCH AB37 9EX.
☎ 01807-580226 (Enquiries);
☎ 01807-580240 (Residence).

DIOCESAN YOUTH CO-ORDINATOR
Mrs. Marie Cooke, Youth Office,
3A Hillpark, INVERNESS IV2 4AL
☎ 01463-232136.

VIII. JUSTICE AND PEACE
Diocesan Promoter: Vacant.

IX. PONTIFICAL MISSION AID SOCIETIES
Diocesan Director: Rev. Deacon John Futers,
Corpus Christi,
16 Dunvegan Avenue,
Portlethen, ABERDEEN AB12 4NE.
☎ 01224-780256.

X. LOCAL ECUMENISM
Diocesan Representative: Contact: Bishop's House.

XI. REGISTRAR FOR DECEASED CLERGY
Diocesan Registrar: c/o Bishop's House,
3 Queen's Cross,
ABERDEEN AB15 4XU.

XII. DIOCESAN FINANCE; MILLENNIUM APPEAL
Appeal Co-ordinator: Mrs. Joyce Webster
Appeal Office: 3 Queen's Cross,
ABERDEEN AB15 4XU.
☎ 01224-208944.
Chairman, Steering Committee: Mr. Patrick Mitchell, LL.B.
Chairman, Events Committee: Mr. Peter MacDonald.
Chairman, Heritage Committee: Mr. Charles Rattray.

CATHEDRAL CHAPTER
(Restored 2nd July, 1892.)

"A Chapter of Canons . . . is a college of priests, whose role is to celebrate the more solemn liturgical functions in a cathedral or a collegiate church. It is for the Cathedral Chapter, besides, to fulfil those roles entrusted to it by law or by the diocesan Bishop" (Canon 503).

Provost:	Right Rev. Mgr. John F. Copland.
Canons:	Very Rev. Hugh Malaney;
	Very Rev. Bernard G. MacDonald;
	Very Rev. Robert A. McDonald;
	Very Rev. John Symon;
	Very Rev. Peter A. Moran;
	Very Rev. William R. T. Anderson
	Very Rev. Alistair M. Doyle.
Honorary Canon:	Very Rev. Duncan Stone;
	Very Rev. Charles T. Stanley.

DEANERIES

A dean is a priest who is placed in charge of a group of parishes with "the duty and the right to promote and co-ordinate common pastoral action."
(Canons 553/555).

1. **St. Mary's:** (City of Aberdeen and Shetland).
   Cathedral; St. Peter's; St. Joseph's, Woodside; Sacred Heart, Torry; Holy Family, Mastrick; St. Francis', Mannofield; Our Lady of Aberdeen Kincorth; University Catholic Chaplaincy; Bridge of Don; Lerwick.
   Dean—Very Rev. William Canon Anderson.

2. **St. Columba's:** (Kincardine and Aberdeenshire).
   Banchory; Blairs; Ballater; Ellon; Fraserburgh; Inverurie; Peterhead; Stonehaven.
   Dean—Very Rev. Peter A. Canon Moran.

3. **St. Thomas':** (Moray and Banffshire).
   Buckie; Banff; Dufftown; Elgin; Fochabers; Forres; Huntly; Keith; Tomintoul.
   Dean—Right Rev. Mgr. John Provost Copland, V.G.

4. **St. Joseph's:** (Highlands and Orkney).
   St. Mary's, Inverness; St. Ninian's, Inverness; Aviemore; Beauly; Brora; Culloden; Dingwall; Dornie; Fort Augustus; Kirkwall; Marydale; Nairn; Stratherrick; Tain; Thurso; Wick.
   Dean—Very Rev. Robert Canon McDonald.

CITY OF ABERDEEN

CATHEDRAL OF ST. MARY OF THE ASSUMPTION
(1860), Huntly Street.

Very Rev. William R. T. Canon Anderson, M.A., F.T.C.L.,
Administrator (1960)
Rev. William H. Joss *(Permanent Deacon)* (1997)

POSTAL ADDRESS: Cathedral Clergy House, 20 Huntly Street, ABERDEEN
AB10 1SH. ☎/Fax: Aberdeen (01224) 640160.

Sunday Masses: Vigil-Mass, 7 p.m.; 8, 11.15 a.m., 6 p.m. Evening
Prayer and Benediction: 4 p.m. (in Nazareth House). Holy Days of
Obligation, Masses: 10 a.m., 12.45, 7.30 p.m. Confessions: Saturday,
10.30 to 11.15 a.m., 6 to 6.50 p.m.
Estimated Catholic population: 1,500.

CONVENT OF THE SACRED HEART, 5 QUEEN'S LANE SOUTH, ABERDEEN AB15
6UZ. ☎ ABERDEEN (01224) 322757. SERVED FROM THE CATHEDRAL.
NAZARETH HOUSE, 34 CLAREMONT STREET, ABERDEEN AB10 6RA. ☎
ABERDEEN (01224) 582091; FAX: 01224-574849. CHAPLAIN: VERY REV.
JOHN CANON SYMON (1953). MASSES: SUNDAY, 9.30 A.M., HOLY DAYS OF
OBLIGATION, 7.15 A.M. EVENING PRAYER AND BENEDICTION, SUNDAY, 4 P.M.
THE ROYAL INFIRMARY, ALBYN HOSPITAL AND OAKBANK RESIDENTIAL
SCHOOL, ALL ATTENDED FROM THE CATHEDRAL.
ST. JOSEPH'S PRIMARY SCHOOL.

ST. COLUMBA, Bridge of Don (1983), Braehead Way.
Served from St. Joseph's.

Rev Brian Kilkerr, K.C.H.S., A.B.I.I.B.A. *(Permanent Deacon)* (1998)

POSTAL ADDRESS: 'Maranatha', 43 Valentine Drive,Danestone,
ABERDEEN AB22 8YF. ☎ Aberdeen (01224) 826555.; Fax: 01224-
820001,

Sunday Mass: 10 a.m. Confessions: First Saturday of the month.
Estimated Catholic population: 500.

ST. FRANCIS OF ASSISI, Mannofield (1958, 1982),
Deeside Drive.

Rev. Christopher Brannan, LL.B. (1983)

POSTAL ADDRESS: St. Francis', 231 Deeside Gardens, ABERDEEN AB15
7PS. ☎/Fax: Aberdeen (01224) 315893.

Sunday Masses: 11 a.m., 6 p.m. Holy Days of Obligation Masses: 9.30
a.m.; 7.45 p.m. Confessions: Wednesday, 6.30 p.m. Saturday, 10 a.m.;
after Mass on request.
Estimated Catholic population: 1,570.

WESTHILL, TRINITY CHURCH, SERVED FROM ST. FRANCIS', MANNOFIELD.
TOR-NA-DEE HOSPITAL, AND ROXBURGHE HOUSE (HOSPICE) ATTENDED FROM
ST. FRANCIS OF ASSISI.
AUMÔNERIE DES CATHOLIQUES DE LANGUE FRANÇAISE (CENTRE FOR FRENCH-
SPEAKING CATHOLICS): MESSE ANTICIPÉE DU DIMANCHE, 18H00 UNE FOIS PAR
MOIS. ☎ INVERURIE (01467) 620319.

THE HOLY FAMILY, Mastrick (1954, 1967), Upper Mastrick Way.

Lay Pastoral Assistant: Mrs. Margaret Coll

POSTAL ADDRESS: Holy Family Church Flat, Deveron Road, ABERDEEN
AB16 6LZ. Tel.: Aberdeen (01224) 692796.

Sunday Mass: 10.15 a.m. Holy Days of Obligation, Mass: 7.30 p.m.
Confessions: before Masses.
Estimated Catholic population: 175.   **A**

WOODEND GENERAL HOSPITAL, HAMEWITH LODGE, ROSEWELL HOME,
BYRON PARK AND CROFT HOUSE ATTENDED FROM THE HOLY FAMILY.
HOLY FAMILY PRIMARY SCHOOL.

ST. JOSEPH, Woodside (1842), Tanfield Walk.

Rev. Gabriel O. Asare, M.A. (1960)
Rev. Joseph Gyim-Austin (1981)

POSTAL ADDRESS: St. Joseph's, 2 Tanfield Walk, ABERDEEN AB24 4AQ.
☎ Aberdeen (01224) 484226.

Sunday Masses: Vigil-Mass, 5 p.m., in Dyce Parish Church Hall; 11.30
a.m, 6 p.m. Holy Days of Obligation, Mass: 7.30 p.m. Confessions:
second Saturday of each month.
Estimated Catholic population: 560.

(ST. PETER'S PRIMARY SCHOOL.)

OUR LADY OF ABERDEEN, Kincorth (1961, 1963), Cairngorm Crescent.

Very Rev. Charles T. Canon Stanley (1960)

POSTAL ADDRESS: Our Lady of Aberdeen, 70 Cairngorm Crescent, ABERDEEN AB12 5BR. ☎ Aberdeen (01224) 876704.
E-mail: cstanley@zetnet.co.uk

Sunday Mass: 11.15 a.m. Holy Days of Obligation, Mass: 7.30 p.m.
Confessions: Saturday, 10.30 to 11 a.m.
Estimated Catholic population: 400 (including Portlethen).

Rev. John R. Futers *(Permanent Deacon)* (1986)
Postal Address: Corpus Christi, 16 Dunvegan Avenue, Portlethen, ABERDEEN AB12 4NE. ☎ Aberdeen (01224) 780256.

PORTLETHEN AND COVE SERVED FROM OUR LADY OF ABERDEEN.
ROYAL CORNHILL HOSPITAL, Aberdeen, AND LETHEN PARK NURSING HOME, Portlethen, ATTENDED FROM OUR LADY OF ABERDEEN.
(ST. JOSEPH 'S PRIMARY SCHOOL.)

ST. PETER, Castlegate (1774, 1803), Justice Street.

Rev. Andrew Mann, B.A., S.T.B. (1980)

POSTAL ADDRESS: 15 Grampian Road, Torry, ABERDEEN AB11 8ED.
☎/Fax: Aberdeen (01224) 878489.
E-mail: acmann@zetnet.co.uk

Sunday Masses: Vigil-Mass, 6 p.m. (5 p.m. in winter); 11.a.m. Holy Days of Obligation, Masses: 10 a.m.; 1.45 p.m. (in St. Peter's School).
Confessions: Saturday, 10.30 to 11 a.m.
Estimated Catholic population: 300.

THE CITY HOSPITAL, URQUHART ROAD, ATTENDED FROM ST. PETER'S.
ST. PETER'S PRIMARY SCHOOL.

SACRED HEART, Torry (1905, 1911), Grampian Road.

Rev. Andrew Mann, B.A., S.T.B. (1980)

POSTAL ADDRESS: Sacred Heart, 15 Grampian Road, Torry, ABERDEEN AB11 8ED. ☎/Fax: Aberdeen (01224) 878489.
E-mail:acmann@zetnet.co.uk

Sunday Mass: 9.45 a.m. Holy Days of Obligation, Mass: 7 p.m.
Confessions: Sunday, 9.15 to 9.30 a.m.
Estimated Catholic population: 100.

ABERDEEN MATERNITY HOSPITAL, ROYAL ABERDEEN CHILDREN'S HOSPITAL AND H.M. PRISON CRAIGINCHES SERVED FROM SACRED HEART.
(ST. JOSEPH'S PRIMARY SCHOOL).

COVE and ALTENS, City of Aberdeen. Served from Our Lady of Aberdeen, Kincorth.

PORTLETHEN MASS CENTRE, Aberdeenshire. Served from Our Lady of Aberdeen, Kincorth.

Sunday Mass: 9.30 a.m. in Jubilee Hall.

CHAPLAINCY FOR CATHOLIC STUDENTS AT ABERDEEN UNIVERSITY (1967, 1972), High Street, Old Aberdeen.

Rev. Richard Copsey, O.Carm. (1971)
Rev. David Waite, O.Carm. (1990)

POSTAL ADDRESS: Elphinstone House, 7 High Street, Old Aberdeen ABERDEEN AB24 3EE. ☎ Aberdeen (01224) 482444.
E-mails: rcopsey@carmelnet.org; dwaite@carmelnet.org

Service times during term: Sunday Masses: 10 a.m., 6.30 p.m. Holy Days of Obligation, Masses: 12.15, 5.15 p.m., during term.
During University vacation, times of Masses on application to the Chaplain. Confessions: on request.

SECONDARY SCHOOLS IN THE CITY OF ABERDEEN designated for the education of Catholic pupils.
Aberdeen Grammar School, Skene Street. ☎ Aberdeen (01224) 642299.
Linksfield Academy, 520 King Street. ☎ Aberdeen (01224) 641343.
Northfield Academy, Granitehill Place. ☎ Aberdeen (01224) 699715.

PARISHES OUTSIDE THE CITY OF ABERDEEN
The name given last before the name of the Church is the Local Authority or Island Council.

ABERLOUR, Moray, The Sacred Heart (1909), Chapel Terrace. Served from Tomintoul.
Sunday Vigil-Mass, 5 p.m. Confessions: by appointment.

THE FLEMING HOSPITAL AND SPEYSIDE HOME, Aberlour, ATTENDED FROM TOMINTOUL (☎ TOMINTOUL (01807) 580226).

ABOYNE, Aberdeenshire, St. Margaret (1874) Gordon Crescent. Served from Ballater.
Sunday Mass: Vigil-Mass, 6.30 p.m. Holy Days of Obligation: 7.30 p.m.

ACHILTIBUIE, Highland. Served from Dingwall.
Nearest Mass, Ullapool. For further information, 'phone Dingwall (01349) 863143.

ACHMORE, Highland. Served from Dornie.
For information, telephone Dornie (Kyle) (01599) 555229.

ALFORD, Aberdeenshire. Served from Inverurie.
Sunday Vigil-Mass, 6 p.m., in St. Andrew's Scottish Episcopal Church (junction of Donside Road and Montgarrie Road,in centre of Alford). Holy Days of Obligation, Mass: as announced.

ALNESS (Easter Ross), Highland, Oratory of St. John Ogilvie (1979, 1977), Coul Park. Served from Tain.

Sunday Vigil-Mass, 6 p.m. Holy Days of Obligation, Mass: 10 a.m. Confessions: Before and after all Masses; by appointment.

LA SAINTE UNION CONVENT, ST. JOHN OGILVIE, COUL PARK, ALNESS IV17 0RD. ☎ ALNESS (01349) 883459.

APPLECROSS (Wester Ross), Highland. Served from Dornie (☎ Dornie (Kyle) (01599) 555229.
Services as announced. For information, contact Dornie, St. Duthac's.

AULTBEA, Highland. Served from Dingwall.
Nearest Sunday Mass, Gairloch. For further information, 'phone
Dingwall (01349) 863143.

AVIEMORE, Highland, St. Aidan (1960,
1951),Grampian Road. Served from Kingussie (Diocese
of Argyll and The Isles). ☎ Kingussie (01540) 661322.

Sunday Masses: Vigil-Mass, 5.30 p.m.; 11 a.m. Holy Days of Obligation,
Masses: as announced locally. Confessions:Saturday, 4.30 to 5.15 p.m.;
on request.
Estimated Catholic population: 160.

IAIN CHARLES HOSPITAL, GRAND VIEW NURSING HOME, GRANT HOUSE AND
MOUNT BARKER RESIDENTIAL HOME, Grantown-on-Spey, ATTENDED FROM
AVIEMORE.

BALINTORE, Highland. Served from Tain.
For Mass times telephone Tain (01862) 892592.

BALLATER, Aberdeenshire, St. Nathalan (1905). Golf
Road. United with Aboyne and Braemar, 1994.

Rev. Derick W.B. McCulloch, B.D., B.A., M.A., S.T.I. (1994)

POSTAL ADDRESS: St. Nathalan's, 48 Golf Road, BALLATER AB35 5RS. ☎
Ballater (01339) 756043.

Sunday Mass: 12 noon. Holy Days of Obligation: Mass, 12 noon.
Confessions: Saturday, 5.30 p.m.; by appointment.
Estimated Catholic population: 190.

BANCHORY, Aberdeenshire, St. Columba (1964,
1931), High Street.

Rev. James Thomson (1988)

POSTAL ADDRESS: St. Columba's, Corsee Cottage, 5 High Street,
BANCHORY AB31 5RP. ☎ Banchory (01330) 822835; Fax: 01330-825654
E-mail: stcolumba@ifb.co.uk.

Sunday Masses: Vigil-Mass, 6 p.m.; 11 a.m. Holy Days of Obligation
Masses: 10 a.m., 7.30 p.m. Confessions: Saturday, after Vigil-Mass; at
call.
Estimated Catholic population: 380.

GLEN-O'-DEE HOSPITAL, Banchory, AND KINCARDINE O'NEIL WAR
MEMORIAL HOSPITAL, Torphins, ATTENDED FROM ST. COLUMBA'S.

BANFF, Aberdeenshire, Our Lady of Mount Carmel (1870), Sandyhill Road.

Rev. Laurence J. Lochrie, S.J. (1957)

POSTAL ADDRESS: Mount Carmel, Sandyhill Road, BANFF AB4 1BE. ☎ Banff (01261) 812204.

Sunday Masses: Vigil-Mass, 6.30 p.m.; 11.30 a.m. Holy Days of Obligation, Masses: 1.10, 7 p.m. Confessions: Saturday, 10.45 to 11.15 a.m.
Estimated Catholic population: 140.

PORTSOY SERVED FROM BANFF.
LADYSBRIDGE MENTAL HOSPITAL, CHALMERS HOSPITAL, Banff, TURRIFF COTTAGE HOSPITAL, Turriff, AND CAMPBELL HOSPITAL, Portsoy, ATTENDED FROM BANFF.

BEAULY, Inverness-shire, Highland, St. Mary (1843, 1864), A862 (village main road).

Rev. Austin Gaskell, O.P., M.A., M.Ed. (1962)

POSTAL ADDRESS: St. Mary's, BEAULY IV4 7AU. ☎ Beauly (01463) 782232.

Sunday Mass: 11 a.m. Holy Days of Obligation, Masses: announced locally. Confessions: Saturday, 10.30 a.m.; on request. **A**
Estimated Catholic population: 380.

LENTRAN HOUSE, AND URRAY HOUSE, (Muir of Ord), SERVED FROM ST. MARY'S.
CATHOLIC CEMETERY.

BETTYHILL, Highland. (Parish of St. Anne, Thurso.)
Nearest Mass, Thurso.

BLAIRS, Aberdeenshire, St. Mary's (1829, 1901).

Rev. James Thomson (1988)
Rev. John Woodside, M.I.S.M. (*Permanent Deacon*) (1994)

POSTAL ADDRESS: The Parish of St. Mary, South Deeside Road, Blairs, ABERDEEN AB12 5YQ. ☎/Fax: Aberdeen (01224) 869424.
E-mail: johnwoodside@blairs.net
Sunday Mass: 9 a.m. Holy Days of Obligation, Vigil-Mass: 7.30 p.m.
Confessions: on request.
Estimated Catholic population: 220. ♿

The Blairs Museum (Scottish Catholic Heritage Collection), South Deeside Road, ABERDEEN AB12 5YQ. ☎ 01224-869424; Fax: 01221-891284. E-mail: Curator@Blairs.net
Open 1st May to 31st October, 2000: Friday, Saturday, Sunday & Monday, 11 a.m. to 4 p.m.   **A**
The Blairs College Chapel Trust, South Deeside Road, Blairs, ABERDEEN AB12 5YQ. ☎/Fax: 01224-869424.
E-mail:BCT@blairs.net
Access to the Chapel: Sunday, 8.30 to 10.30 a.m.; Monday, Tuesday, Thursday, 10 a.m. to 2 p.m.; other times by arrangement.
Website:www.blairs.net
The Friends of Blairs, South Deeside Road, Blairs, ABERDEEN AB12 5YQ. ☎/Fax: 01224-869424.
E-mail: FOB@blairs.net

BONAR BRIDGE, Highland. Served from Brora.

BRAEMAR, Aberdeenshire, St. Andrew (circa 1703, 1839), Auchendryne Square. Served from Ballater.
Sunday Mass: 10 a.m. Holy Days of Obligation: Mass, 10 a.m.   **A**

HUMANAE VITAE HOUSE, (PRO-LIFE CENTRE), CHAPEL BRAE, BRAEMAR AB35 5YT. ☎ BRAEMAR (013397) 41380. FAX: (013397) 41416. RESIDENT PRIEST: REV. JAMES MORROW, PH.L., S.T.L., M.A. (1958).

BRORA Sutherland, Highland, Christ the King (1957, 1973), Gower Street.

Rev. Michael Benedict Seed, O.S.B., S.T.L., B.Sc. (1956)

Postal address: The Bungalow, Gower Street, BRORA KW9 6PU. ☎ Brora (01408) 621388.

Sunday Masses: Vigil-Mass, 6 p.m., 11 a.m. Holy Days of Obligation Masses: 10 a.m., 6 p.m. Confessions: Saturday, 5.30 p.m
Estimated Catholic population: 180.

LAWSON MEMORIAL HOSPITAL, CAMBUSAVIE AND SEAFORTH HOUSE, Golspie, AND MIGDALE HOSPITAL, Bonar Bridge, ATTENDED FROM BRORA.

BUCKIE, Moray, St. Peter (1857), St. Andrew's Square.

Rev. Edward P. Traynor, Ph.B., S.T.B., Lic.Psych., J.P. (1985)

POSTAL ADDRESS: St. Peter's, St. Andrew's Square, BUCKIE AB56 1QN.
☎/Fax: Buckie (01542) 832196; Mobile: 07974-691053.
E-mail: FatherEddie@St.Peter's99.freeserve.co.uk

Sunday Masses: Vigil-Mass, 6.30 p.m., 10 a.m. Holy Days of Obligation,
Masses: 9.30 a.m., 7 p.m. Confessions: Friday, 6 to 7 p.m.; Saturday, 5
to 6 p.m.
Estimated Catholic population: 500.   **A**

PRESHOME AND TYNET SERVED FROM BUCKIE.
SEAFIELD HOSPITAL AND NETHERHA' AND PARKLANDS OLD PEOPLE'S HOMES,
Buckie, SERVED FROM ST. PETER'S.
ST. PETER'S PRIMARY SCHOOL.

CANNICH, Highland. See Marydale (p. 161).

CHAPELTOWN, Braes of Glenlivet, Moray, Our Lady of Perpetual Succour (1829, 1897). Served from Tomintoul.

All sick calls and enquiries should be directed to the parish priest at
Tomintoul (☎ Tomintoul (01807) 580226).

Sunday Mass: 11 a.m., alternately withTomintoul and Tombae. Holy
Days of Obligation Mass as announced. Confessions by appointment.

CATHOLIC CEMETERY.

CROMARTY, Highland. Served from Dingwall (☎ 01349-863143).

Communion Service in St. Regulus' Episcopal Church, Church
Street, Sunday, 7 p.m.

CRUDEN BAY, Aberdeenshire. Served from Peterhead.

For information, telephone 01779-470443.

CULLEN, Moray. Served from Portsoy.

For Mass times, telephone Banff (01261) 812204.

CULLODEN, Highland, St. Columba (1993, 1991).

Rev. Peter R. Barry, B.A. (1969)

POSTAL ADDRESS: 12 Culloden Court, INVERNESS IV2 7DX. ☎ Inverness (01463) 791957.

Sunday Mass: 9.30 a.m. in Duncan Forbes School, 4 p.m. in Ardersier Memorial Hall. Holy Days of Obligation, Mass: 7.30 p.m. in Duncan Forbes School. Confessions: as announced.
Estimated Catholic population: 300.

LA SAINTE UNION SISTER, 6 LOCHLANN TERRACE, CULLODEN, INVERNESS IV1 2PZ. ☎ 01463-793127; FAX: 01463-793779.
RAIGMORE HOSPITAL, Inverness, SERVED FROM ST. COLUMBA'S.

DINGWALL Ross-shire, Highland, St. Lawrence (1902) Castle Street.

Rev . David Kay, S.J. (1981)

POSTAL ADDRESS: St. Lawrence's, 21 Castle Street, DINGWALL IV15 9HU. ☎ Dingwall (01349) 863143.

Sunday Masses: Vigil-Mass, 7.30 p.m.; 10 a.m. Holy Days of Obligation, Mass:10 a.m., 7.30 p.m. Confessions: Saturday, 10 to 10.30 a.m., 6.45 to 7.15 p.m.
Estimated Catholic population: 250.

ROSS MEMORIAL HOSPITAL, Dingwall, STRATHBURN HOUSE, Gairloch, NICHOLSON MEMORIAL HOSPITAL, FODDERTY HOUSE, BALMORAL LODGE AND RAVENSCROFT, Strathpeffer, LOCHBROOM HOUSE AND NURSING HOME, Ullapool, AND FAIRBURN HOUSE, Urray, ATTENDED FROM ST. LAWRENCE'S.

DORNIE, Kintail, Highland, St. Duthac (circa 1703, 1860), Bundalloch Road.

Rev. Gerald A. Livingstone, B.D. (1995)

POSTAL ADDRESS: St. Duthac's, Bundalloch Road, Dornie, KYLE IV40 8EL. ☎ Dornie (Kyle) (01599) 555229; Fax: 01599-555458.
E-mail: gerry.livingstone@zetnet.co.uk

Sunday Masses: Vigil-Mass, 7.30 p.m.; 10.30 a.m. Holy Days of Obligation, Masses: Vigil-Mass, 7.30 p.m.; 10 a.m. Confessions: before any Mass; on request.
Estimated Catholic population: 250.

GRAHAM HOUSE (OLD PEOPLE'S HOME) ATTENDED FROM ST. DUTHAC'S.

DORNOCH, Highland. Served from Brora.

Services held in St. Finnbarr's Episcopal Church, Schoolhill.
Sunday Mass: 4 p.m. Holy Days of Obligation, Mass: 12 noon.

DRUMNADROCHIT, Highland. Served from Beauly.

For times of services, telephone Beauly (01463) 782232.

DUFFTOWN, Moray, Our Lady of the Assumption (1728, 1825), Fife Street.

Rev. Colin M. Stewart, Ph.D., M.Ed., S.T.B.
(*Tomintoul*) (1982)

POSTAL ADDRESS: c/o St. Michael's, Main Street, Tomintoul, BALLINDALLOCH AB37 9EX. ☎/Fax: Tomintoul (01807) 580226.
E-mail: SMCTtoul@aol.com

Sunday Mass: 9 a.m. Confessions by appointment.
Estimated Catholic population (with Aberlour):200.

MOUNT STEPHEN COTTAGE HOSPITAL, Dufftown, THE FLEMING HOSPITAL AND SPEYSIDE HOME, Aberlour, AND CRAGGANMORE HOME, Ballindalloch, ATTENDED FROM TOMINTOUL.

DURNESS, Highland, Served from Brora.

DYCE, City of Aberdeen. Dyce Parish Church Hall, Victoria Street. Served from St. Joseph's, Aberdeen.

☎ Aberdeen (01224) 484226.
Sunday Vigil-Mass: 5 p.m. Confessions, before Mass.

ELGIN, Moray, St. Sylvester (1843).

Very Rev. Alistair Mason Canon Doyle, B.A., Dip.R.E. (1962)

POSTAL ADDRESS: St. Sylvester's, 19 Institution Road, ELGIN IV30 1QT.
☎ Elgin (01343) 542280.

Sunday Masses: Vigil-Mass, 6 p.m.; 11.15 a.m. Holy Days of Obligation,
Masses: 10 a.m., 7 p.m. Confessions: Saturday, 10.20 a.m., 5.20 p.m.;
on request. Lossiemouth, St. Columba's, Sundays and Holy Day Vigils,
Mass, 6.30 p.m.
Estimated Catholic population: 800.

CONVENT OF THE SISTERS OF MERCY, GREYFRIARS,ABBEY STREET, ELGIN IV30 1DB. ☎ ELGIN (01343) 547806. SERVED FROM ST. SYLVESTER'S.
ABBEYSIDE HOME, ANDERSON'S HOME, FLEURS HOME, GREYFRIARS CLOSE, WESTPARK COURT, DR. GRAY'S HOSPITAL AND SPYNIE HOSPITAL ATTENDED FROM ST. SYLVESTER'S. HALLIMAN HOUSE, Lossiemouth, ATTENDED FROM ST. SYLVESTER'S.
ST. SYLVESTER'S PRIMARY SCHOOL.

ELLON, Aberdeenshire, Our Lady and St. John the Baptist (1989, 1992), Union Street.

Rev. Raymond Coyle, B.A. (1977)

POSTAL ADDRESS: The Presbytery, 3 Union Street, ELLON AB41 9BA. ☎ Ellon (01358) 721485.

SUNDAY MASSES: Vigil-Mass, 6 p.m.; 10.30 a.m. Holy Days of Obligation, Masses: Vigil-Mass, 7.30 p.m.; 10 a.m., 7.30 p.m. Confessions: Saturday, 5 p.m., Sunday 12.30 p.m.

FRANCISCAN MISSIONARIES OF MARY, 9 GORDON GROVE, ELLON AB41 9AF. ☎ ELLON (01358) 722388.
KINGSEAT HOSPITAL, New Machar, AND H.M. PRISON, Peterhead, ATTENDED FROM ELLON.

ESKADALE, Highland, St. Mary (1793, 1826). Served from Beauly.

Sunday Mass: 9 a.m. on alternate Sundays.Holy Days of Obligation, Mass: announced locally. Confessions before Mass.　　　　　　　　🅰

SISTERS OF ST. MARY OF NAMUR, CHAPEL CROFT, ESKADALE, KILTARLITY BEAULY IV4 7JR. ☎ BEAULY (01463) 741364.
CATHOLIC CEMETERY.

FETTERNEAR, Aberdeenshire, Our Lady of the Garioch and St. John the Evangelist (1859). Served from Inverurie.

(1$^{1/2}$ miles N.W. of Kemnay; signposted *St. John's Church* on the Burnhervie to Blairdaff Road.)
Sunday Mass 6 p.m., alternately with Inverurie.

CATHOLIC CEMETERY—ST. JOHN'S, FETTERNEAR.

FOCHABERS, Moray, St. Mary (1826), South Street.

Very Rev. Bernard G. Canon MacDonald (1948)

POSTAL ADDRESS: St. Mary's, 22A South Street, FOCHABERS IV32 7ED. ☎ Fochabers (01343) 820285.

Sunday Masses: Vigil-Mass, 6 p.m.;11.15 a.m. Holy Days of Obligation, Mass: 7p.m. Confessions: Saturday, before Vigil-Mass. **A**
Estimated Catholic population: 120.

(ST. SYLVESTER'S PRIMARY SCHOOL, ELGIN; ST. PETER'S PRIMARY SCHOOL BUCKIE)

FORRES, Moray, St. Margaret (1929, 1927), High Street.

Rev. Francis Barnett, S.J. (1963)

POSTAL ADDRESS: St. Margaret's, High Street, FORRES IV36 0BU. ☎ Nairn (01667) 453323/Forres (01309) 672306.

Sunday Masses: 9 a.m., 7 p.m. Evening Service as announced.Holy Days of Obligation, Vigil Mass: 7 p.m. Confessions: Saturday, 10.30 to 11 a.m.
Estimated Catholic population: 310.

LEANCHOIL HOSPITAL, ATTENDED FROM FORRES.

FORT AUGUSTUS Inverness-shire, Highland, St. Peter and St. Benedict's (1842, as St. Peter's; 1999, new Chapel in old Abbey Lodge).

Rev. Keith Paul Bonnici, O.S.B. (1995)

POSTAL ADDRESS: St. Benedict's, The Lodge, Glen Doe Road, FORT AUGUSTUS PH32 4BG.☎/Fax:Fort Augustus (01320) 366451.
E-mail: Fr.Paul@ecosse.net
Sunday Masses: Vigil-Mass, Saturday, 5 p.m. (*June to September*);10 a.m. Holy Days of Obligation, Mass: 7.30p.m. Confessions: Saturday, 4.30 p.m.: Sunday, 9.45 a.m. at call.
Estimated Catholic population (with Stratherrick):94. **A**

STRATHERRICK SERVED FROM FORT AUGUSTUS.
THE TELFORD CENTRE, Fort Augustus, SERVED FROM ST. PETER AND ST. BENEDICT'S.

FORT GEORGE and ARDERSIER, Highland. Served from Culloden.

Mass in Village Hall, Ardersier, Sunday, 4 p.m.

FORTROSE, Highland, St. Peter and St. Boniface, 9 Cathedral Square. Served from Beauly.

Sunday Mass: Vigil-Mass, 6 p.m. Holy Days of Obligation, Mass: announced locally.

FRASERBURGH, Aberdeenshire, Our Lady, Star of the Sea, and St. Drostan (1896), Commerce Street.

Rev. Kevin Firth, B.A., S.T.L. (1977)

POSTAL ADDRESS: 73 Commerce Street, FRASERBURGH AB43 9LR. ☎ Fraserburgh (01346) 518215.

Sunday Mass: 9.40 a.m. Holy Days of Obligation, Masses: 8 a.m., 7.30 p.m. Confessions: Saturday, 11.30 to 11.55 a.m.; at call. Estimated Ctholic population: 316.

FRASERBURGH HOSPITAL (INCLUDING MATERNITY WARD), ATTENDED FROM OUR LADY'S FRASERBURGH.

FYVIE, Aberdeenshire. Served from Inverurie.

GAIRLOCH, Highland. Served from Dingwall.

Sunday Mass: 2.30 p.m. in Community Centre (beside Tourist Information Office). Holy Days of Obligation: Masses in Dingwall, 10 a.m., 7.30 p.m. Confessions: Sunday from 2 p.m. For further information, telephone Dingwall (01349) 863143.

GARVE, Highland. Nearest Sunday Mass, Dingwall.

GLENKINDIE, Aberdeenshire. Served from Inverurie.

GOLSPIE, Highland. Served from Brora. For information apply to Rev. Parish Priest at Brora (℅ Brora (01408) 621388).

GRANTOWN-ON-SPEY, Highland, St. Anne (1960).
Served from Kingussie, Argyll and The Isles. (☎ Kingussie (01540) 661322.)

Sunday Mass, 4.15 p.m.

HATTON OF FINTRAY, Aberdeenshire. Served from Inverurie

HELMSDALE, Highland. Served from Brora.

HUNTLY, Aberdeenshire, St. Margaret (circa 1742, 1834, restored and rededicated, 1990), Chapel Street.

Right Rev. Mgr. John F. Provost Copland, V.G. (1946)

POSTAL ADDRESS: St. Thomas' Rectory, Chapel Street, KEITH AB55 5AL. ☎ Keith (01542) 882352.

Sunday Mass: 9.45 a.m. Holy Days of Obligation, Vigil-Mass, 6.30 p.m. Confessions: Sunday, 9.15 a.m.
Estimated Catholic population: 161.

HUNTLY HOSPITAL, SCOTT HOSPITAL, ROTHIEDEN AND MEADOWS HOME ATTENDED FROM ST. MARGARET'S.

INSCH, Aberdeenshire. Served from Inverurie.

INVERBERVIE, Aberdeenshire. Served from Stonehaven.

Sunday: Vigil-Mass, 6.30 p.m., and Holy Day Vigil-Mass, 7 p.m., in St. David's Episcopal Church, Victoria Terrace.

INVERGORDON Easter Ross, Highland, St. Joseph, (1916, 1958), High Street. Served from Tain.

Sunday Mass: 11.45 a.m. Holy Days of Obligation, Mass: 7.30 p.m. Confessions: Before and after all Masses; by appointment.

INVERNESS, Highland. St. Mary (1837, extended and re-dedicated, 1979).

Very Rev. Robert A. Canon McDonald (1952)
Pastoral Assistants: Sr. Eva Flennery, L.S.U.
Sr. Teresa Naughton, L.S.U.

POSTAL ADDRESS: St. Mary's, Huntly Street, INVERNESS IV3 5PR. ☎
Inverness (01463) 233519; Fax: 01463-718194.

Rev. Jacques Cooke, C.Eng., M.I.Chem.E.
(*Permanent Deacon*) (1986)

POSTAL ADDRESS: 42 Kenneth Street, INVERNESS IV3 5DH. ☎ Inverness
(01463) 230670.

Sunday Masses: Vigil-Mass, 7 p.m. (*June to September*); 10 a.m., 6.30
p.m. Holy Days of Obligation, Masses: Vigil-Mass, 7.30 p.m.; 10 a.m.,
7.30 p.m. Confessions: Saturday, 10.30 a.m.
Estiamted Catholic population: 1,010.

LA SAINTE UNION CONVENT, 32 HUNTLY STREET, INVERNESS IV3 5PR. ☎
INVERNESS (01463) 221086.
ROYAL NORTHERN INFIRMARY, CRAIG-DUNAIN HOSPITAL, CRAIG PHADRIG
HOSPITAL, HIGHLAND HOSPICE AND CHESHIRE HOME, ATTENDED FROM ST.
MARY'S.
ST. JOSEPH'S PRIMARY SCHOOL.

INVERNESS, Highland, St. Ninian (1959, 1977), Culduthel Road.

Rev. Peter R. Barry, B.A., Cert.Ed. (1969)
(*Resident at* 12 Culloden Court, INVERNESS IV2 7DX. Tel: Inverness
(01463) 791957.)
OFFICIAL ADDRESS: St. Ninian's, 21 Culduthel Road, INVERNESS IV2 4AA.
☎ Inverness (01463) 236620.

Rev. John McEwan, S.F.O. (*Permanent Deacon*) (1992)

HOME ADDRESS: 25 Townlands Park, CROMARTY IV11 8YY. ☎ Cromarty
(01381) 600281.

Sunday Masses: Vigil-Mass, 5 p.m.; 11.30 a.m. Vespers and
Benediction, 5 p.m. Holy Days of Obligation, Masses: 12.30 p.m., 6
p.m. Confessions: Saturday, 4 to 5 p.m.; weekdays, on request.
Estimated Catholic population: 600.

Raigmore Hospital ATTENDED FROM ST. COLUMBA'S, CULLODEN .
H.M. PRISON PORTERFIELD ATTENDED FROM ST. NINIAN'S.
(ST. JOSEPH'S PRIMARY SCHOOL).

INVERURIE, Aberdeenshire, The Immaculate Conception (1849, 1852), North Street.

Very Rev. Peter A. Canon Moran, Ph.L., S.T.L., M.A.,
M.Ed., L.T.C.L (1959)

POSTAL ADDRESS: Catholic Church, 116 North Street, INVERURIE AB51
4TL. ☎ Inverurie (01467) 620319.
E-mail: pamoran@tinyworld.co.uk

Sunday Masses: 10.30 a.m.(in hall); 6 p.m. alternately with Fetternear.
Holy Days of Obligation, Masses: as announced. Confessions:
Saturday, 12 noon to 12.30 p.m.; on request or appointment.
Estimated Catholic population: 734.   🅰

INVERURIE HOSPITAL, INSCH AND DISTRICT WAR MEMORIAL HOSPITAL,
GARIOCH NURSING HOME, Inverurie, AND B;YTHEWOOD NURSING HOME,
Port Elphinstone, ATTENDED FROM INVERURIE.
**The Registers of Lumsden (app. 1950 to 1995) are preserved at
Inverurie.**

KEITH, Moray, St. Thomas (circa 1783, 1831), Chapel Street.

Right Rev. Mgr. John F. Provost Copland, V.G. (1946)

POSTAL ADDRESS: St . Thomas' Rectory, Chapel Street, KEITH AB55
5AL. ☎ Keith (01542) 882352.

Sunday Masses: Vigil-Mass, 6.30 p.m.; 11.30 a.m. Holy Days of
Obligation, Masses: 9.15 a.m., 6.30 p.m. Confessions: Saturday, 10.30
to 11 a.m., after Vigil-Mass.
Estimated Catholic population: 335.   🈁 ♿

THE TURNER MEMORIAL HOSPITAL, GLENISLA HOME, TAYLOR COURT AND
WESTON HOUSE ATTENDED FROM ST. THOMAS'.
ST. THOMAS' PRIMARY SCHOOL.

KEMNAY, Aberdeenshire. Served from Inverurie.

KINLOSS, Moray, St. Mary, R.A.F. Kinloss.
See Bishopric of the Forces (p.403).

KINTORE, Aberdeenshire. Served from Inverurie.

KIRKWALL, Orkney Islands, Our Lady and St. Joseph (1939, 1877, 1985). Junction Road.

Rev. Kenneth Nugent, S.J. (1966)

POSTAL ADDRESS: Catholic Presbytery, 31 Main Street, KIRKWALL KW15 1BU. ☎ Kirkwall (01856) 872462.

Sunday Masses: Vigil-Mass, 6 p.m.; 11 a.m.; Mass in Stromness: time on application to the Parish Priest. Holy Days of Obligation, Masses: 10 a.m., 7 p.m.; Confessions: on request.
Estimated Catholic population: 110*

ITALIAN CHAPEL, LAMBHOLM: MASS, FIRST SUNDAY EACH SUMMER MONTH. ORKNEY COUNTY HOME, EASTBANK SANATORIUM AND I.D. HOSPITAL, AND BALFOUR HOSPITAL ATTENDED FROM KIRKWALL.

KISHORN, Wester Ross, Highland. Served from Dornie (☎ Dornie (Kyle) (01599) 555229.

Sunday Vigil-Mass, first Saturday of the month, 4.30 p.m., in Episcopal Church. Confessions beforehand on request.   Ⓐ

KYLE OF LOCHALSH, Highland. Served from Dornie.

LAIRG, Highland. Served from Brora.

LERWICK, Shetland Islands, St. Margaret (1900, 1910), Harbour Street.

Rev. James F. G. Hayes, S.J. (1965)

POSTAL ADDRESS: St. Margaret's, 87 St. Olaf Street, LERWICK ZE1 0ES. ☎ Lerwick (01595) 692233.

Sunday Masses: Vigil-Mass, 5 p.m.; 8.30, 10.30 a.m., 6.30 p.m. Holy Days of Obligation, Masses: Vigil-Mass, 7 p.m.; 8.15 a.m., 12.30, 5.15 p.m. Confessions: Saturday, 10.30 to 10.45 a.m.; on request.
Estimated Catholic population: 250*.   ♋ Ⓐ

GILBERT BAIN HOSPITAL, MONTFIELD HOSPITAL, KANTERSTED HOME, VIEWFORTH HOME AND R.A.F. SAXA-VORD, Unst, ATTENDED FROM LERWICK.

LOCHINVER, Highland. Served from Brora.
Sunday Mass in Fishermen's Mission, Culag Park, 11 a.m. (July and August).

LOSSIEMOUTH, Moray, St. Columba, Union Street. Served from Elgin.

Sunday Mass: 6.30 p.m. Holy Days of Obligation, Vigil-Mass: 6.30 p.m. Confessions before Mass.

HALLIMAN HOUSE ATTENDED FROM ELGIN.

LOSSIEMOUTH, Moray, Our Lady, Star of the Sea, R.A.F. Lossiemouth. See Bishopric of the Forces (p. 403).

LUMSDEN, Aberdeenshire. Served from Inverurie.

MARYDALE, Cannich, Highland, Our Lady and St. Bean (1868). Served from Beauly.
Sunday Mass: 9 a.m. on alternate Sundays.

SANCTI ANGELI BENEDICTINE SKETE, MARYDALE, BEAULY IV4 7LT. TEL.: CANNICH (01456) 415218.

MELVICH, Highland. (Parish of St. Anne, Thurso.) Nearest Mass, Thurso.

NAIRN, Highland, St. Mary (1861,1864), Academy Street.
Rev. Francis Barnett, S.J. (1963)

POSTAL ADDRESS: St. Mary's, 7 Academy Street, NAIRN IV12 4RJ. ☎ Nairn (01667) 453323.

Sunday Masses. Vigil-Mass, 6 p.m.; 11 a.m. Holy Days of Obligation, Masses: 10 a.m., 7 p.m. Confessions: Saturday, 5 to 5.45 p.m. Estimated Catholic population: 310. ♿

NAIRN COUNTY HOSPITAL, CONVALESCENT HOME AND CORSEE HOME ATTENDED FROM ST. MARY'S.

OLDMELDRUM, Aberdeenshire. Served from Inverurie.

ORKNEY. See Kirkwall and Stromness.

PETERHEAD, Aberdeenshire, St. Mary (1847, 1851), St. Peter Street. Served from Fraserburgh.

Rev. Kevin Firth, B.A., S.T.L. (1977)

POSTAL ADDRESS: 73 Commerce Street, FRASERBURGH AB43 9LR. ☎ (Presbytery, Fraserburgh)01346-518215; (Parish Hall, Peterhead): 01779-472453.

Sr. Theresa O'Flynn, F.M.M. *(Pastoral Assistant).*

POSTAL ADDRESS: The Convent, 9 Gordon Grove, ELLON AB41 9AS. ☎ Ellon (01358) 722388.

Sunday Masses: Vigil-Mass, 6.30 p.m.; 11.30 a.m. Holy Days of Obligation, Masses: Vigil-Mass, 7.30 p.m.; 10.30 a.m. Confessions: Saturday, 5.15 to 5.45 p.m.
Estimated Catholic population: 380.   ♿ ♿

PETERHEAD COMMUNITY HOSPITAL ATTENDED FROM ST. MARY'S.

PLOCKTON, Highland. Served from Dornie.
Services as announced.   For information regarding services, telephone Dornie (Kyle) (01599) 555229.

PLUSCARDEN, Moray, Abbey of Our Blessed Lady, St. John the Baptist and St. Andrew. (Founded 1230, re-opened 1948). Benedictines of the Subiaco Congregation.

Right Rev. Hugh Gilbert, O.S.B., B.A., *Abbot* (1982)
Right Rev. Alfred Spencer, O.S.B., *Abbot Emeritus* (1941)
Very Rev. Giles Conacher, O.S.B.,*Prior and Cellarer* (1979)
Rev. Maurus Deegan, O.S.B. (1952)
Rev. Camillus Warner, O.S.B. (1960)
Rev. Mark Savage, O.S.B., LL.B. (1986)
Rev. Benedict Hardy, O.S.B., B.A., B.A.Div. (1995)
Rev. Martin Birrell, O.S.B., M.A. (1979)

POSTAL ADDRESS: Pluscarden Abbey, ELGIN IV30 8UA. ☎ Dallas (01343) 890257; Fax: (01343) 890258.

Sundays and Holy Days of Obligation, Masses: 8, 10 (*Sung Latin*) a.m. Vespers and Benediction: 5.30 p.m.; Weekdays, Mass (*Sung Latin*), 8.45 a.m. Confessions: at call and before Mass (*including French*).
                                                    ♿ ♿

RETREATANTS — MALE AND FEMALE — ARE WELCOME. THEY SHOULD WRITE OR FAX: THE GUEST MASTER, ST. BENEDICT'S (FOR MEN) OR THE WARDEN, ST. SCHOLASTICA'S (FOR WOMEN). NEAREST RAILWAY STATION IS ELGIN, SIX MILES AWAY. BUS SERVICE VERY INFREQUENT.

POOLEWE, Highland. Served from Dingwall.
Nearest Sunday Mass, Gairloch.

PORTMAHOMACK, Highland. Served from Tain.
For information, telephone Tain (01862) 892592.

PORTSOY, Aberdeenshire. The Annunciation (circa 1790, 1829). 54 Aird Street. Served from Banff.
For information ☎ Banff (01261) 812204).
Sunday Mass: 9.30 a.m. Holy Days of Obligation, Mass, announced locally.

PRESHOME, Enzie, Moray, St. Gregory (17th Century 1788). Served from Buckie.
Sunday Mass, 5.30 p.m..

ROTHIENORMAN, Aberdeenshire. Served from Inverurie.

SAUCHEN, Aberdeenshire. Served from Inverurie.

SCOURIE, Highland. Served from Brora.

SHIEL BRIDGE, Glenshiel, Highland. Served from Dornie.
For information, telephone Dornie (Kyle) (01599) 555229.

STONEHAVEN, Aberdeenshire. The Immaculate Conception (1877), Arbuthnott Place.

Rev. Stuart P. Chalmers, Ph.B., S.T.L. (1997)

POSTAL ADDRESS: St. Mary's, Bridgefield, STONEHAVEN AB39 2JE. ☎ Stonehaven (01569) 762433; Fax: 01569-763289.

Sunday Masses: 9, 11 a.m., 6.30 p.m. Holy Days of Obligation, Masses: 8 a.m., 7 p.m. Confessions: Saturday, 10.30 to 11 a.m.; on request. Estimated Catholic population: 750.

KINCARDINE COMMUNITY HOSPITAL AND MOWAT COURT ATTENDED FROM ST. MARY'S.

STRATHDON, Aberdeenshire, Our Lady of the Snows, Corgarff. Served from Ballater.

Enquiries to Rev. Parish Priest, Ballater. ☎ Ballater (013397) 756043.

STRATHERRICK, Highland, The Immaculate Conception (1859). Served from Fort Augustus..☎:Fort Augustus (01320) 366451.

Sunday Mass: 12 noon. Holy Days of Obligation, Mass: 5 p.m. Confessions: Sunday, 11.45 a.m.   Ⓐ

ST. JOHN'S CATHOLIC CEMETERY.

STROMEFERRY (South), Highland. Served from Dornie.

For information, telephone Rev. Parish Priest at Dornie (Kyle) (01599) 555229.

STROMNESS, Orkney Islands. Stella Maris, 'Braemar'. Served from Kirkwall.

Sunday Mass: 6 p.m. or (*Winter*) 5 p.m.

TAIN, Easter Ross, Highland, St. Vincent (1986), Cameron Road.

Very Rev. Hugh Canon Malaney (1947)
Rev. Paul Lippok *(Permanent Deacon)* (1997)

POSTAL ADDRESS: St. Vincent's, Cameron Road, TAIN IVl9 1NN ☎ Tain (01862) 892592.

Sunday Mass: 10 a.m. Holy Days of Obligation, Mass: Vigil-Mass, 7.30 p.m. Confessions: Before and after all Masses; by appointment. Estimated Catholic population: 300.

ALNESS, BALINTORE, INVERGORDON AND PORTMAHOMACK SERVED FROM TAIN. DUTHAC HOUSE RESIDENTIAL HOME, Tain; REDWOOD HOME, Alness; INVERGORDON HOSPITAL, CASTLE GARDENS RESIDENTIAL HOME , MULHALL RESIDENTIAL HOME AND WYVIS HOUSE, Invergordon, SERVED FROM TAIN.

THURSO, Cathness, Highland, St. Anne (1960), Sweyn Road.

Rev. John M. Allen (1985)

POSTAL ADDRESS: St. Anne's, 2 Sweyn Road, THURSO KW14 7NW. ☎ Thurso (01847) 893196.
Sunday Masses: Vigil-Mass, 6.30 p.m.; 9 a.m. Holy Days of Obligation, Mass: 7 p.m. Confessions: Saturday, 6 p.m.
Estimated Catholic population:240.   **A**

DUNBAR HOSPITAL, BAYVIEW NURSING HOME, NAVER HOUSE EVENTIDE HOME AND PENTLAND VIEW ATTENDED FROM ST. ANNE'S.

TOMBAE, Glenlivet, Moray, The Incarnation (1829). Served from Tomintoul.

Sick Calls and enquiries should be directed to the Rev. Parish Priest, Tomintoul. (☎ Tomintoul (01807) 580226).

Sunday Mass: 11 a.m., alternately with Chapeltown and Tomintoul. Holy Days of Obligation, Mass as announced (at Tombae, Chapeltown or Tomintoul; check by telephone). Confessions:as announced or by appointment.

CATHOLIC CEMETERY.

TOMINTOUL, Moray, Our Lady and St. Michael (1837), Main Street.

Rev. Colin M. Stewart, Ph.D., M.Ed., S.T.B. (1982)

POSTAL ADDRESS: St. Michael's, Main Street, Tomintoul, BALLINDALLOCH AB37 9EX. ☎ & Fax: Tomintoul (01807) 580226.
E-mail:SMCTtoul@aol.com

Sunday Mass: 11 a.m. alternately with Chapeltown and Tombae. Holy Days of Obligation, Masses as announced. Confessions: by appointment.   **A**
Estimated Catholic population (with Tombae and Chapeltown): 100.

ST. MICHAEL'S CENTRE, MAIN STREET, TOMINTOUL., BALLINDALLOCH AB37 9EX. ☎/FAX: TOMINTOUL (01807) 580226.
E-mail: SMCTtoul@aol.com
CATHOLIC CEMETERY.

TONGUE, Highland. (Parish of St. Anne, Thurso. ☎ Thurso (01847) 893196.)

Mass, last Sunday in every month, 4 p.m. in Village Hall.

TYNET, Moray, St. Ninian (1755). Served from Buckie.
Sunday Mass: 8.30 a.m.

ULLAPOOL, Wester Ross, Highland, St. Martin of Tours (1988), Mill Street. Served from Dingwall.

Rev. David Kay, S.J. (*Dingwall*)   (1981)

Sunday Mass: 5.30 p.m. Holy Days of Obligation, Masses in Dingwall: 10 a.m., 7.30 p.m. Confessions: Sunday from 5 p.m.
For further information, telephone Dingwall (01349) 863143.   ♿

WESTHILL, Aberdeenshire, Trinity Church (1981), Westhill Drive. Served from St. Francis', Aberdeen (☎ Aberdeen (01224) 315893).

Rev. Christopher Brannan, LL.B.   (1983)

Sunday Mass: 9 a.m. Holy Days of Obligation, Mass: 6.30 p.m.

WICK, Caithness, Highland, St. Joachim (1836), Breadalbane Terrace.

Rev. John M. Allen (1985)

POSTAL ADDRESS: "Amherst", Malcolm Street, Wick KW1 5AG.
☎Thurso (01847) 893196.

Sunday Mass: 11 a.m. Holy Days of Obligation, Vigil-Mass: 7 p.m.
Confessions: Sunday 12.30 p.m.
Estimated Catholic population: 200.

CAITHNESS CENERAL HOSPITAL, PULTENEY HOUSE EVENTIDE HOME,
RIVERSIDE HOME AND SEAVIEW NURSING HOME ATTENDED FROM ST.
JOACHIM'S.

RETIRED CLERGY OF THE DIOCESE

Rev. Patrick Grady, c/o Bishop's House, 3 Queen's Cross, ABERDEEN AB9 2NL.

Very Rev. Duncan Canon Stone, 9 Cathedral Square, FORTROSE IV10 8TB. ☎ Fortrose (01381) 621088.

Very Rev. John Canon Symon, Nazareth House, 34 Claremont Street, ABERDEEN AB10 6RA. ☎ 01124-582091.

Rev. Ronald J. Walls, M.A., Dip.Ed., 54 Aird Street, Portsoy, BANFF AB15 2RB. ☎/Fax: 01261-841950.

INSTITUTES OF CONSECRATED LIFE
AND
SOCIETIES OF APOSTOLIC LIFE

MEN

BENEDICTINES (1876)

(1876, 1999) St. Peter and St. Benedict's,
The Lodge, Glen Doe Road, FORT AUGUSTUS PH32 4DB.
☎ Fort Augustus (01320) 366451.

(1948) Pluscarden Abbey, ELGIN IV30 8UA.
☎ Dallas (01343) 890257; Fax: (01343) 890258.

Christ the King, The Bungalow, Gower Street,
BRORA KW9 6PU.
☎ Brora (01408) 621388.

CARMELITES (1993)

Elphinstone House, 7 High Street,
Old Aberdeen, ABERDEEN AB24 3EE
.☎ Aberdeen (01224) 482444.

DOMINICANS

St. Mary's, BEAULY IV4 7AU.
☎ Beauly (01463) 782232.

JESUITS

Mount Carmel, Sandyhill Road, BANFF B45 1BE.
☎ Banff (01261) 812204.

St. Laurence's, 21 Castle Street, DINGWALL IV15 9HU.
☎ Dingwall (01349) 863143.

Our Lady and St. Joseph, 31 Main Street, KIRKWALL KW15 1BU.
☎ Kirkwall (01856) 872462.

St. Margaret's, 87 St. Olaf Street, LERWICK ZE1 0ES.
☎ Lerwick (01595) 692233

St. Mary's, 7 Academy Street, NAIRN IV12 4RJ.
☎ Nairn (01667) 453323.

WOMEN

FRANCISCAN MISSIONARIES OF MARY(1978)

9 Gordon Grove, Ellon AB41 9AS. ☎ Ellon (01358) 722388.

LA SAINTE UNION (1971)

(1977) La Sainte Union Convent, St. John Ogilvie, Coul Park, ALNESS
IV17 0RD. ☎ Alness (01349) 883459.

(1982) La Sainte Union Convent, 32 Huntly Street, INVERNESS IV3
5PR. ☎ Inverness (01463) 221086.

(1991) 6 Loch Lann Terrace, Culloden, INVERNESS IV1 2PZ. ☎
Inverness (01463) 793127; Fax: 01463-793779.

POOR SISTERS OF NAZARETH(1862)

(1871) Nazareth House, 34 Claremont Street, ABERDEEN AB10 6RA.
☎ Aberdeen (01224) 582091; Fax: 01224-574849.
Chaplain: Very Rev. John Canon Symon (1953).

SISTERS OF ST. MARY OF NAMUR (1978)

Chapel Croft, Eskadale, Kiltarlity, BEAULY IV4 7JR.
☎ Beauly (01463) 741364.

SISTERS OF MERCY (1861)

(1871) Convent of Mercy, Greyfriars, Abbey Street, ELGIN IV30 1DA.
☎ Elgin (01343) 547806.

SOCIETY OF THE SACRED HEART (1895)

(1895, 1993) Convent of the Sacred Heart, 5 Queen's Lane South,
ABERDEEN AB1 6UZ ☎ Aberdeen (01224) 322757.

Diocese of Argyll and The Isles

Bishop of Argyll and The Isles

Right Reverend Ian Murray, B.A.

Born at Lennoxtown, Stirlingshire,15th December 1932; educated St. Machan's Primary School, Lennoxtown, St. Ninian's High School, Kirkintilloch, St. Mary's College, Blairs; Royal Scots College, Valladolid, Spain.; ordained priest at Valladolid, 17th March, 1956; assistant priest, St. Mary's Cathedral, Edinburgh, St. Kenneth's, Lochore, St. Columba's, Edinburgh. vice-rector, Royal Scots College, Valladolid, 1963-70; chaplain, Catholic students at University of Stirling, 1970-78; Open University (B.A.,Hons); parish priest, St. Bride's, Cowdenbeath 1978-85; St. Ninian's, Edinburgh, 1985-87; rector, Royal Scots College, Valladolid, 1987-8, Salamanca, 1988-94; prelate of honour, 1989; parish priest, Our Lady and St. Andrew's, Galashiels, 1994-6; parish priest, St. Francis Xavier's, Falkirk, with Slamannan,1996-99; vicar-general, St. Andrews and Edinburgh,1996-99; nominated bishop of Argyll and The Isles, 3rd November, 1999, and ordained by Keith Patrick O'Brien, archbishop of St. Andrews and Edinburgh, at Oban, 7th December, 1999.

Residence: Bishop's House, Esplanade, Oban PA34 5AB
☎/Fax: 01631-571395.

VICARS-GENERAL
Right Rev. Mgr. Roderick Provost Macdonald, S.T.L., St. Mun's, BALLACHULISH PA39 4JG. ☎ Ballachulish (01855) 811203.
Right Rev. Mgr. Donald W. MacKinnon, B.A., St. Mary's, ARISAIG PH39 4NH.
☎/Fax: Arisaig (01687) 450223.

THE DIOCESAN CURIA
Diocesan Office: St. Columba's Cathedral,
Esplanade,
OBAN   *567 436*
PA34 5AB.
☎/Fax.: Oban (01631) 571003.

Chancellor: Right Rev. Mgr. Thomas Wynne,
St. Margaret's,
ROY BRIDGE
PH31 4RE.
☎ Spean Bridge (01397) 712238.

Acting Treasurer: Mrs. Janie Milne,
Diocesan Office,
St. Columba's Cathedral,
Esplanade,
OBAN
PA34 5AB
☎/Fax: Oban (01631) 571003.
E-mail:rcd.argyll.and.isles@dial.pipex.com

Notary: Very Rev. John A. Canon Galbraith, B.A.
St. Peter's,
Daliburgh,
LOCHBOSDALE
PA81 5SS.
☎/Fax: Lochboisdale (01878) 700305.

College of Consultors: Right Rev. Mgr. Roderick Provost
Macdonald, S.T.L., V.G.;
Right Rev. Mgr. Donald W. MacKinnon
B.A., V.G.
Right Rev. Mgr. Thomas Wynne;
Very Rev. John A. Canon Galbraith;
Rev. Malcolm J. MacLellan;
Very Rev. John Angus Canon Macdonald,
S.T.B., M.A., M.Litt.;
Right Rev. Mgr. Donald W. MacKinnon
B.A., V.G.
Rev. Donald J. MacKay, S.T.B.

Finance Committee: Right Rev. Mgr. Roderick Provost
Macdonald, S.T.L., V.G.;
Right Rev. Mgr. Thomas Wynne;
Mrs. J. Milne;
Mrs. M. MacDonald;
Very Rev. John Angus Canon Macdonald,
S.T.B., M.A., M . Litt .;
Very Rev. Iain Canon MacMaster;
Rev. Donald J. MacKay, S.T.B.;
Rev. Roderick H. Johnston, S.T.B.;
Mr. Alistair MacLeod.

**Representative on
Highland Education
Committee:** Mrs. Catherine Grant,
44 Island Bank Road,
INVERNESS IV2 4QT
☎ Inverness (01463) 230792.

**Representative on Argyll
and Bute Education
Committee:** Very Rev. William Canon Fraser,
St. Margaret's, Argyll Street,
LOCHGILPHEAD PA31 8NE.
☎ Lochgilphead (01546) 602380.

**Representative on Western
Isles Education
Committee:** Awaiting appointment.

**Religious Education
Advisor:** Very Rev. John Angus Canon
Macdonald, S.T.B.,M.A., M.Litt.,
St. Mary's,
Belford Road,
FORT WILLIAM PH33 6BT.
☎ Fort William (01397) 702174.

Director of Vocations: Rev. Roderick M. McAulay,
St. Kieran's,
6 St. John Street,
CAMPBELTOWN PA28 6BQ
☎ Campbeltown (01586) 552160.

**Registrar for Deceased
Clergy:** Very Rev. Iain Canon MacMaster,
St. Andrew's, Columshill Street,
ROTHESAY PA20 0XH.
☎ Rothesay (01700) 502047.

Diocesan Director
for Pontifical Mission
Aid Societies:
Rev. Roderick J.MacNeil,
St. Michael's, Ardkenneth,
Iochdar, LOCHBOISDALE HS8 5RD.
☎/Fax.:Carnan (01870) 610243.

National Youth Council:
Religious of the Assumption,
1 Mossfield Drive,,
Lochyside, FORT WILLIAM
PH33 7PE.
☎ Fort William (01397) 703606..
Diocesan Youth Representative:
Sister Patricia; Sister Claire.

Justice and Peace: Mr. Raymond Madill.

CATHEDRAL CHAPTER
(Restored, 20th August, 1907.)

Provost: Right Rev. Mgr. Roderick Macdonald,
S.T.L., V.G.

Canons: Very Rev. Angus J. MacQueen;
Very Rev. John A. Galbraith, B.A.;
Very Rev. William Fraser;
Very Rev. Iain MacMaster;
Very Rev. John Angus Macdonald,
S.T.B., M.A., M.Litt.

Honorary Canons: Right Rev. Mgr. Ewen MacInnes;
Very Rev. Joseph Terry;
Right Rev. Mgr. Ronald J. K. Hendry.
Very Rev. Calum MacNeill, B.A., S.T.B.

DEANERIES

1. **St. Andrew:** Campbeltown, Dunoon, Rothesay, Lochgilphead, Oban, Taynuilt.
    Dean—Very Rev. Iain Canon MacMaster.

2. **St. Margaret:** Arisaig, Caol, Fort William, Glencoe, Glenfinnan, Kingussie, Mingarry, Morar, Roy Bridge.

    Dean—Right Rev. Mgr. Roderick Provost Macdonald, S.T.L., V.G.

3. **St. Michael:** Ardkenneth, Benbecula, Bornish, Castlebay, Daliburgh, Eriskay, North Bay, Stornoway.

    Dean—Very Rev. Angus J. Canon MacQueen.

CITY OF OBAN

ST. COLUMBA'S CATHEDRAL (1878, 1932), Corran Esplanade.

Very Rev. Michael J. MacDonald, Ph.B., S.T.L.
Administrator (1978)
Rev. Anthony Day (1980)

POSTAL ADDRESS: Cathedral House, Corran Esplanade, OBAN PA34 5AB. ☎/Fax:Oban (01631) 562123.

Sunday Masses: Vigil-Mass, 7 p.m.; 10.30 a.m. Holy Days of Obligation, Masses: 10 a.m., 7 p.m. Confessions: Saturday, 9.30 to 10 a.m., 6.30 to 7 p.m.
Estimated Catholic population: 1,350.

TAYNUILT SERVED FROM THE CATHEDRAL.
CARMELITE MONASTERY, ROCKFIELD ROAD, OBAN PA34 5DQ. SERVED FROM CATHEDRAL.
LORN AND THE ISLES HOSPITAL, EADER GLINN, AND NORTH ARGYLL EVENTIDE HOMES: ALL ATTENDED FROM THE CATHEDRAL.
ST. COLUMBA'S PRIMARY SCHOOL.

PARISHES OUTSIDE THE CITY OF OBAN
The name given last before the name of the Church is the Local Authority or Island Council.

ARDGOUR, Highland. See Glenfinnan.

ARDKENNETH, South Uist, Comhairle nan Eilean Siar (Western Isles), St. Michael (1829).

Rev. Roderick J. MacNeil (1985)
Sr. Mary Claire Ryan, *Pastoral Assistant*

POSTAL ADDRESS: St. Michael's, Ardkenneth, Iochdar, LOCHBOISDALE HS8 5RD. ☎/Fax: Carnan (01870) 610243; Mobile ☎ 0370-866157.
E-mail: rjmacneil@aol.com
Sunday Mass: 11.30 a.m.
Evening Service, 6 p.m. Holy Days of Obligation, Mass: 7 p.m.
Confessions: Saturday, 5 p.m. Services generally in Gaelic.
Estimated Catholic population: 300.

PRIMARY SCHOOL.

ARISAIG Inverness-shire, Highland, St. Mary (1800, 1849).

Right Rev. Mgr. Donald W. MacKinnon, B.A., V.G. (1971)

POSTAL ADDRESS: St. Mary's, ARISAIG PH39 4NH. ☎/Fax: Arisaig (01687) 450223.

Sunday Masses: Vigil-Mass, 6 p.m., 10.30 a.m. Evening Service: as announced. Holy Days of Obligation, Masses: 9.30 a.m., 7 p.m. Confessions: Saturdays, 10 to 10.30 a.m., 5.30 to 5.55 p.m. Estimated Catholic population: 200.

ARRAN, Brodick, North Ayrshire. See Brodick.

BALLACHULISH Argyllshire, Highland. See Glencoe.

BENBECULA, Comhairle nan Eilean Siar (Western Isles), St. Mary (1884).

Rev. John P. Mackinnon, S.T.B. (*Administrator*) (1999)

POSTAL ADDRESS: St. Mary's, Griminish, ISLE OF BENBECULA HS7 5QA. ☎ Benbecula (01870) 602221.

Sunday Masses: Vigil-Mass, 7 p.m.; 11 a.m. Evening Service: 7 p.m. Holy Days of Obligation, Masses: 10 a.m., 7.30 p.m. Confessions: Saturday, 6 to 6.45 p.m.
Estimated Catholic populaton: 600.

DERA RANGE HEBRIDES AND R.A.F. BENBECULA ATTENDED FROM ST. MARY'S. SERVICES AS ANNOUNCED.
LOCHMADDY HOSPITAL, North Uist, AND TRIANAID HOME, Carinish, North Uist, ATTENDED FROM BENBECULA.
SGOIL LIONACLEIT (SECONDARY SCHOOL).

BORNISH, South Uist, Comhairle nan Eilean Siar (Western Isles), St. Mary (1837).

Rev. Donald Ewen Campbell, S.T.B. (1972)

POSTAL ADDRESS: St. Mary's, Bornish, LOCHBOISDALE HS8 5SA. ☎ Bornish (01878) 710350.

Sunday Mass: 10 a.m. (*in English on first Sunday of month*). Evening Service: 6 p.m. Holy Days of Obligation, Mass: 10.30 a.m., 7 p.m. Confessions: Saturday, 5 p.m. Any time on request. Estimated Catholic populaton: 260.

SERVICES IN GAELIC.
PRIMARY SCHOOL.

BROADFORD, Isle of Skye, Highland, served from Dornie (Diocese of Aberdeen).

☎ Dornie (Kyle) (01599) 555229; Fax: 01599-555458.
E-mail: gerry.livingstone@zetnet.co.uk

Sunday Mass: 4 p.m., in the Medical Centre, High Road. Confessions before Mass on request.

BRODICK, Arran, North Ayrshire, Holy Cross (1991, 1983), Douglas Hotel Grounds.

Rev. Noel Colford, Ph.L., S.T.L. (*Administrator*) (1964)

POSTAL ADDRESS: Holy Cross, BRODICK KA27 8AJ. ☎ Brodick (01770) 302030.

Sunday Masses: Vigil Mass, 7.30 p.m. (*June to September*); 9.30(*June to September*), 11 a.m. (*all year*).   Holy Days of Obligation Masses: Vigil-Mass, 7 p.m.; 10 a.m. Confessions: half an hour before Mass. Estimated Catholic population: 100.

WAR MEMORIAL HOSPITAL, Lamlash, ATTENDED FROM HOLY CROSS.

CAMPBELTOWN, Argyll and Bute, St. Kieran (1816, 1850), St. John Street. *Tagu : . 0791 9585 969*

Rev. Roderick M. McAuley (1988)

POSTAL ADDRESS: St. Kieran's, 6 St. John Street, CAMPBELTOWN PA28 6BQ. ☎: Campbeltown (01586) 552160; Fax: 01586-553631.

Sunday Masses: Vigil-Mass, 6.30 p.m.; 10 a.m. Holy Days of Obligation, Masses: as announced. Confessions: Saturday, 9.30 a.m., 5 p.m.; any time on request.
Estimated Catholic population: 380.

CAMPBELTOWN HOSPITAL, AUCHINLEE EVENTIDE HOME AND KINTYRE NURSING HOME SERVED FROM ST KIERAN'S.
ST. KIERAN'S PRIMARY SCHOOL.

CANNA Inverness-shire, Highland, St. Columba. Served from Morar.

☎ Mallaig (01687)462201.
Mass Monthly as annouced.

CAOL Inverness-shire, Highland, St. John the Evangelist (1970), St. John's Road.

Rev. Roderick H. Johnston, S.T.B. (1997)

POSTAL ADDRESS: St. John's, St. John's Road, Caol, FORT WILLIAM PH33 7PR. ☎/Fax: Fort William (01397) 700622.
E-mail:rodjohnston@dial.pipex.com

Sunday Masses: Vigil-Mass, 7 p.m.; 10.30 a.m. Holy Days of Obligation, Masses: Vigil-Mass, 7 p.m.; 10 am. Confessions: Saturday, 9.45 a.m., 6.30 p.m.
Estimated Catholic population: 850.   Ⓐ

SISTERS OF THE ASSUMPTION, I MOSSFIELD DRIVE, LOCHYSIDE, FORT WILLIAM PH33 7PE. ☎ FORT WILLIAM (01397) 703606.
MOSSPARK NURSING HOME attended from ST. JOHN'S.
LOCHYSIDE R.C. PRIMARY SCHOOL.

CASTLEBAY, Barra, Comhairle nan Eilean Siar (Western Isles), Our Lady, Star of the Sea (1888).

Rev. Donald J. MacKay, S.T.B. (1976)

POSTAL ADDRESS: Star of the Sea, CASTLEBAY HS9 5XD. ☎/Fax: Castlebay (01871) 810267.

Sunday Mass: 11 a.m. Holy Days of Obligation, Masses: as announced. Confessions: Saturday, 10 a.m., 5 p.m.
Estimated Catholic population: 720.   🈁 Ⓐ

SISTERS OF NOTRE DAME, 10 GLEN, CASTLEBAY HS9 5UQ. ☎ CASTLEBAY (01871) 810727.
ST. BRENDAN'S HOSPITAL-HOME, Castlebay, SERVED FROM STAR OF THE SEA.

COLL, Argyll and Bute. Served from Oban Cathedral.
Services as announced.

COLONSAY Argyll and Bute.
Served from Lochgilphead.
Mass as announced.

CRAIGSTON, Barra, Comhairle nan Eilean Siar (Western Isles), St. Brendan (1805, 1858). Served from Castlebay.

Sunday Mass: Vigil-Mass, Saturday, 7 p.m. Holy Days of Obligation, Mass as announced.

DALAVICH, Argyll and Bute. Served from Taynuilt.

Mass, as announced.

DALIBURGH, South Uist, Comhairle nan Eilean Siar(Western Isles), St. Peter (1868, 1907).

Very Rev. John A. Canon Galbraith, B.A. (1971)
Sr. Ann Healy, *Pastoral Assistant*

POSTAL ADDRESS: St. Peter's, Daliburgh, LOCHBOISDALE HS8 5SS. ☎ Lochboisdale (01878) 700305; Fax: 01878-700780.
E-mail: PA44@dial.pipex.com

Sunday Masses: Vigil-Mass, 8 p.m.; 11.30 a.m. Evening Service: 6 p.m. (*on alternate Sundays*). Holy Days of Obligation, Masses: 9 a.m., 7.30 p.m. Confessions: Saturday, 6 to 7 p.m. Mass and other Services mainly in Gaelic.
Estimated Catholic population: 950.

SISTERS OF THE SACRED HEARTS OF JESUS AND MARY, LOCH AN EILEAN, ASKERNISH, LOCHBOISDALE HS8 5SY. ☎ LOCHBOISDALE (01878) 700417. DALIBURGH HOSPITAL AND UIST HOUSE ATTENDED FROM DALIBURGH.

DRIMNIN Argyllshire, Highland. Served from Mingarry.

☎ Salen (Fort William) (01967) 431251.
Mass as announced.

DUNBEG, Argyll and Bute, Holy Trinity (1964). Served from Oban.

Enquiries to Cathedral (01631-562123).

DUNOON, Argyll and Bute, Our Lady of the Immaculate Conception and St. Mun (1862, 1931), Alexandra Parade.

Rev. Alexander J. Culley (1986)

POSTAL ADDRESS: Reul-na-Mara, Brandon Street, DUNOON PA23 8BU. ☎ Dunoon (01369) 702125.

Sunday Masses: Vigil-Mass, 6 p.m.; 9, 11 a.m. Evening Service: as announced, Holy Days of Obligation, Masses: 9 a.m., 7.30 p.m. Confessions: Saturday, 5.30 p.m.; on request. Estimated Catholic population: 900.

DUNOON GENERAL HOSPITAL AND COWAL HOSPICE ATTENDED FROM ST. MUN'S. ST. MUN'S PRIMARY SCHOOL.

EIGG, Inverness-shire, Highland, St. Donnan (1810, 1910), Served from Arisaig.
☎ Arisaig (01687) 450223.
Services as announced.

EOLIGARRY, Barra, Comhairle nan Eilean Siar(Western Isles) St. Vincent de Paul. Served from Northbay.
Sunday Mass: 9.30 a.m. Confessions: Saturday, 5 p.m. Other Services as announced. (*Services in Gaelic*)

ERISKAY, Comhairle nan Eilean Siar (Western Isles), St. Michael (1852, 1903).

Rev. Malcolm J. MacLellan (1953)

POSTAL ADDRESS: St. Michael's, Eriskay, LOCHBOISDALE HS8 5JL. ☎ Eriskay (01878) 720201.

Sunday Masses: 10 a.m.   Evening Service: 5 p.m. Holy Days of Obligation, Masses: 9 a.m., 7 p.m. Confessions: Saturday, 5 p.m. Estimated Catholic population: 125.

FORT WILLIAM, Inverness-shire, Highland, The Immaculate Conception (1794, 1934), Belford Road.

Very Rev John Angus Canon Macdonald,
S.T.B., M.A., M.Litt. (1970)

POSTAL ADDRESS: St. Mary's, Belford Road, FORT WILLIAM PH33 6BT. ☎
Fort William (01397) 702174; Fax 01397-706046.

Sunday Masses: Vigil-Mass, 7 p.m.; 9, 11 a.m., 4 p.m. Evening Service
as announced. Holy Days of Obligation, Masses: Vigil-Mass, 7 p.m.;
10.15 a.m., 1.10, 7 p.m. Confessions: Saturday, 9.30 a.m., 4 to 4.30
p.m., 6.30 p.m.; on request. Occasional weekday Masses in Gaelic.
Estimated Catholic population: 1,227. ▨ ᕈ

BELFORD HOSPITAL, BELHAVEN WARD, GLENTOWER NURSING HOME,
HELSDALE NURSING HOME, INVERNEVIS HOUSE (MASS ON MONDAYS, 9.30
A.M.) AND VICTORIA COURT ATTENDED FROM ST. MARY'S.
ST. MARY'S PRIMARY SCHOOL; (LOCHYSIDE R.C. PRIMARY SCHOOL).

GARRYNAMONIE, South Uist, Comhairle nan Eilean Siar(Western Isles), Our Lady of Sorrows (1964). Served from Daliburgh.

Sunday Mass: 10 a.m. Evening Service, 6 p.m. (*on alternate Sundays*).
Holy Days of Obligation, Mass: 10.30 a.m. Confessions: Saturday, 4.30
to 5 p.m. Mass and other Services mainly in Gaelic.

GLENCOE, Argyllshire, Highland, St. Mun (1897, 1837), Ballachulish.

Right Rev. Mgr. Roderick Provost Macdonald, S.T.L., V.G. (1949)

POSTAL ADDRESS: St. Mun's, BALLACHULISH PA39 4JG. ☎ Ballachulish
(01855) 811203.

Sunday Mass: 11 a.m. Holy Days of Obligation, Mass: 7 p.m.
Confessions: Saturday, 3.30 p.m.
Estimated Catholic population: 191.

GLENCOE HOSPITAL, Ballachulish, ATTENDED FROM ST. MUN'S.

GLENFINNAN, Inverness-shire, Highland, SS. Mary and Finnan (1870, 1872). Served from Caol.
Sunday Mass: 1 p.m. Holy Days of Obligation, Mass: 7 p.m.

GLENUIG in Moidart, Inverness-shire, Highland, St. Agnes (1861). Served from Mingarry.
Sunday Mass: 9.30 a.m. Holy Days of Obligation: Vigil-Mass, 7.30 p.m.

HOWBEG, South Uist, Comhairle nan Eilean (Western Isles), St. Joseph (1902). Served from Bornish.

Sunday Vigil-Mass, 6.30 p.m. Confessions: Saturday, 6 p.m.

INVERAILORT, Inverness-shire, Highland. Served from Arisaig.
Sunday Mass: 12.15 p.m. in Inverailort Castle.

INVERARAY, Argyll and Bute. Served from Lochgilphead.
Sunday Mass: 12.30 p.m. in All Saints' Episcopal Church.

INVERGARRY, Inverness-shire, Highland, St. Finnan (1891, 1938), Served from Roy Bridge.

Sunday Mass: 9.15 a.m. Holy Days of Obligation, Mass: 5.50 p.m.

IONA, Argyll and Bute. Served from Oban Cathedral.
Availability of Mass, in Michael Chapel, depends on possible presence of a priest visitor. For information, apply to the Warden (☎ Iona (01681) 700369.

ISLAY, Argyll and Bute. Served from Campbeltown.
1st and 3rd Sunday of each month, Mass in St. Columba's Episcopal Church, Bridgend, at 4.30 p.m. For further information, enquire from St. Kieran's Campbeltown. ☎ Campbeltown (01586) 552160.

JURA, Argyll and Bute. Served from Lochgilphead.
Mass as announced.

KILCHOAN, Invernesshire, Highland. Served from Mingarry. (☎ Salen (Fort William) (01967) 431251).
Mass when announced.

KINGUSSIE, Inverness-shire, Highland, Our Lady of the Rosary and St. Columba (1863, 1932), Newtonmore Road.

Rev. Benedict Lodge, C.P. (1977)

POSTAL ADDRESS: "Loreto," Newtonmore Road, KINGUSSIE PH21 1HF.
☎ Kingussie (01540) 661322.

Sunday Masses: Vigil-Mass, 7 p.m.; 9.30 a.m. Holy Days of Obligation, Masses: as anounced. Confessions: Sunday, 8.30 to 9.30 a.m.; at call. Estimated Catholic population: 120.

ST. VINCENT'S HOME ATTENDED FROM OUR LADY OF THE ROSARY AND ST. COLUMBA'S.
GLEN COVE SHELTERED HOUSING, Newtonmore, SERVED FROM KINGUSSIE. MASS, 1ST SUNDAY OF MONTH, 3 P.M.

KINLOCHLEVEN, Argyllshire, Highland, The Good Shepherd (1961)Riverside Road. Served from Glencoe.

Sunday Mass: 9.30 a.m. Holy Days of Obligation, Mass: 10 a.m.

KNOYDART, Inverness-shire, Highland. "Scottas", Inverie, Knoydart.Served from Morar
☎ Mallaig (01687) 462201.
Services (*Summer only*) as announced.

LOCHAILORT, Inverness-shire, Highland. See Inverailort.

LOCHALINE, Lochaber. Served from Mingarry.
☎ Salen (Fort William) (01967) 431251.
Mass as announced.

LOCHGILPHEAD, Argyll and Bute, St. Margaret (1929), Argyll Street.

Very Rev. William Canon Fraser (1969)

POSTAL ADDRESS: St. Margaret's, Argyll Street, LOCHGILPHEAD PA31 8NE. ☎/Fax: Lochgilphead (01546) 602380.

Sunday Masses: Vigil-Mass (*July and August*), 7.30 p.m.; 10 a.m., 4.30 p.m. (*October to April*), 7.30 p.m. (*May to September*). Holy Days of Obligation, Masses: 8.20 a.m., 7.30 p.m. Confessions: Saturday, 6.30 p.m. Estimated Catholic population: 310.   **A**

ARGYLL AND BUTE HOSPITAL, MID-ARGYLL HOSPITAL, DUNCUAN GERIATRIC HOSPITAL, AN CALA CHILDREN'S HOME, ARDFENAIG HOME AND CALEDONIA COURT ATTENDED FROM ST. MARGARET'S.

LOCHNEVIS, Inverness-shire, Highland. Served from Morar.
Monthly Mass as announced.

MALLAIG, Inverness-shire, Highland, St. Patrick (1935). Served from Morar.
Sunday Mass: 10 a.m. Holy Days of Obligation, Mass: 4 p.m. Confessions: Saturday, 11.30 a.m.

MINGARRY in Moidart, Inverness-shire, Highland, Our Lady of the Angels (1769, 1862).

Rev. Angus McLaughlin, O.P., B.A. (*Administrator*) (1965)

POSTAL ADDRESS: Priest's House, Mingarry, ACHARACLE PH36 4ZX. ☎ Salen (Fort William) (01967) 431251.
E-mail: ANGUSMCLAUGHLIN@TALK21.COM

Sunday Mass: 11 a.m. Holy Days of Obligation, Mass: 7.30 p.m. Confessions: on request.
Estimated Catholic population: 110.

DALMHOR HOUSE, Strontian, ATTENDED FROM OUR LADY OF THE ANGELS.

MORAR, Inverness-shire, Highland, Our Lady of the Perpetual Succour and St Cumin (1782, 1889).

Rev. Michael A. Hutson, Dip.T.Mus.,
Cert.R.C.R.E., B.D. (1994)

POSTAL ADDRESS: Church House, Morar, MALLAIG PH40 4PB ☎ Mallaig (01687) 462201.

Sunday Mass: 11.30 a.m. Holy Days of Obligation, Mass 7 p.m.
Confessions: Saturdays, 5.30 p.m.
Estimated Catholic population: 350.   Ⓐ

MUCK, Inverness-shire, Highland. Served from Arisaig.
Mass in School, as announced.

MULL, Argyll and Bute. Served from Oban Cathedral. See Iona and Tobermory.

NORTHBAY Barra; Comhairle nan Eilean Siar(Western Isles), St. Barr (1907, 1919).

Very Rev. Angus John Canon MacQueen (1951)

POSTAL ADDRESS: St Barr's, Northbay, CASTLEBAY HS9 5YQ. ☎ Northbay (01871) 890228.

Sunday Masses: 11 a.m. Evening Service as announced. Holy Days of Obligation, Masses: Vigil-Mass, 7.30 p.m.; 7.30 p.m. Confessions: Saturday, 6 p.m. (*Services in Gaelic*).
Estimated Catholic population: 318.

NORTH UIST, Comhairle nan Eilean (Western Isles).
Bayhead, Tigh Ceilidh. Served from Benbecula. (☎ 01870-60221).
Sunday Mass once a month, 1 p.m.

ONICH, Inverness-shire, Highland. See Glencoe, Kinlochleven or Fort William.
Via Ballachulish Bridge, nearest church is St. Mun's, Glencoe.

PORTREE, Isle of Skye, Highland, Cille Mhoire, Our Lady of the Assumption (1894, 1919).
Served from Dornie (Diocese of Aberdeen).
☎ Dornie (Kyle) (01599) 555229; Fax: 01599-555458.
E-mail: gerry.livingstone@zetnet.co.uk
Sunday Mass: 2 p.m. Holy Days of Obligation, Mass: 7 p.m.
Confessions, before Mass on request.   **A**

RHUM, Inverness-shire, Lochaber. Served from Morar.
☎ Mallaig (01687) 462201.
Services as announced.

ROTHESAY, Isle of Bute, Argyll and Bute, St. Andrew (1866, 1925), Columshill Street.

Very Rev. Iain Canon MacMaster (1965)

POSTAL ADDRESS: St. Andrew's, Columshill Street, ROTHESAY PA20 0HX.
☎/Fax: Rothesay (01700) 502047.
E-mail: 101533.1701@compuserve.com

Sunday Masses: Vigil-Mass, 7 p.m.; 9, 11.15 a.m. Holy Days of Obligation, Masses: 8.55, 10 a.m., 7 p.m. Confessions: Saturday, 10.30 a.m., 6.15 p.m.; daily, before Mass.
Estimated Catholic population: 685.   **A**

VICTORIA HOSPITAL, VICTORIA ANNEXE, ARDMORE HOME, CRAIGARD HOME, FERFADD COURT, FOLEY COURT, MOUNT CARMEL HOME, ROTHESAY COURT AND THOMSON HOME ATTENDED FROM ST. ANDREW'S.
ST. ANDREW'S PRIMARY SCHOOL.

ROY BRIDGE, Inverness-shire, Highland, St. Margaret (1826, 1929), Braeroy Road.

Right Rev. Mgr. Thomas Wynne, B.D. (1957)

POSTAL ADDRESS: St. Margaret's, ROY BRIDGE PH31 4AE. ☎/Fax: Spean Bridge (01397) 712238.

Sunday Mass: 11.30 a.m. Holy Days of Obligation, Mass: 10 a.m., 8 p.m. Confessions: before Mass.
Estimated Catholic population: 240.

CILLE CHOIRILL CEMETERY CHAPEL: MASS AS ANNOUNCED.

SKYE, See Broadford and Portree.

SPEAN BRIDGE, Inverness-shire, Highland, St. Joseph (1949, 1967). Served from Roy Bridge.
Sunday Vigil-Mass, 6.30 p.m. Holy Days of Obligation, Mass, 7 p.m
Confessions: before Mass.

STORNOWAY, Lewis, Comhairle nan Eilean Siar (Western Isles), Our Holy Redeemer (1961, 1991), Scotland Street.
Rev. Paul Hackett, S.J. (1961)

POSTAL ADDRESS: Our Holy Redeemer's, 71 Kenneth Street, STORNOWAY HS1 2DS. ☎ Stornoway (01851) 702070.

Sunday Masses: Vigil-Mass, 6 p.m. (*Third Saturday in Gaelic*); 10, 11 a.m. Holy Days of Obligation, Masses: 10 a.m., 4, 7.30 p.m. Confessions: Saturday, during Exposition after 12 noon Mass; on request.
Estimated Catholic population: 290.

WESTERN ISLES HOSPITAL ATTENDED FROM OUR HOLY REDEEMER'S.

STRONTIAN, Highland. Served from Mingarry.

TARBERT, Loch Fyne, Argyll and Bute. Served from Lochgilphead.
Mass as announced.

TARBERT on Lochnevis, Inverness-shire, Highland, Our Lady, Star of the Sea. Served from Morar.
☎ Mallaig (01687) 462201.
Services as announced.

TAYNUILT, Argyll and Bute, The Visitation (1902). Served from Oban Cathedral.

Sunday Mass: 12.30 p.m. Holy Days of Obligation, Mass: 7 p.m. Confessions: before Masses of Obligation and at call.

TIGHNABRUAICH, Argyll and Bute. (Parish of St. Andrew, Rothesay). Served from Dunoon.
Mass,in Kamas Community Centre as announced. Contact: ☎ 01700-811656.

TIREE, Argyll and Bute. Served from Oban Cathedral.
Services as announced.

TOBERMORY, Isle of Mull, Argyll and Bute, Our Lady, Star of the Sea, Victoria Street. Served from the Cathedral, Oban.
Sunday Mass or Communion Service 12 noon.

VATERSAY, Comhairle nan Eilean Siar (Western Isles), Our Lady of the Waves and St. John (1913), Uidh. Served from Castlebay, Barra.
Sunday Mass: 3.30 p.m. Holy Days of Obligation, Mass as announced.

WEST GERINISH, South Uist, Comhairle nan Eilean (Western Isles), St. Bride (1966). Served from Ardkenneth.
Sunday Vigil-Mass, 7 p.m. Holy Days of Obligation, Mass: 10 a.m. Confessions: Saturday, 6.30 p.m.

RETIRED PRIESTS OF THE DIOCESE

Right Rev. Mgr. Ronald J. K. Canon Hendry, Nazareth House, 34 Claremont Street, ABERDEEN AB1 6RA ☎ 01224-588082

Rev. Patrick Kennedy, M.A., Nazareth House, 34 Claremont Street, ABERDEEN AB1 6RA ☎ 01224-588082

Rev. Michael Lea, Emmaus; 1 Hillside Avenue, KINGUSSIE PH21 1PA. ☎ Kingussie (01540 661649.

Right Rev Mgr. Ewen Provost MacInnes, Nazareth House, 1647 Paisley Road West, GLASGOW G52 3QT

Very Rev Calum Canon MacNeill, B.A., c/o Diocesan Office, St. Columba's Cathedral, Esplanade, OBAN PA34 5AB.

Rev. Joseph McShane, c/o Margaret McShane, Beltrees, Linwood Road, PAISLEY PA1 2TL

Very Rev. Joseph Canon Terry, c/o Diocesan Office, St. Columba's Cathedral, Esplanade, OBAN PA34 5AB.

INSTITUTES OF CONSECRATED LIFE
AND
SOCIETIES OF APOSTOLIC LIFE

MEN

JESUITS
Our Holy Redeemer, 71 Kenneth Street, STORNOWAY HS1 2DS. ☎
Stornoway (01851) 702070.

PASSIONISTS
Our Lady of the Rosary and St. Columba, "Loreto", Newtonmore
Road, KINGUSSIE PH21 1HF. ☎ Kingussie (01540) 661322.

WOMEN
DISCALCED CARMELITES (1924)
Carmelite Monastery, Rockfield Road, OBAN PA34 5DQ

RELIGIOUS OF THE ASSUMPTION (1972)
Religious of the Assumption, 1 Mossfield Drive, Lochyside, FORT
WILLIAM PH33 7PE. ☎ Fort William (01397) 703606.

SISTERS OF NOTRE DAME (1995)
Notre Dame Convent, Glen, CASTLEBAY HS9 5UQ. ☎ Castle bay
(01871) 810 727.

SISTERS OF THE SACRED HEARTS OF JESUS AND MARY (1896)
(1985) Sacred Heart Convent, Loch an Eilean, Askernish,
LOCHBOISDALE HS8 5SY. ☎ Lochboisdale (01878) 700417.

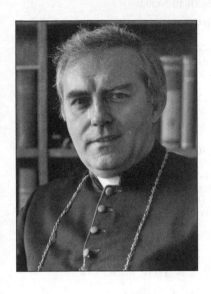

Diocese of Dunkeld

Bishop of Dunkeld
Right Rev. Vincent Logan

Born at Bathgate, West Lothian, 30th June 1941; educated St. Mary's Academy, Bathgate, St. Mary's College, Blairs, St. Andrew's College, Drygrange, Roxburghshir; ordained priest at Edinburgh, 14th March 1964; assistant priest, St. Margaret, Davidson's Mains, Edinburgh, 1964-66; Corpus Christi College, Bayswater, London, (Diploma in Religious Education) 1966-67; chaplain, St. Joseph's Hospital, Rosewell, 1967-77; parish priest, St. Mary's, Ratho, 1977-81; adviser in Religious Education, 1967; director, Religious Education Office, Edinburgh, 1970-81; episcopal vicar, Education, St. Andrews and Edinburgh, 1977-81; nominated bishop of Dunkeld, 26th January 1981, and ordained by Gordon Gray, cardinal archbishop of St. Andrews and Edinburgh, at Dundee, 26th February, 1981.

Residence: Bishop's House, 29 Roseangle, DUNDEE DD1 4LS.
☎ Dundee (01382) 224327; Fax: 01382-205212.
E-mail: vincentlogan@compuserve.com

VICARS-GENERAL

Right Rev. Mgr. Joseph Creegan, B.A., M.Ed., 5/61 Main Street, Invergowrie, DUNDEE DD2 5BA. ☎ Dundee (01382) 561067; Fax: 01382-561963.

Right Rev. Mgr. Hugh F. Canon McInally, J.P., C.A., Ph.B., S.T.B., Our Lady of Victories, 22 Powrie Place, DUNDEE DD1 2PQ. ☎ Dundee (01382) 226384.

THE DIOCESAN CURIA

Diocesan Centre:	24-28 Lawside Road, DUNDEE DD3 6XY. ☎ Dundee (01382) 225453. Fax: Dundee (01382) 204585).
Administrator:	Miss Vera Swifte.
Treasurer:	Right Rev. Mgr. Hugh F. Canon McInally, J.P., C.A., Ph.B., S.T.B., V.G.
Chancellor:	Rev. Michael J. Milton.
Canon Lawyer:	Very Rev. Basil Canon O'Sullivan, J.C.L.
Fabric and Planning Board:	*Secretary:* Rev. Deacon David Fyffe, Dip.Com., B.A.
College of Consultors:	Right Rev. Mgr. Hugh F. Canon McInally, V.G. Right Rev. Mgr. Joseph Creegan, V.G. Very Rev. Charles Canon Hendry, Very Rev. Kenneth Canon McBride, Very Rev. Hugh Canon Sreenan, Rev. John Harty, Rev. Brian McLean.
Director of Vocations:	Rev. John Harty, S.T.B., St. Leonard & St. Fergus, St. Leonard's Place, DUNDEE DD3 9HD. ☎ Dundee (01382) 858151.
Asst. Vocations Director:	Rev. Kevin J. Golden, Our Lady of Sorrows, Finlarig Terrace, Fintry, DUNDEE DD4 9JF ☎ Dundee (01382) 502068.

Directors for the Permanent Diaconate:	Rev. John Harty, S.T.B, St. Leonard & St. Fergus, St. Leonard's Place, DUNDEE DD3 9HD. ☎ Dundee (01382) 858151. Rev. Deacon John Campbell, Dip.Tech.Ed., H.N.C., F.T.C. c/o Our Lady of Victories, 22 Powrie Place, DUNDEE DD1 2PQ.

Church Representatives on Local Authority Education Committees

Dundee:	Right Rev. Mgr. Joseph Creegan, B.A., M.Ed., V.G.
Angus:	Rev. Mark Cassidy, Ph.B., S.T.L.
Clackmannan:	Rev. Kenneth McCaffrey, Dip.Theol., Dip.Ed.
Perth and Kinross:	Mrs. Margaret Martin.
Religious Inspector of Schools:	Right Rev. Mgr. Benjamin Canon Donachie, M.A., Dip.Ed.
Religious Education Office:	Diocesan Centre 24-28 Lawside Road Dundee DD3 6XY. ☎ DUNDEE (01382) 225453. *Co-ordinator:* Rev. Ian Mullen.
Social Care Office:	Diocesan Centre, 24-28 Lawside Road, DUNDEE DD3 6XY. Dundee (01382) 225453, Ext. 23. *Director:* Sister Andrea, F.M.D.M.
Youth Office:	Diocesan Centre 24-28 Lawside Road, DUNDEE (01382) 225453, Ext. 15. *Director:* Rev. Neil Dorward, M.A., B.A. *Youth Officer:* Mrs. Sheena O'Reilly.
Diocesan Newspaper:	*Dunkeld News;* *Editor:* Mr. Andrew Mitchell, Diocesan Centre, 24-28 Lawside Road, DUNDEE DD3 6XY. ☎ Dundee (01382) 225453.
Registrar for Deceased Clergy:	Rev. Michael J. Milton, The Chancellor, Diocesan Centre, 24-28 Lawside Road, DUNDEE DD3 6XY. ☎ Dundee (01382) 225453.
Council of Priests to the Bishop of Dunkeld:	*Secretary,* Rev. William Finnigan, St. John's, 20 Melville Street, PERTH PH1 5PY. ☎ Perth (01783) 622241.

Pontifical Mission Aid Societies:	*Director:* Rev. James Foley, St. Fillan's, 20 King Street, NEWPORT-ON-TAY DD6 8BN.
Diocesan Representatives on Radio Tay Churches Council:	Lt. Col. Denis Naulty (Ret.); Mr Michael Simpson.

CATHEDRAL CHAPTER
(Restored 16th July, 1895.)

Provost:	Very Rev. John J. Connolly.
Canons:	Right Rev. Mgr. Benjamin Donachie *(Secretary);* Very Rev. Charles Hendry; Very Rev. Basil O'Sullivan; Very Rev. Kenneth McBride; Very Rev. Hugh Sreenan; Right Rev. Mgr. Hugh F. McInally. Very Rev. John O'Farrell.
Honorary Canons:	Very Rev. Augustine Klein; Very Rev. Kevin A. Smyth; Very Rev. Rupert Loughlin; Very Rev. Romeo Coia.

DEANERIES

1. **St. Andrew:** Cathedral, Dundee; St. Thomas', Arbroath; St. Anne's, Carnoustie; St. Columba's, Cupar; St. Fergus', Forfar; St. Bride's, Monifieth; St. Margaret's, Montrose; St. Fillan's, Newport-onTay; University Chaplaincy, Dundee.
   Dean—Rev. Neil Gallagher.

2. **St. Mary:** St. Columba's, Dundee; St. Leonard's and St. Fergus', Dundee; Our Lady of Victories, Dundee; St. Patrick's, Dundee; SS. Peter and Paul, Dundee.
   Dean—Rev. John Harty.

3. **St. Ninian:** St. Clement's, Dundee; St. Francis', Dundee; Immaculate Conception, Dundee; St. Joseph's, Dundee; St. Ninian's, Dundee; Wellburn, Dundee; Ninewells Hospital Chaplaincy.
   Dean—Rev. Michael J. Milton.

4. **St. Margaret:** St. Matthew's, Dundee; Our Lady of Good Counsel, Broughty Ferry; Our Lady of Sorrows, Dundee; St. Pius X, Dundee; St. Teresa's, Dundee; St. Vincent de Paul's, Dundee.

   Dean—Rev. Aldo Angelosanto, S.T.L.

5. **St. Fillan:** St. John's, Perth; St. Mary Magdalene's, Perth; Our Lady of Lourdes, Perth; Our Lady of Perpetual Succour, Auchterarder; St. Stephen's, Blairgowrie; St. Fillan's, Crieff; St. Columba's, Dunkeld; St. James', Kinross; St. Bride's, Pitlochry.

   Dean—Rev. Martin Drysdale.

6. **St. Mungo:** St. Mungo's, Alloa; St. John Vianney's, Alva; St. Joseph the Worker, Callander; The Holy Family, Dunblane; St. Serf's, Highvalleyfield; St. Bernadette's, Tullibody.

   Dean—Rev. Kenneth McCaffrey

CITY OF DUNDEE

ST. ANDREW'S CATHEDRAL (1782, 1836), Nethergate.

Very Rev. Kenneth Canon McBride, *Administrator* (1962)

POSTAL ADDRESS: 150 Nethergate, DUNDEE DD1 4EA. ☎ Dundee (01382) 225228.

Sunday Masses: 10.30 a.m., 7 p.m. Holy Days of Obligation, Masses: 10 a.m., 12.15, 7 p.m. Confessions: Saturday, 4.30 to 5.30 p.m.; other times by appointment.
Estimated Catholic population: 500.

FOR MEMBERS OF THE POLISH COMMUNITY: MASS IN THE CATHEDRAL ON THE FIRST SUNDAY OF EACH MONTH AT 3 P.M. CHAPLAIN: THE REV. MARIAN LEKAWA, POLISH CATHOLIC MISSION IN SCOTLAND, 4 PARKGROVE TERRACE, GLASGOW G3 7SD.

FOR MEMBERS OF THE UKRAINIAN COMMUNITY: MASS IN THE UKRAINIAN RITE IN THE CATHEDRAL ON THE LAST SUNDAY OF EACH MONTH AT 4 P.M. CHAPLAIN: REV. LUBOMYR PIDLUSKYJ, UKRAINIAN ST. ANDREW'S PRESBYTERY, 6 MANSION HOUSE ROAD, EDINBURGH EH9 1TZ.

JERICHO HOUSE, 36 ARTILLERY LANE, DUNDEE DD1 1PE. ☎ DUNDEE (01382) 223627.
STRATHMORE LODGE, Courthouse Square, ATTENDED FROM THE CATHEDRAL.
(ST. JOSEPH'S PRIMARY SCHOOL)

ST. CLEMENT, Charleston (1956, 1962), Craigowan Road.

Rev. Ian Mullen (1978)

POSTAL ADDRESS: St. Clement's, Craigowan Road, DUNDEE DD2 4NJ. ☎ Dundee (01382) 621658; Fax: 01382-400905.

Sunday Masses: Vigil-Mass, 6 p.m.; 10.30 a.m. Holy Days of Obligation, Masses: 9.30 a.m., 7 p.m. Confessions: Saturday, 5.30 p.m., after Vigil-Mass.
Estimated Catholic population: 3,000*

LITTLE SISTERS OF THE POOR, ST. JOSEPH'S CONVENT, WELLBURN HOUSE, 118 LIFF ROAD, DUNDEE DD2 2QT. ☎ DUNDEE (01382) 611654. CHAPLAIN: WELLBURN COTTAGE, 120 LIFF ROAD, DUNDEE DD2 2QT. ☎ DUNDEE (01382) 611237.
ST. CLEMENT'S PRIMARY SCHOOL.

ST. COLUMBA, Kirkton (1960, 1963), Derwent Avenue.

Rev. John Harty, S.T.B. (1975)
Rev. Martin McWilliams (1996)

POSTAL ADDRESS: St. Leonard's and St. Fergus', St. Leonard's Place, DUNDEE DD3 9HD. ☎ Dundee (01382) 858151/810739.

Sunday Masses: Vigil-Mass, 6 p.m.; 10.30 a.m. Holy Days of Obligation, Masses: 9.30 a.m., 7 p.m. Confessions: Saturday, 5 to 5.45 p.m. Estimated Catholic population: 1,000.

FRANCISCAN MISSIONARIES OF THE DIVINE MOTHERHOOD, ST. COLUMBA'S, DERWENT AVENUE, DUNDEE DD3 0BE. ☎ DUNDEE (01382) 832063.
STRATHMARTINE HOSPITAL AND HARESTANE HOUSE ATTENDED FROM ST. COLUMBA'S.
ST. COLUMBA'S PRIMARY SCHOOL.

ST. FRANCIS (1932, 1959), Tullideph Road.

Rev. Eugene O'Sullivan (1972)
Rev. Thomas Clark (*Permanent Deacon*) (1994)

POSTAL ADDRESS: St. Francis', Tullideph Road, DUNDEE DD2 2PN. ☎ Dundee (01382) 668007; Fax: 01382-668462.

Sunday Masses: 10, 11.30 a.m., 6.30 p.m. Holy Days of Obligation, Masses: 8, 10 a.m., 6.30 p.m. Confessions: Saturday, 10.30 a.m., 5.30 to 6.30 p.m.
Estimated Catholic population:2,000*.

ST. JOSEPH'S CONVENT OF MERCY, LAWSIDE ROAD, DUNDEE DD3 6BJ. ☎ DUNDEE (01382) 322304. SERVED FROM ST. FRANCIS'. (MASS ON FRIDAYS, 11.45 A.M.).
ANCRUM HOUSE, ST. ANNE'S HOME AND ADULT TRAINING CENTRES FOR THE MENTALLY HANDICAPPED, Dudhope Gardens, ATTENDED FROM ST. FRANCIS'.

THE IMMACULATE CONCEPTION, Lochee (1847, 1866), St. Mary's Lane.

Very Rev. John Canon O'Farrell, O.B.E., R.D., J.P. (1964)

POSTAL ADDRESS: St. Mary's, 41 High Street, Lochee, DUNDEE DD2 3AP. ☎ Dundee (01382) 611282.

Sunday Masses: Vigil-Mass, 6 p.m.; 10, 11.30 a.m. Evening Service: as announced. Holy Days of Obligation, Masses: 9, 10 a.m., 7.30 p.m. Confessions: Saturday, after 10 am. Mass, 4 to 5 p.m.; on call.
Estimated Catholic population: 2,000.

ROYAL DUNDEE LIFF HOSPITAL, Liff, ATTENDED FROM THE IMMACULATE CONCEPTION.
ST. MARY'S PRIMARY SCHOOL.

ST. JOSEPH, PROTECTOR OF THE CHURCH
(1873), Wilkie's Lane.

Right Rev. Mgr. Joseph Creegan, B.A., M.Ed., V.G. (1966)

POSTAL ADDRESS: Flat 5, The Old Rectory, 61 Main Street, Invergowrie, DUNDEE DD2 5BA. ☎ Dundee (01382) 561067; Fax: 01382-561963.. E-mail: Creegan@tesco.net

Sunday Masses: 9.30, 11 a.m. Evening Service (Advent and Lent), 4 p.m. Holy Days of Obligation, Masses: 10 a.m., 6 p.m. Confessions: after weekday and Saturday Mass.
Estimated Catholic population: 400.   &

ST. JOSEPH'S PRIMARY SCHOOL.

ST. LEONARD and ST. FERGUS, Ardler (1956, 1975), St. Leonard's Place.

Rev. John Harty, S.T.B. (1975)
Rev. Martin McWilliams, B.D. (1996)
Rev. David Fyffe, Dip.Com., B.A. (*Permanent Deacon*) (1994)

POSTAL ADDRESS: St. Leonard's and St. Fergus', St. Leonard Place, DUNDEE DD3 9HD. ☎ Dundee (01382) 858151/810739.

Sunday Masses: Vigil-Mass, 6 p.m.; 9.30, 11 a.m., 6 p.m. Holy Days of Obligation, Masses: Vigil-Mass, 7 p.m.; 10 a.m., 7 p.m. Confessions: Saturday, 5 to 5.45 p.m.
Estimated Catholic population: 5,000.

SISTERS OF ST. MARY OF NAMUR, ST. MARY'S, 53 AMERICANMUIR ROAD, DUNDEE DD3 9AD. ☎ DUNDEE (01382) 858064.
ST. LEONARD'S HOUSE AND TURRIFF HOUSE ATTENDED FROM ST. LEONARD'S.
ST. FERGUS PRIMARY SCHOOL; ST. MARGARET'S PRIMARY SCHOOL; LAWSIDE ACADEMY.

ST. MARY, OUR LADY OF VICTORIES, Hilltown
(1851), Forebank Road.

Right Rev. Mgr. Hugh F. Canon McInally,
J.P., C.A., Ph.B., S.T.B., V.G. (1963)
Rev. John Campbell, Dip.Tech.Ed., H.N.C., F.T.C.
(*Permanent Deacon*) (1995)

POSTAL ADDRESS: St. Mary's Rectory, 22 Powrie Place, DUNDEE DD1
2PQ. ☎ Dundee (01382) 226384.

Sunday Masses: 9 a.m., 12 noon. Holy Days of Obligation, Masses: 10
a.m., 7 p.m. Confessions: First and third Fridays, 5 to 5.30 p.m.
Estimated Catholic population: 500.

OUR LADY'S PRIMARY SCHOOL (WITH PROVISION FOR HANDICAPPED
CHILDREN).

ST. MATTHEW, Whitfield (1968, 1974), Whitfield Drive
(linked with Our Lady of Sorrows, Fintry).

Rev. Kevin J. Golden (1990)

POSTAL ADDRESS: Our Lady of Sorrows, Finlarig Terrace, DUNDEE DD4
9JF. ☎ Dundee (01382) 502068.

Sunday Mass: 10 a.m. (Sung Mass, with Children's Liturgy of the
Word). Evening Service (Advent and Lent), 4 p.m. Holy Days of
Obligation, Masses: 9.15 a.m. in St. Luke's and St. Matthew's Primary
School, 6.30 p.m.. Confessions: Saturday. 5.15 to 6 p.m., during
Exposition of the Blessed Sacrament, in Our Lady of Sorrows; at call.
Estimated Catholic population: 300.

CONVENT OF THE GOOD SHEPHERD, 8 PITCAPLE WALK, WHITFIELD,
DUNDEE DD4 0RT ☎ DUNDEE (01382) 503700.
BALLUMBIE COURT NURSING HOME ATTENDED FROM ST. MATTHEW'S
ST. LUKE'S AND ST. MATTHEW'S PRIMARY SCHOOL.

ST. NINIAN, Menzieshill (1963, 1969), Dickson Avenue.

Rev. Michael J. Milton (1988)

POSTAL ADDRESS: St. Ninian's, Dickson Avenue, DUNDEE DD2 4DA. ☎
Dundee (01382) 669966. Fax: 01382-643665.

Sunday Masses: Vigil-Mass, 6 p.m.; 10 a.m. Evening Service as
announced. Holy Days of Obligation, Masses: 9.30 a.m., 6.30 p.m.
Confessions: Saturday, 5.15 to 5.40 p.m.
Estimated Catholic population: 2,000.

ROYAL VICTORIA HOSPITAL AND ROXBURGHE HOUSE ATTENDED FROM ST.
NINIAN'S.
ST. NINIAN'S PRIMARY SCHOOL.

OUR LADY OF GOOD COUNSEL, Broughty Ferry (1904), Westfield Road.

Rev. Anthony McCarthy (1958)

POSTAL ADDRESS: Our Lady of Good Counsel, 29 Westfield Road, Broughty Ferry, DUNDEE DD5 1ED. ☎ Dundee (01382) 778750.

Sunday Masses: 9, 11 a.m., Holy Days of Obligation, Masses: 10 a.m., 6 p.m. Confessions: Saturday, 10.30 a.m., 5 to 6 p.m.; on request. Estimated Catholic population: 800.   &

CRAIGIE HOUSE, RESIDENTIAL AND NURSING HOMES AND DUNDEE LIMB-FITTING CENTRE ATTENDED FROM BROUGHTY FERRY.
(ST. PIUS X PRIMARY SCHOOL)

OUR LADY OF SORROWS, Fintry (1956, 1967), Finlarig Terrace (linked with St. Matthew, Whitfield).

Rev. Kevin J. Golden (1990)

POSTAL ADDRESS: Our Lady of Sorrows, Finlarig Terrace, Fintry, DUNDEE DD4 9JF. ☎ Dundee (01382) 502068.

Sunday Masses: Vigil-Mass, 6.30 p.m.(sung); 11.30 a.m.(sung with Children's Liturgy of the Word). Evening Service, Advent and Lent, 4 p.m. Holy Days of Obligation, Masses: 9.15 (in St. Luke's and St. Matthew's Primary School) a.m., 7.30 p.m. Confessions: Saturday, 5.15 to 6 p.m. during Exposition of the Blessed Sacrament. Estimated Catholic popuation: 1,000.   🦻 Ⓐ

SERVITE HOUSE (SHELTERED HOUSING), 61 FINLARIG TERRACE, DUNDEE. DD4 9JE. ☎ DUNDEE (01382) 453694.
SERVITE HOUSE (SHELTERED HOUSING), FINLAGGAN CRESCENT, DUNDEE. DD4. ☎ DUNDEE (01382) 500010.
ST. LUKE'S AND ST. MATTHEW'S PRIMARY SCHOOL.

ST. PATRICK, Stobswell (1890, 1898), Arthurstone Terrace.

Right Rev. Mgr. Hugh F. Canon McInally,
J.P., C.A., Ph.B., S.T.B., V.G. (1963)
Rev. David H. McFarlane, B Sc., B.Comm.
(*Permanent Deacon*) (1994)

POSTAL ADDRESS: St. Patrick's, 3 Maitland Street, DUNDEE DD4 6RW. ☎
Dundee (01382) 226384.
Sunday Masses: Vigil-Mass, 6 p.m.; 10.30 a.m. Holy Days of Obligation,
Masses: Vigil-Mass, 7 p.m.; 12.30 p.m. Confessions: Second and fourth
Fridays, 5 to 5.30 p.m.
Estimated Catholic population: 600.

CATHOLIC CHAPLAINCY FOR ABVERTAY UNIVERSITY, 3 MAITLAND STREET,
DUNDEE DD4 6RW. ☎ DUNDEE (01382) 668007.
MARIST BROTHERS, 11 NAIRN STREET, DUNDEE DD4 7EN. ☎ DUNDEE
(01382) 450708.
SERVITE SISTERS, 127 PITKERRO ROAD, DUNDEE DD4 7EF. ☎ (01382)
456252.
OUR LADY'S PRIMARY SCHOOL (WITH PROVISION FOR HANDICAPPED
CHILDREN).

SS. PETER AND PAUL, Coldside (1929, 1930), Byron Street.

Very Rev. Ian Wilson, O.S.A., *Prior* (1984)
Rev. Bernard O'Connor, O.S.A. (1955)
Rev. Sean Quinlan, O.S.A. (1967)

POSTAL ADDRESS: SS. Peter and Paul, 29 Byron Street, DUNDEE DD3
6QN. ☎ Dundee (01382) 825067; Fax: 01382-817730.

Sunday Masses: Vigil-Mass, 6 p.m.; 9.30, 11.30 a.m. Holy Days of
Obligation, Masses: Vigil-Mass: 6.30 p.m.;11 a.m., 6.30 p.m.
Confessions: Friday, 6 to 6.30 p.m.; Saturday, 10.15 to 11 a.m., 11.30
a.m. to 12 noon, 4.30 to 5.30 p.m.
Estimated Catholic population:1,250.

KING'S CROSS HOSPITAL AND NINEWELLS HOSPITAL SERVED FROM SS. PETER
AND PAUL.
SS. PETER AND PAUL PRIMARY SCHOOL; ST. JOHN'S HIGH SCHOOL.

ST. PIUS X, Douglas (1955, 1961), Balerno Street.

Rev. Aldo Angelosanto, S.T.L. (1973)

POSTAL ADDRESS: St. Pius X, Balerno Street, Douglas, DUNDEE DD4 8NP. ☎ Dundee (01382) 778449.

Sunday Masses: Vigil-Mass, 6 p.m.; 10.30 a.m. Holy Days of Obligation, Masses: Vigil-Mass, 7 p.m.; 9.30 a.m. Confessions: Saturday, after morning Mass, after Vigil-Mass.
Estimated Catholic population: 2,000.

DOUGLAS HOUSE HOME FOR THE ELDERLY ATTENDED FROM ST. PIUS X.
ST. PIUS X PRIMARY SCHOOL; ST. SAVIOUR'S HIGH SCHOOL.

ST. TERESA OF AVILA (1940, 1955), Graham Street.

Very Rev. John Joseph Provost Connolly (1952)

POSTAL ADDRESS: St. Teresa's, 5 Graham Street, DUNDEE DD4 9AB. ☎ Dundee (01382) 825133.

Sunday Mass: 10 a.m. Evening Service: as announced. Holy Days of Obligation, Masses: 10 a.m., 7 p.m. Confessions: Saturday, after morning Mass.
Estimated Catholic population: 500.

ST. VINCENT DE PAUL, Kingsway East (1950), Pitkerro Drive.

Very Rev. Andrew M. Walls, O.S.M., *Prior* (1956)
Rev Peter M. Conniffe., O.S.M., *Parish Priest* (1965)
Rev. Paul M. Addison, O.S.M. (1965)
Rev Anselm M. Richardson, O.S.M. (1948)
Rev. Philip M. Walsh, O.S.M. (1953)
Sr. Mary Ghent, O.S.M. *(Parish Sister)*

POSTAL ADDRESS: The Servite Priory, 145 Kingsway East, DUNDEE DD4 8AA. ☎ Dundee (01382) 500446 (Priory)/505835 (Parish); Fax: 01382-505835.

Sunday Masses: Vigil-Mass, 5 p.m.; 8, 11 a.m. Holy Days of Obligation, Masses: Vigil-Mass, 7 p.m.; 9.30 a.m., 7 p.m. Confessions: Saturday, 11.30 a.m to 12 noon, 6 to 6.30 p.m.
Estimated Catholic population:400.

SERVITE SISTERS, 127 PITKERRO ROAD, DUNDEE DD4 7EF. ☎ DUNDEE (01382) 456252.
JOAN BARTLETT HOUSE (SHELTERED HOUSING) ATTENDED FROM ST. VINCENT DE PAUL'S.
ST. VINCENT'S PRIMARY SCHOOL.

UNIVERSITY OF DUNDEE CHAPLAINCY FOR CATHOLICS

Very Rev. Kenneth Canon McBride, *Chaplain* (1962)

POSTAL ADDRESS: Catholic Chaplaincy, 42 Wilkie's Lane, DUNDEE DD1 5HR. ☎ Dundee (01382) 223755 (*Secretary:* Dundee (0382) 344157, Ext. 4157). (*Residence:* Cathedral House, 150 Nethergate, DUNDEE DD1 4EA. ☎ Dundee (01382) 225228).

UNIVERSITY CHAPEL, CROSS ROW. SUNDAY MASS: 4.45 P.M. HOLY DAYS OF OBLIGATION, MASS: 1.10 P.M. CONFESSIONS: AT CALL.

CHAPLAINCY TO DUNDEE ROYAL INFIRMARY and NINEWELLS HOSPITAL

Very Rev. Ian Wilson, O.S.A., *Chaplain* (1988)

POSTAL ADDRESS: SS. Peter and Paul, 29 Byron Street, DUNDEE DD3 6QN. ☎ Dundee (01382) 825067/815992. Fax: 01382-817730.

Sunday Mass: 4.15 p.m. in Ninewells Hospital Chapel.

PARISHES OUTSIDE THE CITY OF DUNDEE

The name given last before the name of the Church is the Local Authority.

ABERFELDY, Perth and Kinross, Our Lady of Mercy, Home Street (1885). Served from Pitlochry.

Sunday Mass: 9.30 a.m. Holy Days of Obligation, Mass: 12.30 p.m. Confessions: before Mass.

ABERFOYLE, Stirling. Served from Callander.

ALLOA, Clackmannan, St. Mungo (1853, 1961), Mar Street.

Rev. Kenneth McCaffrey, Dip.Theol. Dip.Ed. (1982)
Rev. James Wallace (*Resident in Tullibody*) (1957)
Rev. Steven P. Mulholland, M.A., S.T.L. (1998)
Rev. John McAviney, C.Q.S.W. (*Permanent Deacon*) (1995)

POSTAL ADDRESS: St. Mungo's, 25 Mar Street, ALLOA FK10 1HR. ☎ Alloa (01259) 212486; Fax: 01259-722711.
E-mail:kenmac@sol.co.uk

Sunday Masses: Vigil-Mass, 6.30 p.m.; 10 a.m. Holy Days of Obligation, Masses: 9 a.m.; evening Mass as announced in Alloa, Tullibody or Alva. Confessions: Saturday, after Vigil-Mass, after any morning Mass, on request.
Estimated Catholic population: 1,600.   Wheelchair facilities in adjacent hall

For members of the Polish Community, Mass as announced.
CLACKMANNAN COUNTY HOSPITAL, SAUCHIE HOSPITAL, SAUCHIE NURSING HOME AND STRUAN HOUSE SCHOOL ATTENDED FROM ST. MUNGO'S.
ST. MUNGO'S PRIMARY SCHOOL. (Transport to St. Modan's High School, Stirling).

ALVA, Clackmannan, St. John Vianney (1913, 1926), East Stirling Street.

Rev. Kenneth J. McCaffrey, Dip.Theol., Dip.Ed.,
(*Resident in Alloa*) (1982)
Rev. James Wallace (*Resident in Tullibody*) (1957)
Rev. Steven P. Mulholland, M.A., S.T.L.
(*Resident in Alloa*) (1998)
Sr. Ethelreda Maher, U.J., *Parish Sister*
Sr. Catherine Ryan, U.J., *Parish Sister*

POSTAL ADDRESS: St. Mungo's, 25 Mar Street, ALLOA FK10 1HR. Tel..: Alloa (01259) 212486; Fax: 01259-722711.
E-mail:kenmac@sol.co.uk

Sunday Masses: 11 a.m.,5.15 p.m. Holy Days of Obligation, Mass: 10 a.m.; evening Mass as announced in Alva, Alloa or Tullibody. Confessions: after any morning Mass; on request.
Estimated Catholic population: 500.   Wheelchair facilities in adjacent hall

URSULINE CONVENT, 16 EAST STIRLING STREET, ALVA FK12 5HA.. ☎ ALVA (01259) 760324.
MENSTRIE HOUSE, Menstrie, ATTENDED FROM ALVA.
H.M. PRISON, GLENOCHIL: MASS, THURSDAY, 10.30 A.M.
(ST. BERNADETTE'S SCHOOL, Tullibody; ST. MUNGO'S SCHOOL, Alloa; transport to St. Modan's High School, Stirling).

ALYTH, Perth and Kinross, St. Luan (1879, 1900).
Served from Blairgowrie.
Sunday Mass: 9.30 a.m. Holy Days of Obligation, Mass: 7 p.m.
Confessions on request.

ARBROATH, Angus, St. Thomas of Canterbury (1839, 1848), Dishlandtown Street.

Right Rev. Mgr. Benjamin Canon Donachie,
M.A., Dip.Ed. (1958)

POSTAL ADDRESS: St. Thomas of Canterbury, 56 Dishlandtown Street,
ARBROATH DD11 1QU. ☎/Fax:Arbroath (01241) 873013.
E-mail: b.rev.donachie@talk21.com

Sunday Masses: Vigil-Mass, 6.30 p.m.; 10.30 a.m. Holy Days of
Obligation, Masses: 11 a.m. in school, 7 p.m. Confessions: weekdays
before daily Mass; Saturdays, 10.30 to 11 a.m.   **A**
Estimated Catholic population: 800.

ARBROATH ROYAL INFIRMARY, LITTLE CAIRNEY NURSING HOME AND ROYAL
MARINES, CONDOR, ATTENDED FROM ST. THOMAS'.
ST. THOMAS' PRIMARY SCHOOL.

**AUCHTERARDER, Perth and Kinross, Our Lady of
Perpetual Succour** (1956, 1879), Castleton Road.

Very Rev. Basil Canon O'Sullivan, J.C.L (1956)

POSTAL ADDRESS: The Catholic Presbytery, Castleton Road,
AUCHTERARDER PH3 1JW. ☎ Dunblane(01786) 822146.
E-mail: basil.osullivan@btinternet.com

Sunday Masses: Vigil-Mass, 5 p.m.; 10 a.m. Evening Service: as
announced. Holy Days of Obligation, Vigil-Mass, 6.30 p.m.
Confessions: Saturday, 4.30 p.m.   **A**
Estimated Catholic population: 350.

KIPPEN HOUSE NURSING HOME, Dunning, ATTENDED FROM OUR LADY OF
PERPETUAL SUCCOUR.
(ST. DOMINIC'S PRIMARY SCHOOL, Crieff.)

AUCHTERMUCHTY, Fife, St. Matthew (1953, 1959), Back Dykes. Served from Cupar, Fife.

Sunday Mass: 9.30 a.m. Holy Days of Obligation, Vigil-Mass, previous evening, 7.15 p.m. Confessions before and after Mass.

BLAIRGOWRIE, Perth and Kinross, St. Stephen (1848, 1856), John Street.

Very Rev. Hugh J. Canon Sreenan (1962)
Rev. Anthony Cousins, M.A., Dip.Ed.
(*Permanent Deacon*) (1996)

POSTAL ADDRESS: St. Stephen's, 8 Bank Street, BLAIRGOWRIE PH10 6DE.
☎ Blairgowrie (01250) 872171.

Sunday Mass: 11 a.m. Evening Service: as announced. Holy Days of Obligation, Mass: 9.15 a.m. Confessions: Saturday, after morning Mass, 5 to 5.30 p.m.
Estimated Catholic population: 750.

THE COTTAGE HOSPITAL, Blairgowrie, VIEWPARK HOME FOR THE MENTALLY HANDICAPPED, Alyth, AND THE COTTAGE HOSPITAL, Meigle, ATTENDED FROM ST. STEPHEN'S.
ST. STEPHEN'S PRIMARY SCHOOL.

BLAIRHALL, Fife. Served from Highvalleyfield.

BRECHIN, Angus, St. Ninian's (1888, 1964), Bank Street. Served from Montrose.

Sunday Mass: 10 a.m. Holy Days of Obligation, Mass: 6.30 p.m.

CALLANDER, Stirling, St. Joseph the Worker (1958). Glenartney Road.

Rev. James R. McCruden, M.A., Dip.Ed. (1988)

POSTAL ADDRESS: 2A Ancaster Square, CALLANDER FK17 8ED. ☎ Callander (01877) 330702.

Sunday Masses: Vigil-Mass (*May to October*), 5.30 p.m.; 11.30 a.m. Holy Days of Obligation, Mass: 7.30 p.m. Confessions: before and after Mass.
Estimated Catholic population: 500.

CARNOUSTIE, Angus, St. Anne (1928, 2000), Thomas Street.

Rev. Mark Cassidy, Ph.B., S.T.L. (1988)

POSTAL ADDRESS: St. Anne's, 100 Dundee Street, CARNOUSTIE DD7 7PH. ☎ Carnoustie (01241) 853386.

Sunday Masses: Vigil-Mass, 5 p.m.; 9.30 a.m. Holy Days of Obligation, Masses: Vigil-Mass, 7 p.m.; 9.30 a.m. Confessions: Saturday, 4 to 4.30 p.m.
Estimated Catholic population: 500.

CAMUS HOUSE, WILLOWBANK HOUSE, BROOKFIELD RESIDENTIAL HOME AND LOUSEN PARK SHELTERED HOUSING ATTENDED FROM ST. ANNE'S.

COMRIE, Perth and Kinross, St. Margaret (1914), Drummond Street. Served from Crieff.
Sunday Mass: 9.30 a.m. Holy Days of Obligation, Mass: 6 p.m. Confessions before Mass.

COUPAR ANGUS, Perth and Kinross, St. Mary (1966). Served from Blairgowrie.
Sunday Vigil-Mass, 6.30 p.m. Holy Days of Obligation, Vigil-Mass, 6.30 p.m. Confessions, on request.

CRIEFF, Perth and Kinross, St. Fillan (1799, 1871), Ford Road.

Rev. Martin Drysdale, Ph.L., S.T.L. (1975)

POSTAL ADDRESS: St. Fillan's, Ford Road, CRIEFF PII7 3HN. ☎ Crieff (01764) 3269.

Sunday Masses: Vigil-Mass, 5.30 p.m.; 11 a.m. Holy Days of Obligation, Masses: 9.30 a.m., 7 p.m. Confessions: Saturday, 4.30 to 5.15 p.m.
Estimated Catholic population: 750*.

CRIEFF COTTAGE HOSPITAL, RICHMOND HOUSE, BRITISH LIMBLESS EX-SERVICEMEN'S ASSOCIATION HOME AND CULTYBRAGGAN ARMY CAMP ATTENDED FROM CRIEFF.
ST. DOMINIC'S PRIMARY SCHOOL.

CUPAR, Fife, St. Columba (1864, 1964), Kirkgate.

Rev. Patrick J. McInally, S.T.B., Dip.Lit. (1972)

POSTAL ADDRESS: St. Columba's, Ashlar Lane, CUPAR KY15 4AN. ☎
Cupar (01334) 653000.
E-mail:FATHERPAT@CUPARFIFE.FREESERVE.CO.UK
Website:http//welcome.to/st.columbas

Sunday Masses: Vigil-Mass, 6.30 p.m.; 11 a.m. Holy Days of Obligation,
Masses: 9.30 a.m., 7.15 p.m. Confessions: Saturday, 6 p.m.; on request.
Estimated Catholic population:650.

FRANCISCAN SISTERS OF THE DIVINE MOTHERHOOD, ST. MARY'S CONVENT,
BIRKWOOD, WESTFIELD ROAD, CUPAR KY15 5AR. ☎ CUPAR (01334) 657009.
STRATHEDEN HOSPITAL, ADAMSON HOSPITAL, Cupar, AND PITLAIR HOUSE,
Bow of Fife,ATTENDED FROM ST. COLUMBA'S .
ST. COLUMBA'S PRIMARY SCHOOL.

DOUNE, Stirling, SS. Fillan and Alphonsus (1875), Main Street. Served from Callander.
Sunday Mass: 9.45 a.m. Holy Days of Obligation, Mass: 6 p.m.
Confessions before Mass.

DUNBLANE, Stirling, The Holy Family (1878, 1934), Claredon Place.

Very Rev. Basil Canon O'Sullivan, J.C.L. (1956)

POSTAL ADDRESS: St. Clare, Claredon Place, DUNBLANE FK15 9HB. ☎
Dunblane (01786) 822146.
E-mai: basil.osullivan@btinternet.com

Sunday Masses: Vigil-Mass, 7 p.m.; 8.45, 11.30 a.m. Evening Service as
announced. Holy Days of Obligation. Masses: 8.30, 10 a.m., 7.30 p.m.
Confessions: Saturday, 10.30 a.m.
Estimated Catholic population: 750.

QUEEN VICTORIA SCHOOL, Dunblane, ATTENDED FROM DUNBLANE. MASS AS
ANNOUNCED.

DUNBLANE, Stirling, Society of African Missions (1976).

Very Rev. Patrick N. McGuire, S.M.A., S.T.B., F.C.C.A. (1987)
Rev. Michael J. Walsh, S.M.A., M.A., Dip.Ed. (1942)
Rev. Gerald A. Toner, S.M.A., M.A. (1987)

POSTAL ADDRESS: S.M.A. Fathers, St. Theresa's, Abbey House, Claredon Place, DUNBLANE FK15 9HB. ☎ Dunblane (01786) 824002; Fax: 01786-825997.

DUNKELD, Perth and Kinross, St. Columba (1924, 1932), St. Mary's Road, Birnam. Served from St. John's, Perth.

All enquiries to Perth (01738) 622241.
Sunday Mass: 11.30 a.m.

FORFAR, Angus, St. Fergus (1946, 1963), Gallowshade.

Rev. Neil Gallagher   (1971)
Rev. Ian Gordon, M.A. (*Permanent Deacon*) (1994)

POSTAL ADDRESS: St. Fergus', Gallowshade, FORFAR DD8 1NG. ☎ Forfar (01307) 462104; Fax: 01307-466926..

Sunday Masses: 11 a.m., 6.30 p.m. Holy Days of Obligation, Masses: 8 a.m., 7.30 p.m. Confessions: Saturday, 7.30 to 8 p.m.
Estimated Catholic population: 700.

FORFAR INFIRMARY AND WHITEHILLS OLD PEOPLE'S HOSPITAL SERVED FROM ST. FERGUS'.

NORANSIDE YOUNG OFFENDERS' INSTITUTION (SUNDAY MASS, 1.30 P.M., OPEN TO PUBLIC) SERVED FROM ST. FERGUS'.

HIGHVALLEYFIELD, Fife, St. Serf (1913, 1922), Chapel Street.

Rev. Brian F. McLean, Ph.B., S.T.B., J.C.L., (1986)

POSTAL ADDRESS: St. Serf's, 14 Chapel Street, Highvalleyfield, DUNFERMLINE KY12 8SJ. ☎ Newmills (01383) 880366.

Sunday Masses: Vigil-Mass, 6.30 p.m.; 11.30 a.m. (*also 10 a.m. in Kincardine on-Forth*). Holy Days of Obligation, Masses: Vigil-Mass, 7 p.m.; 10 a.m. (*also 7 p.m. in Kincardine-on-Forth*). Confessions: Saturday, 5 to 5.30 p.m.
Estimated Catholic population: 600.

Facilities in hall

ST. SERF'S PRIMARY SCHOOL; (HOLY NAME PRIMARY SCHOOL,Oakley).

KEIR HOUSE, Dunblane, Stirling, St. Margaret (1912).
Semi-public Oratory. Served from Dunblane. Mass as announced.

KILLIN, Stirling. Served from Callander.
Sunday Mass: 2.30 p.m. in Episcopal Church, Killin. Confessions before services.

KINCARDINE-ON-FORTH, Fife, St. Thenew and St. Serf (1970), Kilbagie Street. Served from High-valleyfield.
Sunday Mass: 10 a.m. Holy Days of Obligation, Mass: 7 p.m. Other Services as announced.

KINNOULL, Perth, Perth and Kinross, Our Lady of Perpetual Succour (1866, 1868), Hatton Road. Redemptorist Fathers.

Very Rev. Padraig Gallagher, C.Ss.R., *Rector* (1982)
Rev. James McManus, C.Ss.R. (1964)
Rev. Joseph Doherty, C.Ss.R. (1969)
Rev. Oliver Keyes, C.Ss.R. (1973)
Rev. Professor Hamish Swanston, Obl.C.Ss.R.
Bro. Malachy, C.Ss.R.
Bro. Pius, C.Ss.R.

POSTAL ADDRESS: St. Mary's Mission and Renewal Centre, Hatton Road, Kinnoull, PERTH PH2 7BP. ☎ Perth (01738) 624075; Fax: 01736- 442071.
E-mail: copiosa@aol.com.
Sunday Mass: 10 a.m. Evening Service as announced. Holy Days of Obligation, Mass: 8 a.m. Confessions at call.

Applications for Missions, Retreats and Residential Courses should be addressed to the Very Rev. Father Rector, C.Ss.R., St. Mary's Mission and Renewal Centre, Kinnoull, Perth PH2 7BP.

The Centre offers a range of Retreats and Courses for Clergy, Religious and Lay People.

KINROSS, Perth and Kinross, St. James (1955, 1956), High Street.

Rev. Neil Dorward, M.A., B.D. (1992)

POSTAL ADDRESS: St. James', 5 High Street, KINROSS KY13 7AW. ☎/Fax: Kinross (01577) 863329.
E-mail: neil.dorward@st.jamesrc.freeserve.co.uk

Sunday Masses: Vigil-Mass, 7 p.m.; 10, 11.30 a.m. Holy Days of Obligation, Masses: 9 a.m., 7 p.m. Confessions: Saturday, 5 to 6 p.m.
Estimated Catholic population: 500.

(facilities in hall only.)

ASHLEY HOUSE, LEVENGLEN, ROUND HOUSE CHILDREN'S HOSPICE, RUMBLING BRIDGE NURSING HOME AND H.M. PRISON PERTH ATTENDED FROM ST. JAMES'.
(ST. JOHN'S PRIMARY SCHOOL, PERTH.; TRANSPORT TO ST. COLUMBA'S HIGH SCHOOL, PERTH).

KIRRIEMUIR, Angus, St. Anthony (1950, 1987), 3 St. Mary's Close, Roods. Served from Forfar.

(☎ Kirriemuir (01575) 74220).
Sunday Mass: 9.30 a.m. Holy Days of Obligation, Mass: 6 p.m. Confessions: Sunday, 9 to 9.15 a.m.

LEUCHARS, Fife. St. Michael's Chapel, R.A.F. Station, attended from Newport-on-Tay.

Sunday Vigil-Mass: 6 p.m. Holy Days of Obligation, Mass: 5.15 p.m. Confessions: on request.

MONIFIETH, Angus, St. Bride (1880, 1983), Brook Street.

Very Rev. Romeo Canon Coia, M.A., B.A   (1959)
Rev. David Forsyth (*Permanent Deacon*)   (1996)

POSTAL ADDRESS: St. Bride's, 9 Muirnwood Place, Monifieth, DUNDEE DD5 4JL. ☎ Monifieth (01382) 534557.

Sunday Masses: Vigil-Mass, 6 p.m.; 10.30 a.m., 6.15 p.m. Holy Days of Obligation, Masses: 10 a.m., 4, 7 p.m. Confessions: Saturdays, 11 a.m. to 12 noon, 5 to 5.45 p.m.
Estimated Catholic population: 950.

ST. MARY'S HOME FOR THE ELDERLY, PANMURE STREET, MONIFIETH, DUNDEE DD5 4EG. ☎ MONIFIETH (01382) 533376. MASS, TUESDAY AND THURSDAY; COMMUNION SERVICE EVERY OTHER DAY.
ASHLUDIE HOSPITAL, SOUTH GRANGE NURSING HOME AND TIG-NA-MUIR HOME FOR THE ELDERLY, ATTENDED FROM ST. BRIDE'S

MONTROSE, Angus, St. Margaret (1883, 1886), Market Street.

Rev. James H. High, M.A (1986)

POSTAL ADDRESS: St. Margaret's, Market Street, MONTROSE DD10 8NB. ☎ Montrose (01674) 672208.

Sunday Mass: Vigil-Mass (*July to September*), 6 p.m.; 11.30 a.m. Holy Days of Obligation, Masses: 10 a.m., 7.30 p.m. Confessions: Friday, 7 to 7.30 p.m.; on request.
Estimated Catholic population: 400.

STRACATHRO HOSPITAL, SUNNYSIDE HOSPITAL, ROYAL INFIRMARY, Montrose, ROYAL INFIRMARY, Brechin, AND ROSSIE FARM SCHOOL ARE ATTENDED FROM MONTROSE.
U.S. NAVAL BASE, EDZELL, SERVED BY U.S. NAVAL CHAPLAIN. SUNDAY MASS: 9 A.M. HOLY DAYS OF OBLIGATION, MASSES: AS ANNOUNCED.
ST. MARGARET'S PRIMARY SCHOOL.

NEWPORT-ON-TAY, Fife, St. Fillan (1886, 1893), King Street.

Rev. James Foley (1964)

POSTAL ADDRESS: St. Fillan's, 20 King Street, NEWPORT-ON-TAY DD6 8BN. ☎ Newport-on-Tay (01382) 542324.

Sunday Mass: 11.30 a.m. Holy Days of Obligation, Mass: 7 p.m. Confessions: after Mass; Saturday, 10.30 to 11 a.m.
timated Catholic population: 350.

R.A.F. STATION, LEUCHARS, SERVED FROM NEWPORT. ST. MICHAEL'S CHAPEL. SUNDAY VIGIL-MASS, 6 P.M., HOLY DAYS OF OBLIGATION, MASS: 5.15 P.M. CONFESSIONS: ON REQUEST.
(ST. COLUMBA'S PRIMARY SCHOOL, Cupar; GREYFRIARS PRIMARY SCHOOL, St. Andrews.)

PERTH, Perth and Kinross, St. John the Baptist (1821, 1893), Melville Street.

Very Rev. Charles Canon Hendry (1955)
Rev. William F. Finnigan, Dip. Theol. (1995)
Rev. Colin K. Golden, Dip. Theol. (1998)
Rev. David W. Connelly *(Permanent Deacon)*(1997)

POSTAL ADDRESS: St. John's, 20 Melville Street, PERTH PH1 5PY. ☎ Perth (01738) 622241.

Sunday Masses: Vigil-Mass, 6.30 p.m.; 9, 11 a.m., 6.30 p.m. Holy Days of Obligation, Masses: Vigil-Mass, 7.30 p.m.; 10, 11.15 a.m., 7.30 p.m. (In school term, Mass on Holy Days of Obligation in St. Columba's High School: 9 a.m.) Confessions: Saturday, after 10 a.m. Mass, 5 to 6 p.m.; at call.
Estimated Catholic population: 2,500.

FOR MEMBERS OF THE POLISH COMMUNUITY: MASS ON THE THIRD SUNDAY OF EACH MONTH, 3 P.M.
MARIST SISTERS, 16 MELVILLE STREET, PERTH PH1 5PY. ☎ PERTH (01738) 626303.
THE ROYAL INFIRMARY, STRATHTAY, MURRAY ROYAL HOSPITAL, BEECHGROVE, CRAIGIEKNOWES NURSING HOME, OCHIL HOUSE, NORTH INCH HOME AND UPPER SPRINGLANDS AND TAYSIDE NURSING HOME ATTENDED FROM ST. JOHN'S.
ST. JOHN'S PRIMARY SCHOOL; ST. COLUMBA'S HIGH SCHOOL.

PERTH, Perth and Kinross, St. Mary Magdalene, Craigie (1962, 1959), Glenearn Road. Temporarily served from St. John's, Perth.

Very Rev. Charles Canon Hendry (1955)
Rev. William F. Finnigan, Dip. Theol. (1995)
Rev. Colin K. Golden, Dip. Theol. (1998)
Rev. David W. Connelly *(Permanent Deacon)*(1997)

POSTAL ADDRESS: St. John's, 20 Melville Street, PERTH PH1 5PY. ☎ Perth (01738) 622241
.
Sunday Masses: 10 a.m. Holy Days of Obligation, Mass: 8 a.m.

PERTH, Perth and Kinross, Our Lady of Lourdes, Letham (1959), Struan Road, Letham.

Rev. David Francis Ward, F.S.A.Scot. (1962)

POSTAL ADDRESS: 42 Struan Road, Perth PH1 2JP. ☎ Perth (01738) 623902.
E-mail:DWard39187@aol.com

Sunday Masses: 10 a.m., 6 p.m. Evening Service, 4 p.m. as announced. Holy Days of Obligation, Masses: 8, 10 a.m., 7 p.m. Confessions: Saturday, 5.20 to 6.20 p.m.; at call.
Estimated Catholic population: 1,500.

BEECH GROVE HOUSE AND OCHIL NURSING HOME ATTENDED FROM OUR LADY OF LOURDES.
OUR LADY'S PRIMARY SCHOOL.

PITLOCHRY, Perth and Kinross, St. Bride (1949, 1969), Rie-Achan Road.

Very Rev. Rupert Canon Loughlin (1944)

POSTAL ADDRESS: St. Bride's, Rie-Achan Road, PITLOCHRY PH16 5AL. ☎ Pitlochry (01796) 472174.

Sunday Mass: Vigil-Mass (*June to September*), 6 p.m.; 11.30 a.m. Holy Days of Obligation, Mass: 7.30 p.m. (*May to August, also 9.30 a.m.*). Confessions: after Mass; at call.
Estimated Catholic population:180.

COTTAGE HOSPITAL AND DALWEEM HOME FOR THE ELDERLY, Aberfeldy, AND COTTAGE HOSPITAL, Pitlochry, ATTENDED FROM ST. BRIDE'S.

RANNOCH, Killiechonan, Perth and Kinross, Sacred Heart (1928). Served from Pitlochry.
Sunday Mass: 3 p.m. in Community Hall, Allt Mhor Place, Kinloch Rannoch. Masses at all other times as announced. Confessions before Mass.

STRATHTAY, Perth and Kinross, Holy Cross (1876). Served from Pitlochry.
For times of services on Sundays and Holy Days of Obligation phone Rev. Parish Priest (☎ Pitlochry (01796) 472174).

TAYPORT, Fife, Our Lady, Star of the Sea (1939). Served from Newport-on-Tay.

Sunday Mass: 10 a.m. Holy Days of Obligation, Mass: 10 a.m. Confessions: Saturday, 11.30 to 12 noon .

TILLICOULTRY, Clackmannan. Served from Alloa and Tullibody.
Community Centre, Sunday Mass: 9 a.m.

TULLIBODY, Clackmannan, St. Bernadette (1958, 1963), Baingle Brae.

Rev. James Wallace (*Priest in Charge*)   (1957)
Rev. Kenneth McCaffrey
(Resident in Alloa) (1982)
Rev. Steven P. Mulholland, M.A., S.T.L.
(Resident in Alloa) (1998)

POSTAL ADDRESS: St. Bernadette's, Baingle Brae, TULLIBODY FK10 2SG. ☎ Alloa (01259) 213274.

Sunday Mass: 12 noon. Rosary and Benediction, 11.40 a.m. Holy Days of Obligation, Masses: Vigil-Mass, 7.30 p.m.; 9 a.m. (*School, 11 a.m.*), 7 p.m. Confessions: daily before Mass; Saturday, 11 to 11.30 a.m., 4 to 4.30 p.m.; at call.
Estimated Catholic population: 850.

H.M. YOUNG OFFENDERS INSTITUTION GLENOCHIL SERVED FROM ST. BERNADETTE'S. MASS AS ANNOUNCED.
ORCHARD HOUSE NURSING HOME, ATTENDED FROM ST. BERNADETTE'S.
PRIMARY SCHOOL.

RETIRED PRIESTS OF THE DIOCESE

Very Rev. Augustine Canon Klein, Wellburn Home, 118 Liff Road, DUNDEE DD2 2QT.
Very Rev. Kevin Canon Smyth, Crossroads Cottage, Leitfie, Meigle, BLAIRGOWRIE PH11 8NZ. ☎ Meigle (018284) 338.

INSTITUTES OF CONSECRATED LIFE
AND
SOCIETIES OF APOSTOLIC LIFE

MEN

AUGUSTINIANS (1950)

SS. Peter and Paul, 29 Byron Street, DUNDEE DD3 6QN. ☎ Dundee (01382) 825067; Fax: 01382-817730.

REDEMPTORISTS (1867)

St. Mary's, Hatton Road, Kinnoull, PERTH PH2 7BP. ☎ Perth (01738) 624075; Fax: 01738-442071.

SERVITES (1950)

St. Vincent de Paul, 145 Kingsway East, DUNDEE DD4 8AA. ☎ Dundee (01382) 500446/505835; Fax: 01382-505835.

SOCIETY OF AFRICAN MISSIONS (1976)

S.M.A. Fathers, St. Theresa's, Abbey House, Claredon Place, DUNBLANE FK15 9HB. ☎ Dunblane (01786) 824002; Fax: 01786-825997.

MARIST BROTHERS (1859)

(1996) Marist Brothers, 11 Nairn Street, DUNDEE DD4 7EN. ☎ Dundee (01382) 450708.

WOMEN

FRANCISCAN MISSIONARIES OF THE DIVINE MOTHERHOOD (1974)

(1990) St. Columba's, Derwent Avenue, DUNDEE DD3 0BE. ☎ Dundee (01382) 832063.
(1993) St. Mary's Convent, Birkwood, Westfield Road, CUPAR KY15 5AR. ☎ Cupar (01334) 657009.
E-mail:FMDM.CUPAR@TESCO.NET

CONGREGATION OF THE GOOD SHEPHERD (1984)

Good Shepherd Sisters, 8 Pitcaple Walk, Ormiston Crescent, Whitfield, DUNDEE DD4 0RT. ☎ Dundee (01382) 503700.

LITTLE SISTERS OF THE POOR (1863)

St. Joseph's Convent, Wellburn Home, 118 Liff Road, Lochee, DUNDEE DD2 2QT. ☎ Dundee (01382) 622212.
Chaplain: Rev. Gerard Ratcliffe, C.Ss.R. (1946), Wellburn Cottage, 120 Liff Road, Lochee, DUNDEE DD2 2QT

MARIST SISTERS(1982)

16 Melville Street, PERTH PH1 5PY. ☎ Perth (01738) 626303.

SISTERS OF ST. MARY OF NAMUR (1964)

(1982) St. Mary's, 53 Americanmuir Road, DUNDEE DD3 9AD. ☎ Dundee (01382) 858064.

SISTERS OF MERCY (1859)

St. Joseph's Convent of Mercy, Lawside Road, DUNDEE DD3 6BJ. ☎Dundee (01382) 322304/224011..
St. Anne's Cottage, 30 Lawside Road, DUNDEE DD3 6BJ. ☎Dundee (01382) 228597.

SERVITE SISTERS (1984)

(1990) Servite Sisters, 127 Pitkerro Road, DUNDEE DD4 7EF. ☎ Dundee (01382) 456252.

URSULINES OF JESUS(1995)

St. John Vianney's, 16 East Stirling Street, ALVA FK12 5HA. ☎ Alva (01259) 760324.

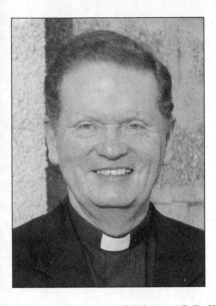

Diocese of Galloway

Bishop of Galloway
Right Rev. Maurice Taylor, S.T.D.

Born at Hamilton, Lanarkshire, 5th May 1926; educated St. Aloysius'
College, Glasgow, Our Lady's High School, Motherwell; St. Mary's
College, Blairs; army service, Second World War: Royal Army Medical
Corps, 1944-47; Scots College, Rome (S.T.L., Gregorian University,
Rome, 1951); ordained priest at Rome, 2nd July 1950; assistant priest,
St. Bartholomew, Coatbridge, 1951-52; Scots College, Rome (S.T.D.
bene probatus, 1954, Gregorian University, Rome); assistant priest, St.
Bernadette, Motherwell, 1954-55; on staff of St. Peter's College,
Cardross, 1955-65; rector, Royal Scots College, Valladolid, Spain,
1965-74; prelate of honour, 1971; parish priest, Our Lady of Lourdes,
East Kilbride, 1974-81; nominated bishop of Galloway, 4th April 1981,
and ordained by Gordon Gray, cardinal archbishop of St. Andrews
and Edinburgh, at Coodham, Ayrshire, 9th June 1981.

Residence: Candida Casa, 8 Corsehill Road, Ayr KA7 2ST.
☎ Ayr (01292) 266750.

VICAR-GENERAL

Right Rev. Mgr. Joseph V. Canon Boyd, St. Paul's, 2 Peggieshill
Place, Belmont, Ayr KA7 3RF. ☎ Ayr (01292) 260197.

THE DIOCESAN CURIA

Diocesan Office:	8 Corsehill Road, Ayr KA7 2ST. ☎/Fax: Ayr (01292) 266750. E-mail:stninian@globalnet.co.uk
Diocesan Pastoral Office:	8 Corsehill Road, Ayr KA7 2ST. ☎ Ayr (01292) 289888.
Chancellor:	Right Rev. Mgr. Joseph V. Canon Boyd, V.G.
Notary:	Rev. William R. McFadden, Ph.B., S.T.L., M.S.
College of Consultors:	Right Rev. Mgr. Joseph V. Canon Boyd, V.G.; Rev. Matthew F. McManus; Rev. Patrick McSorley; Rev. Joseph Boland; Rev. Eamonn Flynn; Rev. George Thompson; Rev. William R. McFadden.
Council of Priests:	*Chairman,* Rev.William R. McFadden *Secretary,* Rev. Stephen Latham, St. Joseph's, Lewis Street, Stranraer DG9 7AL. ☎ Stranraer (01776) 703125
Link Persons for Re.igious:	Sr. Anne Smyth,29 Shore Road, Skelmorlie PA17 5EH. ☎ 01475-520213. Sr. Teresa Nolan,69 Lainshaw Street, Stewarton, Kilmarnock KA3 5BX ☎ 01560-483322.
Diocesan Finance Committee:	Right Rev. Mgr. Joseph V. Canon Boyd, V.G.; Rev. Michael Lynch; Rev. Alistair G. Tosh; Rev. Martin D. Poland; Mr. John Mulhern

Ongoing Formation of Priests Programme: *Leader:* Rev. Martin D. Poland.

Church Representatives on Local Authority Education Committees

North Ayrshire: Rev Matthew F. McManus, St. Winin's, St. Winning's Lane, KILWINNING KA13 6EP.
☎ ilwinning (01294) 552276
Fax.:01294-558606..

South Ayrshire: Mr Hugh Hasson, 50 Samson Avenue, KILMARNOCK KA1 3ED.
☎ Kilmarnock (01563) 526764

East Ayrshire: Mr. John McHugh, 17 Bannoch Place, KILWINNING KA13 7JY.
☎ Kilwinning (01294) 554 556.

Dumfries and Galloway: Very Rev. John Canon Walls, St. Teresa's, Glasgow Road, DUMFRIES DG2 9DE.
☎ 01387-252603.

Education Strategy Group: *Chairperson:* Mr. Thomas Gilbey, 7 Carnoustie Court, KILWINNING KA13 6QY..
☎ (01294)551806.

Religious Education Advisers:
Primary Schools: Sr. Dorothy McCaffrey, S.N.D., 55 St. Phillans Avenue, AYR KA7 3DD.
☎ Ayr (01292) 290689.

Secondary Schools: Mr. Peter Maxwell, 61 North Hamilton Street, KILMARNOCK KA1 2QJ
☎ Kilmarnock (01563) 541792.

Directors of Vocations: Rev. Patrick Keegans, St. Margaret's, 27 John Street, AYR KA8 0BS
☎ 01292-263488.
Rev. Stephen Latham, St. Joseph's, Lewis Street, STRANRAER DG9 7AL.
☎ Stranraer (01776) 703125

Liturgy Co-ordinator: Rev. Michael D. Farrington.

Christian Unity Co-ordinator: Rev. Archibald Brown.

Marriage and Family Life Co-ordinators: Mr. Frank Ward,
11 Fotheringham Road,
AYR KA8 0EY.
☎ 01292-267539
Mr. David Mackey,
27 Langholm Street,
NEWCASTLETON TD9 0QX.
☎ 013873-75345.

Justice and Peace Co-ordinator: Mrs. Margaret Donnelly
111 Mill Road,
IRVINE KA12 0JS
☎ 01294-271835.

R.C.I.A.: *Diocesan Co-ordinator:*
Rev. William R. McFadden,
St. John's,
92 Glaisnock Street,
CUMNOCK KA18 1JU
☎ Cumnock (01290) 421031.

Youth: *Diocesan Youth Officer:*
Miss Bernadette McFadden,
7c Westend,
DALRY KA24 5DU.
☎ Dalry (01294) 833357.
Chaplain:
Rev. James Hayes,
St. Cuthbert's Presbytery,
28 Dailly Road,
MAYBOLE KA19 7AU.
☎ Maybole (01655) 882145,

Social Care Committee: Mr. Daniel McMonagle,
5 Rowan Crescent,
AYR KA7 3NA.
☎ Ayr (01292) 284985.

The Galloway Newsletter: *Editor,* Diocesan Pastoral Office,
8 Corsehill Road,
AYR KA7 2ST.
☎ Ayr (01292) 289888.

Diocesan Media Officer: Mrs. Mary McClune,
3 Recawr Park,
AYR KA7 4SW.
☎/Fax: 01292-442223.

Registrar for Deceased Clergy: Right Rev. Mgr. Joseph V. Canon Boyd,
V.G.,
St. Paul's, 2 Peggieshill Place,
AYR KA7 3RF.
☎ 01292-260197.

Pontifical Mission Aid Societies: *Diocesan Director,* Rev. John A. McGee
Cathedral House,
27 Dalmilling Crescent,
AYR KA8 0QL.
☎ Ayr (01292) 265716.

CATHEDRAL CHAPTER
(Erected 23rd December, 1901)

Provost: Very Rev. Thomas J. Murphy.

Canons: Very Rev. Eugene Mathews;
Very Rev. John P. Flannery;
Very Rev. Samuel McGinness;
Right Rev. Mgr. Joseph V. Boyd;
Very Rev. Denis F. Quinlan *(Secretary)*;
Very Rev. Alexander McGarry.

Honorary Canons: Right Rev. Mgr. Francis Duffy;
Right Rev. Mgr. Stephen Kennedy;
Very Rev. George McCafferty;
Very Rev. John Donnelly;
Very Rev. John Walls;
Very Rev. Mgr. Thomas K. Conway:
Very Rev. John J. Crowley.
Very Rev. Thomas J. McGread.

DEANERIES

1. **St. Margaret.** Good Shepherd Cathedral, Ayr; St. Margaret, Ayr; St. Paul, Ayr; Drongan; Girvan; Maybole; Mossblown; Prestwick; Troon; Waterside.
   Dean—Rev. Patrick McSorley.

2. **St. Andrew.** Annan; Castle Douglas; Dalbeattie; St. Andrew, Dumfries; St. Teresa, Dumfries; Gatehouse of Fleet; Gretna; Kinharvie Centre; Kirkconnel; Kirkcudbright; Langholm; Lockerbie; Moffat; New Abbey; Newton Stewart; Stranraer; Whithorn; Wigtown.
   Dean—Rev. George Thompson.

3. **St. Joseph.** Auchinleck; Catrine; Cumnock; Galston; Hurlford; St. Joseph, Kilmarnock; St. Matthew, Kilmarnock; St. Michael, Kilmarnock; Our Lady of Mount Carmel, Kilmarnock; Nazareth House, Kilmarnock; Muirkirk; Stewarton.
   Dean—Rev. Joseph Boland.

4. **St. Mary.** Beith; Dalry; St. John Ogilvie, Irvine; St. Margaret, Irvine; St. Mary, Irvine; Kilbirnie; Kilwinning; Sacred Heart Fathers, Kilwinning.
   Dean—Rev. Matthew M. McManus.

5. **St Columba.** Ardrossan, Largs; Millport; St. Brendan, Saltcoats; Our Lady, Star of the Sea, Saltcoats; Stevenston; West Kilbride.
   Dean—Rev. Eamonn Flynn.

CITY OF AYR

GOOD SHEPHERD CATHEDRAL (1957), Dalmilling Crescent.

Very Rev. John A. McGee, S.T.L.,
Administrator (1970)

POSTAL ADDRESS: Cathedral House, 37 Dalmilling Crescent, AYR KA8 0QL. ☎ Ayr (01292) 265716.

Sunday Masses: 11.30 a.m., 6 p.m. Holy Days of Obligation, Masses: 9.30 a.m., 7 p.m. Confessions: Saturday, after Mass; on request
Estimated Catholic population: 1,100..

ST. JOHN'S PRIMARY SCHOOL — GOOD SHEPHERD CAMPUS..

ST. MARGARET (1822, 1827), John Street.

Rev. Patrick Keegans, S.T.B. (1970)

POSTAL ADDRESS: St. Margaret's, 27 John Street, AYR KA8 0BS. ☎ Ayr (01292) 263488.

Sunday Masses: Vigil-Mass, 6 p.m.; 10, 11.30 a.m. Holy Days of Obligation, Masses: 10 a.m., 7 p.m. Confessions: Saturday, after 10 a.m. Mass, after Vigil-Mass.
Estimated Catholic population: 1,600.

AYR HOSPITAL AND AYR HOSPICE ATTENDED FROM ST. MARGARET'S, AYR.
ST. JOHN'S PRIMARY SCHOOL.

ST. PAUL, Belmont (1967), Peggieshill Road.

Right Rev. Mgr. Joseph V. Canon Boyd, V.G. (1957)
Rev. Stephen J. Cochrane, B.Sc., M.A., B.D. (1998)

POSTAL ADDRESS: St. Paul's, 2 Peggieshill Place, Belmont, AYR KA7 3RF. ☎ Ayr (01292) 260197.

Sunday Masses: Vigil-Mass 6.30 p.m.; 10 a.m., 12 noon. Holy Days of Obligation, Masses: 10 a.m., 7.30 p.m. Confessions: Saturday, after morning Mass, after Vigil-Mass.
Estimated Catholic population: 1,535.

Sisters of St. Joseph of Cluny, St. Ninian's, 30 Meadowpark, Ayr KA7 2LR. ☎ Ayr (01292) 263518.
Ailsa Mental Hospital and Carrick Glen Hospital attended from St. Paul's.
Wonder West World attended from Maybole.
Queen Margaret Academy; (St. John's Primary Schools).

Parishes Outside the City of Ayr
*The name given last before the name of the Church
is the Local Authority.*

ANNAN, Dumfries and Galloway, St. Columba (1839, 1906), Scott's Street.

Rev. G. Stuart Campbell, S.T.B. (1992)

Postal address: St. Columba's, 40 Scott's Street, Annan DG12 6JG. ☎/Fax: Annan (01461) 202776.

Sunday Masses: Vigil-Mass, 6 p.m.; 11 a.m. Holy Days of Obligation, Masses: 9 a.m., 7 p.m. Confessions: Saturday, 5.30 to 5.50 p.m., after Vigil-Mass.
Estimated Catholic population: 390.

Annan Hospital, Kiltarra Nursing Home and "Lydiafield" Old People's Home, Standalane, Annan, Served from St. Columba's.
St. Columba's Primary School.

ANNBANK, See Mossblown, Page 238.

ARDROSSAN, North Ayrshire, St. Peter-in-Chains (1945,1938), South Crescent Road.

Rev. Michael Lynch (1955)

Postal address: St. Peter's, 1 South Crescent Road, Ardrossan KA22 8DU. ☎ Ardrossan (01294) 464063; Fax 01294-466737.
E-mail: m.lynch@lineone.net

Sunday Masses: Vigil-Mass, 6.30 p.m.; 10 a.m., 12 noon, 6.30 p.m. Holy Days of Obligation, Masses: Vigil-Mass, 7 p.m.; 9.30 a.m., 7 p.m. Confessions: Friday, 7.30 p.m.; Saturday, 10 a.m., 7.30 p.m.; on request.
Estimated Catholic population: 4,000.

Franciscans of the Immaculate Conception, 25 McKellar Avenue, Ardrossan KA22 7AS. ☎ Ardrossan (01294) 603457.
Abbotsford House Nursing Home; George Aitken Court, Currie Court and Montgomerie Court (Sheltered Accommodation); all attended from St. Peter's.
St. Peter's Primary School.

AUCHINLECK, East Ayrshire, Our Lady of Lourdes and St. Patrick (1867, 1964), Sorn Road.

Very Rev. Thomas Joseph Provost Murphy (1943)

POSTAL ADDRESS: Our Lady of Lourdes and St. Patrick's, 35 Sorn Road, Auchinleck, CUMNOCK KA18 2HR. ☎ Cumnock (01290) 421521.

Sunday Masses: 10 a.m. Holy Days of Obligation, Masses: 10 a.m., 7 p.m. Devotional Vigil, First Saturdays, 7 p.m. Confessions: Saturday, 6.30 to 7 p.m.; any time. 🅰 ♿
Estimated Catholic population:365.

Facilities in adjoining Hall

AFFLECK HOUSE, NIGHTINGALE HOME AND CARRICK VIEW HOUSE ATTENDED FROM OUR LADY OF LOURDES AND ST. PATRICK.
The Registers of Our Lady and St. Patrick's, Birnie Knowe, and the older Registers of St. Joseph's, Catrine, are preserved in Auchinleck. ST. PATRICK'S PRIMARY SCHOOL.

BEITH, North Ayrshire, Our Lady of Perpetual Succour (1947, 1816), Mitchell Street.

Rev. John Kinsler (1965)

POSTAL ADDRESS: Our Lady of Perpetual Succour, 2 Crummock Street, BEITH KA15 2BD. ☎ Beith (01505) 502392.

Sunday Mass: 10 a.m. Holy Days of Obligation, Masses. 10 a.m., 7 p.m. Confessions, Saturday, after morning Mass; on request.
Estimated Catholic population: 400. 🅰

(ST. BRIDGET'S PRIMARY SCHOOL, Kilbirnie).

CASTLE DOUGLAS, Kirkcudbrightshire, Dumfries and Galloway, St. John the Evangelist (1867), Abercromby Road. Served from Kirkcudbright.

Rev. Neil O'Donnell, B.A., B.D., Dip.Ed., Dip.R.E. (1991)

POSTAL ADDRESS: St. Andrew's and St. Cuthbert's, High Street, Kirkcudbright DG6 4JW. ☎/Fax: Kirkcudbright (01557) 330687.

Sunday Mass: Vigil-Mass, 6 p.m. Holy Days of Obligation, Mass: 7 p.m. Confessions: Saturday, 5.15 to 5.45 p.m.
Estimated Catholic population: 450. 🅿

CASTLE DOUGLAS HOSPITAL AND CARLINGWARK HOUSE ATTENDED FRON ST. JOHN'S.
(ST. PETER'S PRIMARY SCHOOL, Dalbeattie).

CATRINE, East Ayrshire, St. Joseph (1867, 1960), Ballochmyle Street.

Very Rev. John P. Canon Flannery (1948)

POSTAL ADDRESS: St. Joseph's, 14 Ballochmyle Street, Catrine, MAUCHLINE KA5 6QP. ☎ Mauchline (01290) 551408.

Sunday Masses: 10.30 a.m., 6 p.m. Holy Days of Obligation, Masses: 9.45 a.m., 7 p.m. Confessions: Saturday, 7 to 7.30 p.m.; after Masses. Estimated Catholic population: 300.

BALLOCHMYLE HOSPITAL AND WOODSIDE NURSING HOME, Mauchline, ATTENDED FROM ST. JOSEPH'S.
The older Registers of St. Joseph's, Catrine, are preserved at Our Lady and St. Patrick's, Auchinleck.
(ST. PATRICK'S PRIMARY SCHOOL, Auchinleck).

CUMNOCK, East Ayrshire, St. John the Evangelist (1850, 1882), Glaisnock Street.

Rev. William R. McFadden, Ph.B., S.T.L., M.S. (1985)

POSTAL ADDRESS: St. John's, 92 Glaisnock Street, CUMNOCK KA18 1JU. ☎/Fax: Cumnock (01290) 421031.
E-mail: wrmcf299@aol.com

Sunday Masses: Vigil-Mass, 6 p.m.; 11.45 a.m. Holy Days of Obligation, Masses: 9.30 a.m., 7 p.m. Confessions: Saturday, after Vigil-Mass; on request; by appointment.
Estimated Catholic population: 1,000 (including New Cumnock).

HOLMHEAD HOSPITAL, AND HILLSIDE SCHOOL, ATTENDED FROM ST. JOHN'S.
ST. JOHN'S PRIMARY SCHOOL; ST. JOSEPH'S ACADEMY, CUMNOCK CAMPUS.

DALBEATTIE, Kirkcudbrightshire, Dumfries and Galloway, St. Peter (circa 1745, 1814), Craignair Street.

Rev. George Thompson, M.A., Dip.Ed. (1989)

POSTAL ADDRESS: St. Peter's, Craignair Street, DALBEATTIE DG5 4AX. ☎ Dalbeattie (01556) 610358.

Sunday Masses: Vigil-Mass,6.30 p.m.; 10 a.m. Holy Days of Obligation, Masses: 9 a.m., 7 p.m. Confessions: Saturday, 6 to 6.30 p.m.
Estimated Catholic population: 200.

SOUTHERNESS HOLIDAY VILLAGE: SUNDAY MASS: EASTER SUNDAY, 4 P.M.; 25TH JUNE TO 24TH SEPTEMBER, BOTH INCLUSIVE, 4 P.M.
ALMA HOUSE, Dalbeattie; BARLOCHAN AND CLIFFORD HOUSE, Palnackie, HERRIESDALE HOUSE, Haugh of Urr, AND MUNCHES PARK, Dalbeattie, ATTENDED FROM ST. PETER'S.
ST. PETER'S PRIMARY SCHOOL.

DALRY, North Ayrshire, St. Palladius (1848, 1851), Aitken Street.

Rev. Matthew F. McManus (1965)
Rerv. Patrick J. Lawson (1996)

POSTAL ADDRESS: St. Palladius', 10 Aitken Street, DALRY KA24 4BX.
☎ Dalry (01294) 832181/552266; Fax: 01294-558606.
E-mail: St.Winins@Virgin.net

Sunday Masses: Vigil-Mass, 6.30 p.m.; 9.00 a.m. Holy Days of Obligation Masses: Vigil-Mass, 7 p.m.; 10 a.m. Confessions: by request. Estimated Catholic population: 450.   **A**

ST. PALLADIUS' PRIMARY SCHOOL.

DARVEL, East Ayrshire, Our Lady of the Valley, 4 West Donington Street. Served from Galston.

Sunday Mass: 10 a.m. Holy Days of Obligation, Vigil-Mass, 7 p.m.   **A**

DRONGAN, East Ayrshire, St. Clare (1965, 1967), Watson Terrace. Served from Good Shepherd Cathedral, Ayr.

Rev. John A. McGee, S.T.L. (1970)

POSTAL ADDRESS: Cathedral House, Dalmilling Crescent, AYR KA8 0QL. ☎ Ayr (01292) 265716.

Sunday Mass: 9.45 a.m. Holy Days of Obligation, Vigil-Mass, 7 p.m. Confessions on request.
Estimated Catholic population: 300.   🎗

DUMFRIES, Dumfries and Galloway, St. Andrew (1810, 1964), Shakespeare Street.

Rev. Michael D. Farrington, S.T.L., Ph.L. (1968)
Rev. Stephen Sharkey, B.D., Dip.Ph. (1999)

POSTAL ADDRESS: St. Andrew's, 27 Brooke Street, DUMFRIES DG1 2JL. ☎ Dumfries (01387) 254281.

Sunday Masses: Vigil-Mass, 6 p.m.; 9, 11 a.m. Holy Days of Obligation, Masses: 10 a.m., 7 p.m. Confessions: Saturday, 10.30 to 11 a.m.; on request.
Estimated Catholic population: 2,000.   🎗 &

Marist Brothers, Carrick House, Craigs Road, Dumfries DG1 4QL. ☎ Dumfries (01387) 269473.
Marist Centre, Kinharvie House, New Abbey, Dumfries DG2 8DZ. ☎ New Abbey (11357) 850433.
Sisters of Charity of St. Vincent de Paul, St. Vincent's Convent, Brooke Street, Dumfries DG1 2JL. ☎ Dumfries (01387) 254093.
Sisters of Notre Dame de Namur, 6 Carnegie Street, Dumfries DG1 1PD. ☎ Dumfries (01387) 263394.
The Royal Infirmary, Crichton Royal Institute and Cresswell Maternity Hospital attended from St. Andrew's.
St. Andrew's Primary School; St. Joseph's College.

DUMFRIES, Dumfries and Galloway, St. Teresa (1958), Glasgow Road.

Very Rev. John Canon Walls, S.T.L. (1961)
Sr. Eileen Igoe *(Pastoral Assistant)*

Postal address: St. Teresa's, Glasgow Road, Dumfries DG2 9DE.
☎ Dumfries (01387) 252603; Fax: 01387-245354.
E-mail: john@walls40.freeserve.co.uk.

Sunday Masses: 10.45 a.m., 6 p.m. Holy Days of Obligation, Masses: 10 a.m., 7 p.m. Confessions: Saturday, 10.30 to 11a.m.; by appointment. Estimated Catholic population:1,900.

Lochduar and Dalawoodie Nursing Homes attended from St. Teresa's.
H.M. Young Offenders' Institution: Chaplain, Very Rev. John Canon Walls.
St. Teresa's Primary School; (St. Andrew's Primary School).

GALSTON, East Ayrshire, St. Sophia (1883, 1886), Bentinck Street.

Rev. Martin D. Poland (1982)

Postal address: St. Sophia's, Bentinck Street, Galston KA4 8HT.
☎ Galston (01563) 820339; Fax:01563-829054..

Sunday Masses: Vigil-Mass, 6 p.m.; 11.30 a.m. Holy Days of Obligation, Masses: 10 a.m., 7 p.m. Confessions: Saturday, 10.30 to 11 a.m., before Vigil-Mass.
Estimated Catholic population: 820.

St. Sophia's Primary School.

GATEHOUSE OF FLEET, Dumfries and Galloway, Church of the Resurrection (1971), Riverbank. Served from Kirkcudbright.

Sunday Mass: 10.45 a.m. Holy Days of Obligation, Vigil-Mass: 6 p.m.
Confessions: by appointment.   Ⓐ

GIRVAN, South Ayrshire, The Sacred Hearts of Jesus and Mary (1850, 1860), Harbour Lane.

Very Rev. Eugene Canon Mathews, J.C.L. (1946)
Rev. John Boyce, M.A., B.D. (1997)

POSTAL ADDRESS: Sacred Hearts, 17 Harbour Street, GIRVAN KA26 9AJ.
☎ Girvan (01465) 713331.

Sunday Masses: Vigil-Mass, 7 p.m.; 9, 11 a.m. Holy Days of Obligation,
Masses: 10 a.m., 7.30 p.m. Confessions: Saturday, 10.30 to 11 a.m., 6
to 7 p.m.; any time on request.   Ⓐ
Estimated Catholic population: 850.

SISTERS OF ST. JOSEPH OF CLUNY, ST. JOSEPH'S CONVENT, CLUNY COURT,
HENRIETTA STREET, GIRVAN KA26 9AL. ☎ GIRVAN (01465) 713673.
JERICHO BENEDICTINES, TROCHRAGUE GUEST HOUSE, GIRVAN KA26 9QA.
☎ GIRVAN (01465) 712074.
DAVIDSON COTTAGE HOSPITAL, ATTENDED FROM GIRVAN.
SACRED HEART PRIMARY SCHOOL.

GRETNA, Dumfries and Galloway, St. Ninian (1925, 1918), Victory Avenue. Served from Annan.

Sunday Mass: 4 p.m. Holy Days of Obligation, Mass. 11 a.m.
Confessions: before Sunday Mass.
Estimated Catholic population: 100.   ⚚ Ⓐ

HURLFORD, East Ayrshire, St. Paul (1883, 1913), Galston Road.

Rev. Gerard Magee (1985)

POSTAL ADDRESS: St. Paul's, 53 Galston Road, Hurlford, KILMARNOCK
KA1 5HT. ☎/Fax: Kilmarnock (01563) 525963.
E-mail:stpaulshurlford.freeserve.co.uk

Sunday Masses: Vigil-Mass, 6.30 p.m.; 10.30 a.m. Holy Days of
Obligation, Masses: Vigil-Mass, 7 p.m.; 10 a.m., 7 p.m. Confessions:
Saturday, after VigilMass.
Estimated Catholic population: 800   ⚚

CESSNOCK CARDENS RESIDENTIAL HOME, KERRMUIR HOSTEL FOR MENTALLY
HANDICAPPED AND TORRANCE LODGE NURSING HOME ATTENDED FROM ST.
PAUL'S.

IRVINE, North Ayrshire, St. John Ogilvie, Bourtreehill (1976, 1979), Crofthead, Village Centre.

Rev. John Dugdale, S.C.J. (1970)

POSTAL ADDRESS: St. John Ogilvie's, Village Centre, Bourtreehill, IRVINE KA11 1JX. ☎ Irvine (01294) 212587.
E-mail:J.Dugdale@tesco.net

Sunday Masses: Vigil-Mass, 6 p.m.;10.30 a.m., 5.30 p.m. Holy Days of Obligation, Masses: 10 a.m., 7.30 p.m. Confessions: Saturday, 10.30 to 11 a.m.; 5.15 to 5.45 p.m.,7 to 7.30 p.m.
Estimated Catholic population: 2,000.

MISSIONARY SISTERS OF OUR LADY OF AFRICA, 4 KILSYTH CRESCENT, BOURTREEHILL, IRVINE KA11 1JL. ☎ IRVINE (01294) 214158.
SHALOM NURSING HOME, Dreghorn, ATTENDED FROM ST. JOHN OGILVIE'S.
ST. JOHN OGILVIE'S PRIMARY SCHOOL.

IRVINE, North Ayrshire, St. Margaret of Scotland (1976, 1982), Castlepark Circle.

Rev. William Boyd (1984)

POSTAL ADDRESS: St. Mary's, West Road, IRVINE KA12 8RE. ☎ Irvine (01294) 279130/272852.

Sunday Mass: 10.30 a.m. Holy Days of Obligation, Mass: 7 p.m. Confessions: by appointment.
Estimated Catholic population: 700.

AYRSHIRE CENTRAL HOSPITAL AND CUMBRAE LODGE NURSING HOME., ATTENDED FROM ST. MARGARET'S.
(ST. MARK'S PRIMARY SCHOOL).

IRVINE, North Ayrshire, St. Mary (1862, 1875), West Road.

Rev. William Boyd (1984)

POSTAL ADDRESS: St. Mary's, West Road, IRVINE KA12 8RE. ☎ Irvine (01294) 279130/272852.

Sunday Masses: Vigil-Mass, 6.30 p.m.; 9 a.m., 12 noon. Holy Days of Obligation, Mass: 10 a.m. Confessions: Saturday, 10.30 to 11 a.m.,
Estimated Catholic population: 1,400.

RAVENSPARK HOSPITAL, SERVED FROM ST. MARY'S.
ST. MARK'S PRIMARY SCHOOL.

KILBIRNIE, North Ayrshire, St. Brigid (1862), Newton Street.

Very Rev. Alexander Canon McGarry (1958)

POSTAL ADDRESS: St. Brigid's, 30 Newton Street, KILBIRNIE KA25 6HW.
☎ Kilbirnie (01505) 682215.

Sunday Masses: Vigil-Mass, 6.30 p.m.; 11 a.m. Evening Service as announced. Holy Days of Obligation, Masses: 10 a.m., 7.30 p.m. Confessions: Saturday, 10.30 a.m., 5.30 to 6.15 p.m.
Estimated Catholic population: 1,200.

MONTGOMERIE COURT AND CONNELL COURT SERVED FROM ST. BRIGID'S.
ST. BRIDGET'S PRIMARY SCHOOL.

KILMARNOCK, East Ayrshire, St. Joseph (1847), Hill Street.

Very Rev. Denis F. Canon Quinlan (1958)

POSTAL ADDRESS: St. Joseph's, 15A Hill Street, KILMARNOCK KA3 1HA.
☎ Kilmarnock (01563) 521832; Fax: 01563-526628.

Sunday Masses: Vigil-Mass, 6 p.m.; 10 a.m., 12 noon. Holy Days of Obligation, Masses: Vigil-Mass, 7 p.m.; 10 a.m., 12.30 p.m. Confessions: Friday, after 10 a.m. Mass; Saturday, 9.20 to 9.45 a.m., 6.45 to 7.15 p.m.; on request.
Exposition of the Blessed Sacrament, Tuesday: 10.30 a.m. to 8 p.m.
Short Exposition with Benediction, Saturday, after 10 a.m. Mass.
Estimated Catholic population: 2,200.

CROSSHOUSE HOSPITAL. SUNDAY MASS: 3 P.M. CONFESSIONS: ON REQUEST. ☎ 01563-521133. CHAPLAINS:
    REV. GERARD MAGEE, HURLFORD. ☎ 01563-525963.;
    REV. DAVID BORLAND, ST. MICHAEL'S, KILMARNOCK.☎ 01563-525993.

NAZARETH HOUSE, HILL STREET, KILMARNOCK KA3 1HG. ☎ KILMARNOCK (01563) 522835. CHAPLAIN: RIGHT REV. MGR. FRANCIS CANON DUFFY (1938). ☎ KILMARNOCK (01563) 537872.
ARGYLL, DEAN, GRACELAND, GRANGE, HIGHFIELD, KIRKLEA, LIZDEAN, LONGPARK, ROSEBANK, SPRINGHILL STRATHLEA AND THORTOUN NURSING HOMES ATTENDED FROM ST. JOSEPH'S.
ST. COLUMBA'S PRIMARY SCHOOL.

KILMARNOCK, East Ayrshire, St. Matthew, New Farm Loch (1974, 1977), Grassyards Road.

Rev. Joseph Boland (1969)

POSTAL ADDRESS: St. Matthew's, Grassyards Road, New Farm Loch, KILMARNOCK KA3 7SH. ☎ Kilmarnock (01563) 533587; Fax:01563-550355.
E-mail: joe@rboland.freeserve.co.uk

Sunday Masses: Vigil-Mass, 6.30 p.m.; 9.30, 11 a.m. Holy Days of Obligation, Masses: 10 a.m., 11.30 a.m. (*in Primary School*), 7 p.m. Confessions: Saturday, 9.30 a.m., 6 p.m.; on request.
Estimated Catholic population: 900. [A]

KILMARNOCK PRISON, ATTENDED FROM ST. MATTHEW'S (MASS, THURSDAY, 7 P.M.)
ST. JOSEPH'S ACADEMY; ST. MATTHEW'S PRIMARY SCHOOL.

KILMARNOCK, East Ayrshire, St. Michael (1953), Treeswoodhead Road.

Rev. David M. Borland, B.D. *(Administrator)*(1998)

POSTAL ADDRESS: St. Michael's, Treeswoodhead Road, Bellfield, KILMARNOCK KA1 4NX. ☎ Kilmarnock (01563) 525993.

Sunday Masses: Vigil-Mass, 6 p.m.; 10 a.m. Holy Days of Obligation, Masses: 10 a.m., 7 p.m. Confessions: Saturday, after 10 a.m. Mass and after Vigil-Mass; at call.
Estimated Catholic population: 800.

CROSSHOUSE HOSPITAL, KIRKLANDSIDE HOSPITAL AND CRAIGIE NURSING HOME Kilmarnock, ATTENDED FROM ST. MICHAEL'S.
(ST. COLUMBA'S PRIMARY SCHOOL).

KILMARNOCK, East Ayrshire, Our Lady of Mount Carmel, Onthank (1963), Kirkton Road.

Rev. John Murphy, M.A. (1993)

POSTAL ADDRESS: Mount Carmel, Kirkton Road, Onthank, KILMARNOCK KA3 2DF. ☎ Kilmarnock (01563) 523822.

Sunday Masses: Vigil-Mass, 6.30 p.m.; 10 a.m. Holy Days of Obligation, Masses: as announced. Confessions: before any Mass; on request.
Exposition of the Blessed Sacrament: Wednesday and Friday, 10.30 a.m. to 1 p.m.
Estimated Catholic population: 1,500. [A]

HALLHOUSE NUSING HOME,Fenwick, ATTENDED FROM MOUNT CARMEL.
MOUNT CARMEL PRIMARY SCHOOL.

KILWINNING, North Ayrshire, St. Winin (1872, 1937), St.Winning's Lane.

Rev. Matthew F. McManus (1965)
Rev. Patrick Lawson (1996)

POSTAL ADDRESS: St. Winin's, St. Winning's Lane, Kilwinning KA13 6EP. ☎ Kilwinning (01294) 552276; Fax: 01294-558606.(Hall: ☎ 01294-558337.)
E-mail: st.winins@virgin.net
Wev Site:st.Winins.org.uk

Sunday Masses: Vigil-Mass, 6.30 p.m.; 10 a.m., 12 noon. Holy Days of Obligation, Masses: Vigil-Mass, 7.30 p.m.; 9, 11 (*St. Luke's School*) a.m., 7.30 p.m. Confessions: Saturday, 10.30 a.m., 5.30 p.m.
Estimated Catholic population: 3,500   .

SISTERS OF THE HOLY CROSS AND PASSION, 23 STEVENSTON ROAD, KILWINNING KA13 6LG. ☎ KILWINNING (01294) 552278.
BUCKREDDAN RETIREMENT HOME AND CHALYBEATE RETIREMENT FLATS ATTENDED FROM ST. WININ'S.
ST. LUKE'S PRIMARY SCHOOL; ST. WINNING'S PRIMARY SCHOOL; ST. MICHAEL'S ACADEMY.

KILWINNING, North Ayrshire, Sacred Heart Fathers (1970), Smithstone House of Prayer and Spirituality.

Very Rev. Constant Botter, S.C.J., *Superior* (1960)
Bro. John Cochrane, S.C.J.

POSTAL ADDRESS: Smithstone House, Dalry Road, KILWINNING KA13 6PL. ☎ Kilwinning (01294) 552515; Fax: 01294-559081.

For days or evenings of retreat, please contact the community.

KIRKCONNEL, Dumfries and Galloway, St. Conal (1921, 1922), Main Street. Served from St. Teresa's, Dumfries.

Sunday Mass: Vigil-Mass, 5.30 p.m. Holy Days of Obligation Mass: Vigil-Mass, 7 p.m.

KIRKCUDBRIGHT, Dumfries and Galloway, SS. Andrew and Cuthbert (1845, 1886), High Street.

Rev. Neil O'Donnell, B.A., B.D., Dip.Ed., Dip.R.E. (1991)

POSTAL ADDRESS: St. Andrew's and St. Cuthbert's, High Street, KIRKCUDBRIGHT DG6 4JW. ☎/Fax: Kirkcudbright (01557) 330687.

Sunday Mass: 9 a.m. Holy Days of Obligation, Mass: 9.30 a.m. Confessions: Saturday: 10.30 to 11 a.m. Estimated Catholic population: 450*. Ⓐ

KIRKCUDBRIGHT HOSPITAL AND MERSE HOUSE ATTENDED FROM KIRKCUDBRIGHT.
ST. CUTHBERT'S PRIMARY SCHOOL.

LANGHOLM, Dumfries and Galloway St. Francis (1960), Drove Road. Served from Annan.

Sunday Mass: 9 a.m. in Langholm Day Centre for the time being. Holy Days of Obligation, Vigil-Mass, 7.30 p.m., in Day Centre for the time being. Confessions: before Sunday Mass. Estimated Catholic population: 60.

THOMAS HOPE HOSPITAL AND DALARRAN NURSING HOME ATTENDED FROM ANNAN.

LARGS, North Ayrshire, St. Mary, Star of the Sea (1869, 1962), Greenock Road.

Rev. Alistair G. Tosh (1963)

POSTAL ADDRESS: St. Mary's, 28 Greenock Road, LARGS KA30 8NE. ☎ Largs (01475) 672324.
E-mail: user682215@aol.com

Sunday Masses: Vigil-Mass, 6.30 p.m.; 9, 11.30 a.m. Evening Service: as announced. Holy Days of Obligation, Masses: Vigil-Mass, 7 p.m.; 10 a.m., 7 p.m. Confessions:Friday, after 7 p.m. Mass; Saturday, after 10 a.m. Mass, after Vigil-Mass; on request.
Estimated Catholic population: 1,500. 🎵 ♿

BENEDICTINE ADORERS OF THE SACRED HEART (TYBURN NUNS), BENEDICTINE PRIORY, MACKERSTON PLACE, LARGS KA30 8BY. ☎ LARGS (01475) 687320.
SISTERS OF NOTRE DAME DE NAMUR, LINCLUDEN, 29 SHORE ROAD, SKELMORLIE PA17 5EH. ☎ WEMYSS BAY (01475) 520213.
BROOKSBY HOUSE HOSPITAL AND HAYLIE HOUSE AND ALL PRIVATE RESIDENTIAL HOMES IN LARGS AND SKELMORLIE ATTENDED FROM ST. MARY'S.
ST. MARY'S PRIMARY SCHOOL.

LOCKERBIE, Dumfries and Galloway, Holy Trinity (1968, 1874, 1972), High Street.

Rev. Gerald Donnelly, M.A. (1993)

POSTAL ADDRESS: The Presbytery, 1 Sherwood Crescent, LOCKERBIE DG11 2DY. ☎ Lockerbie (01576) 202563.

Sunday Masses: Vigil-Mass, 7 p.m.; 11.15 a.m. Holy Days of Obligation, Mass: 7.30 p.m. Confessions: Saturday, 6.15 to 6.45 p.m.; before and after any Mass.
Estimated Catholic population: 800.

LOCHMABEN HOSPITAL, Lochmaben, AND COTTAGE HOSPITAL, Moffat, ATTENDED FROM LOCKERBIE.
Parish previously known as St. Mungo's. Registers prior to 1972 are preserved at Holy Trinity, Lockerbie.

MAYBOLE, South Ayrshire, Our Lady and St. Cuthbert (1878), Dailly Road.

Rev. James Hayes (1993)

POSTAL ADDRESS: St. Cuthbert's Presbytery, 28 Dailly Road, MAYBOLE KA19 7AU. ☎/Fax:: Maybole (01655) 882145.

Sunday Masses: Vigil-Mass, 6.30 p.m.; 10 a.m. Holy Days of Obligation, Masses: 10 a.m., 7 p.m. Confessions: Saturday, before and after Vigil-Mass; on request.
Estimated Catholic population: 500.

MAYBOLE DAY HOSPITAL ATTENDED FROM MAYBOLE.
ST. CUTHBERT'S PRIMARY SCHOOL.

MILLPORT, Cumbrae, North Ayrshire, Our Lady of Perpetual Succour (1939, 1958), College Street.

Rev. John A. Collins (1969)

POSTAL ADDRESS: The Presbytery, 1 George Street, MILLPORT KA28 0BG. ☎ Millport (01475) 530537.

Sunday Mass: Vigil-Mass, 7 p.m.; 10 a.m. (*September to Easter*); 9 a.m., 12 noon (*Easter to September*). Holy Days of Obligation, Masses: Vigil-Mass, 7 p.m.; 10 a.m., 7 p.m. Confessions: before and after Masses; on request.
Estimated Catholic population: 80.

LADY MARGARET HOSPITAL, CRAIG-EN-ROS, MANSEWOOD, MILLBURN AND TOWERS HOMES FOR THE ELDERLY, ATTENDED FROM MILLPORT.

MOFFAT, Dumfries and Galloway, St. Luke (1886), Mansfield Place. Served from Lockerbie.

Sunday Mass: 9.30 a.m. Holy Days of Obligation, Mass: 6 p.m. Confessions: before and after Mass.

MONIAIVE, Dumfries and Galloway, Maxwelton Chapel. Served from St. Teresa's, Dumfries.

MOSSBLOWN, South Ayrshire, St. Ann (1898), Annbank Road.

Rev. John McLean, B.A., M.Sc., A.T.I. (1987)

POSTAL ADDRESS: St. Ann's, 27 Annbank Road, Mossblown, AYR KA6 5DZ. ☎ Annbank (01292) 520204.

Sunday Masses: Vigil-Mass, 6.15 p.m.; 11 a.m. Holy Days of Obligation, Masses: 9.30 a.m., 7.30 p.m. Confessions: Saturday, 5.30 to 6 p.m.
Estimated Catholic population: 450.

TEMPLE HOUSE NURSING HOME SERVED FROM ST. ANN'S.
ST. ANN'S PRIMARY SCHOOL.

MUIRKIRK, East Ayrshire, St. Thomas, Apostle (1856, 1906), Wellwood Street.

Rev. William R. McFadden, Ph.B., S.T.L., M.S. (1985)

POSTAL ADDRESS: St. John's, 92 Glaisnock Street, CUMNOCK KA18 1JU.
☎/Fax: Cumnock (01290) 421031.
E-mail: wrmcf299@aol.com

Sunday Mass: 10 a.m. Holy Days of Obligation, Masses: 9.30 a.m., 7p.m. Confessions: on request.
Estimated Catholic population: 150.

(ST. JOHN'S PRIMARY SCHOOL, Cumnock)

NEW ABBEY, Dumfries and Galloway, St. Mary (1815, 1825). Served from St. Andrew's, Dumfries.

Sunday Mass: 10 a.m. Confessions on request.   Ⓐ

NEWTON STEWART, Wigtownshire, Dumfries and Galloway, Our Lady and St. Ninian (1825, 1876), Windsor Road.

Rev. David A. Conroy, M.A., M.M.S., I.M.S.(Dip.) (1992)

POSTAL ADDRESS: St. Ninian's Presbytery, Windsor Road, NEWTON STEWART DG8 6HP. ☎/ Fax: Newton Stewart (01671) 402182.

Sunday Mass: 10 a.m. Holy Days of Obligation, Masses: Vigil-Mass, 7.30 p.m.; 10 a.m. Confessions: Friday after Mass.
Estimated Catholic population: 430* (including Whithorn).

H. M. PRISON PENNINGHAM, NEWTON STEWART HOSPITAL, CORNWALL PARK HOME AND CUMLODEN MANOR NURSING HOME, Newton Stewart, ATTENDED FROM ST. NINIAN'S .
WHITHORN AND WIGTOWN SERVED FROM NEWTON STEWART.
ST. NINIAN'S PRIMARY SCHOOL.

PATNA, East Ayrshire. See Waterside.

PRESTWICK, South Ayrshire, St. Quivox (1938, 1933), St. Quivox Road.

Rev. Patrick McSorley　(1960)

POSTAL ADDRESS: St. Quivox, 34 St. Quivox Road, PRESTWICK KA9 1LU. ☎/ Fax: Prestwick (01292) 478068.

Sunday Masses: 10, 11.30 a.m., 6 p.m. Holy Days of Obligation, Masses: 9 a.m., 7.30 p.m. Confessions: Saturday, 9.30 to 10 a.m., 7 to 7.30 p.m.
Estimated Catholic population: 1,200.

FRANCISCAN SISTERS OF THE IMMACULATE CONCEPTION, 4 LAIGHLAND, PRESTWICK KA9 2JE. ☎ PRESTWICK (01292) 475016.
BIGGART HOSPITAL SERVED FROM ST. QUIVOX.
ST. NINIAN'S PRIMARY SCHOOL.

SALTCOATS, North Ayrshire, St. Brendan (1965), Corrie Crescent.

Rev. Edward McGhee, M.Ed.　(1972)

POSTAL ADDRESS: St. Brendan's, 63 Corrie Crescent, SALTCOATS KA21 6JN. ☎/ Fax: Saltcoats (01294) 463843.

Sunday Masses: Vigil-Mass, 6.30 p.m.; 10 a.m., 12 noon. Holy Days of Obligation, Masses: 9 a.m., 7 p.m. Confessions: Saturday, 10 a.m., after Vigil-Mass.
Estimated Catholic population: 1,200.

ARRAN VIEW NURSING HOME ATTENDED FROM ST. BRENDAN'S.
ST. ANTHONY'S PRIMARY SCHOOL.

SALTCOATS, North Ayrshire, Our Lady, Star of the Sea (1853, 1856), Ardrossan Road.

Rev. Eamonn Flynn　(1966)

POSTAL ADDRESS: Our Lady, Star of the Sea, 10 Ardrossan Road, SALTCOATS KA21 5BW. ☎ Saltcoats (01294) 463461.

Sunday Masses: 10 a.m., 12 noon, 6.30 p.m. Evening Service: as announced. Holy Days of Obligation, Masses: Vigil-Mass, 7 p.m.; 10 a.m., 7 p.m. Confessions: Friday, 6.15 p.m., Saturday, 10.30 a.m.
Estimated Catholic population: 1,400.

SEABANK NURSING HOME, BARNETT COURT, CANAL COURT AND EGLINTON COURT SERVED FROM OUR LADY, STAR OF THE SEA.
ST. ANDREW'S ACADEMY; (ST. ANTHONY'S PRIMARY SCHOOL).

SANQUHAR, Dumfries and Galloway. See Kirkconnel.

SOUTHERNESS, Dumfries and Galloway. See Dalbeattie.

STEVENSTON, North Ayrshire, St. John (1905, 1963), Hayocks Road.

Rev. Martin Chambers, S.T.B. (1989)
Sr. Eithne Foley, *Pastoral Assistant*
Sr. Rita Deegan, *Pastoral Assistant*

POSTAL ADDRESS: St. John's, Hayocks Road, STEVENSTON KA20 4DE. ☎ Stevenston (01294) 463225.

Sunday Masses: Vigil-Mass, 6.30 p.m., 9.30, 11.30 a.m. Holy Days of Obligation, Masses: 10 a.m., 7 p.m. Confessions: Saturday, after Masses
Estimated Catholic population: 2,200..

MISSIONARY SISTERS OF ST. COLUMBAN, 4 KERELAW AVENUE, STEVENSTON KA20 4EH. ☎ STEVENSTON (01294) 603913
AFTON COURT, BONNIE LESLIE COURT, CALEY COURT AND KERELAW RESIDENTIAL SCHOOL ATTENDED FROM ST. JOHN'S.
ST. JOHN'S PRIMARY SCHOOL.

STEWARTON, East Ayrshire, Our Lady and St. John (1974) Lainshaw Street (Parish of Our Lady of Mount Carmel, Kilmarnock).

Rev. John Murphy, M.A. (1993)
Sr. Teresa Nolan, S.M.R. *(Pastoral Co-ordinator).*

POSTAL ADDRESS: Our Lady and St. John's, Lainshaw Street, Stewarton, KILMARNOCK KA3 5BX. ☎ Stewarton (01560) 483322.

Sunday Masses: Vigil-Mass, 5 p.m.; 11.45 a.m. Holy Days of Obligation, Masses: as announced. Confessions: on request.
Estimated Catholic population: 900.

SISTERS OF MARIE REPARATRICE, OUR LADY AND ST. JOHN'S, LAINSHAW STREET, STEWARTON. KILMARNOCK KA3 5BX ☎ STEWARTON (01560) 483322.
MANSFIELD NURSING HOME ATTENDED FROM OUR LADY AND ST. JOHN'S.
MOUNT CARMEL PRIMARY SCHOOL, Kilmarnock.

STRANRAER, Wigtownshire, Dumfries and Galloway, St. Joseph (1846, 1853), Lewis Street.

Rev. Stephen Latham (1997)

POSTAL ADDRESS: St. Joseph's, Lewis Street, STRANRAER DG9 7AL. ☎ Stranraer (01776) 703125; Fax: 01776-706523.
E-mail:latham@calnet.uk.com

Sunday Masses: Vigil-Mass, 6.30 p.m.; 10 a.m. Holy Days of Obligation, Masses: 9.30 a.m., 7.30 p.m. Confessions: Saturday, 10.30 to 11 a.m.; by arrangement.
Estimated Catholic population: 700.　　　　　　　　　　　　　🅰

> SISTERS OF ST. JOSEPH OF CLUNY, ST. JOSEPH'S CONVENT, LEWIS STREET, STRANRAER DG9 7AL. ☎ STRANRAER (01776) 702856.
> GARRICK HOSPITAL AND DALRYMPLE HOSPITAL, ATTENDED FROM ST. JOSEPH'S.
> ST. JOSEPH'S PRIMARY SCHOOL.

THORNHILL, Dumfries and Galloway. Served from St. Teresa's, Dumfries.

TROON, South Ayrshire, Our Lady of the Assumption and St. Meddan (1883, 1911), St. Meddan's Street.

Rev. Archibald Brown, S.T.B., B.A. (1972)

POSTAL ADDRESS: Our Lady and St. Meddan's, 4 Cessnock Road, TROON KA10 6NJ. ☎ Troon (01292) 313541.

Sunday Masses: Vigil-Mass, 6 p.m.; 9, 11.15 a.m. Holy Days of Obligation, Masses: 10 a.m., 7 p.m. Confessions: after both Masses on Saturday.
Estimated Catholic population: 1,750.　　　　　　🐦　🅰

> ALL NURSING HOMES IN TROON ATTENDED FROM OUR LADY AND ST. MEDDAN'S.
> ST. PATRICK'S PRIMARY SCHOOL.

WATERSIDE, Dunaskin, East Ayrshire, St. Francis Xavier (1860, 1895), Dalmellington Road. Served from St. Paul's, Ayr.

Right Rev. Mgr. Joseph V. Canon Boyd, V.G. (1957)
Rev. Stephen J. Cochrane, B.Sc., M.A., B.D. (1998)

POSTAL ADDRESS: St. Paul's, 2 Peggieshill Place, Belmont, AYR KA7 3RF.
☎ Ayr (01292) 260197.

Sunday Masses: Vigil-Mass, 1st, 3rd and 5th Sunday, 6 p.m.; 2nd and 4th Sunday, 10 a.m. Holy Days of Obligation, Masses: morning Mass in St. Xavier's School, during school term; 6.30 p.m. Confessions, before Mass.
Estimated Catholic population: 400   Ⓐ

GLEBE HOUSE NURSING HOME AND KNOWE VIEW NURSING HOME, Dalmellington, AND BURNFOOT NURSING HOME AND DOONBANK NURSING HOME, Patna, ATTENDED FROM ST. PAUL'S, AYR.
ST. XAVIER'S PRIMARY SCHOOL.

WEST KILBRIDE, North Ayrshire, St. Bride (1947, 1908) Hunterston Road.

Very Rev. Samuel Canon McGinness (1956)

POSTAL ADDRESS: St. Bride's, 9 Hunterston Road, WEST KILBRIDE KA23 9EX. ☎/Fax: West Kilbride (01294) 823188.

Sunday Masses: Vigil-Mass, 6.30 p.m.; 10.30 a.m. Holy Days of Obligation, Mass: 7.30 p.m. Confessions: Saturday, after Vigil-Mass.
Estimated Catholic population: 400.

(ST. PETER'S PRIMARY SCHOOL, Ardrossan).

WHITHORN, Wigtownshire, Dumfries and Galloway, St. Martin and St. Ninian (1880, 1960), George Street.

Rev. David A. Conroy, M.A., M.M.S., I.M.S.(Dip.) (1992)

POSTAL ADDRESS: St. Ninian's Presbytery, George Street, Whithorn, NEWTON STEWART DG8 8PZ. ☎ Whithorn (01988) 500396; Newton Stewart (01671) 402182.

Sunday Mass, 12 noon. Holy Days of Obligation, Mass: 7.30 p.m. Confessions: after weekday Mass.
Estimated Catholic population: cf. Newton Stewart.　　　　　　Ⓐ

WIGTOWN, Dumfries and Galloway, The Sacred Heart (1879), South Main Street. Served from Newton Stewart.
Sunday Vigil-Mass, 6 p.m. Holy Days of Obligation, Mass: 6 p.m. Confessions: Saturday, after Mass.

ALL SOULS PRIMARY SCHOOL.

RETIRED PRIESTS OF THE DIOCESE

Very Rev. Mgr. Thomas K. Canon Conway, 3 Essex Park Cottages, Kellwood Place, Georgetown, DUMFRIES DG1 4JA. Tel: Dumfries (01387) 267039.

Very Rev. John J. Canon Crowley, 68 Homemount House, Gogoside Road, LARGS KA30 9LS. ☎ Largs (01475) 686991.

Very Rev. John Canon Donnelly, 41 Overmills Road, AYR KA7 3LH. ☎ Ayr (01292) 285865.

Right Rev. Mgr. Francis Canon Duffy, Nazareth House, 23 Hill Street, KILMARNOCK KA3 1HG. ☎ Kilmarnock (01563) 537872.

Right Rev. Mgr. Stephen Canon Kennedy, 15 Dalmellington Road, AYR KA7 3TH ☎ Ayr (01292) 286001.

Rev. John Kerr, c/o Candida Casa, 8 Corsehill Road, Ayr KA7 2ST. Very Rev. George Canon McCafferty, 18 Solway Place, TROON KA10 7EJ. ☎ Troon (01292) 314989.

Rev. Thomas McCann, 25 Monro Avenue, DUMFRIES DG1 4YH. ☎ Dumfries (01387) 251611.

Very Rev. Thomas J. Canon McGread, 4 Southbrae Drive, GLASGOW G13 1PX. ☎ 0141-576 8766.

Rev. Ralph Mancini, 1 Oakfield Drive, Georgetown, DUMFRIES DG1 4PD. ☎ Dumfries (01387)263047.

Rev. F. Paul G. Moore, 40 Woodcroft Avenue, LARGS KA30 9EW. ☎ Largs (01475) 673177.

Rev. F. Gilmour Ommer, 464 Downall Green, North Ashton, WIGAN WN4 0NA. ☎ 01942-721712.

Rev. John Walsh, 31 Mansfield Road, PRESTWICK KA9 2DN. ☎ Prestwick (01292) 476179.

SCHOOL CHAPLAINS

Ayr, Queen Margaret Academy	Rev. James Hayes.
Dumfries, St. Joseph's College	Rev. Gerald Donnelly & Rev. Stephen Sharkey.
Kilmarnock, St. Joseph's Academy	
Kilwinning, St. Michael's Academy	
Saltcoats, St. Andrew's Academy	Rev. Edward McGhee

INSTITUTES OF CONSECRATED LIFE
AND
SOCIETIES OF APOSTOLIC LIFE

MEN

SACRED HEART FATHERS (ST. QUENTIN) (1970)

(1970) Smithstone House, Dalry Road, KILWINNING KA13 6PL.
☎ Kilwinning (01294) 552515; Fax: 01294-559081.

(1976) St. John Ogilvie's, Village Centre, Bourtreehill, IRVINE KA11
1JX. ☎ Irvine (01294) 212587.

JERICHO BENEDICTINES (1994)

Trochrague Guest House, GIRVAN KA26 9QB.
☎ Girvan (01465) 712074.

MARIST BROTHERS (1872)

(1873) Craigs House, Craigs Road, DUMFRIES DG1 4OL.
☎ Dumfries (01387) 269473.

WOMEN

BENEDICTINE ADORERS OF THE SACRED HEART OF JESUS
MONTMARTRE
(TYBURN NUNS) (1992)

(1988) Benedictine Priory, Mackerston Place, LARGS KA30 8BY.
☎ Largs (01475) 687320.

DAUGHTERS OF CHARITY OF ST. VINCENT DE PAUL (1892)

St. Vincent's Convent, Brooke Street, DUMFRIES DG1 2JL.
☎ Dumfries (01387) 254093.

FRANCISCANS OF THE IMMACULATE CONCEPTION (1982)

Franciscan Convent, 25 McKellar Avenue, ARDROSSAN KA22 7AS.
☎ Ardrossan (01294) 603457.

(1998) Franciscan Convent, 4 Laighland, PRESTWICK KA9 2JE.
☎ Prestwick (01292)475016

MISSIONARY SISTERS OF OUR LADY OF AFRICA (1991)
(THE WHITE SISTERS)

Missionary Sisters of Our Lady of Africa, 4-5 Kilsyth Crescent,
Bourtreehill, IRVINE KA11 1JL. ☎ Irvine (01294) 214158.

MISSIONARY SISTERS OF ST. COLUMBAN (1992)

Missionary Sisters of St. Columban, 4 Kerelaw Avenue, STEVENSTON KA20 4EH. ☎ Stevenston (01294) 603913.

SOCIETY OF MARIE REPARATRICE (1987)

(1999) Sisters of Marie Reparatrice, 69 Lainshaw Street, Stewarton, KILMARNOCK KA3 5BX
☎ Kilmarnock (01560) 483322.

SISTERS OF THE MOST HOLY CROSS AND PASSION (1896)

(1985) Monkrigg, 23 Stevenston Road, KILWINNING KA13 6LG.
☎ Kilwinning (01294) 552278.

SISTERS OF NOTRE DAME DE NAMUR (1902)

(1902) Notre Dame Apostolic Centre, Lincluden, 29 Shore Road, SKELMORLIE PA17 5EH. ☎ Wemyss Bay (01475) 520213.

(1983) Sisters of Notre Dame, 6 Carnegie Street, DUMFRIES DG1 1PD. ☎ Dumfries (01387) 263394.

(1999) 55 St. Phillans Avenue, AYR KA7 3DD.
☎ Ayr (01292) 290689.

SISTERS OF ST. JOSEPH OF CLUNY (1879)

(1879) St. Joseph's Convent, Cluny Court, Henrietta Street, GIRVAN KA26 9AL. ☎ Girvan (01465) 713673; Fax: 01465-712248.

(1897) St. Joseph's Convent, Lewis Street, STRANRAER DG9 7AL.
☎ Stranraer (01776) 702856.

(1992) St. Ninian's, 30 Meadowpark, AYR KA7 2LR.
☎/Fax:: Ayr (01292) 263518.

POOR SISTERS OF NAZARETH (1890)

(1902) Nazareth House, 23 Hill Street, KILMARNOCK KA1 3HG.
☎ Kilmarnock (01563) 522835; Fax: 01563-574980..

Chaplain: Right Rev. Mgr. Francis Canon Duffy (1938).
☎ Kilmarnock (01563) 537872.

MIXED

MARISTS

Marist Centre, Kinharvie House, New Abbey, DUMFRIES DG2 8DZ. ☎ New Abbey (01387) 850433; Fax: 01387-850465.
E-mail: kinharvieh@aol.com

Archdiocese of Glasgow

Specialis filia romanae ecclesiae

Archbishop and Metropolitan
His Eminence Cardinal Thomas Joseph Winning
K.C.*H.S., S.T.L., D.C.L., D.D., D.Univ., LL.D., F.E.I.S.

Born at Wishaw, 3rd June, 1925; educated at Our Lady's High School, Motherwell; St. Mary's College, Blairs; St. Peter's College, Bearsden; Scots College, Rome (S.T.L., 1949, Gregorian University, Rome); ordained priest at Rome, 18th December, 1948, assistant priest, Chapelhall, 1949-50; Scots College, Rome (D.C.L. *cum laude* 1953, Gregorian University, Rome), assistant priest, St. Mary, Hamilton, 1953-57, Cathedral, Motherwell, 1957-58; chaplain, Franciscans of the Immaculate Conception, Bothwell, 1958-61; diocesan secretary, Motherwell, 1956-61; spiritual director, Scots College, Rome, 1961-1966; advocate of the Sacred Roman Rota, 1965; parish priest, St. Luke's, Motherwell, 1966-1970; officialis and vicar episcopal of Motherwell diocese, 1966-1970; first president Scottish Catholic Marriage Tribunal, 1970, nominated titular bishop of Louth (and auxiliary bishop), 22nd October 1971, and ordained by James Donald Scanlan, archbishop of Glasgow, at Glasgow, 30th November, 1971; parish priest, Our Holy Redeemer's, Clydebank, 1972-1974; translated to Glasgow, 23rd April 1974; honorary D.D. (University of Glasgow) 1983, honorary Fellow of the Educational Institute of Scotland, 1986, Grand Prior of the Scottish Lieutenancy of the Equestrian Order of the Holy Sepulchre of Jerusalem, 1989; honorary D.Univ. (University of Strathclyde), 1992; created Cardinal Priest of the title of S. Andrea delle Fratte, 26th November 1994; honorary LL.D. (University of Aberdeen), 1996; honorary Professor of Faculty of Divinity (University of Glasgow) 1996.

Residence: 40 Newlands Road, GLASGOW G43 2JD

VICAR GENERAL

Right Rev. Mgr. James T. Canon Clancy, Ph.L., S.T.B.,
Saint Andrew's Cathedral, 90 Dunlop Street, Glasgow, G1 4ER Tel: 0141-221 3096
email: JClancy-VG@rcag.org.uk

THE DIOCESAN CURIA

---

*"The diocesan curia consists of those institutions and persons which furnish assistance to
the bishop in the governance of the entire diocese, especially in directing pastoral activity,
in providing for the administration of the diocese and in exercising judicial power." (The
Code of Canon Law, canon 469)*

Curial Offices:
Address:
> *Curial Offices, 196 Clyde Street, Glasgow, G1 4JY.*
> *Telephone: 0141-226 5898. Fax: 0141-225 2600.*

E-mail

> *In addition to these general email addresses, individual addresses are given after the
> names of those who have a direct email address. Please check in individual departments
> if you wish to email a specific person directly.*

Curia:	Curia@rcag.org.uk
Estates Office:	Estates@rcag.org.uk
Flourish:	Flourish@rcag.org.uk
Finance:	Finance@rcag.org.uk
Pastoral Office:	PastoralOffice@rcag.org.uk
Personnel Office:	PersonnelOffice@rcag.org.uk
Religious Education:	RE@rcag.org.uk
Social Care:	Social-care@rcag.org.uk

Homepage   http:\\www.rcag.org.uk

> *All official communications should be addressed to "The Chancellor" All press
> inquiries should be made through the national Press Office or the Director of
> Communications at the above address and telephone number*

> *The Curial Offices are opened on weekdays from 9.00am to 5.00pm. The offices
> are closed on Holy Days (Christmas Day, Holy Thursday, Good Friday,
> Ascension Thursday, St. Peter and Paul, Assumption, All Saints, Saint Andrew's
> Day) and on Public Holidays.*

The Episcopal Council:

The Cardinal, The Vicar General, The Vicars Episcopal

Moderator of the Curia and Chancellor:

Rt. Rev. Mgr. Peter Smith, JCL, (Chancellor@rcag.org.uk)
Tel: Office 0141-226 5898; Home Phone and Fax: 0141-810 4976

Vice-Chancellor:

Sister Mary Veronica McGrath OSF, MA (Vice-Chancellor@rcag.org.uk)

PASTORAL BRANCH

Pastoral Office:

Pastoral Offices, 196 Clyde Street, Glasgow, G1 4JY.
Tel: 0141-226 5898.   Fax No: 0141 225 2600

Email: PastoralOffice@rcag.org.uk

Unless otherwise noted, all Pastoral Commission, Ecclesial Agencies and Support Groups may be contacted at the above address.

Where a priest is named as head of a commission or agency, he may be contacted through his parish.

Vicar Episcopal for Pastoral Action:

Rev. Paul M. Conroy, Ph.L, STL (VE-Pastoral@rcag.org.uk)

Assistant: Rev. Paul Murray, B.Sc., Ph.B., S.T.L. (Assist-VE@rcag.org.uk)

Secretary: Miss Christina O'Donnell (Secretary-Pastoral@rcag.org.uk)

Youth Development Officer: Chris Docherty BA (Hons), P.G.C.C.Y.S. (Youth@rcag.org.uk)

Diocesan Pastoral Team:

The Cardinal, Rev. Paul Conroy, Rev. David Brown, Rev. Paul Murray, Rev. James Lawlor, Sr. Terry O'Byrne, Mrs. Patricia Sheridan, Mr. Russel Rodger, Mrs. Irene McCann, Mr. Michael Murphy, Rev. Gerard Nugent, Rev. Joseph Mackle, Sr. Bridget McNally, Mr. David Quail

The Pastoral Action of the Diocese is divided into three types of group according to their function. (Approved by Diocesan Pastoral Council, October 4th, 1997)

Commissions: The Pastoral Commissions discern needs, plan and programme within a specific area in the pastoral life of the diocese.

Agencies: Ecclesial Agencies provide the means and the resources that enable commissions to achieve their targets.

Support Groups: Support groups provide the opportunity to associate togethe and for mutual support to different vocational groups and to those who hav particular needs within the community.

PASTORAL COMMISSIONS

Pastoral Commissions discern needs, plan and programme within a specific area in the pastoral life of the diocese. (Cf. Book of Structures: Card 15.3)

Department 1 - Pastoral Care of Community (Rev. Paul Murray)

Pastoral Care of All as Community	Rev. Paul Murray
Pastoral Care of Neighbourhood Groups	to be appointed
Pastoral Care of the Family	Mrs. Josephine McMahon

Department 2 - Pastoral Care of Specific Groups (Right Rev. Mgr. John Gilmartin)

Diocesan Youth Movement	Rev. Paul McAlinden - Pastoral Office

Department 3 - Church in Dialogue with Others (Rev. Peter Sweeney)

Church in Dialogue with Others	Rev. Peter Sweeney - St. John Ogilvie's

Department 4 - Specific Pastoral Services (Mr. David Ramsay)

Commission for Catechesis	to be appointed
Catholic Schools Commission	Mrs. Anna Keegan
Liturgy Commission	Rev. Andrew McKenzie - Scotus College
Social Care Commission	Miss Agnes Malone

Justice and Peace Commission	to be appointed
Commission for Mission Awareness	to be appointed

Department 5 - Pastoral Care for Ministries (Rev. Michael Conroy)

Commission for Doctrinal Formation	Rev. Joseph Sullivan
Commission for Ministry to Priests	Rev. William McGinley – Saint Conval's
Commission for Vocations	Rt. Rev. Mgr. James Ryan - Saint Peter's, Partick

Department 6 - Support Structures (Rev. Paul Conroy)

Commission for Social Communication	Mr. Ronnie Convery
Commission for Finance & Fabric	Rev. Joseph Coyle
Commission for the fora of dialogue	To be appointed

ECCLESIAL AGENCIES...SERVING PASTORAL PLANNING

Ecclesial Agencies provide the means and resources that enable commissions to achieve their targets.

Adult Faith Development	Rev. Brian Reilly
Approval of Catholic Teachers	Apply to Personnel Office
Archdiocesan Pro-Life and Bishops' Conference of Scotland, Pro-Life	Miss Roseanne Reddy - Pro Life Office 274 Bath Street Glasgow G2 4JR. Tel: 0141.332.8220
Catholic Marriage Care	Mrs. M. McGuigan
Church Music (G.A.C.M.A.)	Right Rev. Mgr. P. G. Fitzpatrick - St Leo's

Council for Christians and Jews	Rev. Brian Reilly
Doctrinal Resources	Rev. Joseph Sullivan
Families 2000	Sr. Mary Agnes S.N.D.
Family Faith Agency	Sr. Doreen Grant S.N.D. Family Faith Centre, 694 Balmore Road, Glasgow, G22 6QS. Tel: 0141-347 0637
Glasgow Churches Together *This Ecumenical body was formally inaugurated on 1st September, 1991. The Archdiocese of Glasgow takes full part in Glasgow Churches Together, and is represented by six members in the central group.*	Chairman: Rt. Rev. Mgr. J. Noel Woods, M.P.S. Address: C/o The Presbytery of Glasgow, 260 Bath Street, Glasgow, G2 4JP Tel/Fax: 0141 332 6606 Email: COFS.Glasgow.Presbytery@dail.pipex.com
Information and Resources	Mr. Ronald P. Convery, M.A. (Hons.)
Liturgical Resources	Rev. Andrew McKenzie - Scotus College
Mass Media	Mr. Ronald P. Convery, M.A. (Hons.)
Ministry to Priests	Rev. William McGinley – Saint Conval's
Fertility Care Scotland	Mrs. Lucille McQuade
R.C.I.A.	Rev. Andrew McKenzie – Scotus College
R.E. Centre	Rev. Brian Reilly
S.P.R.E.D.	Sr. Agnes Nelson
SERRA	Mr. Alec Duncan
Spiritual & Pastoral Formation of Pastoral Workers	Diocesan Pastoral Team
Spirituality of the Diocesan Community	Diocesan Pastoral Team

St Margaret's Child and Family Care Society	Contact: The Chairman 274 Bath Street Glasgow G2 4JR.
Support of the Terminally Ill	Miss Agnes Malone
Victims of Child Abuse	Mr. David Ramsay
Vocations Promotion	Rt. Rev. Mgr. James Ryan - Vocations Director
Youth	Mr. Chris Docherty

SUPPORT GROUPS

Support Groups provide the opportunity to associate together and for mutual support to different vocational groups and to those who have particular needs within the diocesan community. They can be contacted through the Pastoral Office

Beginning Experience
Bereavement Support
Doctors' Guild
Health Care Workers
Nurses' Guild
Police Guild
SCIM
Support for Older People
Teachers' Guild
Union of Catholic Mothers

ADMINISTRATIVE BRANCH

The following departments are all situated in the Archdiocesan Offices, 196 Clyde Street, Glasgow, G1 4JY.
Tel: 0141-226 5898 Fax: 0141-225 2600

All official communications should be addressed to "The Chancellor"

Vicar Episcopal for Administrative Affairs:

Rt. Rev. Mgr. Peter Smith, JCL (Chancellor@rcag.org.uk)

Directors:

> *As well as responsibility for their own department, as listed below, the Directors have responsibility within their own competence for the relevant aspects of every administrative department.*

Director of Care Services – Mr. David Ramsay
(Director-Care@rcag.org.uk)
Director of Development - Mr. Kenneth Crilley,
A.R.I.C.S., Dip. Proj. Man (Director-Development@rcag.org.uk)
Director of Finance - Miss Louise Devine, B. Acc., C.A.
(Director-Finance@rcag.org.uk)
Director of Personnel - Miss Sue Jardine, B.Sc. (Hons), M.I.P.M.
(Director-Personnel@rcag.org.uk)
Director of Communications – Mr. Ronald P. Convery
(Director-Communications@rcag.org.uk)

1. APPROVAL OF CATHOLIC TEACHERS:
Email: Approval@rcag.org.uk

> *All applications for Catholic Teacher Approval should be addressed to the Personnel Department*

2. ARCHIVES:
E-mail Archives@rcag.org.uk

Archivist:

Right Rev. Mgr. Hugh N. Canon Boyle, Ph. L., S.T.L., F.S.A.Scot.
Assistant: Miss Mary McHugh, B. A., M. Litt., Ph.D, LL.B, F.S.A.Scot.

3. COMMUNICATIONS OFFICE:
Director of Communications:

Mr. P. Ronald P. Convery, M.A. (Hons.) (Director-Communications@rcag.org.uk)

Archdiocesan Newspaper:

Flourish, 196 Clyde Street, Glasgow, G1 4JY.
Tel: 0141-226 5898. Fax No: 0141-225 2600

Email: Flourish@rcag.org.uk

Editor:

Mr. Vincent Toal (Editor-Flourish@rcag.org.uk)

Secretary: Mrs. Mary McMahon (Secretary-Flourish@rcag.org.uk)

4. DEVELOPMENT AND ESTATES OFFICE

Email: Estates@rcag.org.uk

Director of Development:

Mr. Kenneth Crilley, A.R.I.C.S., Dip. Proj. Man.
(Director-Development@rcag.org.uk)

Fabric and Planning Board:

The Cardinal, Right. Rev. Mgr. James T. Clancy, V.G.; Very. Rev. Michael Canon Mooney; Rev. Joseph Coyle; Rt. Rev. Mgr. Patrick Osborne, Rev. Andrew McKenzie.

Matters for the attention of the Fabric and Planning Board should be addressed to "The Chancellor"

Estates Officers:

Mr. Kevin Moran, B.Eng. (Hons)   Mr. Malcolm MacAulay
(Kevin.Moran@rcag.org.uk)   (Calum.MacAulay@rcag.org.uk)

Health and Safety Advisor

Health and Safety matters should be brought to the attention of the Estates Department.

St. Peter's Cemetery

Manager: Mr. Liam McGrath, Tel: 0141-778 1183 (Dalbeth@rcag.org.uk)

Administrative Assistance:

Miss Sharon Scullion (Sharon.Scullion@rcag.org.uk)

5. Finance Section
Treasurer:

Very Rev. Michael Canon Mooney

Assistant Treasurer: Rt. Rev. Mgr. Owen Gallagher

Director of Finance:

Miss Louise Devine, B. Acc., C.A. (Director-Finance@rcag.org.uk)

Managers: Mrs. Kathleen Barratt (Kathleen.Barratt@rcag.org.uk)
Miss Maureen Walsh (Maureen.Walsh@rcag.org.uk)

Sales Ledger Administrator: Miss Donna Hendry
(Donna.Hendry@rcag.org.uk)
Purchase Ledger Administrator: Miss Margaret Kelly
(Margaret.Kelly@rcag.org.uk)

Payroll Administrator: Mrs. Maureen Gallagher
(Maureen.Gallagher@rcag.org.uk)

Covenant Administrator: Mrs. Joanne McLeod
(Covenant@rcag.org.uk)

Finance Council:

The Cardinal, Right Rev. Mgr. James T. Clancy, V.G., Very Rev.
Michael Canon Mooney, Rt. Rev. Mgr. Owen Gallagher, Miss Eleanor
Donnachie, Prof. Alfred L. Brown, K.C.S.G., Mr. Kevin Sweeney, C.A.,
Ll.B., Rev. Peter Gallacher

Finance Co-ordinating Group:

Rev. John McAuley, Very Rev. Michael Canon Mooney, Rt. Rev. Mgr.
Owen Gallagher, Rev. Noel Barry; Right. Rev. Mgr. Daniel Hart; Rev.
Thomas Hendry; Rev. Denis Hurley; Rev. Edward Kelly; Very. Rev.
William Canon Tobin.

7. Liturgical Celebrations
Email: Liturgy@rcag.org.uk

*In organising and preparing for Diocesan Liturgical Celebrations and Liturgies
involving the Cardinal parishes and organisations are required to consult with the
Director of Liturgy and/or the Diocesan Master of Ceremonies.   Concelebration
Vestments and Chalices may also be arranged through the under-noted offices.*

Diocesan Director of Liturgy: Rev. Andrew McKenzie, Scotus College, 2
Chesters Road, Bearsden, G61 4AG. Tel 0141 942 8384

Diocesan Master of Ceremonies: Rt. Rev. Mgr. Peter Smith, Curial offices, 196 Clyde Street, Glasgow, G1 4JY. Tel 0141 226 5898

Diocesan Concelebration Vestments and Concelebration Chalices: Mrs. Margaret Hamill, Nazareth House, 1647 Paisley Road West, Glasgow, G52 3QT. Tel: 0141 891 5024

8. PERSONNEL
Director of Personnel:

Miss Sue Jardine, B.Sc. (Hons), PGDip.Pers.Mgt., M.I.P.D.M.I.P.M. (Director-Personnel@rcag.org.uk)

Personnel Administrator: Miss Kelly Harkins, Assoc.I.P.D. (Kelly.Harkins@rcag.org.uk)

Personnel Assistants: Mrs Ann McGarvey (Ann.McGarvey@rcag.org.uk) Miss Louise Malley (Louise.Malley@rcag.org.uk)

9. RELIGIOUS EDUCATION CENTRE
Email: RE@rcag.org.uk

Address:
Religious Education Centre, 196 Clyde Street, Glasgow, G1 4JY.
Tel: 0141-226 5898. Fax No: 0141 225 2600

Director of Religious Education Centre:

Rev. Brian C. Reilly, M.A., S.T.B., L.S.S. (DRE@rcag.org.uk)

Assistant: Rev. John J. McGrorry, Ph. B, S.T.L., M.A. (ADRE@rcag.org.uk)

Deputy Directors:

Primary - Miss Patricia Lockhart, B.A., Dip. C.E. (Primary-RE@rcag.org.uk)

Secondary – Mr. William Horton, B. Sc. (Hons), Dip. R.E. (Secondary-RE@rcag.org.uk)

Secretary: Janette Russell (Secretary-RE@rcag.org.uk)

10. SECRETARIAL/CLERICAL

Secretary: Mrs. Annette Moran (Secretary-Curia@rcag.org.uk)

Telephonist: Mrs. Eileen McKiernan

11. SOCIAL CARE SERVICES
Social-Care@rcag.org.uk

Address: Archdiocesan Social Services Centre, 196 Clyde Street, Glasgow, G1 4JY. Tel: 0141-226 5898. Fax: 0141-225 2600.

Director of Care Services:

Mr. David Ramsay (Director-Care@rcag.org.uk)

Personal Assistant:

Miss Catherine Sloey (Catherine.Sloey@rcag.org.uk)

Funding Resources Manager

Mr. Rod Fleming (Rod.Fleming@rcag.org.uk)

District Managers

Mr. Charles Dickson
(Charlie.Dickson@rcag.org.uk)

Mr. Michael Mesarowicz
(Michael.Mesarowicz@rcag.org.uk)

Mrs. Liz McPake
(Liz.McPake@rcag.org.uk)

Mr. Michael Lynch
(Mick.Lynch@rcag.org.uk)

Ms. Sheena Gault
(Sheena.Gault@rcag.org.uk)

Training Officer

Mr. Brian Smith (Brian.Smith@rcag.org.uk)

Secretarial

Awaiting appointment

JUDICIAL BRANCH

The Scottish National Tribunal deals with many judicial matters, especially as regards marriage annulments.

Address: 22 Woodrow Road, Glasgow G41 5PN.
Tel 0141-427 3036.

Officialis: Rev. Gerard Tartaglia, Ph.B, S.T.B, J.C.L.; Officialis

Officials of the Tribunal from the Archdiocese of Glasgow:

Rev. Gerard Tartaglia, Ph.B, S.T.B, J.C.L.; Officialis

Sister Ishbel MacPherson, SND JCD

Judges: Right. Rev. Mgr. James T. Canon Clancy, S.T.B, Ph.L., V.G.; Rev. John Chalmers D.C.L.; Right. Rev. Mgr. Daniel Hart, Ph.L, S.T.L., MA, Dip. Ed.; Rev. John McAuley S.T.B.; Rev. Joseph McAuley, LL.B., Ph.B. S.T.L.

Defender of the Bond: Rt. Rev. Mgr. Peter Smith, J.C.L.

Judicial matters not within the remit of the Scottish National Tribunal are dealt with by the Curia and communication should be addressed to The Chancellor.

ADVISORS TO THE CARDINAL

College of Consultors:

Right. Rev. Mgr. James T. Clancy, V.G., Revv. Michael Conroy, Right. Rev. Mgr. Daniel Hart, Rt. Rev. Mgr. John Gilmartin, Rev. Joseph Mackle, Rt. Rev. Mgr. James Ryan, Rev. Paul Conroy, Rt. Rev. Mgr. Peter Smith, V. Rev. Neil Donnachie; Rt. Rev. Mgr Owen Gallagher; Revv. John McGrorry; Joseph Chambers

Council of Priests:

Chairman: Rev. Gerard Nugent
Vice-Chairman: Rt. Rev. Mgr. Daniel Hart
Secretary: Rev. John Carroll, St. Joseph's, Tollcross.

Representatives on Education Committees:

Representative for Glasgow:

Rev. Joseph Chambers,
Our Lady of Good Counsel, 6 Broompark Circus, Glasgow, G31 2JF.
Tel/Fax: 0141 554 1558

Representative for East Dunbartonshire

Very Rev. Mgr. Hugh Bradley,
Saint Matthew's, 2 South Crosshill Road, Bishopbriggs,
Tel: 0141 772 1619

Representative for West Dunbartonshire

Rev. John McGrorry,
St. Joseph's, 3 Buchanan Street, Milngave, Glasgow, G62 8DZ.
Tel: 0141-956 1400

Representative for North Lanarkshire

Mr. Anthony Quinn, (Diocese of Motherwell), 8 Arthur Avenue, Airdrie, ML6 9EZ

Representative for Argyll and Bute

Very Rev. William Canon Fraser, Diocese of Argyll and The Isles

Pontifical Mission Aid Societies:
Archdiocesan Director:

Awaiting Appointment

Registrar for Deceased Clergy:

Rt. Rev. Mgr. Hugh N. Canon Boyle, Ph.L., S.T.L., F.S.A.Scot.,
The Lindens, 36 Mansionhouse Road, Glasgow, G41 3DW

THE CATHEDRAL CHAPTER (RESTORED 13TH JANUARY, 1884):

Provost:

Right Rev. Mgr. Martin Quinlan

Canons:

Right. Rev. Mgr. Thomas Murray, Very Rev. Michael Meechan, Right. Rev.
Mgr. Hugh N. Boyle, Very Rev. Mgr. Gaetano Rossi, Right. Rev. Mgr. James
McShane, Very Revv. Patrick J. Kelly, Right. Revv. Mgri. James T. Clancy,
Matthew Coakley, Very Revv. John Bennett, Bernard Devine, Michael
Henretty, James Simcox, Hugh O'Donnell

Honorary Canons:

Very Revv. Jeremiah O'Flynn, John Brannan, Michael Mooney, Thomas
Murphy, William Tobin, Nicholas Rowan, Thomas Glen, Francis Mallon.

DEANERIES:

*Deaneries are structures whereby the Diocesan Bishop can exercise his ministry
in a more effective way. They are therefore smaller areas allowing more
localised pastoral and administrative action, in harmony with the diocesan
vision and planning.*

*Deaneries are placed under the care of a dean who is to assist the Diocesan
Bishop in his ministry. Each deanery also has a deanery co-ordinator who
works with the dean and the deanery co-ordinating team at local level and the
diocesan bishop and his pastoral team at the diocesan level. Deaneries
therefore form an integral part of the diocesan structure.*

CITY-EAST:

St. Andrew's Cathedral, Glasgow; St. Aloysius, Garnethill; St. Anne,
Dennistoun; St. Alphonsus, Glasgow; St. Mary, Calton; St. Michael, Parkhead.
Our Lady of Fatima, Dalmarnock; Our Lady of Good Counsel, Dennistoun;
Sacred Heart, Bridgeton; Strathclyde University Chaplaincy.

Dean: Awaiting appointment

Deanery Co-ordinator: Mr. Stephen Boyd (C/o Sacred Heart Parish)

KELVIN:

St. Charles, North Kelvinside; St. Gregory, Wyndford; St. Patrick, Anderston; St. Peter, Partick; St. Simon, Partick; Glasgow University Chaplaincy.

Dean: Rt. Rev. Mgr. James Ryan

Deanery Co-ordinator: Rev. Joseph Keenan

EASTMUIR:

St. Barnabas, Shettleston; St. Joachim, Carmyle; St. Joseph, Tollcross; St. Jude, Barlanark; St. Mark, Carntyne; St. Paul, Shettleston.

Dean: Awaiting Appointment

Deanery Co-ordinator: Rev. John Campbell

GOVANHILL-LAURIESTON:

Holy Cross, Crosshill; Our Lady of Consolation, Govanhill; St. Albert, Pollokshields; Blessed John Duns Scotus, Gorbals, St. Brigid, Toryglen

Dean: Rev. Anthony Bancewicz

Deanery Co-ordinator: Mary Clare Corr (C/o Holy Cross Parish)

CATHKIN:

Christ the King, King's Park; St. Bartholomew, Castlemilk; St. Margaret Mary, Castlemilk; St. Martin, Castlemilk.

Dean: Awaiting appointment

Deanery Co-ordinator: Rev. Allan Cameron

CART VALLEY:

Holy Name, Mansewood; St. Mary Immaculate, Pollokshaws; St. Gabriel, Merrylee; St. Helen, Langside; St. Vincent de Paul, Thornliebank.

Dean: V. Rev. Hugh Canon O'Donnell

Deanery Co-ordinator: Rev. Gerard Tartaglia, Ph.B., S.T.B., J.C.L.

POLLOK:

St. Bernard, South Nitshill; St. Conval, Pollok; St. James, Crookston; St. Louise, Arden; St. Robert Bellarmine, Househillwood.

Dean: Rev. Laurence McMahon

Deanery Co-ordinator: Rev. Joseph McAuley LL.B, Ph.B, S.T.L.

CRAIGTON:

Our Lady of Lourdes, Cardonald; Our Lady and St. George, Penilee; Our Lady and St. Margaret, Kinning Park; St. Anthony, Govan; St. Constantine, Govan; St. Saviour, Govan.

Dean: Rt. Rev. Mgr. John Gilmartin

Deanery Co-ordinator: To be appointed

SCOTSTOUN-KNIGHTSWOOD:

Corpus Christi, Scotstounhill; Our Lady of Perpetual Succour, Broomhill; St. Brendan, Yoker; St. Ninian, Knightswood; St. Paul, Whiteinch.

Dean: Rt. Rev. Mgr. Owen Gallagher

Deanery Co-ordinator: Sister Alice Garrity (C/o St. Ninian's)

GARSCADDEN:

Immaculate Conception, Maryhill; St. Benedict, Drumchapel; St. Laurence, Drumchapel, St. Pius X, Drumchapel; St. Andrew, Bearsden, St. Joseph, Milngavie.

Dean: Rev. William Donnelly

Deanery Co-ordinator: To be appointed

GARSCUBE-MILTON:

Our Lady of the Assumption, Ruchill; St. Agnes, Lambhill; St. Augustine, Milton; St. Monica, Milton; St. Columba, Glasgow; St. Teresa, Possilpark.

Dean: Rev. Thomas Hendry

Deanery Co-ordinator: Mr. Jim Dean (C/o Our Lady of the Assumption)

ST. ROLLOX:

Immaculate Heart of Mary, Balornock; All Saints, Barmulloch; St. Aloysius, Springburn, St. Catherine Laboure, Balornock, St. Mungo, Townhead; St. Philomena, Provanmill, St. Roch, Garngad

Dean: Rev. John McAuley

Deanery Co-ordinator: Mr. John Harkins, C/o All Saints

PROVAN:

St. Bernadette, Carntyne; St. John Ogilvie, Easterhouse; St. Maria Goretti, Cranhill; St. Philip, Ruchazie; St. Thomas, Riddrie

Dean: Very Rev. Michael Canon Henretty

Deanery Co-ordinator: Rev. Peter Sweeney

DUMBARTON:

St. Michael, Dumbarton; St. Patrick, Dumbarton; St. Peter, Dumbarton; Our Lady and St. Mark, Alexandria; St. Kessog, Balloch; St. Ronan, Bonhill; St. Mahew, Cardross; Our Lady, Star of the Sea, Garelochhead, St. Joseph, Helensburgh; St. Martin, Renton; St. Gildas, Rosneath.

Dean: Rev. George Bradburn

Deanery Co-ordinator: Rev. Sean FitzGerald

CLYDEBANK:

Our Holy Redeemer, Clydebank; St. Eunan, Clydebank; St. Margaret, Clydebank; Our Lady of Loreto, Dalmuir, St. Stephen, Dalmuir; St. Mary, Duntocher; St. Joseph, Faifley; St. Patrick, Old Kilpatrick.

Dean: Rev. Philip Tartaglia

Deanery Co-ordinator: Awaiting Appointment

STRATHKELVIN:

St. Dominic, Bishopbriggs, St. Matthew, Bishopbriggs; Holy Family and St. Ninian, Kirkintilloch; St. Flannan, Kirkintilloch; St. John of the Cross, Twechar.

Dean: Rev. Denis A. Hurley

Deanery Co-ordinator: Mr. John Coultas (C/o Saint Dominic's)

CUMBERNAULD:

Sacred Heart, Cumbernauld; St. Joseph, Cumbernauld, St. Lucy, Cumbernauld, Our Lady and St. Helen, Condorrat, Holy Cross, Croy.

Dean: Rt. Rev. Mgr. Patrick Osborne

Deanery Co-ordinator: Mrs. Elizabeth Dornan (C/o Our Lady & Saint Helen's, Condorrat)

Churches and Clergy of the Archdiocese

CITY OF GLASGOW

ST. ANDREW'S CATHEDRAL (1816), Clyde Street.

Right Rev. Mgr. James T. Canon Clancy, S.T.B., Ph.L.,V.G.,
Administrator (1967)
Rev.William F. Clarke (1957)
Rev.Thomas A. Kilbride, M.A., S.T.B., S.S.L. (1996)

POSTAL ADDRESS: St. Andrew's Cathedral House, 90 Dunlop Street,
GLASGOW G1 4ER. ☎/Fax: 0141-221 3096.
E-mail: administrator@cathedral12.freeserve.co.uk

Sunday Masses: Vigil-Mass, 6.30 p.m.; 10 a.m., 12 noon, 5 p.m. Holy
Days of Obligation, Masses: Vigil-Mass, 5.15 p.m.; 8, 10.30 a.m., 12
noon, 1.00, 5.15 p.m. Weekday Masses: 8.15 a.m., 1.00 and (except
Saturday) 5.15 p.m. Confessions: weekdays (except Holy Days), 7.45 to
8.10 a.m., 12.30 to 1.00 p.m., 4.45 to 5.10 p.m.; Saturday, 7.45 to 8.10
a.m., 12 noon to 1.00 p.m., 4 to 6.30 p.m.
Exposition of the Blessed Sacrament, Monday to Friday (except Holy
Days of Obligation), 8.45 a.m. to 5.10 p.m.; Saturday, 8.45 a.m. to
6.15p.m.
Estimated Catholic population: 200.

ROYAL MATERNITY HOSPITAL, ROTTENROW AND CITY MORTUARY, JOCELYN
SQUARE ATTENDED FROM THE CATHEDRAL.
(ST. MUNGO'S PRIMARY SCHOOL)

ST. AGNES, Lambhill (1884, 1894), Balmore Road.

Rev. Joseph Noel Burke, S.T.B (1965)

POSTAL ADDRESS: St. Agnes', 694 Balmore Road, GLASGOW G22 6QS.
☎ 0141-336 8175.

Sunday Masses: Vigil-Mass, 6 p.m.; 10 a.m., 12 noon. Holy Days of
Obligation, Masses: 10 a.m., 7 p.m. Confessions: Saturdays, 10.30 a.m.,
after Vigil-Mass to 7.15 p.m.
Estimated Catholic population: 2,800.

KINGARTH OLD PEOPLE'S HOME ATTENDED FROM ST. AGNES'. FAMILY FAITH CENTRE, 694 BALMORE ROAD, GLASGOW G22 6QS. ☎ 0141-347 0637. FRANCISCANS OF THE IMMACULATE CONCEPTION, FRANCISCAN CONVENT, 27 HILLEND ROAD, GLASGOW G22 6NE. ☎ 0141-336 8136. (SERVED FROM ST. TERESA'S).
SISTERS OF MERCY, 59 HERMA STREET, GLASGOW G23 5AN. ☎ 0141-946 4939.
ST. AGNES' PRIMARY SCHOOL; ST. JOAN OF ARC SPECIAL NEEDS SECONDARY SCHOOL; (ST. AUGUSTINE'S PRIMARY SCHOOL).

ST. ALBERT, Pollokshields (1965, 1967), Albert Drive.

Very Rev. John Canon Bennett (1951)

POSTAL ADDRESS: St. Albert's, 180 Albert Drive, GLASGOW G41 2NH. ☎0141-429 5287.

Sunday Masses: Vigil-Mass, 6.30 p.m.; 9, 11 a.m., 6 p.m. Holy Days of Obligation, Masses: 10 a.m., 12.15, 7.30 p.m. Confessions: Saturdays, 10.30 a.m., after Vigil-Mass.
Estimated Catholic population: 1,200.

MARIST BROTHERS, ST. BENET'S, 227 NITHSDALE ROAD, GLASGOW G41 5HA. ☎ 0141-427 1750.
DAUGHTERS OF CHARITY, ST. VINCENT'S CONVENT, 347 ALBERT DRIVE, GLASGOW G41 5PH. ☎ 0141-427 3408.
DUNREATH (A STUDY CENTRE FOR MEN WHOSE PASTORAL CARE IS ENTRUSTED TO THE OPUS DEI PRELATURE), 231 NITHSDALE ROAD, GLASGOW G41 5HB. ☎0141-427 3236; FAX: 0141-427 7547. RESIDENT PRIESTS: REV. GONZALO GONZALES, LL.D., D.C.L. (1955); REV. STEFAN HNYLYCIA, B.SC. (1986).
DANIEL HOUSE, ST. ANDREW'S HOUSE PROJECT, CHILDREN'S HOMES; ELMTREE NURSING HOME, GLENAFTON NURSING HOME, BRIAR HA' HOUSE, NITHSDALE LODGE NURSING HOME, ST. ANDREW'S NURSING HOME, AND TAYFORD HOUSE, HOMES FOR THE ELDERLY; ALL ATTENDED FROM ST. ALBERT'S.
ST. ALBERT'S PRIMARY SCHOOL; (ST. BRIDE'S PRIMARY SCHOOL).

ALL SAINTS, Barmulloch (1969, 1971), Broomfield Road.

Rev. Michael Woodford, Ph.B., S.T.B., Dip. Past. Theol. (1974)

POSTAL ADDRESS: All Saints', 567 Broomfield Road, GLASGOW G21 3HW. ☎0141-558 7824.
E-mail: 106507,1545@compuserve.com

Sunday Masses: Vigil-Mass, 5.30 p.m.; 10.30 a.m., 12.15 p.m. Holy Days of Obligation, Masses: Vigil-Mass, 7.30 p.m.; 10 a.m. Confessions: Saturday, after morning Mass, 5 to 5.20 p.m., after Vigil-Mass if required.
Estimated Catholic population: 2,500.

BROOMFIELD COURT NURSING HOMEATTENDED FROM ALL SAINTS.
(ST. CATHERINE'S PRIMARY SCHOOL; ST. MARTHA'S PRIMARY SCHOOL.)

ST. ALOYSIUS, Garnethill (1866, 1910), Rose Street.

Rev. John Twist, S.J., *Parish Priest* (1973)
Rev.Alan Fortune, S..J. (1973)
Rev. Gerard Hassay, S.J. (1965)
Rev. Vincent McAtamney, S.J. (1947)
Rev. Fintan Creaven, S.J. (1968)
Rev. Peter Granger-Banyard, S.J. (1966)
Rev. Michael Spencer, S.J. (1958)
Bro. James Spence, S.J.

POSTAL ADDRESSES: Parish Office, 27 Hill Street, GLASGOW G3 6RL.
☎0141-332 3039.
St. Aloysius' Residence, 10 Woodside Place, GLASGOW G3 7QF.
☎ 0141-332 3039.
E-mail:aloychurch@garnet92.freeserve.co.uk
Web-site:http://www.aloysius.glasgow.ukgateway.net

Rev. Adrian Porter, S.J., *Superior* (1988)
Rev. Peter Brook, S.J. (1988)
Rev. James Christie, S.J. (1970)

POSTAL ADDRESS: Flat 3, 56 Bentinck Street, GLASGOW G3 7TT.

Sunday Masses: Vigil-Mass, 5.45 p.m.; 9, 10.30 a.m., 12 noon (Sung Mass
during school term), 9 p.m. Holy Days of Obligation, Masses:
Vigil-Mass, 5.45 p.m.; 8 a.m., 12.30, 5.45 p.m. Confessions: Monday to
Friday, 11.30 a.m. to 12.15 p.m. 5.15 to 5.40 p.m.; Saturday 10.30 a.m.
to 12.25 p.m., 2 to 5.30 p.m. (during Exposition).
Estimated Catholic population: 600.   ♿ ♿

ST. ALOYSIUS' COLLEGE, 45 HILL STREET, GLASGOW G3 6RJ. ☎0141-332
3190; FAX: 0141-353 0426.
CRAIGHEAD INSTITUTE OF LIFE AND FAITH, 26 ROSE STREET, GLASGOW G3
6RE. ☎0141-332 2733. FAX: 0141-353 1192.
GARNETHILL CENTRE, 28 ROSE STREET, GLASGOW G3 6RE. ☎0141-333 0730;
FAX: 0141-333 0737.
CONVENT OF MERCY, 62 HILL STREET, GLASGOW G3 6RH. ☎0141-332 0895.
IGNATIAN SPIRITUALITY CENTRE, 7 WOODSIDE PLACE, GLASGOW G3 7AF.
☎0141-354 0077.
(ST JOSEPH'S PRIMARY SCHOOL)

ST. ALOYSIUS, Springburn (1856, 1882), Hillkirk Street.

Rev. Noel Murray, B.Th. (1954)

POSTAL ADDRESS: St. Aloysius', 10 Hillkirk Street, Springburn, GLASGOW
G21 1TH. ☎0141-558 5495.

Sunday Masses: Vigil-Mass, 6 p.m.; 9, 11 a.m. Holy Days of Obligation,
Masses: Vigil-Mass, 6 p.m.; 10 a.m., 6 p.m. Confessions: daily after 10 a.m.
Mass; Saturday, 5 to 5.30 p.m. Exposition of the Blessed Sacrament,
Monday, Tuesday, Thursday, Friday, after 10 a.m. Mass to 4 p.m.
Estimated Catholic Population: 1,200.   [A]

ST. ALOYSIUS' PRIMARY SCHOOL; (ST. STEPHEN'S PRIMARY SCHOOL).

ST. ALPHONSUS, Calton (1946, 1905), London Road.

Rev. Francis Gallagher (1968)

POSTAL ADDRESS: St. Alphonsus', 18 Stevenson Street, GLASGOW G40 2ST.
☎0141-552 0519; Fax: 0141-552 1991.
E-mail:st.alphonsus@virgin.net
Web-site:http://homes.arealcity.comStAlphonsus/

Sunday Masses: Vigil-Mass, 5 p.m.; 10, 11 a.m., 12 noon, 4.45 p.m. Holy Days of Obligation, Masses: Vigil-Mass, 5.30 p.m.; 12.30, 5.30 p.m. Confessions: Saturday, 12.30p.m.
Estimated Catholic population: 650.

JAMES DUNCAN HOUSE, GREAT EASTERN HOTEL (HOSTEL) AND MONTEITH HOTEL (HOSTEL), ATTENDED FROM ST. ALPHONSUS'.
(SACRED HEART PRIMARY SCHOOL, Bridgeton; ST. ANNE'S PRIMARY SCHOOL, Crownpoint Road)

ST. ANNE, Dennistoun (1898, 1933), Whitevale Street.

Rev. Gerard F. Barnes (1986)

POSTAL ADDRESS: St. Anne's, 21 Whitevale Street, GLASGOW G31 1QW .
☎0141-554 0285.

E-mail: FADGE@stannes33.freeserve.co.uk

Sunday Masses: Vigil-Mass, 6 p.m.; 11 a.m., 5 p.m. Holy Days of Obligation, Masses: Vigil-Mass, 7 p.m.; 9.30 a.m., 7 p.m. Confessions: Saturday, after 9.30 a.m. Mass,5.30 to 5.45 p.m.; any time on request. Estimated Catholic population; 2,000.

SISTERS OF ST. JOSEPH OF CLUNY, ST. JOSEPH'S CONVENT, 23 WHITEVALE STREET, GLASGOW G31 IQW. ☎0141-554 9055.
ST. DENIS' PRIMARY SCHOOL; (ST. ANNE'S PRIMARY SCHOOL).

ST. ANTHONY, Govan (1861, 1878), Govan Road.

Rev. Edward Kelly (1955)

POSTAL ADDRESS: St. Anthony's, 62 Langlands Road, GLASGOW G51 3BD.
☎0141-445 1416.

Sunday Masses: Vigil-Mass, 5.30p.m.; 11.15 a.m. Holy Days of Obligation, Masses: 9.30 a.m. (for school), 12.30 p.m., 5.30 p.m. Confessions: Tuesday and Thursday, before 12.30 p.m. Mass and before Novena; Saturday, before and after 11 a.m. Mass, after Vigil-Mass.
Estimated Catholic population: 1,000.

(ST. ANTHONY 'S PRIMARY SCHOOL.)

ST. AUGUSTINE, Milton (1953, 1956), Ashgill Road.

Rev. Gerard C. Hill, Ph.L., S.T.L., M.A. (1968)

POSTAL ADDRESS: St. Augustine's, 393 Ashgill Road, GLASGOW G22 7HN.
☎0141-772 1905.

Sunday Masses: Vigil-Mass: 7 p.m.; 10 a.m., 12 noon. Holy Days of
Obligation, Masses: Vigil-Mass, 7 p.m.; 10 a.m. Confessions: Saturday
after 10 a.m. Mass, before and after Vigil-Mass.
Estimated Catholic population: 2,100   🗲

DAUGHTERS OF MARY, HELP OF CHRISTIANS (SALESIAN SISTERS), 138/140
RONALDSAY STREET, GLASGOW G22 7AR. ☎0141-762 3420.

ASHGILL NURSING HOME, TARANSAY COURT (SHELTERED HOUSING) AND
MILTON SPECIAL NEEDS   SECONDARY SCHOOL ATTENDED FROM ST.
AUGUSTINE'S.
ST. AUGUSTINE'S PRIMARY SCHOOL; ST. AMBROSE'S PRIMARY SCHOOL; (ST.
ALOYSIUS' PRIMARY SCHOOL).

ST. BARNABAS, Shettleston (1950, 1962), Darleith Street.

Rev. Francis Balmer (1983)

POSTAL ADDRESS: St. Barnabas', 140 Wellshot Road, GLASGOW G32 7BH.
☎0141-778 2861.

Sunday Masses: Vigil-Mass, 6 p.m.; 9.30, 11 30 a.m. Holy Days of
Obligation, Masses: Vigil-Mass 7 p.m; 9 30 a.m., 11 a.m. in school, 6
p.m.   Confessions: Saturday, before and after morning Mass and
Vigil-Mass.
Estimated Catholic population:1,500.   🗲

LIGHTBURN HOSPITAL, ATTENDED FROM ST. BARNABAS'.
ST. TIMOTHY'S PRIMARY SCHOOL; ST ANDREW'S SECONDARY SCHOOL; (ST.
PAUL'S PRIMARY SCHOOL).

ST. BARTHOLOMEW, Castlemilk (1955, 1958), Croftfoot Drive.

Very Rev. Francis Canon Mallon (1954)
Rev. Paul G. Murray, B.Sc., Ph.B., S.T.L. (1988)

POSTAL ADDRESS: St. Bartholomew's, 32 Croftoot Drive, GLASGOW G45
0NG. ☎0141-634 2051; Fax: 0141-630 0958.
E-mail:saint.bartholomew@btinternet.com

Sunday Masses: Vigil-Mass, 6.30 p.m.; 10.30 a.m., 12 noon, 6.30 p.m. Holy
Days of Obligation, Masses: Vigil-Mass 7.30 p.m; 9.30 a.m., 7.30 p.m.
Confessions: Thursday after Novena, 7.30 p m; Saturday, after morning
Mass, before and after Vigil-Mass.
Estimated Catholic population: 2,500.

ST BARTHOLOMEW'S PRIMARY SCHOOL.

ST. BENEDICT, Drumchapel (1960,1991), Drumchapel Road.

Rev. Anthony Sweeney (1974)

POSTAL ADDRESS: St. Benedict's, 60 Drumchapel Road, GLASGOW G15 6QE.
☎0141-944 1767.

Sunday Masses: Vigil-Mass, 6 p.m.; 10 a.m., 12 noon, 6 p.m. Holy Days of
Obligation, Masses: Vigil-Mass, 7 p.m.; 10 a.m., 7 p.m. Confessions:
Saturday, after 9.30 a.m. Mass, 5.30 to 5.50 p.m.
Estimated Catholic population: 2,500.

DRUMCHAPEL HOSPITAL SERVED FROM ST. BENEDICT'S.
(ST. PIUS' PRIMARY SCHOOL; ST. NINIAN'S PRIMARY SCHOOL).

ST. BERNADETTE, Carntyne (1950, 1934), Carntyne Road.

Rev. Joseph Cairns (1964)

POSTAL ADDRESS: St. Bernadette's, 361 Carntyne Road, GLASGOW G32 6JL.
☎0141-778 3060.

Sunday Masses: Vigil-Mass, 6.30 p.m.; 11 a.m. Holy Days of Obligation,
Masses: Vigil-Mass, 6.30 p.m.; 9.30 a.m. Confessions: Saturdav, 10 a.m.,
5.45 p.m

Estimated Catholic population: 1,750.

CARNTYNE GARDENS (SHELTERED HOUSING), CARNTYNE HOUSE CARE UNIT.
ALEXANDRA COURT AND GREENFIELD PARK (NURSING HOMES) ATTENDED FROM
ST. BERNADETTE'S
ST. AIDAN'S SPECIAL NEEDS SECONDARY SCHOOL (ST. MARK'S PRIMARY
SCHOOL; ST. MICHAEL'S PRIMARY SCHOOL; ST. TIMOTHY'S PRIMARY SCHOOL
ST THOMAS' PRIMARY SCHOOL).

ST. BERNARD, South Nitshill (1960, 1963), Wiltonburn Road.

Rev. Joseph L. McAuley, LL.B, Ph.B, S.T.L. (1984)

POSTAL ADDRESS: St. Bernard's, 18 Wiltonburn Road, GLASGOW G53 7JF.
☎ & Fax: 0141-876 9012.
E-mail: joseph.mcauley@stbernard42procserve.co.uk

Also in residence:

Rev. Eustace Cassidy, C.P. (☎ *0141-876 1230*) (1957)

Sunday Masses: Vigil-Mass, 5.30 p.m.; 11 a.m. Evening Prayer and
Benediction, 5 p.m. Holy Days of Obligation, Masses: Vigil-Mass, 5.30
p.m.; 11 a.m. Confessions: Saturday, 5 p.m. and after Vigil-Mass.
Estimated Catholic population: 1,000.

MANOR PARK NURSING HOME   AND PARKHOUSE MANOR NURSING HOME
ATTENDED FROM ST. BERNARD'S.
ST. BERNARD'S PRIMARY SCHOOL; (ST. ANGELA'S PRIMARY SCHOOL).

ST. BRENDAN, YOKER (1946, 1949), Kelso Street.

Rev. Edward Brian McNaught, S.T.B., B.A. (1973)
Sr. Stephanie McAuley, R.S.C. *(Pastoral Assistant)*

POSTAL ADDRESS: St. Brendan's, 187 Kelso Street, GLASGOW G13 4BH.
☎0141-952 1471.

Sunday Masses: Vigil-Mass, 5.30 p.m.; 9.30 , 11.30 a.m., 6 p.m. Holy Days
of Obligation, Masses: Vigil-Mass, 7.30 p.m.; 9.30 a.m., 7.30 p.m.
Confessions: Monday, after 7.30 p.m. Devotions; Saturday, after 10 a.m.
Mass, after Vigil-Mass.
Estimated Catholic population: 3,200.

KELSO HOUSE RESPITE CENTRE, 287 KELSO STREET, GLASGOW G13 4PA.
☎0141-951 1821.
BLAWARTHILL GERIATRIC HOSPITAL AND QUAYSIDE NURSING HOME ATTENDED
FROM ST. BRENDAN'S.
ST. BRENDAN'S PRIMARY SCHOOL.

ST. BRIGID, Toryglen (1955, 1957), Prospecthill Road.

Rev. Brian C. Reilly, M.A., S.T.B,, L.S.S. (1977)
Very Rev. Nicholas Canon Rowan (1947)

POSTAL ADDRESS: St. Brigid's, 12 Prospecthill Crescent, Toryglen, GLASGOW G42 0JN. ☎ 0141-647 3585.
E-mail: father@brianr99.freeserve.co.uk

Sunday Masses: Vigil-Mass, 6.30 p.m.; 10 a.m., 12 noon, 5 p.m. Evening Devotions: as announced. Holy Days of Obligation, Masses: Vigil-Mass, 6.30 p.m.; 8.30, 10 a.m., 6.30 p.m. Confessions: Saturday, 9.30 a.m., 5.30 to 6.20 p.m.
Estimated Catholic population: 4,000.

ST BRIGID'S PRIMARY SCHOOL.

ST. CATHERINE LABOURE, North Balornock (1950, 1953), Lamont Road.

Rev. Aidan Martin, Ph.B., S.T.B. (1982)
Rev. Thomas S. Cunningham *(Retired)* (1953)

POSTAL ADDRESS: St. Catherine's, 90 Lamont Road, GLASGOW G21 3PP. ☎ 0141-558 6723; Fax: 0141-558 6723.

Sunday Masses: Vigil-Mass, 6.30 p.m.; 9.30, 11.30 a.m., 6.30 p.m. Holy Days of Obligation, Masses: as announced.. Confessions: Thursday, after Novena; Saturday, 10 a.m., 6 to 6.30 p.m., after Vigil-Mass.
Estimated Catholic population: 2,500.

HEATHER BANK NURSING HOME AND WALLACEWELL CHILDREN'S HOME ATTENDED FROM ST. CATHERINE'S.
ST. CATHERINE'S PRIMARY SCHOOL; ALL SAINTS' SECONDARY SCHOOL; (ST. MARTHA'S PRIMARY SCHOOL).

ST. CHARLES, North Kelvinside (1899, 1960), Kelvinside Gardens East.

Rev. Sabatino Tedeschi (1959)

POSTAL ADDRESS: St. Charles', 1 Kelvinside Gardens, GLASGOW G20 6BG ☎ 0141-946 2769.

Also in Residence:

Rev. William J. Slavin, C.Psychol. *(Hospital Chaplain)* (1964)
(☎ & Fax: 0141-946 7622; E-mail: wslavin@compuserve.com)

Sunday Masses: Vigil-Mass, 6 p.m.;11 a.m.,6 p.m. Holy Days of Obligation, Masses: 10 a.m., 6.30 p.m. Confessions: after daily Mass; Saturday, after Vigil-Mass.
Estimated Catholic population: 940.

FAITHFUL COMPANIONS OF JESUS, FLAT 2/1, 8 QUEEN MARGARET ROAD, GLASGOW G20 6DP. ☎ 0141-946 4644.
QUEEN MOTHER HOSPITAL AND ROYAL HOSPITAL FOR SICK CHILDREN. CHAPLAIN: REV. WILLIAM J. SLAVIN, ST. CHARLES'. ☎/FAX: 0141-946 7622, (HOSPITAL: 0141-201 0000).
ST. CHARLES' PRIMARY SCHOOL; (NOTRE DAME PRIMARY SCHOOL).

CHRIST THE KING, King's Park (1934, 1960), Carmunnock Road.

Rev. Peter M. Gallacher, Ph.B., S.T.L., S.L.L. (1979)
Rev. James Cosker (1961)
Rev. John Keenan (1995)

POSTAL ADDRESS: Christ the King, 220 Carmunnock Road, GLASGOW G44 5AP. ☎0141-637 2882; Fax: 0141-637 1601.
E-mail:christtheking@btinternet.com.

Sunday Masses: Vigil-Mass, 6.30 p.m.; 9, 10.30 a.m., 12 noon, 6.30 p.m. Evening Service: as announced. Holy Days of Obligation, Masses: Vigil-Mass, 6.30 p.m.; 8, 10, 11 a.m., 7.30 p.m. Confessions (until further notice): Thursdays, 6.30 to 7p.m., after Novena to 7.45 p.m.; Saturdays, 9.30 to 10 a.m., 10.30 to 10.45 a.m., 6 to 6.30, 7.15 to 7.45 p.m.
Estimated Catholic population: 6,500.

ST. FILLAN'S PRIMARY SCHOOL; ST. MIRIN'S PRIMARY SCHOOL.

ST. COLUMBA, Woodside (1906, 1941), Hopehill Road.

Rev. David Trainer (1968)

POSTAL ADDRESS: St. Columba's, 74 Hopehill Road, GLASGOW G20 7HH. ☎0141-332 4530; Fax: 0141-331 0287.

Sunday Masses: Vigil-Mass, 6 p.m.; 11 a.m., 5 p.m. Holy Days of Obligation, Masses: 10 a.m., 7 p.m. Confessions: Saturday, 10.30 a.m., 5.15 p.m.
Estimated Catholic population:1,650.

BURNBANK HOME FOR THE ELDERLY, BURNBANK GARDENS, AND DAVENPORT NURSING HOME, BURNBANK TERRACE, ATTENDED FROM ST. COLUMBA'S.
ST. JOSEPH'S PRIMARY SCHOOL.

ST. CONSTANTINE, Govan (1921), Uist Street.

Rev. Robert McCann (1980)
Rev. John McGrath (1999)

POSTAL ADDRESS: St. Constantine's, 54 Uist Street, GLASGOW G51 3XW.
☎0141-445 1434.

Sunday Masses: Vigil-Mass, 6 p.m.; 10 a.m., 12 noon, 6 p.m. Holy Days
of Obligation, Masses: Vigil-Mass, 7 p.m.; 8, 10 a.m., 7 p.m.
Confessions: Saturday, after 10 a.m. Mass, after Vigil-Mass.
Estimated Catholic population: 4,000.

DAVID LEA HOME ATTENDED FROM ST. CONSTANTINE'S.
THE SOUTHERN GENERAL HOSPITAL. CHAPLAIN: REV. BERNARD CONNELL,
OUR LADY OF PERPETUAL SUCCOUR, BROOMHILL. ☎0141-339 1324
(HOSPITAL.: 0141-201 1100)
ST. JEROME'S PRIMARY SCHOOL; (ST. ANTHONY'S PRIMARY SCHOOL).

ST. CONVAL, Pollok (1949, 1956), Hapland Road.

Rev. William McGinley (1962)
Right Rev. Mgr. Peter Smith, J.C.L. (*Diocesan Chancellor*) (☎.& Fax:
0141-810 4976) (1984)

POSTAL ADDRESS: St. Conval's, 21 Hapland Road, GLASGOW G53 5NT.
☎ 0141-882 5265.

Sunday Masses: Vigil-Mass, 6 p.m.; 10.30 a.m., 12 noon. Holy Days of
Obligation, Masses: 10 a.m., 7 p.m. Confessions: Saturday, after
morning Mass, after Vigil-Mass.
Estimated Catholic population: 2,400.

MISSIONARIES OF CHARITY, 186 BRAIDCRAFT ROAD, GLASGOW G53 5DZ. ☎
0141-883 2785.
ST. EDMUND'S PRIMARY SCHOOL; ST. MARNOCK'S PRIMARY SCHOOL.

CORPUS CHRISTI, Scotstounhill (1969, 1972), Lincoln Avenue.

Rev. Joseph Mills (1967)
Rev. Mark Morris, Dip. Theol.*(Hospital Chaplain)*(1993)
Sr. Marie Molloy, R.S.C. *(Pastoral Assistant)*

POSTAL ADDRESS: Corpus Christi,42 Lincoln Avenue, GLASGOW G13 3RG.
☎0141-954 3777.

Sunday Masses: Vigil-Mass, 6 p.m.; 9, 11 a.m., 5.30 p.m. Holy Days of
Obligation, Masses: Vigil-Mass, 6 p.m.; 9.30 (on schooldays), 11 a.m., 6
p.m. Confessions: Saturday, after 10 a.m. Mass, after Vigil-Mass.
Exposition of the Blessed Sacrament: Sundays, 1 to 4 p.m.;Tuesdays,
10.30 a.m. to 4 p.m.
Estimated Catholic population:1,500.

MORRISON HOUSE (HOME FOR THE ELDERLY) ATTENDED FROM CORPUS
CHRISTI.
GARTNAVEL ROYAL AND GENERAL HOSPITALS. CHAPLAIN: REV. MARK MORRIS,
CORPUS CHRISTI. ☎0141-954 3777. ROYAL HOSPITAL: SUNDAY MASS, 10 A.M.
(IN CHAPEL), GENERAL HOSPITAL: SUNDAY MASS, 11 A.M. (ON GROUND FLOOR).
CORPUS CHRISTI PRIMARY SCHOOL; (ST. BRENDAN'S PRIMARY SCHOOL).

ST. GABRIEL, Merrylee (1955, 1957), Merrylee Road.

Rev. Christopher Gilfedder (1954)
Rev. Joseph Mackle, Dip.Theol. (1989)

POSTAL ADDRESS: St. Gabriel's, 83 Merrylee Road, GLASGOW G43 2QY.
☎0141-637 4138.

Sunday Masses: Vigil-Mass, 6 p.m.; 8.30, 10, 11.15 a.m., 12.30, 6 p.m.
Holy Days of Obligation, Masses: 7, 10, 11 a.m., 8 p.m. Confessions:
Saturday after 10 a.m. Mass, 5 to 6 p.m.
Estimated Catholic population:2,500.

SCHOENSTATT SISTERS OF MARY, 30 LANGSIDE DRIVE, GLASGOW G43 2QQ.
☎0141-637 3316.
CARTVALE NURSING HOME AND MERRYLEE LODGE (HOME FOR THE ELDERLY)
SERVED FROM ST. GABRIEL'S.
OUR LADY OF THE ANNUNCIATION PRIMARY SCHOOL; ST. OSWALD'S SPECIAL
NEEDS SECONDARY SCHOOL; (OUR LADY OF THE MISSIONS PRIMARY
SCHOOL).

ST. GREGORY, Wyndford (1965, 1971),Kelvindale Road.

Rev. Carlo Centra (1950)

POSTAL ADDRESS: St. Gregory's, 136 Kelvindale Road, GLASGOW G20 8DP.
☎0141-946 3009.

Sunday Masses: Vigil-Mass, 6 p.m.; 9, 10.30 a.m., 12 noon. Holy Days of
Obligation, Masses: Vigil-Mass, 7 p.m.; 7 p.m. Confessions: Saturday, 9
to 9.30 a.m., 10 to 10.30 a.m., 5.30 to 6 p.m. Exposition of the Blessed
Sacrament, Saturday, after 9.30 a.m. Mass.
Estimated Catholic population: 3,000.

EASTPARK HOME, GLENFINNAN SHELTERED HOUSING AND WYNDFORD
SHELTERED HOUSING ATTENDED FROM ST. GREGORY'S.
GLENALVON (A CULTURAL CENTRE FOR WOMEN WHOSE PASTORAL CARE IS
ENTRUSTED TO THE OPUS DEI PRELATURE), 5 KIRKLEE GARDENS, GLASGOW
G12 0SG. ☎/FAX: 041-339 3234.
ST. GREGORY'S PRIMARY SCHOOL.

ST. HELEN, Langside (1966, 1968), Langside Avenue.

Right Rev. Mgr. Daniel J. C. Hart, Ph.L., S.T.L.,
M.A., Dip.Ed. (1956)

POSTAL ADDRESS: St. Helen's, 165 Camphill Avenue, GLASGOW G41 3DR.
☎0141-632 2626.

Sunday Masses: Vigil-Mass, 5.30 p.m.; 9, 11 a.m., 12.30, 5 p.m. Evening
Service: 6 p.m. as announced. Holy Days of Obligation, Masses: Vigil-
Mass, 5.30 p.m.; 8, 10 a.m., 12.30, 7.30 p.m. Confessions: Thursday, 7.30
p.m.; Saturday, 10.30 to 11.15 a.m., 6.20 to 7 p.m.
Estimated Catholic population: 2,000.

CARMELITE MONASTERY, 29 MANSIONHOUSE ROAD, GLASGOW G41 3DN.
BON SECOURS HOSPITAL, 36 MANSIONHOUSE ROAD, GLASGOW G41 3DW.
☎0141-632 9231.
ST. JOHN'S RESIDENTIAL HOME, THORNWOOD HALL, OXTON HOUSE AND
CROSSMYLOOF RESOURCE CENTRE (EVENTIDE HOMES) ATTENDED FROM ST.
HELEN'S.
(ST. BRIDE'S PRIMARY SCHOOL; ST. CONVAL'S PRIMARY SCHOOL.)

HOLY CROSS, Crosshill (1886, 1911), Dixon Avenue.

Rev. Anthony Bancewicz (1965)
Rev. Thomas Holloran (1957)
Rev. Stephen Hannah (*Hospital Chaplain*) (1988)

POSTAL ADDRESS: Holy Cross, 113 Dixon Avenue, GLASGOW G42 8ER.
☎0141-423 0105.

Sunday Masses: Vigil-Mas, 6 p.m.; 9.30, 11 a.m., 12.15, 8 p.m. Holy Days
of Obligation, Masses: Vigil-Mass, 6 p.m.; 9.30 a.m., 12.30, 6 p.m.
Confessions: Saturday, 10 to 11 a.m., after Vigil-Mass to 7.30 p.m.
Exposition of the Blessed Sacrament, Monday to Saturday, 10 a.m. to 8
p.m.
Estimated Catholic population:4,500.

FRANCISCAN CONVENT OF THE IMMACULATE CONCEPTION, 92 DIXON AVENUE,
GLASGOW G41 8EJ. MANSIONHOUSE ROAD, GLASGOW G41 3DN. ☎0141 423
4501.
VICTORIA INFIRMARY (SUNDAY MASS, 4 P.M., DOCTORS' DINING ROOM, FLOOR
F), MANSIONHOUSE UNIT (MASS, FIRST SUNDAY, 2.30 P.M.) AND MCQUAKER
BUILDING (WARDS 20 & 21). CHAPLAINS: REV. STEPHEN HANNAH, HOLY
CROSS; SISTER ELIZABETH ANN, BON SECOURS.
HOLY CROSS PRIMARY SCHOOL; ST. BRIDE'S PRIMARY SCHOOL;
HOLYROOD SECONDARY SCHOOL.

HOLY NAME, Mansewood (1975, 1984) Hillside Road.

Very Rev . Patrick J . Canon Kelly (1951)

Postal address: Holy Name, 200 Hillside Road, GLASGOW G43 1BU .
☎0141-649 9668.

Sunday Masses: Vigil-Mass, 6 p.m.; 10.30 a.m., 12.15, 5.15 p.m. Holy
Days of Obligation, Masses: 10 a.m., 6.30 p.m. Confessions: Saturday,
10.30 a.m., before and after Vigil-Mass.
Estimated Catholic population: 1,400.

DAUGHTERS OF ST. PAUL, MARYLAND CONVENT, 24 HILLSIDE ROAD, GLASGOW
G43 1DB. ☎0141-571 0608.
WOODVALE RESIDENTIAL HOME SERVED FROM HOLY NAME.

IMMACULATE CONCEPTION, Maryhill (1851, 1991), Maryhill Road.

Rev. William Mone (1955)
Very Rev.Thomas Canon Murphy (<i>Retired</i>) (1948)

POSTAL ADDRESS: Immaculate Conception, 2049 Maryhill Road, GLASGOW G20 0AA. ☎0141-946 2071.

Sunday Masses: Vigil-Mass, 6.30 p.m.; 9, 10.30 a.m., 12 noon, 6.30 p.m. Holy Days of Obligation, Masses: as announced. Confessions: Thursday, 7 until Mass at 7.30 p.m.; Saturday, 9.45 to 10.15 a.m., 5 to 6 p.m. Estimated Catholic population: 4200.

LORETTO SHELTERED HOUSING, 2045 MARYHILL ROAD, GLASGOW G20 0AA. ☎0141-945 3008.
SISTERS OF ST. JOSEPH OF PEACE, 17 CALDERCUILT ROAD, GLASGOW G20 0AE. ☎0141-579 6061.
FERGUSON-ANDERSON HOME ATTENDED FROM IMMACULATE CONCEPTION.
ST. BLANE'S PRIMARY SCHOOL; ST. MARY'S PRIMARY SCHOOL; JOHN PAUL ACADEMY; (ST. AGNES' PRIMARY SCHOOL).

THE IMMACULATE HEART OF MARY, Balornock (1946,1951), Broomfield Road.

Rev. Peter Lennon (1961)
Rev. Stephen Dunn, B.Sc., B.D. (<i>Hospital Chaplain</i>) (1994)

POSTAL ADDRESS: Immaculate Heart of Mary, 162 Broomfield Road, GLASGOW G21 3UE. ☎0141-558 5025.

Sunday Masses: Vigil-Mass, 6 p.m.; 9.30, 11.30 a.m., 6 p.m. Evening Service: 5 p.m. Holy Days of Obligation, Masses: Vigil-Mass, 7 p.m.; 9.30, 11 a.m., 7 p.m. Confessions: Thursday, after Novena; Saturday, after 9.30 a.m. Mass, 5 to 5.45 p.m., after Vigil-Mass. Estimated Catholic population: 1,500.

SPRINGBURN HOME AND GRAMPIAN HOME ATTENDED FROM THE IMMACULATE HEART.
STOBHILL HOSPITAL AND HUNTERSHILL NURSING HOME. CHAPLAIN, REV. STEPHEN DUNN, IMMACULATE HEART (☎0141-558 5025). MASS IN STOBHILL HOSPITAL (CHAPLAINCY, BESIDE WARD 14); SUNDAY, 2 P.M.; HOLY DAYS OF OBLIGATION, 1 P.M.
ST. MARTHA'S PRIMARY SCHOOL.

ST. JAMES, Crookston (1949, 1968), Crosstobs Road.

Right Rev. Mgr. Matthew Canon Coakley (1951)

POSTAL ADDRESS: St. James', 20 Beltrees Road, GLASGOW G53 5TE .
☎/Fax: 0141-882 4927.

Sunday Masses: Vigil-Mass, 5.30 p.m.; 10 a.m., 12 noon. Holy Days of
Obligation, Masses: Vigil-Mass, 7 p.m.; 10 a.m., 7 p.m. Confessions:
Thursdays, 6.45 p.m.; Saturdays, 9.45 a.m., 6.15 to 7 p.m. Exposition of
the Blessed Sacrament, Tuesday and Wednesday: 10.30 a.m. to 8 p.m.
Estimated Catholic population: 2,500.

HANDMAIDS OF THE SACRED HEART OF JESUS, 29 LEVERNSIDE CRESCENT,
GLASGOW G53 5LA. ☎0141-810 3882; FAX: 0141-882 0504.
LEVERNDALE HOSPITAL SERVED FROM ST. JAMES' (SUNDAY MASS, 11 A.M.).
THE MEADOWS NURSING HOME AND MOSHEN NURSING HOME SERVED FROM
ST. JAMES'.
ST. MONICA'S PRIMARY SCHOOL.

ST. JOACHIM, Carmyle (1954, 1957), Inzievar Terrace.

Rev. John O'Hagan (1955)

POSTAL ADDRESS: St. Joachim's, 102 Inzievar Terrace, Carmyle, GLASGOW
G32 8JT. ☎0141-641 1517.

Sunday Masses: Vigil-Mass, 6.30 p.m.; 10, 11.30 a.m.. Holy Days of
Obligation, Masses: Vigil-Mass, 7 p.m.; 9.30 a.m., 7.30 p.m. Confessions:
Wednesday, after 9.30 a.m. Mass: Saturday after 10 a.m. Mass, after
Vigil-Mass.
Estimated Catholic population: 1,300.

ST. JOACHIM'S PRIMARY SCHOOL.

BLESSED JOHN DUNS SCOTUS, Gorbals (1993 by union of parishes of St. Francis of Assisi [erected 1992 by union of parishes of St. Francis and St. Bonaventure] and St. Luke [with which parish of St. John the Evangelist was united in 1982]; church opened as St. Luke's, 1975), Ballater Street.

Rev. Brian McGrath, O.F.M., *Guardian, Parish Priest* (1954)
Rev. Donald Walsh, O.F.M., *Vicar* (1983)
Rev. Noel O'Dwyer, O.F.M., *Director, F.M.U.* (1953)
Rev. Peter Hall, O.F.M. (1982)

POSTAL ADDRESS: Blessed John Duns Scotus, 270 Ballater Street,
GLASGOW G5 0YT. ☎0141-429 0740; Fax: 0141-418 0413.

Sunday Masses: Vigil-Mass, 5.30 p.m.; 10 a.m., 12 noon, 6 p.m. Holy Days of Obligation, Masses: Vigil-Mass, 7 p.m.; 10 a.m., 7 p.m. Confessions: Tuesday, before and after 10 a.m. Mass, after Novena, 8 p.m.; Saturday, before and after 10 a.m. Mass, 4 to 5 p.m., after Vigil-Mass.
Estimated Catholic population: 3,000.

PRINCE AND PRINCESS OF WALES HOSPICE, CARLTON PLACE, ATTENDED FROM BL. JOHN DUNS SCOTUS.
ST. FRANCIS PRIMARY SCHOOL; ST. JOHN'S PRIMARY SCHOOL.

ST. JOHN OGILVIE, Easterhouse (1957, 1960), Newhills Road.

Rev. Peter Sweeney (1975)

POSTAL ADDRESS: St. John Ogilvie's, 97 Wellhouse Crescent, GLASGOW G33 4HF. ☎0141-771 3125.
E-mail:stjohnogilvglasg76@hotmail.com

Sunday Masses: Vigil-Mass, 6 p.m.; 11.30 a.m. Holy Days of Obligation, Masses: 10 a.m., 6.30 p.m. Confessions: Thursday,6.30 p.m.; Saturday, 10.30 a.m., after Vigil-Mass.
Estimated Catholic population: 1,000.

NEWHILLS SCHOOL FOR HANDICAPPED CHILDREN ATTENDED FROM ST. JOHN OGILVIE'S.
OGILVIE PRIMARY SCHOOL.

ST. JOSEPH, Tollcross (1893, 1976), Fullarton Avenue.

Right Rev. Mgr. John Noel Woods, M.P.S. (1958)
Rev. John J. Carroll, S.T.B (1989)
Sr. Genevieve Gaffney, *Pastoral Assistant*
POSTAL ADDRESS: St. Joseph's, 14 Fullarton Avenue, GLASGOW G32 8NA. ☎ 0141-778 1054.
E-mail:jnwoods@dial.pipex.com

Sunday Masses: Vigil-Mass, 5.30 p.m.; 9.30, 11.30 a.m., 6 p.m. Holy Days of Obligation, Masses: 7.30, 9.30 a.m., 7.30 p.m. Confessions: Friday, 5 to 6 p.m.; Saturday, 10 a.m., after Vigil-Mass. Exposition of the Blessed Sacrament, Friday, 10 a.m. to 6.30 p.m.
Estimated Catholic population: 3,500.

BRAIDFAULD HOUSE, DUNVEGAN HOUSE, EASTVIEW NURSING HOME AND FOXLEY HOUSE ATTENDED FROM ST. JOSEPH'S.
ASSISI HOUSE, HOME FOR PEOPLE WITH LEARNING DIFFICULTIES, 41 EASTERHILL STREET, GLASGOW G32 8LN. ☎0141-778 6445; CAUSEWAYSIDE STREET PROJECT, 133 CAUSEWAYSIDE STREET, GLASGOW G32 8LP. ☎0141-763 2262.
ST. PAUL'S PRIMARY SCHOOL; ST. VINCENT'S SPECIAL NEEDS SCHOOL; (ST. JOACHIM'S PRIMARY SCHOOL, CARMYLE).

ST. JUDE, Barlanark (1954, 1956), Pendeen Road.

Rev. Thomas Hurley (1960)

POSTAL ADDRESS: St. Jude's, 159 Pendeen Road, Barlanark, GLASGOW G33 4SH. ☎0141-771 5004

Sunday Masses: Vigil-Mass, 6 p.m.; 11 a.m., 5.30 p.m. Evening Service as anounced. Holy Days of Obligation, Masses: 10 a.m., 7 p.m. Confessions: Monday to Friday, 9.30 a.m.; Saturday, 9.30 a.m., 5.30 p.m. Estimated Catholic population: 1,600.

NOTRE DAME CONVENT, 3 KENTALLON ROAD, GLASGOW G33 4QY.
☎0141-771 4783.
ST. JUDE'S PRIMARY SCHOOL.

ST. LAURENCE, Drumchapel (1954, 1957), Kinfauns Drive.

Rev. Gerard M. Bacon (1986)

POSTAL ADDRESS: St. Laurence's, 215 Kinfauns Drive, GLASGOW G15 7UD. ☎0141-944 2063; Emergency Mobile: 09737-89502.

Sunday Masses: Vigil-Mass, 6 p.m.; 11 a.m. Holy Days of Obligation, Masses: 9.30a.m., 7 p.m. Confessions: Saturday, 5.15 to 5.45 p.m.; on request.
Estimated Catholic population: 1,650.

(ST. CLARE'S PRIMARY SCHOOL).

ST. LEO THE GREAT, Dumbreck (1962, 1976), Beech Avenue.

Right Rev. Mgr. Patrick G. Fitzpatrick, L.R.A.M., B.Mus.Sac., L.C.G., B.Mus.Hons., S.T.L., D.C.E. (1964)

POSTAL ADDRESS: St . Leo's, 5 Beech Avenue, GLASGOW G41 5BY. ☎/Fax: 0141-427 0293.

E-mail: gerry.fitzpatrick@mc.mail.com

Sunday Masses: Vigil-Mass, 6 p.m.; 9.30, 11 a.m. Holy Days of Obligation, Masses: 10 a.m., 7 p.m. Confessions: Saturday, 5.15 p.m. Estimated Catholic population:1,200.

HAZELWOOD HOUSE FOR RETIRED NURSES, ATTENDED FROM ST. LEO'S.
(ST. ALBERT'S PRIMARY SCHOOL; OUR LADY OF LOURDES PRIMARY SCHOOL; OUR LADY OF THE ROSARY PRIMARY SCHOOL; ST. SAVIOUR'S PRIMARY SCHOOL.)

ST. LOUISE, Deaconsbank (1973, 1983), Nitshill Road.

Rev. Charles Kane (1955)

POSTAL ADDRESS: St. Louise's, 4 Inverewe Avenue, Deaconsbank, GLASGOW G46 8TA. ☎0141-638 4709.

Sunday Masses: Vigil-Mass, 6.30 p.m.; 10, 11.30 a.m., 6 p.m. Holy Days of Obligation, Masses: 10 a.m., 6.30 p.m. Confessions: Saturday, 10.30 a.m., 6 p.m., after Vigil-Mass if required; on request.
Estimated Catholic population:3,500.

DARNLEY COURT NURSING HOME AND WHITECRAIGS GRAMPIAN NURSING HOME ATTENDED FROM ST. LOUISE'S.
ST. ANGELA'S PRIMARY SCHOOL; ST. LOUISE'S PRIMARY SCHOOL; (ST. CADOC'S PRIMARY SCHOOL.)

ST. MARGARET MARY, Castlemilk (1957, 1959), Dougrie Road.

Very Rev. Bernard V. Canon Devine (1951)
Rev. Alexander E. Strachan, B.D. (1996)

POSTAL ADDRESS: St. Margaret Mary's, 99 Dougrie Road, GLASGOW G45 9NT. ☎0141-634 6152.

Sunday Masses Vigil-Mass, 6 p.m.; 9.30, 11 a.m., 12.30, 6 p.m. Holy Days of Obligation, Masses: 8, 10 a.m., 7 p.m. Confessions: Monday, 7.30 p.m.; Saturday, 10.30 a.m., 6.30 to 7.30 p.m.
Estimated Catholic population: 3,000.

DOWNCRAIG HOUSE AND GLENWOOD LODGE, ATTENDED FROM ST. MARGARET MARY'S.
ST. JULIE'S PRIMARY SCHOOL; ST. MARGARET MARY'S PRIMARY SCHOOL; ST. MARGARET MARY'S SECONDARY SCHOOL; ST. RAYMOND'S SPECIAL NEEDS SCHOOL.

ST. MARIA GORETTI, Cranhill (1953, 1956), Bellrock Street.

Very Rev. Michael Canon Henretty (1951)
Rev. Thomas P. White, Ph.B., S.T.B. (1999)

POSTAL ADDRESS: St. Maria Goretti's, 259 Bellrock Street, GLASGOW G33 3LN. ☎0141-774 4151.

Sunday Masses: Vigil-Mass, 6 p.m.; 10 a.m., 12 noon. Holy Days of Obligation, Masses: Vigil-Mass, 7.30 p.m.; 10 a.m., 7.30 p.m. Confessions: Saturday, 10.30 to 11 a.m., 6.45 to 7.15 p.m. Estimated Catholic population: 1,600.   🐿 Ⓐ

SISTERS OF MERCY, 6/30 BELLROCK COURT, GLASGOW G33 3JF. ☎0141-774 2093.
ST. ELIZABETH SETON PRIMARY SCHOOL; ST. MODAN'S PRIMARY SCHOOL.

ST. MARK, Shettleston (historically known as: St. Mark's, Carntyne) (1906, 1980), Muiryfauld Drive.

Very Rev. Raymond Armstrong, C.M., M.A.,
Superior, Parish Priest (1965) .

POSTAL ADDRESS: St. Mark's, 80 St. Mark Street, GLASGOW G32 7EA.
☎0141-778 1011.

Sunday Masses: Vigil-Mass, 5.30 p.m.; 10.30 a.m., 5 p.m. Holy Days of Obligation, Masses: 10 a.m., 7 p.m. Confessions: Saturday, 10.15 to 10.45 a.m., 5 to 5.30, 6 to 6.30 p.m.; on request.   🐿 Ⓐ
Estimated Catholic population: 1,100.

ST. MARK'S PRIMARY SCHOOL.

ST. MARTIN, Castlemilk (1958, 1961), Ardencraig Road.

Rev. William A. Monaghan (1974)
Rev. Allan P. Cameron (1987)

POSTAL ADDRESS: St. Martin's, 201 Ardencraig Road, GLASGOW G45 0JJ.
☎0141-634 2262.

Sunday Masses: Vigil-Mass, 6 p.m.; 9.30, 11.30 a.m. Holy Days of Obligation, Masses: Vigil-Mass, 7 p.m.; 9.30 a.m. Confessions: Thursday, 6.30 to 6.50 p.m.; Saturday, 5.30 to 6 p.m.
Estimated Catholic population: 2,000.   🐿 Ⓐ

SISTERS OF THE SACRED HEART OF MARY, 111 ARDENCRAIG DRIVE, GLASGOW G45 0HZ. ☎0141-630 0048.
WINDLAW HOUSE OLD PEOPLE'S HOME attended from ST. MARTIN'S.
ST. DOMINIC'S PRIMARY SCHOOL; ST. MARTIN'S PRIMARY SCHOOL; (ST. RAYMOND'S SPECIAL NEEDS SCHOOL).

ST. MARY, Calton (1842), Abercromby Street.

Rev. Eamon Friel, Ph. L., S.T.L., B.A (Hons.) (1962)

POSTAL ADDRESS: St. Mary's, 89 Abercromby Street, GLASGOW G40 2DQ.
☎0141-554 0872.

Sunday Masses: Vigil-Mass, 6 p.m.; 9.30, 11.30 a.m., 6 p.m. Holy Days of
Obligation, Masses: Vigil-Mass, 6 p.m.; 8.15 a.m., 12.15, 6 p.m.
Confessions: Saturday, 10 to 10.30 a.m., 5 to 6 p.m.
Estimated Catholic population: 1,200.

DAUGHTERS OF WISDOM (LA SAGESSE), 1 GREEN STREET, GLASGOW G40 2HL.
☎0141-556 1064.
KERRVALE NURSING HOME ATTENDED FROM ST. MARY'S.
(ST. ANNE'S PRIMARY SCHOOL; ST. DENIS' PRIMARY SCHOOL; SACRED HEART
PRIMARY SCHOOL.)

ST. MARY IMMACULATE, Pollokshaws (1849,1865)
Shawhill Road.

Very Rev . Hugh Canon O' Donnell (1953)
Rev. Gerard Tartaglia, Ph.B., S.T.B., J.C.L. (1985)

POSTAL ADDRESS: St. Mary's, 150 Shawhill Road, GLASGOW G43 1SY.
☎0141-632 1726.

Sunday Masses: Vigil-Mass, 6 p.m.; 10 a.m., 12 noon, 5 p.m. Evening
Service, as announced. Holy Days of Obligation, Masses: 7.30, 9, 10
a.m.. 7.30 p.m. Confessions: Thursday, 7, 8 p.m.; Saturday, 9.30, 10.30
a.m., 5.30, 7 p.m.
Estimated Catholic population: 3,025.

HECTOR HOUSE AND LANGSIDE NURSING HOME ATTENDED FROM ST. MARY'S.
ST. CONVAL'S PRIMARY SCHOOL.

ST. MICHAEL, Parkhead (1876, 1970), Gallowgate

Rev. Francis O'Rourke (1955)
Very Rev. Michael Canon Mooney (*Retired*) (1944)

POSTAL ADDRESS: St. Michael's, 1350 Gallowgate, GLASGOW G31 4DJ.
☎0141-554 0530.

Sunday Masses: Vigil-Mass, 5.30 p.m., 10.30 a.m., 12 noon, 5.30 p.m.
Holy Days of Obligation, Masses: Vigil-Mass, 5.30 p.m.; 10 a.m., 12.30,
5.30 p.m. Confessions: daily, 12.15 p.m.; Saturdays, 6 to 7 p.m.
Estimated Catholic population: 2,500.

BELVIDERE HOSPITAL AND PARKHEAD HOSPITAL ATTENDED FROM ST. MICHAEL'S.
ST. ANNE'S PRIMARY SCHOOL; ST. MICHAEL'S PRIMARY SCHOOL; ST. MUNGO'S
ACADEMY; (ST. MARK'S PRIMARY SCHOOL).

ST. MONICA, Milton (1969, 1974), Castlebay Street.

Rev. Peter Murphy (1969)

POSTAL ADDRESS: St. Monica's, 171 Castlebay Street, GLASGOW G22 7NE
☎0141-772 4348.

Sunday Masses: Vigil-Mass, 6 p.m.; 11 a.m. Holy Days of Obligation
Masses: Vigil-Mass, 7 p.m.; 10 a.m. Confessions: Saturday, after 10 a.m
Mass, after Vigil-Mass.

Estimated Catholic population: 1,000.

(ST. AMBROSE'S PRIMARY SCHOOL; ST. AUGUSTINE'S PRIMARY SCHOOL).

ST. MUNGO, Townhead (1850, 1869), Parson Street.

Very Rev. Paul Francis Spencer, C.P., *Rector* (1980)
Rev. Dermot Gallagher, C.P., *Vicar* (1989)
Rev. Hubert Hurley, C.P. (1947)
Rev. Augustine Hourigan, C.P. (1969)
Rev. John O'Kane, C.P., *Hospital Chaplain* (1992)
Rev. Eustace Cassidy, C.P. (*Resident at St. Bernard's, Nitshill*) (1957)

POSTAL ADDRESS: St. Mungo's Retreat, 52 Parson Street, GLASGOW G4
0RX ☎0141-552 1823. Fax.: 0141-553 1838

Sunday Masses: Vigil-Mass, 6 p.m.; 10 a.m., 12 noon, 7 p.m. Holy Days
of Obligation, Masses: Vigil-Mass, 6 p.m.; 10 a.m., 12.15 p.m., 7 p.m.
also 9.30 a.m. in St. Stephen's School, 11 a.m. in St. Kevin's School
Confessions: Monday to Friday, 10.30 a.m. to 12 noon., 5.30 to 6 p.m.
Saturday, 10.30 a.m. to 12 noon, 4.30 to 6 p.m., 7 to 8 p.m.

Exposition of the Blessed Sacrament: Wednesday, 10.30 a.m. to 12
noon, 6.30 to 7.30 p.m., Saturday, 10.30 a.m. to 12 noon, 7 to 8 p.m.
Estimated Catholic population: 2,000.

SISTERS OF THE CROSS AND PASSION, 17/2 PINKSTON DRIVE, SIGHTHILL,
GLASGOW G21 1PQ. ☎0141-558 5087/4308.
ROYAL INFIRMARY ATTENDED FROM ST. MUNGO'S. SUNDAY MASS: 4.30 P.M.
PETER MCCANN HOUSE ATTENDED FROM ST. MUNGO'S.
ST. MUNGO'S PRIMARY SCHOOL; ST. STEPHEN'S PRIMARY SCHOOL; ST.
KEVIN'S S.E.N. PRIMARY SCHOOL..
APPLICATIONS FOR MISSIONS OR RETREATS SHOULD BE MADE TO THE RECTOR.

ST. NINIAN, Knightswood (1927, 1959), Knightswood Cross.

Right Rev. Mgr. Owen Gallagher (1958)
Rev. David Brown (1975)
Rev. William McMahon (1999)

POSTAL ADDRESS: St. Ninian's, 5 Baldwin Avenue, GLASGOW G13 2EE.
☎0141-959 1308.
Sunday Masses: Vigil-Mass, 7 p.m.; 8, 9.30, 11 a.m., 12.15, 5 p.m. Holy
Days of Obligation, Masses: Vigil-Mass, 6 p.m.; 8, 10 a.m., 7 p.m.
Confessions: Saturday, 10.30 a.m., 6 to 7 p.m.

Estimated Catholic population: 3,500.

HELPERS OF THE HOLY SOULS, OUR LADY OF PEACE, 38 ARCHERHILL ROAD, GLASGOW G13 3NW. ☎0141-959 4638.
SISTER OF NOTRE DAME, FLAT 1, 1010 GREAT WESTERN ROAD, GLASGOW G13 0NR
KNIGHTSWOOD HOSPITAL, HOMEOPATHIC HOSPITAL, THE GLASGOW NUFFIELD HOSPITAL, CLAYTHORN HOUSE, CLEVEDEN LODGE, FLANDERS HOUSE, RAVELSTON HOUSE, STONELEIGH HOUSE, RANNOCH HOUSE, PROVIDENCE HOUSE AND KNIGHTSWOOD NURSING HOME ATTENDED FROM ST. NINIAN'S.
GARTNAVEL HOSPITALS: SEE CORPUS CHRISTI, SCOTSTOUNHILL
ST. NINIAN'S PRIMARY SCHOOL; (CORPUS CHRISTI PRIMARY SCHOOL).

OUR LADY OF THE ASSUMPTION, Ruchill (1952, 1956), Bilsland Drive.

Rev. John Lyons, B.D. (1980)

POSTAL ADDRESS: Our Lady of the Assumption, 493 Bilsland Drive, GLASGOW G20 9JN. ☎0141-946 2683.

Sunday Masses: Vigil-Mass, 5.30 p.m.; 11 a.m. Holy Days of Obligation, Masses: 10 a.m. (when school is open), 7 p.m. Confessions: Saturday, 5 to 5.30 p.m.
Estimated Catholic population: 450.

SOLIDARITY SHOP. ☎0141-342 4089.
FOUR HILLS NURSING HOME, WYNDFORD LOCKS NURSING HOME, THE ORCHARDS AND HAWTHORN STREET SHELTERED HOUSING ATTENDED FROM OUR LADY OF THE ASSUMPTION.
OUR LADY OF THE ASSUMPTION PRIMARY SCHOOL.

OUR LADY OF CONSOLATION, Govanhill (1966, 1971), Inglefield Street.

Rev. Joseph Walsh, S.T.L. (1978)
Sr. Lucy Cairns, D.C., *Pastoral Assistant*

POSTAL ADDRESS: Our Lady of Consolation, 113 Dixon Avenue, GLASGOW G42 8ER. ☎0141-423 5188.

Sunday Masses: Vigil-Mass, 6.30 p.m.; 10, 11.30 a.m., 7 p.m. Holy Days of Obligation, Masses: 10 a.m., 12 noon, 6 p.m. Confessions: Saturday, 10 a.m., 6 p.m.
Estimated Catholic population: 1,800.

WOMEN'S HOSTEL, ATTENDED FROM OUR LADY OF CONSOLATION.
(ST. BRIDE'S PRIMARY SCHOOL; HOLY CROSS PRIMARY SCHOOL).

OUR LADY OF FATIMA, Dalmarnock (1950,1953), Springfield Road.

Rev. James M. Lawlor, M.A.(Oxon.) (1987)

POSTAL ADDRESS: Our Lady of Fatima, 75 Millerfield Road, GLASGOW G40 4RP. ☎0141-554 5008; Fax: 0141-554 2795..

Sunday Masses: Vigil-Mass, 5.15 p.m.; 11.30 (with Children's Liturgy of the Word) a.m. Evening Service as announced. Holy Days of Obligation, Masses: 10 a.m., 7 p.m. Confessions: Saturday, 10 a.m., 6 p.m.
Estimated Catholic population: 700.

RACHEL HOUSE , 505 BALTIC STREET, GLASGOW G40.☎ 0141-556 5465.
KIRKHAVEN, ATTENDED FROM OUR LADY OF FATIMA.
(ST. MICHAEL'S PRIMARY SCHOOL; SACRED HEART PRIMARY SCHOOL).

OUR LADY OF GOOD COUNSEL, Dennistoun (1962, 1965), Craigpark.

Rev. Thomas J. Chambers, B.A (1967)

POSTAL ADDRESS: Our Lady of Good Counsel, 6 Broompark Circus, GLASGOW G31 2JF. ☎ & Fax: 0141-554 1558.

E-mail: jchambers@claranet.co.uk

Sunday Masses: Vigil-Mass 5.30 p.m.; 10 a.m., 12 noon, 5.30 p.m. Holy Days of Obligation, Masses: 10 a.m., 6 p.m. Confessions: Saturday, 10 a.m., 6 p.m.; on request.
Estimated Catholic population:1,190.

FRANCISCAN CONVENT, 1 BROOMPARK CIRCUS, GLASGOW G31 2JF. ☎0141-554 1415.
FRANCISCAN CONVENT, 41 CIRCUS DRIVE, GLASGOW G31 2JQ. ☎0141-556 6941.
GLASGOW CALEDONIAN UNIVERSITY. CHAPLAIN: REV. THOMAS J. CHAMBERS, B.A., OUR LADY OF GOOD COUNSEL.
GOLFHILL NURSING HOME ATTENDED FROM OUR LADY OF GOOD COUNSEL.
(ST. DENIS' PRIMARY SCHOOL).

OUR LADY OF LOURDES, Cardonald (1906, 1939), Lourdes Avenue.

Right Rev. Mgr. John Gilmartin (1968)
Rev. Joseph E. Sullivan, Ph.B., S.T.L. (1986)
Rev. Paul Friel, B.D. (1992)

POSTAL ADDRESS: Our Lady of Lourdes, 51 Lourdes Avenue, Cardonald, GLASGOW G52 3QU. ☎0141-882 1024.

Sunday Masses: Vigil-Mass, 7 p.m.; 8 (in Nazareth House), 9.30, 11 a.m., 12.15 p.m.; 6 p.m. Evening Service, as announced. Holy Days of Obligation, Masses: Vigil-Mass, 7 p.m.; 9, 10, 11 a.m., 7 p.m. Confessions: Saturday, 10.30 a.m., 5.45 to 6.45 p.m. Exposition of the Blessed Sacrament: Saturday: 5.45 to 6.45 p.m.
Estimated Catholic population: 6,000.

NAZARETH HOUSE, 1647 PAISLEY ROAD WEST, GLASGOW G52 3QT. ☎0141-882 1741; FAX:0141-882 8178.
COMBONI SISTERS' CONVENT, COMBONI HOUSE, 124 BERRYKNOWES ROAD, GLASGOW G52 2TT. ☎0141-883 6139.
LOURDES COURT (LORETTO SHELTERED HOUSING), LOURDES AVENUE.
FORFAR HOUSE, GRAMPIAN HOME, MARTHA HOUSE AND WILMAR NURSING HOME ATTENDED FROM OUR LADY OF LOURDES.
OUR LADY OF LOURDES PRIMARY SCHOOL; OUR LADY OF THE ROSARY PRIMARY SCHOOL; LOURDES SECONDARY SCHOOL.

OUR LADY OF PERPETUAL SUCCOUR, Broomhill (1962, 1965), Mitre Road .

Rev. George F. Gillespie, Ph.L., S.T.B. (1961)
Rev. Bernard Connell (1962)
(*Hospital Chaplain.*☎ *0141-339 1324*)

POSTAL ADDRESS: Our Lady of Perpetual Succour, 17 Mitre Road, GLASGOW G11 7EF. ☎0141-334 5330.

Sunday Masses: Vigil-Mass, 6 p.m.; 10.30 a.m. Holy Days of Obligation, Masses: Vigil-Mass, 7 p.m.; 10 a.m. Confessions: Saturday, before and after 10 a.m. Mass, after Vigil-Mass.
Estimated Catholic population: 1,400.

SISTERS OF NOTRE DAME, NOTRE DAME CONVENT, 14 MARLBOROUGH AVENUE, GLASGOW G11 7BW. ☎0141-339 4882.
FOCOLARE, 152 BEECHWOOD DRIVE, GLASGOW G11 7DX. ☎0141-339 2280.
CLARENCE COURT NURSING HOME ATTENDED FROM OUR LADY OF PERPETUAL SUCCOUR.
THE SOUTHERN GENERAL HOSPITAL. CHAPLAIN: REV. BERNARD CONNELL. ☎0141-339 1324 (HOSPITAL: 0141-201 1100). SUNDAY MASS: 11 A.M. IN MATERNITY OUTPATIENTS DEPT.
ST. THOMAS AQUINAS SECONDARY SCHOOL; (CORPUS CHRISTI, ST. NINIAN'S, NOTRE DAME, ST. PAUL'S AND ST. PETER'S PRIMARY SCHOOLS).

OUR LADY AND ST. GEORGE, Penilee (1949, 1958), Sandwood Road.

Rev. Paul M. Conroy, Ph.L., S.T.L. (1980)
Rev. Paul McAlinden (1993)
Rev. Robert Bradley, S.T.D.*(Retired)* (1947)

POSTAL ADDRESS: Our Lady and St. George's, 50 Sandwood Road, GLASGOW G52 2QE. ☎0141-882 4868; Fax: 0141-883 1644,.

Sunday Masses: Vigil-Mass, 6.30 p.m.; 9.30, 11 a.m., 5.30 p.m. Holy Days of Obligation, Masses: 9, 10.30 a.m., 7 p.m. Confessions: Saturday, 10.30 a.m., 5.30 to 6 p.m.
Estimated Catholic population: 4,000.

SISTERS OF NOTRE DAME, 67 MOORPARK AVENUE, GLASGOW G52 4ET. ☎0141-810 4214.
ROSS HALL HOSPITAL AND DEANFIELD NURSING HOME ATTENDED FROM OUR LADY AND ST. GEORGE'S.
ST. GEORGE'S PRIMARY SCHOOL; (OUR LADY OF LOURDES PRIMARY SCHOOL; OUR LADY OF THE ROSARY PRIMARY SCHOOL.)

OUR LADY AND ST. MARGARET (1874, 1983), Portman Street.

Rev. David Tracey (1962)

.POSTAL ADDRESS: Our Lady and St. Margaret's, 20 Marine Gardens, GLASGOW G51 1HH. ☎0141-427 7505.
Sunday Masses: Vigil-Mass, 6 p.m.; 11.30 a.m. Holy Days of Obligation, Masses: 12.35, 7 p.m. Confessions: Saturday, 5.30 p.m.
Estimated Catholic population: 700.

AILSA CRAIG NURSING HOME, KINNING PARK NURSING HOME AND LAMBHILL COURT NURSING HOME ATTENDED FROM OUR LADY AND ST. MARGARET'S.
(ST. SAVIOUR'S PRIMARY SCHOOL).

ST. PATRICK, Anderston (1850, 1898), North Street.

Rev. Gerard Nugent (1967)

POSTAL ADDRESS: St. Patrick's, 137 William Street, GLASGOW G3 8UR. ☎0141-221 3579.

Sunday Masses: Vigil-Mass, 6 p.m.; 10 a.m., 12 noon. Holy Days of Obligation, Masses: Vigil-Mass, 6 p.m.: 10 a.m., 12.35 p.m. Exposition of the Blessed Sacrament, Thursday, 1.00 with Holy Hour, 7 to 8 p.m.Confessions: Saturday, 10.30 to 11 a.m., 5.15 to 5.45 p.m.
Estimated Catholic population: 1,400.

MARGARET BLACKWOOD CENTRE, PARK NURSING HOME AND CHEAPSIDE MEN'S HOSTEL ATTENDED FROM ST. PATRICK'S.
ST. PATRICK'S PRIMARY SCHOOL.

ST. PAUL, Shettleston (1850, 1959), Shettleston Road.

Rev. John J.N. Burns (1954)
Rev. John G. Campbell (1987)

POSTAL ADDRESS: St. Paul's, 1653 Shettleston Road, GLASGOW G32 9AR.
☎0141-778 1014; Mobile:07801-736681..

Sunday Masses: Vigil-Mass, 6.30 p.m.; 9, 10.30 (Family Mass with Children's Liturgy) a.m., 12 noon, 6.30 (Youth Liturgy) p.m. Evening Service (Avent and Lent), 4 p.m. Holy Days of Obligation, Masses: Vigil-Mass, 7.30 p.m.; 9.30 a.m., 1.00, 7.30 p.m. Confessions: Saturday, 10 a.m., 5.30 to 6.20 p.m., after Vigil-Mass; on request.
Estimated Catholic population: 2,500.

SISTERS OF NOTRE DAME, COMBONI HOUSE, BAILLIESTON ROAD, GLASGOW G32 0TG. ☎/FAX: 0141-771 5242.
ST. JOHN'S RESIDENTIAL SCHOOL, SPRINGBOIG, EASTBANK NURSING HOME AND MOUNT VERNON NURSING HOME, ATTENDED FROM ST. PAUL'S.
(ST. BRIDGET'S PRIMARY SCHOOL; ST. PAUL'S PRIMARY SCHOOL; ST. TIMOTHY'S PRIMARY SCHOOL.)

ST. PAUL, Whiteinch (1903, 1960), Dumbarton Road.

Right Rev. Mgr. John Sheridan (1956)
Rev. Joseph McNulty (*Hospital Chaplain,* ☎0141-954 9203) (1988)

POSTAL ADDRESS: St. Paul's, 1213 Dumbarton Road, GLASGOW G14 9UP.
☎0141-950 2488.

Sunday Masses: Vigil-Mass, 6.30 p.m.; 10 a.m., 11.30 a.m., 6.30 p.m.
Holy Days of Obligation, Masses: Vigil-Mass, 6.30 p.m.; 10 a.m., 6.30 p.m. Confessions: Saturday, 10.30 a.m., 5.30 to 6.30 p.m.
Estimated Catholic population: 2,000.

STELLA MARIS SEAFARERS' CENTRE (APOSTLESHIP OF THE SEA), 937 DUMBARTON ROAD, GLASGOW G14 9UF. ☎0141-339 6657.
SISTERS OF NOTRE DAME, 39 VICTORIA PARK DRIVE SOUTH, GLASGOW G14 9QP. ☎0141-959 4103.
ST. PAUL'S PRIMARY SCHOOL.

ST. PETER, Partick (1855, 1903), Hyndland Street.

Right Rev. Mgr. James Ryan, M.R.Ed. (1967)
Rev. Joseph Keenan (1992)
Rev. Leonard A. Purcell (*Chaplain to the Deaf*) (1985)
(☎(*Minicom Voice and Text*) 0141-357 5772)

POSTAL ADDRESS: St. Peter's, 46 Hyndland Street, GLASGOW G11
5PS.☎0141-576 1378; Fax: 0141-334 6976.

Sunday Masses: Vigil-Mass, 6 p.m.; 9, 10.30 a.m., 12 noon, 6 p.m.
Evening Service, Advent, Lent, May and October, 5 p.m. Holy Days of
Obligation, Masses: Vigil-Mass, 6 p.m.; 8, 10 a.m., 6 p.m. Confessions:
weekdays (except Holy Days), 9.40 a.m.; Saturday, from 9.40 a.m., after
10 a.m. Mass, 5.30 to 6 p.m., after Vigil-Mass.
Estimated Catholic population: 3,500.

WESTERN INFIRMARY. CHAPLAIN: REV. JOSEPH MCNULTY, ST. PAUL'S,
WHITEINCH. SUNDAY MASS, 11 A.M. ☎0141-954 9203.
MARIST BROTHERS, 10 PARTICKHILL ROAD, GLASGOW G11 5BL. ☎0141-339
8259.
FRANCISCAN MISSIONARIES OF MARY, ST. HELEN'S CONVENT, 5 KINGSBOROUGH
GARDENS, GLASGOW G12 9NH. ☎0141-339 6789.
NOTRE DAME CONVENT, 38 KINGSBOROUGH GARDENS, GLASGOW G12 9NJ.
☎0141-339 3567.
NOTRE DAME CONVENT, 55 WHITE STREET, GLASGOW G11 5EQ. ☎0141-339
2986.
NOTRE DAME PRIMARY SCHOOL; ST. PETER'S PRIMARY SCHOOL; NOTRE DAME
GIRLS' HIGH SCHOOL.

ST. PHILIP, Ruchazie (1954, 1958), Drumlochy Road.

Rev. Joseph Boyle (1975)

POSTAL ADDRESS: St. Philip's, 150 Drumlochy Road, GLASGOW G33 3RF.
☎0141-774 5688.

Sunday Masses: 11 a.m., 5.30 p.m. Holy Days of Obligation, Masses: 10
a.m., 7.30 p.m. Confessions: Saturday, after 10 a.m. Mass, 6 to 7 p.m.
Estimated Catholic population: 1,500.

SISTERS OF ST. JOSEPH OF PEACE, 150 DRUMLOCHY ROAD, GLASGOW G33 3RF.
☎0141-774 2677.
ST. PHILIP'S PRIMARY SCHOOL.

ST. PHILOMENA, Provanmill (1939, 1940), Royston Road.

Rev. John McAuley, S.T.B. (1970)

POSTAL ADDRESS: St. Philomena's, 1255 Royston Road, GLASGOW G33 1EH. ☎0141-770 4237; Fax: 041-770 6660.
E-Mail: john@mena.freeserve.co.uk

Sunday Masses: Vigil-Mass, 6 p.m.; 10 a.m. 12 noon, 5 p.m. Holy Days of Obligation, Masses: 10 a.m., 6 p.m. Confessions: Saturday, 10.30 a.m., 6.45 to 7.15 p.m.
Estimated Catholic population: 2,800.

FRANCISCAN MISSIONARIES OF MARY CONVENT, 19-21 MOODIESBURN STREET, GLASGOW G33 1DA. ☎0141-770 8628.
LITTLE SISTERS OF THE POOR, ST. JOSEPH'S, 14 CUMNOCK ROAD, GLASGOW G33 IQT. ☎0141-558 5114.
HOGGANFIELD NURSING HOME ATTENDED FROM ST. PHILOMENA'S.
ST. PHILOMENA'S PRIMARY SCHOOL; (ST. GILBERT'S PRIMARY SCHOOL).

ST. PIUS X, Drumchapel (1954, 1957), Bayfield Terrace.

Rev. Michael Savage *(on Sabbatical)* (1983)
Rev. Jim Rooney, Dip.Theol. *(Administrator)* (1995)
Sr. Una Casey, R.S.C., *Pastoral Assistant*

POSTAL ADDRESS: St. Pius X, 4 Bayfield Terrace, GLASGOW G15 7EJ. ☎0141-944 2044.
E-mail: mikemoriah@aol.com

Sunday Masses: Vigil-Mass, 5.30 p.m.; 11 a.m. Holy Days of Obligation, Masses: 9.30 a.m., 7 p.m. Confessions: daily, after 9.30 a.m. Mass; Saturday, 6 to 6.25p.m.
Estimated Catholic population: 1,000.

DRUMRY HOUSE, HARROW COURT AND PINEWOOD COURT ATTENDED FROM ST. PIUS X.
ST. PIUS PRIMARY SCHOOL; (ST. CLARE'S PRIMARY SCHOOL).

ST. ROBERT BELLARMINE, Househillwood (1941, 1959), Peat Road.

Rev. Lawrence McMahon (1960)

POSTAL ADDRESS: St. Robert's, 310 Peat Road, GLASGOW G53 6SA. ☎0141-881 1137.

Sunday Masses: Vigil-Mass, 6 p.m.; 10 a.m., 12 noon, 6 p.m. Holy Days of Obligation, Masses: Vigil-Mass, 7 p.m.; 10 a.m., 7 p.m. Confessions: Saturday, 10.30 a.m., 5.30 to 7.15 p.m. (except during Vigil-Mass).
Estimated Catholic population: 3,400.

DAUGHTERS OF THE CROSS AND PASSION, 201 GLENLORA DRIVE, GLASGOW G53 6JS. ☎0141-881 2147.
COWGLEN HOSPITAL ATTENDED FROM ST. ROBERT'S.
ST. ROBERT'S PRIMARY SCHOOL; BELLARMINE SECONDARY SCHOOL;
(ST. BERNARD'S PRIMARY SCHOOL).

ST. ROCH, Garngad (1907), Royston Road.

Rev. Angus MacDonald (1970)

POSTAL ADDRESS: St. Roch's, 311 Roystonhill, GLASGOW G21 2HN.
☎0141-552 2945; Fax: 0141-552 2156..

Sunday Masses: Vigil-Mass, 6 p.m.; 9, 11.30 a.m. Holy Days of Obligation, Masses: Vigil-Mass, 7 p.m.; 10 a.m., 7 p.m. Confessions: Monday to Saturday, 9 to 9.50 a.m.; Saturday, 5.30 to 5.50 p.m.
Estimated Catholic population: 3,000.

INSTITUTE OF THE BLESSED VIRGIN MARY, FLAT 10/1, 160 CHARLES STREET, GLASGOW G21 2QG. ☎ 0141-553 2314.
ST. GILBERT'S PRIMARY SCHOOL; ST. ROCH'S PRIMARY SCHOOL;
ST. ROCH'S SECONDARY SCHOOL.

SACRED HEART, Bridgeton (1873, 1910), Old Dalmarnock Road.

Rev. John G. McGinley (1985)

POSTAL ADDRESS: Sacred Heart, 50 Old Dalmarnock Road, GLASGOW G40 4AU. ☎0141-554 0806.

Sunday Masses: Vigil-Mass, 5 p.m.; 9.30, 11.30 a.m. Holy Days of Obligation, Masses: 10 a.m., 6 p.m. Confessions: Saturday, 10.30 a.m., 6 to 6.30 p.m.
Estimated Catholic population: 1,350.

CARMICHAEL HOUSE AND MAXTON HOUSE ATTENDED FROM SACRED HEART.
SACRED HEART PRIMARY SCHOOL.

ST. SAVIOUR, Govan (1897, 1900), Merryland Street.

Rev. Peter C. McKelvie (1963)

POSTAL ADDRESS: St. Saviour's, 39 Merryland Street, GLASGOW G51 2QG.
☎0141-445 1166.

Sunday Masses: Vigil-Mass, 6 p.m.; 11 a.m. Holy Days of Obligation, Masses: Vigil-Mass, 7 p.m.; 10 a.m. Confessions: Thursday, 7.40 p.m.; Saturday, 5 to 5.45 p.m.
Estimated Catholic population: 2,000.

ST. SIMON, Partick (1855, 1858; re-established as separate parish, 1945), Partick Bridge Street.

Rev. John Chalmers, D.C.L (1952)

Postal address: St. Simon's, 33 Partick Bridge Street, Glasgow G11 6PQ. ☎0141-339 7618.

Sunday Masses: 10 a.m., 12.15 p.m., 6.30 p.m. Holy Days of Obligation, Masses: 10.30 a.m., 12.30, 7.30 p.m. Confessions: daily, 10 a.m.; Saturday, 3 to 4 p.m.
Estimated Catholic population: 350.

Queen Mother Hospital and Royal Hospital for Sick Children. Chaplain: Rev. William J. Slavin, St. Charles'. ☎0141-946 7622. (Hospital: 0141-201 0000).
Kelvin School for Children with Visual Impairment and Additional Learning Difficulties, Nairn Street, Yorkhill, attended from St. Simon's.
(St. Peter' Primary School)

FOR MEMBERS OF THE POLISH COMMUNITY See entry on page 297.

ST. STEPHEN, Sighthill (1968, closed 1999).

The Registers of St. Stephen's Parish have been deposited at St. Mungo's, Townhead.

ST. TERESA OF LISIEUX, Possilpark (1932, 1960), Saracen Street.

Rev. Thomas J. Hendry (1966)

Postal address: St. Teresa's, 86 Saracen Street, Glasgow G22 5AD. ☎/Fax: 0141-336 8212.

Sunday Masses: Vigil-Mass, 6 p.m.; 10.30 a.m., 5.30 p.m. Holy Days of Obligation, Masses: Vigil-Mass, 7 p.m.; 10 a.m. Confessions: Saturday, 10.30 a.m., 5.30 p.m., after Vigil-Mass.
Estimated Catholic population: 3,000.

Franciscans of the Immaculate Conception, St. Teresa's, 86 Saracen Street, Glasgow G22 5AD. ☎0141-336 3027; Fax:0141-336 4096. E-mail:SKELLY5507@aol.com

Sheltered Housing, Barloch Street, Sheltered Housing, Gourlay Street, and Allander Court Nursing Home, Denmark Street, attended from St. Teresa's.

St. Cuthbert's Primary School; St. Teresa's Primary School.

ST. THOMAS APOSTLE, Riddrie (1924, 1957), Smithycroft Road.

Rev. Peter McBride (1981)
Rev. John Mulholland , B.D. (1999)

Postal address: St. Thomas', 826 Cumbernauld Road, Glasgow G33 2EE. ☎0141-770 4057.

Sunday Masses: Vigil-Mass, 6.30 p.m.; 9.30, 11 a m., 12.15 p.m. Evening Service as announced. Holy Days of Obligation, Masses: 10 a.m., 7 p.m. Confessions: Saturday, after 10 a.m. Mass, 5.45 to 6.15 p.m. Estimated Catholic population: 1,500.

Sisters of Notre Dame, 135 Smithycroft Road, Glasgow G33 2RD. ☎0141-770 5287.

Fairhome, Riddrie House, Riddrie Knowes, Riddrievale Sheltered Housing, Smithycroft Road, and Peter McEachran Home, Kennyhill. attended from St. Thomas'.

St. Thomas' Primary School.

ST. VINCENT DE PAUL, Thornliebank (East Renfrewshire) (1942,1960), Main Street .

Rev. Oscar de la Torre, S.X., M.Div. (1987)
Rev. Patrick Duffy, S.X. (1998)

Postal address: St. Vincent's, 22 Main Street, Thornliebank, Glasgow G46 7SH. ☎0141-638 0750.

Sunday Masses: Vigil-Mass, 6 p.m.; 9.30, 11.30 a.m. Holy Days of Obligation, Masses: 9.30 a.m., 7 p.m. Confessions: half an hour before daily Mass and weekend Mass, and on reasonable request. Estimated Catholic population: 2,400.

Our Lady of the Missions Primary School; St. Vincent de Paul's Primary School; St. Ninian's High School.

DEAF PEOPLE, CHAPLAINCY FOR

Rev. Leonard A. Purcell, *Chaplain* (1985)

POSTAL ADDRESS: St. Vincent's Centre for Deaf People, 51 Tobago Street, GLASGOW G40 2RH. ☎0141-554 8897 (voice); 0141-550 1616 (Text). Fax: 0141-551 8904.

CHAPLAIN'S RESIDENCE: St. Peter's, 46 Hyndland Street, GLASGOW G11 5PS. ☎0141-576 1378; *(Minicom Voice and Text)* 0141-357 5772; Fax: 0141-334 6976.

Sunday Mass: 7 p.m. Holy Days of Obligation, Mass: 7 p.m. Confessions: Sunday, 6.30 p.m. Mass is celebrated in sign language for deaf people.

POLISH COMMUNITY, CHAPLAINCY FOR

Rev. Marian Antoni Lekawa, S.A.C., *Rector, Polish Catholic Mission in Scotland* (1972)

POSTAL ADDRESS: Polish Catholic Mission in Scotland, 4 Park Grove Terrace, GLASGOW G3 7SD. ☎0141-339 9163.

Services in St. Simon's Church, Partick Bridge Street. Sunday Mass, 11 a.m.

UNIVERSITIES, CHAPLAINCY PARISHES.

University of Glasgow (Chaplaincy established 1925, church of St. Mungo opened 1956, Parish erected 1975).

Rev. Robert J. Hill, B.Sc., Cert. Ed.
Chaplain, Parish Priest (1977)
Sr. Brigid McNally, R.S.M., B.Ed., *Assistant Chaplain*

POSTAL ADDRESS: Turnbull Hall, 15 Southpark Terrace, GLASGOW G12 8LG. ☎0141-339 4315 (Students: 0141-334 2942); Fax: 0141-330 5567. E-mail: RCChaplaincy@gla.ac.uk

Sunday Mass: Vigil-Mass, (October to June), 6.15 p.m.; 11.30 a.m., 6.15 p.m. Holy Days of Obligation, Mass: 12.05 p.m., 1.05, 5.05 p.m. Confessions: Friday, 12.30 to 1.00 p.m.; any time on request. **Ⓐ**

University of Strathclyde (Chaplaincy established 1965, Parish erected 1975).

Rev. Gilbert Markus, O.P.,B.D., B.A., M.Th., S.T.L.,
Chaplain, Parish Priest (1987)

POSTAL ADDRESSES: Ecumenical Chaplaincy Centre, St. Paul's Building, 90 John Street, GLASGOW G1 1JH. ☎0141-553 4144/ (Mobile)07775-743-665,

Residence: Blackfriars, 36 Queen's Drive, GLASGOW G42 8DD. ☎0141-423 2971. Fax/Ans.: 0141-423 4575.

Sunday Mass (Chaplaincy Centre): 11 a.m. Holy Days of Obligation, Masses: 10.10 a.m. (Chaplaincy Centre), 12.10 and 1.10 p.m. (in Students' Union), 5.10 p.m. (Jordanhill). Confessions at call.Weekday Services outside University Term as announced.

COLUMBAN FATHERS (1974).

Very Rev. Declan McNaughton *Superior* (1973)
Rev. Gerard Dunn, M.B. (1967)

POSTAL ADDRESS: St. Columban's, 31 Kingsborough Gardens, GLASGOW G12 9NH. ☎0141-334 1602. E-mail: declan.mcnaughton@gisp.net

COMBONI MISSIONARIES (Verona Fathers) (1979, 1992).

Very Rev. Antonio Benetti, M.C.C.J., *Superior* (1977)
Rev. Charles Duffin, M.C.C.J. (1955)
Rev. Anthony Wolstenholme, M.C.C.J. (1957)

POSTAL ADDRESS: Comboni Missionaries, 138 Carmyle Avenue, Carmyle, GLASGOW G32 8DL. ☎/Fax: 0141-641 4399.

DISCALCED CARMELITES (1988), Mount Carmel Retreat Centre, Pollokshields.

Very Rev. John Grennan, O.C.D. *Prior* (1970)
Rev. Norbert Cummins, O.C.D. (1940)
Rev. Terence Carey, O.C.D. (1958)
Rev. Anthony Parsons, O.C.D. (1995)
Bro. Patrick Walsh, O.C.D.

POSTAL ADDRESS: Mount Carmel, 61 Hamilton Avenue, GLASGOW G41 4HA . ☎0141-427 0794. Fax.: 0141-427 9950.

DOMINICANS (1981).

Very Rev. Gordian Marshall, O.P., B.Ed., *Superior* (1963)
E-mail: Gordian@op_Glasgow.demon.co.uk
Rev. Robert Pollock, O.P., B.A., M.A., Ph.D., F. R.Anth.I. (1956)
E-mail: Pollock@op_Glasgow.demon.co.uk
Rev. Angus McLaughlin,O.P., B.A.,
Administrator, Our Lady of the Angels, Mingarry
(Diocese of Argyll and The Isles) (1965),
Rev. Gilbert Markus, O.P., B.D., B.A., M.Th., S.T.L.,
Chaplain to Strathclyde University (1987)
E-Mail: Gilbert@op_Glasgow.demon.co.uk

POSTAL ADDRESS: Blackfriars, 36 Queen's Drive, GLASGOW G42 8DD.
☎0141-423 2971. Fax: 0141-423 4575.

JESUITS (1859, 1999), Ignatian Spirituality Centre.

Rev. Fintan Creaven, S.J. (1968)
(Resident at St. Aloysius', 10 Woodside Place, Glasgow G3 6RL)
Rev. Brian McClorry, S.J. (1971)
(Resident at Wellcross, 193 Nithsdale Road, Glasgow G41 5EX)

POSTAL ADDRESS: Ignatian Spirituality Centre, 7 Woodside Place,
GLASGOW G3 7QF. ☎0141-354 0077. Fax: 0141-354 0099.

Wellcross (Jesuit Community House)

Very Rev. Brian McClorry, S.J., *Superior* (1971)
Rev. William Forrester, S.J. (1956)
Rev. Peter Harrison, S.J (1943)
Rev. Michael Spencer, S.J. (1958)
Bro. James Spence, S.J.
Bro. John McPake, S.J.

POSTAL ADDRESS: Wellcross, 193 Nithsdale Road, GLASGOW G41 5EX.
☎0141-423 3005.

MILL HILL MISSIONARIES (1948, 1985).

Very Rev. Joseph Holmes, M.H.M., *Rector* (1963)
Rev. Gerard Hamill, M.H.M. (1974)
Rev. Thomas O'Brien, M.H.M., B.D., Ph.L. (1974)

POSTAL ADDRESS: St. Joseph's House, 30 Lourdes Avenue, GLASGOW G52
3QU. ☎0141-883 0139. Fax: 0141-882 5791.

Parishes Outside the City of Glasgow

The name given last before the name of the Church is the Local Authority.

ALEXANDRIA, West Dunbartonshire, Our Lady and St. Mark (1859, 1926), Ferryfield.

Rev. Francis Courtney (1953)
Rev. Brendan J. Murtagh, B.A (1985)

POSTAL ADDRESS: Our Lady and St. Mark's, Ferry Loan, Bank Street, ALEXANDRIA G83 0UW ☎Alexandria (01389) 752091.

Sunday Masses: Vigil-Mass, 5.30 p.m.; 9.30, 11 a.m., 6.30 p.m. Holy Days of Obligation, Masses: Vigil-Mass, 7.30 p.m.; 8, 10 a.m., 7.30 p.m. Confessions: Thursday, 8 p.m.; Saturday, before and after morning and Vigil Masses.
Estimated Catholic population: 1,300.

VALE OF LEVEN GENERAL HOSPITAL, VALE OF LEVEN MATERNITY HOSPITAL AND VALE OF LEVEN HEALTH CARE OF THE ELDERLY, ALEXANDRIA, ATTENDED FROM ST. MARK'S. (MASS ON SECOND SUNDAY OF THE MONTH AT 3 P.M. IN THE HOSPITAL CHAPEL.)
LEVEN COTTAGE HOME; BRIDGE COURT, GRAY STREET, OAKBANK AND THE CROFT SHELTERED HOUSING ATTENDED FROM ST. MARK'S.
ST. MARY'S PRIMARY SCHOOL.

ARROCHAR, Argyll and Bute, SS. Peter and Paul (1953), served from Garelochhead.

Sunday Masses: Easter Sunday to end of September, 8.30 a.m.; October to Palm Sunday, 11.30 a.m. Holy Days of Obligation, Mass: 8.15 p.m.

BALLOCH, West Dunbartonshire, St. Kessog (1952, 1958), Balloch Road.

Rev. Sean M. FitzGerald (1963)
St. Philomena Reid, R.S.C. *(Pastoral Assistant)*

POSTAL ADDRESS: St. Kessog's, Balloch Road, Balloch, ALEXANDRIA G83 8LQ. ☎Alexandria (01389) 721586.

Sunday Masses: Vigil-Mass, 6 p.m.; 9.30, 11.30 (with Children's Liturgy) a.m., 7 p.m. Holy Days of Obligation, Masses: 8, 10 a.m., 7.30 p.m. Confessions: Thursday, 8 p.m.; Saturday, 10 a.m., 6.45 p.m. Adoration of the Blessed Sacrament, Monday and Tuesday, 10 a.m. to 6 p.m. Estimated Catholic population: 3,100.

MANSE GARDENS AND SUNNINGDALE (HOMES FOR THE ELDERLY) ATTENDED FROM ST. KESSOG'S.
ST. KESSOG'S PRIMARY SCHOOL; (ST. MARY'S PRIMARY SCHOOL, Alexandria).

BEARSDEN, East Dunbartonshire, St. Andrew (1967, 1987), Roman Road.

Rev. William B. Donnelly (1965)
Rev. Stephen Connolly (1987)

POSTAL ADDRESS: St. Andrew's, 29 Roman Road, Bearsden, GLASGOW G61 2SN. ☎0141-942 4635.

Sunday Masses: Vigil-Mass, 6 p.m.; 9, 10.30 a.m., 12 noon. Holy Days of Obligation, Masses: Vigil-Mass, 7 p.m.; 10 a.m., 7 p.m. Confessions: Saturday, after 10 a.m. Mass, after Vigil-Mass to 7.30 p.m.
Estimated Catholic population: 3,155.

SISTERS OF NOTRE DAME, 'NOTRE DAME', 19 BURNSIDE, BEARSDEN, GLASGOW G61 4PX. ☎0141-942 5973.
ST. ANDREW'S CAMPUS, UNIVERSITY OF GLASGOW, DUNTOCHER ROAD, BEARSDEN, GLASGOW G61 4NP. ☎0141-943 1424. CHAPLAIN: REV. JOHN HUGHES, M.A., DIP. ED., PH.B., S.T.L., SC.P. (1984), CHAPLAIN'S RESIDENCE, ST. ANDREW'S COLLEGE, DUNTOCHER ROAD, BEARSDEN, GLASGOW G61 4NP. ☎0141-942 7719.
CANNIESBURN HOSPITAL, ABBOTSFORD HOME, BUCHANAN HOUSE HOME, BUCHANAN LODGE HOME, CRAIGHOLME HOME FOR THE DEAF, LYNEDOCH HOME AND SCHAW COURT HOME ATTENDED FROM ST. ANDREW'S.
ST. ANDREW'S PRIMARY SCHOOL.

BEARSDEN, East Dunbartonshire, Scotus College, National Major Seminary under the patronage of Blessed John Duns Scotus (1993, Church dedicated, 1997), Chesters Road.

RESIDENT STAFF

Very Rev. Neil Donnachie, *Rector* (1971)
Rev. Michael B. Regan, B.A., M.Litt., M.Th., D.E.A.,
Vice-Rector and Director of Liturgy (1982)
Rev. Thomas H. Boyle, Dip.Theol., *Spiritual Director* (1986)
Rev. Paul Kelly, M.A., D.Phil., *Director of Studies* (1985)
Rev. Andrew McKenzie, M.A.,*Pastoral Director* (1988)
In Residence
Rev. George Donaldson, Ph.L., S.T.L., Dip.R.E. (1961)

VISITING STAFF
Rev. David Boyd, M.A. (1985)
Rev. Patrick Boylan, L.S.S. (1977)
Rev. Gerard J. Conroy, Ph.B., S.T.B., L.S.S. (1982)
Rev. John A. Hughes, Ph.B., S.T.L.
Sc.P. M.A., Dip.Ed. (1984)
Rev. John Keenan, LL.B., Ph.L., S.T.B. (1995)
Rev. William McFadden, Ph.B., S.T.L. (1985)
Rev. Michael McMahon, Ph.B., S.T.B., L.S.S (1985)
Rev. Paul G. Milarvie, Ph.B., S.T.L. (1993)
Rev. Dominic Quinn, Ph.B., S.T.L. (1988)
Rev. Joseph E. Sullivan, Ph.B., S.T.L. (1985)
Rev. Gerard Tartaglia, Ph.B., S.T.B., J.C.L (1985)
Mrs. Elizabeth M. Kearney, M.A., LL.B., B.D., Ph.D.
Dr. Mary McHugh, B.A., M.Litt., Ph.D.
Sr. Catherine Mulligan, S.N.D., M.A., M.Ed., Dip, Ed.Psych., M.A.C.P.
Ms. Linda O'Kane, B.Sc., D.C.E., Post.Dip.Couns.Sup.
Prof. Parick Reilly, M.A., B.Litt.
Ms. Margaret Tomlinson, B.A., L.R.A.M., L.G.S.M., F.E.S.B
Prof. Peter Walsh, K.C.S.G., M.A., F.R.S.E., D.Litt

POSTAL ADDRESS: Scotus College, 2 Chesters Road, Bearsden, GLASGOW G61 4AG. ☎0141-942 8384 (General Enquiries and Staff); Students: Main House:0141-942 9489; West Block: 0141-941 8348/942 3674 . Fax: 0141-943 1767.

E-mail: office@scotus.demon.co.uk

BISHOPBRIGGS, East Dŭnbartonshire, St. Dominic (1973, 1977), Kirriemuir Road.

Rev. Andrew Tolan (1956)
Rev. Michael Maloney, B.D. (1991)

POSTAL ADDRESS: St. Dominic's, 21 Kirriemuir Road, Woodhill, Bishopbriggs, GLASGOW G64 1DL. ☎0141-762 1154. (Hall: 0141-762 0971).

Sunday Masses: Vigil-Mass, 6 p.m.; 8.30, 10 a.m., 12 noon, 5 p.m. Holy Days of Obligation, Masses: Vigil-Mass, 6 p.m.; 7.30, 9.30, 11 a.m., 6 p.m. Confessions: Saturday, 10 a.m., 6.45 to 7.15 p.m.; on request.

Estimated Catholic population: 3,100.

ST. HELEN'S PRIMARY SCHOOL.

BISHOPBRIGGS, East Dunbartonshire, St. Matthew (1946, 1950), Kirkintilloch Road.

Right Rev. Mgr. Peter O'Farrell, B.Th. (1962)
Very Rev. Mgr. Hugh Bradley, B.A., Ph.B., S.T.B., L.H.E. (1989)

POSTAL ADDRESS: St. Matthew's, 2 South Crosshill Road, Bishopbriggs, GLASGOW G64 2LZ. ☎0141-772 1619.

Sunday Masses: Vigil-Mass, 6.30 p.m.; 9.30, 11 a.m., 12.15, 6 p.m. Evening Service, as announced. Holy Days of Obligation, Masses: Vigil Mass, 7.30 p.m.; 7.30, 10 a.m., 7.30 p.m. Confessions: Saturdays, 10.30 to 11 a.m., 5.30 to 6.15 p.m.; after weekday Masses by request. Estimated Catholic population: 4,000.

ST. MARY'S RESIDENTIAL SCHOOL, KENMURE, ATTENDED FROM ST. MATTHEW'S. (SUNDAY MASS BY ARRANGEMENT).
MAVIS BANK NURSING HOME ATTENDED FROM ST. MATTHEW'S.
ST. MATTHEW'S PRIMARY SCHOOL; TURNBULL HIGH SCHOOL.

BONHILL, Ladyton, West Dunbartonshire, St. Ronan (1973, 1976).

Rev. John Sheary, S.T.L. (1969)

POSTAL ADDRESS: St. Ronan's, Ladyton Estate, Bonhill, ALEXANDRIA G83 9EA. ☎Alexandria (01389) 759457.

Sunday Masses: Vigil-Mass, 6.30 p.m.; 9.30, 11.30 a.m., 5 p.m. Holy Days of Obligation, Masses: Vigil-Mass, 7 p.m.; 9.30 a.m., 7 p.m. Confessions: Saturday, after 9.30 a.m. Mass; before and after Vigil-Mass. Estimated Catholic population: 1,500.

ST. RONAN'S PRIMARY SCHOOL.

CARDROSS, Argyll and Bute, St. Mahew (1978, 6th cent., rebuilt 1467, restored 1955), Darleith Road.

Rev. Dominic Doogan, M.P.S. (1971)

POSTAL ADDRESS: St. Mahew's, "Dunollie", Main Road, Cardross, DUMBARTON G82 5NY. ☎/Fax.: Cardross (01389) 841784.

Sunday Masses: Vigil-Mass, 5.30 p.m.; 10 a.m. Evening Service: as announced. Holy Days of Obligation, Masses: 10 a.m., 7.30 p.m. Confessions: Saturday, 10.15 to 10.45 a.m., 6.45 to 7.15 p.m. Estimated Catholic population: 200.

BLOOMHILL NURSING HOME AND CARDROSS PARK HOME ATTENDED FROM ST. MAHEW'S.
(ST. JOSEPH'S PRIMARY SCHOOL, HELENSBURGH).

CLYDEBANK, West Dunbartonshire, St. Eunan (1948, 1951), East Thomson St .

Rev. Charles J. McElwee (1984)

POSTAL ADDRESS: St. Eunan's, 2 Gilmour Street, CLYDEBANK G81 2BW.
☎0141-952 1108.

Sunday Masses: Vigil-Mass, 6.30 p.m.; 10 a.m., 12 noon, 6.30 p.m.
Evening Service: as announced. Holy Days of Obligation, Masses: Vigil-Mass, 7 p.m.; 9, 11 a.m., 7 p.m. Confessions: Saturday, after 9.30 a.m.
Mass, after Vigil-Mass to 8 p.m. Exposition of the Blessed Sacrament,
Monday to Saturday, 10 a.m. to 4 p.m.
Estimated Catholic population: 2,100.

ST. EUNAN'S PRIMARY SCHOOL; ST. COLUMBA'S HIGH SCHOOL.

CLYDEBANK, West Dunbartonshire, St. Margaret (1969, 1972), Sinclair Street.

Right Rev. Mgr. James Canon McShane,
K.C.H.S., S.T.L., L.S.S. (1947)

POSTAL ADDRESS: St. Margaret's, Sinclair Street, CLYDEBANK G81 1AE.
☎0141-952 9508.

Sunday Masses: Vigil-Mass, 6 p.m.; 10 a.m., 12 noon. Holy Days of
Obligation, Masses: Vigil-Mass, 7 p.m.; 9.30 a.m., 7 p.m. Confessions:
Saturday after 9.30 a.m. Mass, 5 to 5.45 p.m., after Vigil-Mass.
Estimated Catholic population: 2,800.

ST. MARGARET'S HOSPICE, (RELIGIOUS SISTERS OF CHARITY), EAST BARNS
STREET, CLYDEBANK G81 IEG. ☎0141-952 1141; FAX:0141-951 4206..
CHAPLAIN: REV. BERNARD CONNELL, OUR LADY OF PEROPETUAL SUCCOUR,
BROOMHILL. SUNDAYS AND HOLY DAYS OF OBLIGATION, MASS: 11.30 A.M.
OUR HOLY REDEEMER'S PRIMARY SCHOOL; (ST. EUNAN'S PRIMARY SCHOOL).

CLYDEBANK, West Dunbartonshire, Our Holy Redeemer (1888, 1903), Glasgow Road

Rev. James Martin (1952)

POSTAL ADDRESS: Our Holy Redeemer's, South Bank Street, CLYDEBANK
G81 1PH. ☎0141-952 1293.

Sunday Masses: Vigil-Mass, 6.30 p.m.; 10, 11.30 a.m. Holy Days of
Obligation, Masses: Vigil-Mass, 7.30 p.m.; 9.30 a.m., 12 noon, 7.30 p.m.
Confessions: Saturday, after morning Mass, 5.15 to 6.15 p.m.
Estimated Catholic population: 1,000.

ST. ANDREW'S HIGH SCHOOL; (OUR HOLY REDEEMER'S PRIMARY SCHOOL).

CONDORRAT, North Lanarkshire, Our Lady and St. Helen (1974, 1978), Achray Road.

Rev. Michael Conroy, B.A., M.Sc., M.Th., C.Psychol.,
Dip. Couns., A.F.B.Ps.S (1974)
Rev. Paul G. Milarvie, Ph.B., S.T.L (1993)

POSTAL ADDRESS: Our Lady and St. Helen's, 117 Achray Road, Condorrat, Cumbernauld, GLASGOW G67 4JG. ☎Cumbernauld (01236) 731258.
E-mail: olsh@olsthelens.freeserve.co.uk

Sunday Masses: Vigil-Mass, 6 p.m.; 10 a.m., 12 noon, 6 p.m. Holy Days of Obligation, Masses: Vigil-Mass, 7.30 p.m.; 10 a.m., 7.30 p.m. Confessions: Saturdays, 10.30 a.m. 7 to 7.30 p.m.
Estimated Catholic population: 4,000.

RANNOCH LODGE NURSING HOME, MCAULEY CENTRE AND ROSE STREET CENTRE ATTENDED FROM OUR LADY AND ST. HELEN'S.
ST. FRANCIS OF ASSISI PRIMARY SCHOOL; ST. HELEN'S PRIMARY SCHOOL; ST. MAURICE'S HIGH SCHOOL.

CROY, North Lanarkshire, Holy Cross (1902, 1958), Constarry Road.

Rev. Patrick G. Currie (1973)

POSTAL ADDRESS: Holy Cross, Croy, Kilsyth, GLASGOW G65 9JG. ☎Kilsyth (01236) 822148.

Sunday Masses: Vigil-Mass, 6 p.m.; 9.30, 11.40 a.m. Evening Service when announced. Holy Days of Obligation, Masses: Vigil-Mass 7 p.m.; 10 a.m., 7 p.m. Confessions: after weekday morning Mass; Saturday 7 to 7.30 p.m.
Exposition of The Blessed Sacrament, Thursday, 10.30 a.m. to 7 p.m.
Estimated Catholic population: 2,900.

CARRICKSTONE HOUSE AND DAY HOSPITAL ATTENDED FROM HOLY CROSS.
HOLY CROSS PRIMARY SCHOOL.

CUMBERNAULD, North Lanarkshire, St. Joseph (1967, 1971), Broomlands Road, South Carbrain.

Rev. Harry McKay, Ph.L. (1966)

POSTAL ADDRESS: St. Joseph's Presbytery, Broomlands Road, South Carbrain, Cumbernauld, GLASGOW G67 2PT. ☎Cumbernauld (01236) 722897.

Sunday Masses: Vigil Mass, 7 p.m.; 10 a.m., 12 noon, 6.30 p.m. Holy Days of Obligation, Masses: 10 a.m., 7 p.m. Confessions: Thursday, 7.15 to 7.30 p.m. Saturday, 10.15 to 10.30 a.m., 6 to 6.40 p.m.
Estimated Catholic population: 3,000.

CUMBERNAULD GRAMPIAN NURSING HOME AND GLENCRYAN SCHOOL FOR THE HANDICAPPED ATTENDED FROM ST. JOSEPH'S.
ST. JOSEPH'S PRIMARY SCHOOL; ST. MARY'S PRIMARY SCHOOL; OUR LADY'S HIGH SCHOOL.

CUMBERNAULD, North Lanarkshire, St. Lucy (1973, 1976), Hornbeam Road, Abronhill.

Rev. John Casey (1984)

POSTAL ADDRESS: St. Lucy's, 9 Pine Crescent, Abronhill, Cumbernauld, GLASGOW G67 3BB. ☎Cumbernauld (01236) 724894; (Hall: 722168).

Sunday Masses: Vigil-Mass, 6.30 p.m.; 10.30 a.m., 12 noon. Holy Days of Obligation, Masses: 9.30, 11 a.m., 7.30 p.m. Confessions: Saturday, 10 a.m, 5.45 to 6.15 p.m., after Vigil-Mass; on request.
Estimated Catholic population: 2,800.

ST. LUCY'S PRIMARY SCHOOL.

CUMBERNAULD, North Lanarkshire, Sacred Heart (1958, 1964), Kyle Road, Kildrum.

Right Rev. Mgr. Patrick Osborne (1959)
Rev. Colman F. McGrath, Ph.L. (1962)

POSTAL ADDRESS: Sacred Heart Church, Kyle Road, Cumbernauld, GLASGOW G67 2DY. ☎Cumbernauld (01236) 721387.
E-mail: sacredheart@classicfm.net

Sunday Masses: Vigil-Mass, 6 p.m.; 9, 10.30 a.m., 12 noon, 5.30 p.m. Holy Days of Obligation, Masses: 7.30, 10 a.m., 7.30 p.m. Confessions: Saturday, 10.30 a.m., 5.30 to 6 p.m.; after Vigil-Mass; on request.
Estimated Catholic population: 3,000.

REDBURN SPECIAL SCHOOL, ANTONINE DAY CARE CENTRE, DARROCH NURSING HOME, OCHIL VIEW NURSING HOME AND VILLAGE NURSING HOME ATTENDED FROM SACRED HEART.
SACRED HEART PRIMARY SCHOOL; (ST. JOSEPH'S PRIMARY SCHOOL; ST. MARY'S PRIMARY SCHOOL).

DALMUIR, West Dunbartonshire, Our Lady of Loreto (1975, 1977), Dumbarton Road.

Rev. James Lafferty (1961)

POSTAL ADDRESS: Our Lady of Loreto, 707 Dumbarton Road, Dalmuir, CLYDEBANK G81 4HD. ☎0141-952 9795.

Sunday Masses: Vigil-Mass, 6 p.m.; 9.30, 11 a.m. Holy Days of Obligation, Masses: Vigil-Mass, 6 p.m.; 9 (school), 10.30 a.m. Confessions: Wednesday, 9.30 a.m.; Saturday, after 10 a.m. Mass and Vigil-Mass.
Estimated Catholic population: 3,000.

AUCHENTOSHAN SCHOOL AND HANDICAPPED CENTRE, FRANK DOWNIE HOME FOR THE ELDERLY, HILLVIEW NURSING HOME AND H.C.I. HOSPITAL SERVED FROM OUR LADY OF LORETO.
OUR LADY OF LORETTO PRIMARY SCHOOL.

DALMUIR, West Dunbartonshire, St. Stephen (1907,1958),Park Road.

Rev. Gerard J. Conroy, Ph.B., S.T.B., L.S.S. (1982)
Rev. James A. Burns *(Retired)* (1962)

POSTAL ADDRESS: St. Stephen's, 12 Park Road, Dalmuir, CLYDEBANK G81 3LD. ☎0141-952 1461.

Sunday Masses: Vigil-Mass, 5.30 p.m.; 10 a.m., 12 noon. Holy Days of Obligation, Masses: 10 a.m., 7 p.m. Confessions: Friday, after Novena; Saturday, after 10 a.m. Mass, after Vigil-Mass.
Estimated Catholic population: 2,600.

BOQUHANRAN OLD PEOPLE'S HOME AND RAMSEY HOUSE ATTENDED FROM ST. STEPHEN'S.
ST. STEPHEN'S PRIMARY SCHOOL.

DUMBARTON, West Dunbartonshire, St. Michael, Dalreoch (1946, 1954), Cardross Road.

Rev. George Bradburn, S.T.L. (1965)
Rev. Alfred McKenzie, Ph.B., S.T.L.
(Resident, Chaplain to the Convents) (1979)

POSTAL ADDRESS: St. Michael's, 7 Cardross Road, DUMBARTON G82 4JE.
☎/Fax: Dumbarton (01389) 762709 (Hall:01389-732894).

Sunday Masses: Vigil-Mass, 6.30 p.m.; 8, 11 a.m., 6.30 p.m. Holy Days of Obligation, Masses: Vigil-Mass, 6.30 p.m.; 8, 10 a.m., 6.30 p.m. Confessions: weekdays after 10 a.m. Mass; Saturday, 10.30 a.m., 5.30 to 6.30 p.m.
Estimated Catholic population: 3,200.

NOTRE DAME CONVENT, CRAIGEND HOUSE, 74A CARDROSS ROAD, DUMBARTON G82 4JH. ☎DUMBARTON (01389) 733222.
NOTRE DAME CONVENT, 47 OXHILL ROAD, DUMBARTON G82 4JG. ☎DUMBARTON (01389) 731795.
CARMELITE MONASTERY, 17 HELENSLEE ROAD, DUMBARTON G82 4AN.
DUMBARTON JOINT HOSPITAL AND DALREOCH HOME FOR THE ELDERLY ATTENDED FROM ST. MICHAEL'S.
ST. MICHAEL'S PRIMARY SCHOOL; OUR LADY AND ST. PATRICK'S HIGH SCHOOL.

DUMBARTON, West Dunbartonshire, St. Patrick (1830, 1903), Strathleven Place.

Right Rev. Mgr. Desmond Maguire (1954)
Rev. David J. Wallace, Ph.B., S.T.L. (1999)
Rev. Daniel Friel, Ph.L., S.T.L. *(Retired)* (1957)

POSTAL ADDRESS: St. Patrick's Presbytery, Strathleven Place, DUMBARTON G82 1BA. ☎Dumbarton (01389) 762503.

E-mail: stpatricks@altavista.NET

Sunday Masses: Vigil-Mass, 6.30 p.m.; 10 a.m., 12 noon, 5.30 p.m. Holy Days of Obligation, Masses: Vigil-Mass, 7 p.m.; 7, 10 a.m., 7 p.m. Confessions: daily, after 10 a.m. Mass; Saturday, 10.30 a.m., 5 to 6.20 p.m.
Estimated Catholic population: 2,800.

DEVERON HOUSE, LANGCRAIGS RESOURCE CENTRE, ROCK VIEW AND WILLOX PARK ATTENDED FROM ST. PATRICK'S.
ST. PATRICK'S PRIMARY SCHOOL.

DUMBARTON, West Dunbartonshire, St. Peter, Bellsmyre (1966, 1971), Howatshaws Road.

Rev. Thomas O'Rourke (1961)
Very Rev. Michael Canon Meechan, S.T.L. (*Retired*) (1939)

POSTAL ADDRESS: St. Peter's Presbytery, Howatshaws Road, DUMBARTON G82 3DR. ☎/Fax: Dumbarton (01389) 764131.

Sunday Masses: Vigil-Mass, 6 p.m.; 11 a.m., 6 p.m. Evening Service: as announced. Holy Days of Obligation, Masses: Vigil-Mass, 7 p.m.; 10 a.m., 7 p.m. Confessions: weekdays, after all Masses; Fridays, 7 to 8 p.m.; Saturdays, 10.30 to 11 a.m., 5 to 5.30 p.m.
Estimated Catholic population: 1,940.

ST. PETER'S PRIMARY SCHOOL; (ST. PATRICK'S PRIMARY SCHOOL).

DUNTOCHER, West Dunbartonshire, St. Mary (1841, 1954), Chapel Road.

Rev. Philip Tartaglia, Ph.B., S.T.D. (1975)
Rev. Neil McGarrity, Dip.Theol. (1989)

POSTAL ADDRESS: St. Mary's, Chapel Road, Duntocher, CLYDEBANK G81 6DL. ☎Duntocher (01389) 873280.

Sunday Masses: Vigil-Mass, 7 p.m.; 8.30, 10.30 a.m., 12 noon, 6.30 p.m. Evening Service: 5.30 p.m.or as announced. Holy Days of Obligation, Masses: Vigil-Mass, 7.30 p.m.; 7.30, 9.30 a.m., 12 noon, 7.30 p.m. Confessions: Friday, 8 p.m.; Saturday, 10 to 11 a.m., 6 to 7 p.m
Estimated Catholic population: 3,700.

ST. MARY'S PRIMARY SCHOOL.

FAIFLEY, Clydebank, West Dunbartonshire, St. Joseph (1957,1997), Faifley Road.

Rev. Joseph Coyle, S.T.D. (1958)

POSTAL ADDRESS: St. Joseph's, Faifley, CLYDEBANK G81 5EZ. ☎Duntocher (01389) 872236.

Sunday Masses: Vigil-Mass, 6 p.m.; 9.30, 11.30 a.m. Holy Days of Obligation, Masses: Vigil-Mass, 7 p.m.; 9.30 a.m., 7 p.m. Confessions: before and after all Services.
Estimated Catholic population:1,800.

EDINBARNET NURSING HOME ATTENDED FROM ST. JOSEPH'S.
ST. JOSEPH'S PRIMARY SCHOOL.

GARELOCHHEAD, Argyll and Bute, Our Lady, Star of the Sea (1964, 1968), Feorlin Way.

Rev. John F. Ward, B.A. (1969)

POSTAL ADDRESS: "Dunavard," Station Road, Garelochhead, HELENSBURGH G84 0DB. ☎Garelochhead (01436) 810498. E-mail:jfw@gareloch88.freeserve.co.uk

Sunday Mass: 10 a.m. Holy Days of Obligation, Mass: 7 p.m. Confessions: Saturday, after 10 a.m. Mass; on request. SS. Peter and Paul, Arrochar, served from Garelochhead. Estimated Catholic population:120.   **A**

ARDMAY (Arrochar), GULLY BRIDGE (Shandon) AND ROCKVILLE (Garelochhead) NURSING HOMES SERVED FROM OUR LADY, STAR OF THE SEA. ST. PETER'S, H.M.S. NEPTUNE (CLYDE SUBMARINE BASE, FASLANE), R.N. CHAPLAIN. ☎GARELOCHHEAD (01436) 674321, EXT. 6216 (OFFICE). SUNDAY MASS, 9 A.M. HOLY DAYS OF OBLIGATION, MASS: 12 NOON. CONFESSIONS BEFORE MASS. CHAPEL OF ST. MARGARET, CHURCHILL SQUARE, HELENSBURGH. SUNDAY MASS, 10.30 A.M.
(ST. JOSEPH'S PRIMARY SCHOOL, HELENSBURGH).

HELENSBURGH, Argyll and Bute, St. Joseph (1865, 1912), Lomond Street.

Right Rev. Mgr. Maurice Ward, Ph.L., S.T.L. (1960)

POSTAL ADDRESS: St. Joseph's, 41 Lomond Street, HELENSBURGH G84 7ET. ☎ & Fax: Helensburgh (01436) 672463.

Sunday Masses: Vigil-Mass, 7 p.m.; 11 a.m., 5.30 p.m. Holy Days of Obligation, Masses: Vigil-Mass, 7.30 p.m.; 10 a.m., 7.30 p.m. Confessions: weekdays after all Masses; Thursday after Novena, 7.30 p.m.; Saturday, 12 noon to 12.30 p.m., 6 to 6.50 p.m. Exposition of the Blessed Sacrament: Monday and Tuesday, 10.30 a.m. to 9 p.m.; Wednesday and Thursday, 10.30 a.m. to Devotions at 7 p.m.; Friday, 1 to 9 p.m.; Saturday, during evening confessions; First Saturday, 8 p.m. to Sunday, 10.45 a.m. Estimated Catholic population: 2,150.

RED TOWERS, 4 DOUGLAS DRIVE WEST, HELENSBURGH G84 9AL ☎HELENSBURGH (01436) 679137. VICTORIA INFIRMARY, JEANNIE DEANS GERIATRIC HOSPITAL, ARGYLE LODGE, BALVAIRD, CAIRNDHU, CLYDEVIEW EVENTIDE, DRUMADOON NURSING HOME, MARDON HOUSE, MORAR LODGE, NORTHWOOD HOUSE, Helensburgh; CHILDREN'S HOME, Blairvadoch, ATTENDED FROM ST. JOSEPH'S. ST. JOSEPH'S PRIMARY SCHOOL.

KILCREGGAN. See Rosneath page 313.

KIRKINTILLOCH, East Dunbartonshire, St. Flannan (1948, 1970) Hillhead Road.

Rev. John Conway (1955)
Rev. Patrick J. Boyle, B.D. (1996)

POSTAL ADDRESS: St. Flannan's, 79 Hillhead Road, Kirkintilloch, GLASGOW G66 2HY. ☎0141-776 2310.

Sunday Masses: Vigil-Mass, 7 p.m.; 10 a.m., 12 noon, 6.30 p.m. Holy Days of Obligation, Masses: Vigil-Mass, 7 p.m.; 10 a.m., 7 p.m. Confessions: Saturday, 10.30 a.m., 6 to 7 p.m., after Vigil-Mass. Exposition of the Blessed Sacrament, Friday, 10.30 am. to 6.30 p.m. Estimated Catholic population: 4,000.

CAMPSIE VIEW NURSING HOME (MASS, LAST THURSDAY OF THE MONTH, 2 P.M.), AND MERKLAND SPECIAL NEEDS SCHOOL SERVED FROM ST. FLANNAN'S.
ST. FLANNAN'S PRIMARY SCHOOL; (ST. AGATHA'S PRIMARY SCHOOL).

KIRKINTILLOCH, East Dunbartonshire, The Holy Family and St. Ninian (1874, 1893), Union Street.

Rev. Denis A. Hurley (1954)
Rev. Paul T. Brooks, Ph.B., S.T.L. (1997)

POSTAL ADDRESS: Holy Family and St. Ninian's, 20 Union Street, Kirkintilloch, GLASGOW G66 1DH. ☎0141 -776 1063.

Sunday Masses: Vigil-Mass, 6.30 p.m.; 9, 11 a.m., 12.15, 6 p.m. Holy Days of Obligation, Masses: 10 a.m., 7.30 p.m. Confessions: Saturday, 9.30 to 10, 10.30 to 11 a.m., 7 to 8 p.m. Estimated Catholic population: 4,000.

CARMELITE CONVENT, WATERSIDE, KIRKINTILLOCH, GLASGOW G66 3PE. SERVED FROM ST. NINIAN'S. SUNDAY MASS: 9 A.M. EVENING SERVICE: 5.15 P.M. HOLY DAYS OF OBLIGATION, MASS: 9 A.M.
LENZIE CONVALESCENT HOME AND WOODILEE MENTAL HOSPITAL, ATTENDED FROM ST. NINIAN'S.
HOLY FAMILY PRIMARY SCHOOL; ST. NINIAN'S HIGH SCHOOL.

MILNGAVIE, East Dunbartonshire, St. Joseph (1865, 1980), Station Road.

Rev. John J. McGrorry, Ph.B., S.T.L., M.A. (1982)

POSTAL ADDRESS: St. Joseph's House, 3 Buchanan Street, Milngavie, GLASGOW G62 8DZ. ☎0141-956 1400.

Sunday Masses: Vigil-Mass, 5.30 p.m.;10, 11.30 a.m. Evening Service: as announced. Holy Days of Obligation, Masses: 9.30 a.m., 7.30 p.m. Confessions: Saturday, 10 a.m.; any time on request.

Estimated Catholic population: 1,700.

ST. JOSEPH'S PRIMARY SCHOOL.

OLD KILPATRICK, West Dunbartonshire, St. Patrick (1946, 1980), Dumbarton Road.

Rev. Desmond J. McGinty, B.A. (1968)

POSTAL ADDRESS: St. Patrick's, 252 Dumbarton Road, Old Kilpatrick, GLASGOW G60 5LJ. ☎Duntocher (01389) 873044.

Sunday Masses: Vigil-Mass, 6 p.m.; 9, 11 a.m., 6 p.m. Holy Days of Obligation, Masses: Vigil-Mass, 7 p.m.; 10 a.m., 7 p.m. Confessions: Saturday, 10.30 a.m., 5.30 p.m.
Estimated Catholic population: 950.

MOUNT PLEASANT HOUSE, OLD PEOPLE'S HOME, ATTENDED FROM ST. PATRICK'S.
(ST. MARY'S PRIMARY SCHOOL, DUNTOCHER; OUR LADY OF LORETTO PRIMARY SCHOOL, DALMUIR.)

RENTON, West Dunbartonshire, St. Martin of Tours (1899, 1970), Main Street.

Very Rev. James Canon Simcox, B.A. (1953)

POSTAL ADDRESS: St. Martin's, 331 Main Street, Renton, DUMBARTON G82 4PZ. ☎Alexandria (01389) 752089.

Sunday Masses: Vigil-Mass, 6 p.m.; 10.30 a.m., 5 p.m. Evening Service: 4 p.m. when announced. Holy Days of Obligation, Masses: Vigil-Mass, 5 p.rn.; 9.30 a.m., 5 p.m. Confessions: Saturday, before and after 9 a.m. Mass, 5.30 to 6 p.m., after Vigil-Mass.
Estimated Catholic population: 830.

DALMOAK CASTLE NURSING HOME ATTENDED FROM ST. MARTIN'S.
ST. MARTIN'S PRIMARY SCHOOL.

ROSNEATH, Argyll and Bute, St. Gildas (1951, 1968), Main Road.
Rev. Francis McPartlin (1958)

POSTAL ADDRESS: St. Gildas', Rosneath, HELENSBURGH G84 0RJ. ☎Clynder (01436) 831357.

Sunday Masses: Vigil-Mass, 6 p.m.; 10 a.m. Holy Days of Obligation, Masses: Vigil-Mass, 7 p.m.; (on school days) 9 a.m., 10 a.m. Confessions: Saturday, after Vigil-Mass and on request.
Estimated Catholic population: 200.

TWECHAR, East Dunbartonshire, St. John of the Cross (1945, 1969), St. John's Way, Main Street.
Rev. William McLellan (1962)

POSTAL ADDRESS: St. John's Presbytery, St. John's Way, Main Street, Twechar, Kilsyth, GLASGOW G65 9TA. ☎/Fax.: Kilsyth (01236) 822263.

Sunday Masses: 10 a.m., 5 p.m. Evening Service, as announced. Holy Days of Obligation, Masses: 10 a.m., 7 p.m. Confessions: Saturday, after 10 a.m. Mass; Sunday, before Masses; on request.
Estimated Catholic population: 500.   **A**

(ST. AGATHA'S PRIMARY SCHOOL.)

PARISHES, CHURCHES or CHAPELS NOW CLOSED
St. Bonaventure, Oatlands; opened 1952, closed 1992:
Registers deposited at Blessed John Duns Scotus, Ballater Street.
St. Francis, Cumberland Street; opened 1868, closed 1992:
Registers deposited at Blessed John Duns Scotus, Ballater Street.
St. Francis of Assisi, Cumberland Street; opened 1992, closed 1993:
Registers deposited at Blessed John Duns Scotus, Ballater Street.
Good Shepherd, London Road, Dalbeth; opened 1948, closed 1975:
Registers deposited at St. Michael's, Parkhead.
St. John the Evangelist, Portugal Street; opened 1846, closed 1982:
Registers deposited at Blessed John Duns Scotus, Ballater Street.
St. Joseph, North Woodside Road, Cowcaddens; opened 1850, closed 1984: Registers deposited at St. Columba's, Hopehill Road.
St. Luke, Ballater Street, Hutchesontown; opened, 1905,
renamed Blessed John Duns Scotus, 1993.
St. Nicholas', David Street, Milend; opened 1949, closed 1979:
Registers deposited at St. Michael's, Parkhead.
Our Lady, Queen of Peace, Queenslie; opened 1978, closed 1987:
surviving Registers deposited at St. John Ogilvie's, Easterhouse.
St. Stephen, Sighthill; opened 1968, closed 1999: Registers deposited at St. Mungo's, Townhead.
St. Vincent de Paul, Duke Street; opened 1857, closed 1902:
Registers deposited at St. Andrew's Cathedral.

RETIRED PRIESTS OF THE ARCHDIOCESE

Rev. Felix Beattie, Nazareth House, 1647 Paisley Road West, GLASGOW G52 3QT. ☎0141-882 9375.

Rev. John Boles, Woodville, 18 Greenhead Road, DUMBARTON G82 1EL.

Rev. Robert Bradley, Our Lady and St. George's, 50 Sandwood Road, GLASGOW G52 2QE. Tel.: 0141-882 4868.

Very Rev. John Canon Brannan, Nazareth House, 1647 Paisley Road West,GLASGOW G52 3QT. ☎0141-882 9375.

Rev. John D. Broderick, Nazareth House, 1647 Paisley Road West, GLASGOW G52 3QT.

Rev. James Burns, St. Stephen's, 12 Park Road, Dalmuir, CLYDEBANK G81 3LD

Rev, Jeremiah Carroll, 7 Lartigue Place, Ballybunion, Co. Kerry, Ireland.

Rev. Daniel Clancy, Coolydoody, Ballyduff, Co. Waterford, Ireland.

Rev. Peter Clinton, Roadside Cottage, Auchenstarry, Kilsyth, GLASGOW G65 0DF. ☎01236-821946.

Rev. John Collins, The Presbytery, 1 George Street, MILLPORT KA28 0BG. ☎01475-530537.

Rev. Thomas Cunningham, St. Catherine's, 90 Lamont Road, GLASGOW G21 3PP. ☎ 0141-558 6723.

Rev. David Currie, 10 Risk Street, DUMBARTON G82 1SE.

Rev. Richard Dunne, Nazareth House, 1647 Paisley Road West, GLASGOW G52 3QT. ☎ 0141-810 4359..

Rev. Daniel Friel, St. Patrick's, Strathleven Place, DUMBARTON G82 1BA. ☎01389-762505.

Rev. Francis H. Gilfedder, c/o Irvine, 2/1 Canal Street, RENFREW PA4 8QD.

Very Rev. Thomas Canon Glen, Nazareth House, 1647 Paisley Road West, GLASGOW G52 3QT.

Rev. Philip Hastings, St. Joseph's, 14 Cumnock Road, GLASGOW G33 1QT.

Rev. Edward Higgins, 8 Inverewe Avenue, Deaconsbank, GLASGOW G46 8TA. ☎0141-638 5624.

Rev. Francis Jaconelli, 17 Baronscourt Road, PAISLEY PA1 2TW. ☎0141-889 6793.

Rev. Hugh Kearns, St. Margaret's Hospice, East Barns Street, CLYDEBANK G81 1EG.

Rev. Michael Keating, c/o Ferry, Sheskinbeg, Derrybeg, Letterkenny, Co. Donegal, Ireland. ☎Eire (00353) 75-44102.

Rev. Edward Lindsay, St. Joseph's, 14 Cumnock Road, Robroyston, GLASGOW G33 1QT.

Rev. John Loughlin, St. Joseph's, 14 Cumnock Road, Robroyston, GLASGOW G33 1QT. ☎0141-558 6149.

Rev. Peter McCafferty, 182 King's Park Road, GLASGOW G44 4SU. ☎0141-649 3880.

Rev. Charles MacFadden, 31 Muirpark Drive, Bishopbriggs, GLASGOW G64 1RD.

Rev. George McGarrigle, Flat 1/2, 2 Gadsburn Court, GLASGOW G21 3LS. ☎0141-557 5270.

Right Rev. Mgr. Eugene McGee, Gleneagles Court, 3e Hilton Road, Bishopbriggs, GLASGOW G64 3DZ. ☎ 0141-772 2761.

Rev. John Manning, Genazzano, Cahergal Gardens, Ballyvolane Road, Cork, Ireland.

Rev. Thomas G. Mannion, 48 Greenock Road, PAISLEY PA3 2LB.

Rev. Francis Meagher, Flat 6, Clifford Court, 271 Nithsdale Road, GLASGOW G41 5LS.

Very Rev. Michael Canon Meechan, St. Peter's, Howatshaws Road, Bellsmyre, Dumbarton G82 3DR. ☎ 01389-764131.

Very Rev. Michael Canon Mooney, St. Michael's, 1350 Gallowgate, GLASGOW G31 4DJ. ☎0141-554 0530.

Rev. George Morgan, c/o Diocesan Office, 196 Clyde Street, <u>Glasgow</u> G1 4JY.

Rev. John Muldoon, St. Joseph's, 14 Cumnock Road, GLASGOW G33 1QT.

Rev. Francis Murphy, 88 Slieve Rua Drive, Stillorgan, Blackrock, Co. Dublin, Ireland.

Rev. Joseph Murphy, Ballydesmond, Mallow, Co. Cork, Ireland.

Very Rev. Thomas Canon Murphy, Immaculate Conception, 2049 Maryhill Road, GLASGOW G20 0AA. ☎ 0141-946 2071.

Right Rev. Mgr. Thomas Canon Murray, 7 Moore Drive, South Colgrain, HELENSBURGH G84 7LE. ☎ 01436-676531.

Very Rev. Jeremiah Canon O'Flynn, Beaumont Residential Care, Woodvale Road, Beaumont, Ballintemple, Cork, Ireland.

Rev. Michael O'Keeffe, Derryvillane, Mitchelstown, Co. Cork, Ireland.

Rev. Sean O'Neill, 1 Earn Road, TROON KA10 7DS. ☎01292-318913.

Rev. James E. O'Reilly, Flat 2, Clifford Court, 271 Nithsdale Road, GLASGOW G41 5LS ☎ 0141-419 0844.

Rev. Henry Parkinson, 25F Skaterigg Gardens, GLASGOW G13 1ST. ☎ 0141-954 2877.

Right Rev. Mgr. Martin Provost Quinlan, Nazareth House, 1647 Paisley Road West, GLASGOW G52 3QT. ☎ 0141-882 9375.

Rev. Frederick Rawlings, Tig-na-Sagart, Portnoo, Co. Donegal, Ireland.

Rev. James V. Reilly, 3 Ardenvohr, Main Road, Cardross, DUMBARTON G82 5JX. ☎ 01389-841194.

Very Rev. Mgr. Gaetano Canon Rossi, 16 Heriot Crescent, Bishopbriggs, GLASGOW G64 3NG. ☎ 0141-772 7989.

Rev. Patrick Tobin, Castletown, Killeagh, Co. Cork, Ireland. ☎Eire (00353) 21 668304.

Very Rev. William Canon Tobin, 98 Balmuildy Road, Bishopbriggs, GLASGOW G64 3EP.

Rev. Daniel Toy, 93 Holmscroft Street, GREENOCK PA15 4DF

Rev. Anthony Walsh, 3 Warren Street, GLASGOW G42 8AQ. ☎ 0141-423 4607.

HOSPITALS IN THE CITY OF GLASGOW

(Where no individual Priest is named, the Hospital is attended by the Clergy of the Parish as a whole.)

Bon Secours Hospital—Right Rev. Mgr. Hugh N. Canon Boyle, Bon Secours. ☎0141-649 9226 (Hospital: 0141-632 9231).

Gartnavel Royal and General Hospitals—Rev. Mark Morris, Corpus Christi. ☎0141-954 3777.

Queen Mother Hospital and Royal Hospital for Sick Children, Yorkhill—Rev. William Slavin, St. Charles.☎ 0141-946 7622 (Hospital: 0141-201 0000).

Royal Infirmary—Rev. John O'Kane, C.P., St. Mungo's. ☎0141-552 1823.

Southern General Hospital—Rev. Bernard Connell, Our Lady of Perpetual Succour. ☎0141 339 1324. (Hospital: 0141-201 1100)

Stobhill Hospital and Huntershill Nursing Home—Rev. Stephen Dunn, Immaculate Heart of Mary. ☎0141-558 5025.

Victoria Infirmary , Mansionhouse Unit and Mcquaker Building—Rev. Stephen Hannah, Holy Cross. ☎0141-423 0105.

Western Infirmary—Rev. Joseph McNulty, St. Paul's, Whiteinch. ☎0141-954 9203.

Belvidere Hospital—St. Michael's. ☎0141-554 0530.

Blawarthill Geriatric Hospital—St. Brendan's. ☎0141-952 1471.

Cowglen Hospital—St. Robert Bellarmine's. ☎0141-881 1137.

Darnley Court Nursing Home—St. Louise's. ☎0141-638 4709.

Drumchapel Hospital—St. Benedict's. ☎0141-944 1767.

Gartloch Hospital—St. Benedict's Easterhouse (Diocese of Motherwell). ☎0141-771 1991.

Homeopathic Hospital—St. Ninian's. ☎0141-959 1308.

Knightswood Hospital—St. Ninian's. ☎0141-959 1308.

Leverndale Hospital—St. James'. ☎0141-882 4927.

Lightburn Hospital—St. Barnabas'. ☎0141-778 2861.

Nuffield Hospital—St. Ninian's. ☎0141-959 1308.

Parkhead Psychiatric Hospital—St. Michael's. ☎0141-554 0530.

Ross Hall Hospital—Our Lady and St. George's. ☎0141-882 4868.

Royal Hospital for Sick Children (Country Branch)—St. Benedict's. ☎0141-944 1767.

Royal Maternity Hospital, Rottenrow—St. Andrew's Cathedral. ☎0141-221 3096.

St. Francis' Nursing Home—St. Saviour's. ☎0141-445 1166.

SCHOOL CHAPLAINS

All Saints'	Rev. Patrick Boyle.
Holyrood	Rev. John Keenan.
Lourdes	Rev. Paul Friel.
Notre Dame	Rev. Joseph Keenan.
St. Aloysius' College	Rev. Gerard Mitchell, S.J.
St. Andrew's	Rev. John Campbell.
Bellarmine	Rev. Paul McAlinden.
John Paul Academy	Rev. Stephen Connolly.
St. Margaret Mary's	Rev. Alex Strachan.
St. Mungo's Academy	Rev. John Carroll.
St. Roch's	Rev. John Carroll.
St. Thomas Aquinas'	Rev. Joseph Keenan.
St. Andrew's, Clydebank	Rev. Neil McGarrity.
St. Columba's, Clydebank	Rev. Neil McGarrity.
St. Maurice's, Condorrat	Rev. Paul Milarvie.
St. Ninian's, Eastwood	Rev. Allan Cameron.
St. Ninian's, Kirkintilloch	Rev. Paul Brooks.
Our Lady and St. Patrick's, Dumbarton	Rev. Jim Rooney.
Our Lady's High, Cumbernauld	Rev. Paul Milarvie.
Turnbull High, Bishopbriggs	Rev. Michael Maloney

INSTITUTES OF CONSECRATED LIFE

AND

SOCIETIES OF APOSTOLIC LIFE
MEN

COLUMBAN FATHERS (1974)
St. Columban's, 31 Kingsborough Gardens, Hyndland, GLASGOW G12
9NH. ☎0141-334 1602.
E-mail: declan.mcnaughton@gisp.net

COMBONI MISSIONARIES OF THE SACRED HEART (1979)
(Verona Fathers)
(1992) Comboni Missionaries, 138 Carmyle Avenue, Carmyle, GLASGOW
G32 8DL. ☎0141-641 4399.

DISCALCED CARMELITES (1988)
Mount Carmel, 61 Hamilton Avenue, GLASGOW G41 4HA. ☎0141-427
0794; Fax.: 0141-427 9950

DOMINICANS (1965)
(1981) Blackfriars, 36 Queen's Drive, GLASGOW G42 8DD. ☎0141-423
2971; Fax: 0141-423 4575.
Catholic Chaplaincy for Strathclyde University Students, Chaplaincy
Centre, St. Paul's Building, 90 John Street, GLASGOW Gl 1JH.
☎0141-553 4144. (Residence: 0141-423 2971).

FRANCISCANS (1868)
(1993) Blessed John Duns Scotus, 270 Ballater Street, GLASGOW G5 0YT.
☎0141-429 0740; Fax: 0141-418 0413.

JESUITS (1859) 0141 ∅ 3323190
St. Aloysius', 10 Woodside Place, GLASGOW G3 7QF. ☎0141-332 3039
(Parish)/3659 (Community).. Fr John McCabe SJ
St. Aloysius' College, 45 Hill Street, GLASGOW G3 6RJ. ☎0141-332 3190.
Flat 3, 56 Bentinck Street, Glasgow G3 7TT. JMcCabe J Staloys.us. org
(1999) Ignatian Spirituality Centre, 7 Woodside Place, GLASGOW G3
7QF. ☎0141-354 0077; Fax: 0141-354 0099.
(1999) Wellcross, 193 Nithsdale Road, GLASGOW G41 5EX.☎0141-423
3005.

MILL HILL MISSIONARIES (1936)
(1948, 1985) St. Joseph's House, 30 Lourdes Avenue, Cardonald,
GLASGOW G52 3QU. ☎0141-883 0139; Fax.: 0141-882 5791.

PASSIONISTS (1865)
St. Mungo's, 52 Parson Street, GLASGOW G4 0RX. ☎0141-552 1823; Fax.:
0141-553 1838.

VINCENTIANS (1859)

(1990) St. Mark's, 80 St. Mark Street, GLASGOW G32 7EA. ☎0141-778 1011.

XAVERIAN FATHERS (1948)

(1999) St. Vincent de Paul's, 22 Main Street, Thornliebank, GLASGOW G46 7SH. ☎ 0141-638 0750

MARIST BROTHERS (1858)

(1906) St. Kentigern's, 10 Partickhill Road, GLASGOW G11 5BL. ☎0141-339 8259.

(1948) St. Benet's, 227 Nithsdale Road, GLASGOW G41 5HA. ☎0141-427 1750.

WOMEN

BON SECOURS SISTERS (1948)

Bon Secours Convent, 32 Mansionhouse Road, GLASGOW G41 3DW. ☎ 0141-632 8030.

Bon Secours Hospital, 36 Mansionhouse Road, GLASGOW G41 3DW. ☎ 0141-632 9231; Fax.: 0141-636 5066.

Chaplain: Right Rev. Mgr. Hugh N. Canon Boyle, Ph.L., S.T.L., F.S.A.Scot. (1962), The Lindens, Bon Secours Hospital, 36 Mansionhouse Road, GLASGOW, G41 3DW. ☎0141-649 9226.

CARMELITES (1918)

(1918) The Carmelite Monastery of the Nativity of the Blessed Virgin Mary, 29 Mansionhouse Road, GLASGOW G41 3DN. ☎0141-649 3311; Fax: 0141-636 6424.

(1934) The Carmelite Monastery of the Holy Ghost, 17 Helenslee Road, Dumbarton G82 4AN. ☎/Fax: Dumbarton (01389) 764000. E-mail: Carmel.dumbarton@classicfm.net

(1953) The Carmelite Monastery of St. Joseph, Waterside Road, Kirkintilloch, GLASGOW G66 3PE. ☎0141-578 3188; Fax: 0141-578 3264.

COMBONI MISSIONARY SISTERS (1973)
(Verona Sisters)

Comboni House, 124 Berryknowes Road, Cardonald, GLASGOW G52 2TT. ☎0141-883 6139.

DAUGHTERS OF CHARITY OF ST. VINCENT DE PAUL (1856)

(1972) St. Vincent's Convent, 347 Albert Drive, Pollokshields, GLASGOW G41 5PH. ☎0141-427 3408.

(1988) Daughters of Charity, 15-21 Dalserf Street, GLASGOW G31 4AR.

(1991) Daughters of Charity, 139 Maryhill Road, GLASGOW G20 7XN. ☎0141-353 3317.

DAUGHTERS OF MARY, HELP OF CHRISTIANS
(SALESIAN SISTERS) (1978)
(1985) Salesian Sisters, "Marywood", 138/140 Ronaldsay Street, GLASGOW G22 7AR. ☎0141-762 3420; Fax: 0141-762 1935..

DAUGHTERS OF ST. PAUL (1969)
Daughters of St. Paul, Maryland Convent, 24 Hillside Road, GLASGOW G43 1DB. ☎0141-571 0608.

St. Paul MultiMedia, 5A/7 Royal Exchange Square, GLASGOW G1 3HA. ☎0141-226 3391; Fax: 0141-226 4719.
E-Mail:Glasgow@stpaulmultimedia.co.uk

DAUGHTERS OF WISDOM (1970)
(1980) Daughters of Wisdom (La Sagesse), 1 Green Street, Glasgow G40 2HL. ☎0141-556 1064.

FAITHFUL COMPANIONS OF JESUS (1889)
(1999) Faithful Companions, Flat 2/1, 8 Queen Margaret Road, GLASGOW G20 6DP. ☎ 0141-946 4644.

FRANCISCAN SISTERS MINORESSES (1946)
St. Francis' Convent, 54 Merryland Street, GLASGOW G51 2QD. ☎0141-445 6067.

FRANCISCAN MISSIONARIES OF MARY (1946)
(1975) St. Helen's Convent, 5 Kingsborough Gardens, GLASGOW G12 9NH. ☎ 0141-339 6789.
(1975) John Ogilvie House, 1245 Royston Road, GLASGOW G33 1EH. ☎ 0141-770 8628.

FRANCISCANS OF THE IMMACULATE CONCEPTION (1847)
(1962) St. Mary's Convent, 1 Broompark Circus, GLASGOW G31 2JF. ☎0141-554 1415.
(1978) Franciscan Convent, 27 Hillend Road, GLASGOW G22 6NY. ☎0141-336 8136; Fax: 0141-336 3494.
(1981) Franciscan Convent of the Immaculate Conception, 92 Dixon Avenue, GLASGOW G42 8EJ. ☎0141-423 4501.
(1998) (Generalate) Franciscan Convent, St. Teresa's, 86 Saracen Street, GLASGOW G22 5AD. ☎ 0141-336 3027; Fax:0141-336 4096.
(1998) Franciscan Sisters, 41 Circus Drive, GLASGOW G31 2JQ. ☎ 0141-556 6941.

HANDMAIDS OF THE SACRED HEART OF JESUS (1987)
29 Levernside Crescent, GLASGOW G53 5LA. ☎0141-810 3882; Fax:0141-882 0504.

HELPERS OF THE HOLY SOULS (1914)

(1990) Our Lady of Peace, 38 Archerhill Road, GLASGOW G13 3NW.☎0141-959 4638.

INDIVIDUALLY CONSECRATED SISTERS (1976)

c/o Archdiocesan Office, 196 Clyde Street, GLASGOW G1 4JY. ☎0141-226 5898.

INSTITUTE OF THE BLESSED VIRGIN MARY (1966)
(Loreto Sisters)

Flat 10/1, 160 Charles Street, GLASGOW G21 2QQ. ☎0141-553 2314.

LITTLE SISTERS OF THE POOR (1862)

St. Joseph's, 14 Cumnock Road, Robroyston, GLASGOW G33 1QT. ☎0141-558 5114; Fax: 0141-558 7934.

Chaplain: Rev. John Roberts (1953), Flat 7, Maryville Flats,14 Cumnock Road, Robroyston, GLASGOW G33 1QT. ☎0141-558 2185.

MISSIONARIES OF CHARITY (1985)

(1994) 186 Braidcraft Road, GLASGOW G53 5DZ. ☎0141-883 2785.

POOR SISTERS OF NAZARETH (1902)

(1906) Nazareth House, 1647 Paisley Road West, GLASGOW G52 3QT. ☎0141-882 1741; Fax.: 0141-882 8178.

RELIGIOUS SISTERS OF CHARITY (1948)

St. Margaret's Hospice, East Barns Street, CLYDEBANK G81 IEG. Tel.: (Convent) 0141-952 2780; (Hospice) 0141-952 1141.

SCHOENSTATT SISTERS OF MARY (1965)

Ardmory, 30 Langside Drive, GLASGOW G43 2QQ. ☎ 0141-637 3316.

SISTERS OF MERCY (1849)

(1867, 1877, 1980) Convent of Mercy, 62 Hill Street, GLASGOW G3 6RH. ☎ 0141-332 0895.

(1988) Convent of Mercy, 6/30 Bellrock Court, GLASGOW G33 3JF. ☎ 0141-774 2093.

(1993) Convent of Mercy, 59 Herma Street, Lambhill, GLASGOW G23 5AN. ☎ 0141-946 4939.

SISTERS OF THE MOST HOLY CROSS AND PASSION (1982)

Cross and Passion Convent, 201 Glenlora Drive, GLASGOW G53 6JS. ☎0141-881 2147.

(1999) 17/2 Pinkston Drive, Sighthill, GLASGOW G21 1PQ. ☎0141-558 5087/4308.

SISTERS OF NOTRE DAME DE NAMUR (1894)

(1894, 1984) Notre Dame Convent, 38 Kingsborough Gardens, GLASGOW G12 9NJ. ☎ 0141-339 3567.

(1979) Notre Dame Sisters, 53 & 55 White Street, GLASGOW G11 5EQ. ☎ (53) 0141-337 6435; (55) 0141-334 7152.

(1982) Notre Dame Convent,3 Kentallen Road, Barlanark, GLASGOW G33 4QY. Tel.: 0141-771 4783.

(1983) Notre Dame Convent, 14 Marlborough Avenue, GLASGOW G11 7BW. ☎ 0141 -339 4882.

(1992) 135 Smithycroft Road, GLASGOW G33 2RD.☎ 0141-770 5287.

(1992) 39 Victoria Park Drive South, GLASGOW G14 9QP. ☎ 0141-959 4103.

(1993) Sisters of Notre Dame, Comboni House, 151 Baillieston Road, GLASGOW G32 0TG. ☎/Fax.: 0141-771 5242.

(1994) Sisters of Notre Dame, 326 West Princes Street, <u>Glasgow</u> G4 9HA. ☎ 0141-339 8174.
E-mail: ismyth@bigfoot.com

(1983) Sisters of Notre Dame, 67 Moorpark Avenue, GLASGOW G52 4ET. ☎ 0141-810 4214.

(1970) Notre Dame, 19 Burnside, Bearsden, GLASGOW G61 4PX. ☎ 0141-942 5973.

(1912) Notre Dame Convent, Craigend House, 74a Cardross Road, DUMBARTON G82 4JH. ☎ Dumbarton (01389) 733222.

(1994) Sisters of Notre Dame, 47 Oxhill Road, DUMBARTON G82 4DQ. ☎ Dumbarton (01389) 731795.

SISTERS OF ST. JOSEPH OF ANNECY (1980)

(1995) St. Joseph's, Our Lady of Fatima Parish House, 75 Millerfield Road, GLASGOW G40 4RP. ☎ 0141-554 2795.

SISTERS OF ST. JOSEPH OF CLUNY (1946)

(1992) St. Joseph's Convent, 23 Whitevale Street, GLASGOW G31 IQW. ☎/Fax: 0141-554 9055.

SISTERS OF ST. JOSEPH OF PEACE (1924)

(1987) 17 Caldercuilt Road, Maryhill Park, GLASGOW G20 0AE. ☎0141-579 6061.

(1994) 150 Drumlochy Road, Ruchazie, GLASGOW G33 3RF. ☎0141-774 2677.

SISTERS OF THE SACRED HEART OF MARY (1978)

(1994) 111 Ardencraig Drive, GLASGOW G45 0HZ. ☎ 0141-583 7671
E-mail: RSHM@dtn.ntl.com

Diocese of Motherwell

SECTAMINI CARITATEM

Bishop of Motherwell
Right Rev. Joseph Devine, Ph.D.

Born at Glasgow, 7th August 1937; educated St. Ninian's Primary School, Kirkintilloch, St. Mary's College, Blairs, St. Peter's College, Cardross; ordained Priest at Glasgow, 29th June 1960; Scots College, Rome (Ph.D., 1964, Gregorian University, Rome); private secretary, Archbishop of Glasgow, 1964-65; assistant priest, St. Robert Bellarmine, Glasgow, 1965-67, St. Joseph's, Helensburgh, 1967-72; on staff of St. Peter's College, Cardross, 1967-74; assistant chaplain Catholic chaplaincy at University of Glasgow, 1974-77; episcopal vicar, Lay Apostolate, 1974-83; nominated titular Bishop of Voli (and auxiliary bishop), 5th May 1977, and ordained by Thomas Joseph Winning, Archbishop of Glasgow, in St. Francis' Church, Glasgow, 31st May, 1977; translated to Motherwell, 13th May, 1983.

Residence: 22 Wellhall Road, HAMILTON ML3 9BG
☎ Hamilton (01698) 423058; *Fax:* 01698-307093.

VICARS-GENERAL
Right Rev. Mgr. John J. Burns, Ph.L., S.T.L.
St. Bride's, Fallside Road, Bothwell, GLASGOW G71 8BA
☎ (01698) 852710

Right Rev. Mgr. Alexander Devanny,
St. Mary's, 120 Cadzow Street, HAMILTON ML3 6HX
☎ (01698) 423552

THE DIOCESAN CURIA

Diocesan Centre, Coursington Road, MOTHERWELL ML1 1PP
☎ (01698) 269114/5, (01698) 275655
Fax: (01698) 275630
The Diocesan Centre is open from 9.00 am to 4.30 pm on week days
All correspondence should be addressed to the Chancellor

1. CENTRAL ADMINISTRATION

Moderator:	Right Rev. Mgr. Alexander Devanny, V.G.
Chancellor:	Mr. Frank Cassidy
Treasurer:	Rev. Raymond Dempsey
Finance Assistant & Covenant Administrator:	Mrs. Caroline Melvin
Accounts Clerkess:	Mrs. Isabelle Kain
Diocesan Auditor for the National Tribunal:	Mr. Robert Smith.
Fabric:	Mr. Joseph McNally
Administrative Assistant:	Mrs. Margaret Docherty

FINANCE COMMITTEE
Bishop Joseph Devine; Right Rev. Mgr. John J. Burns, V.G.; Right Rev. Mgr. Alex Devanny, V.G.; Rev. Raymond Dempsey; Mr. Frank Cassidy; Mrs. Caroline Melvin; Miss Jane McKenna..
The Committee meets on the second Tuesday of each month.
All matters for the Agenda must be notified to the Chancellor one week before the meeting.

FABRIC & PLANNING COMMITTEE
Bishop Joseph Devine; Right Rev. Mgr. John McIntyre; Rev. Robert Curley; Rev. Thomas O'Hare; Mr. Donal Toner; Mr. Frank Cassidy(Chancellor); Mr. Desmond O'Donnell.
The Committee meets on the third Thursday of each month.
All matters for the Agenda must be notified to the Chancellor one week before the meeting.

2. RELIGIOUS EDUCATION
(a) Religious Education Centre

Diocesan Centre, Coursington Road, MOTHERWELL ML11PP
☎ (01698) 252447
Fax: (01698) 275630

R.E. Advisorate:	Rev. Dominic Douglas, Ph.B., S.T.L.
	Mr. William Liston, Ph.L., S.T.B.
Secondary Sector:	Mr. William Liston, Ph.L., S.T.B.
Primary Sector:	Rev. Dominic Douglas
Special Education:	Rev. Gerard Haddock
S.P.R.E.D. Centre:	Mrs. Anne McLaughlin
	S.P.R.E.D. Centre
	Pastoral/Retreat Centre
	50 Bonkle Road, Newmains.
	Wishaw ML2 9AP
	☎ (01698) 384208
R.E. Services:	Mr. Allan Wright

(b) Representatives on Local Education Committees

North Lanarkshire:	Mr. J. A. Quinn, B.Sc.
	8 Arthur Avenue,
	AIRDRIE ML6 9EZ
	☎ (01236) 762364
South Lanarkshire:	Miss Susan McCormick, M.A., Dip.Ed.
	1 Elm Crescent
	Viewpark, Uddingston,
	GLASGOW G71 5AD
	☎ (01698)
City of Glasgow:	Rev. Thomas J. Chambers,, B.A.
	Our Lady of Good Counsel
	6 Broompark Circus
	GLASGOW G31 2JF
	☎ (0141) 554 1558

3. PASTORAL OFFICE

Pastoral Centre, 50 Bonkle Road, Newmains, WISHAW ML2 9AP
☎ (01698) 385397; Fax: (01698) 381924

Vicar General for Pastoral Care and Planning:	Right Rev. Mgr. John J. Burns, Ph.L., S.T.L., V.G.
Director:	Rev. Henry O'Brien, S.T.D.
Assistant:	Rev. James G. Higgins
Assistant:	Miss Helen Ward
Youth Development Officer:	Mr. Kieran McQuaid, M.A.

DIOCESAN AGENCY LEADERS
PASTORAL CARE

Family Life:	Mrs. Evelyn Lochrin
Mission - Lapsed:	Rev. Brian Logue (01236) 763370
Mission - R.C.I.A.:	Rev. James Naughton (01236) 872608
Social Concerns:	Rev. Thomas Gibbons (0141) 647 6034
Youth:	Rev. Stephen Reilly (01698) 852710
Justice & Peace:	Mrs. Betty Gillick (01236) 768473)

PASTORAL PLANNING

Adult Formation:	Rev. Henry O'Brien, S.T.D. (01698) 385397
Christian Unity:	Rev. James Foley, Ph.L., S.T.L., L.S.S. (01236) 423044
Liturgy:	Rev. James Grant, S.T.B.(01698)843165
Vocations:	Rev. Charles O'Farrell, B.Sc., S.T.B. (01698) 384730
Community Building:	Mr. Michael Webster (01555) 750153

PASTORAL PLANNING TEAM

Chairman:	Bishop Joseph Devine
Co-ordinator:	Rev. Paul Morton
Secretary:	Mr. Raymond Lunny
Members:	Mgr. John J. Burns, Mr. James Quinn
	Rev. Henry O'Brien, Miss Helen Ward
	Rev. Thomas Welsh, S.X.,
	Mrs. Sadie Welsh, Mr. Frank Cassidy
	Mrs. Mary Cushley

PASTORAL COUNCIL

Chairman:	Mr. James Quinn (01501) 820607
Vice-Chair:	Mrs. Mary Cushley (01698) 853044\

SOCIAL CONCERNS

Secretary:	Mr. James Johnston
	14 Ellis Wynd
	MOTHERWELL ML1 2PM
	☎(01698) 253838

4. ADVISORS TO THE BISHOP

Episcopal Vicars:

Diocesan Administration:	Right Rev. Mgr. Alexander Devanny,V.G.
Christian Unity:	Rev. James Foley, Ph.L., S.T.L., L.S.S.
Education:	Rev. Dominic Douglas, Ph.B., S.T.L.

College of Consultors:	Right Rev. Mgr. John J. Burns, V.G. Right Rev. Mgr. Alexander Devanny,V.G. Rev. James Foley, Rev.Gerard J. Chromy, Rev. George Donaldson, Rev. James Naughton, Rev. Daniel Rooney, Rev. Raymond Dempsey
Council of Priests:	Chairman: Rev. Robert Kane, St. Edward's, Lady Ann Crescent, AIRDRIE ML6 9PZ ☎ (01236) 754545
	Secretary: Rev. James Morris, St. Gabriel's 1 Cedar Drive, Viewpark, Uddingston, GLASGOW G71 5LF. ☎ (01698) 817609.
Special Advisor:	Mr. Alan Draper, M.A. The Old School Kingoldrum, KIRRIEMUIR DD8 5HW ☎ (01575) 575656
Child Care Advisor:	Mrs. Margaret Campbell (01236) 767828

Child Protection Co-ordination:
Co-ordinator:	Mr. David McCann. ☎ /Fax Information line: 0141-572 0253.

CONTINUING FORMATION OF THE CLERGY
Bishop Joseph Devine, Rev. Wiliam Nolan *(Chairman)* Canon M. McCarthy, Revv. T. Devine, F. McGachey, I. McLaren, P. Morton, C. O'Farrell, D. Towey.

PERMANENT DIACONATE
Co-ordinator:	Rev. Gerard Chromy, St. Patrick's, 71 Shieldmuir Street, WISHAW ML2 7TH ☎ (01698) 351921

VOCATIONS
Co-Directors of Vocations:	Rev. Dominic Towey St. John Ogilvie's, Broompark Road, Blantyre, GLASGOW G72 9XD ☎(01698) 828774 Rev. Andrew Nelson Cathedal House, Coursington Road MOTHERWELL ML1 1PP ☎ (01698) 263045
Director of Junior Vocations:	Rev. Charles O'Farrell, B.Sc., St. Aidan's, 298 Coltness Road, Wishaw ML2 7EX ☎ 01698-384730

LITURGY

Liturgy Agency Leader: Rev. James Grant,
Holy Family, 57 Hope Street,
Mossend, BELLSHILL ML4 1QA
☎ (01698) 843165

Master of Ceremonies: Rev. Alexander Stewart,
Our Lady of Lourdes', 30 Canberra Drive,
East Kilbride, GLASGOW G75 8DG.
☎ (01355)224511

Assistant M.C.: Rev. Gerard Haddock,
St. Bernadette's, 200 Logans Road,
MOTHERWELL ML1 3PH
☎ (01698) 263945

SCOTTISH NATIONAL TRIBUNAL

*Many judicial matters, especially with regard to marriage annulments, are
dealt with by the Scottish National Tribunal, 22 Woodrow Road, GLASGOW
G41 5PN.* ☎ *0141-427 3036*

Officialis: Rev. Gerard Tartaglia, Ph.B., S.T.B., J.C.L.
Officials of the Tribunal from the Diocese of Motherwell:
Right Rev. Mgr. John J. Burns, V.G.
Rev. George Donaldson, Ph.L., S.T.L., Dip. R.E
Rev. John F. Givens
Rev. James O'Kane, S.T.B., J.C.L.
Rev. Walter Scott, M.A., LL.B., S.T.L.

Pontifical Mission Aid Societies: Rev. Isaac McLaren. St. Stephen's,
Paddock Street, Sikeside, COATBRIDGE
ML5 4PG. ☎ (01236) 420585.

Registrar for Deaceased Clergy: Right Rev.Mgr. Hugh N. Canon
Boyle, Ph.L., S.T.L., F.S.A.Scot.,
The Lindens, Bon Secours,
36 Mansionhouse Road,
GLASGOW G41 3DW
☎ (0141) 649 9226.

CATHEDRAL CHAPTER

(Erected 8th November, 1952.)

Provost: Very Rev. Noel Carey; **Canons:** Very Rev. Henry McGinn;
Very Rev. George Boyd; Very Rev. Niall Hayes; Very Rev. Kieran
O'Farrell; Very Rev. Patrick Moss; Very Rev James Ashe; Very Rev.
Andrew Reen; Very Rev. Michael McCarthy; Very Rev. Patrick O'Hare.

Honorary Canons: Very Rev. Anthony Kilcoyne; Very. Rev. Alphonsus
Woods; Very Rev. Thomas Barry; Very Very Rev. Gerald Maher; Very
Rev. John Gallacher; Very Rev. Denis Keane, Very Rev. Patrick
McGovern; Very Rev. Herbert Flack.

DEANERIES

1. **Northern Deanery:** St. Bridget, Baillieston; St. Francis of Assisi, Baillieston; St. Kevin, Bargeddie; St. Dominic, Craigend; St. Benedict, Easterhouse; St. Clare, Easterhouse; St. Mungo, Garthamlock; St. Michael, Moodiesburn; St. Barbara, Muirhead; St. Joseph, Stepps.
   Dean—Right Rev. Mgr. John McIntyre.

2. **East Kilbride Deanery:** St. Bride; St. Leonard; Our Lady of Lourdes; St. Vincent de Paul.
   Dean—Rev. Michael Ryan.

3. **Rutherglen Deanery:** St. Bride, Cambuslang; St. Cadoc, Halfway; St. Anthony, Rutherglen; St. Columbkille, Rutherglen; St. Mark, Rutherglen.
   Dean—Rev. James O'Hara

4. **Coatbridge Deanery:** St. Augustine, St. Bartholomew; St. Bernard; St. James; St. Mary; St. Monica; St. Patrick; St. Stephen; Our Lady and St. Joseph, Glenboig.
   Dean—Rev. James Foley.

5. **Airdrie Deanery:** St. Andrew; St. Edward; St. Margaret; St. Serf; Corpus Christi, Calderbank; St. Mary, Caldercruix; St. Aloysius, Chapelhall; Holy Trinity and All Saints, Coatdyke; St. Catherine, Harthill; St. David, Plains.
   Dean—Rev. Paul Morton.

6. **Central Deanery:** St. Gerard, Bellshill; Sacred Heart, Bellshill; St. Bride, Bothwell; Christ the King, Holytown; Holy Family, Mossend; St. John the Baptist, Uddingston; St. Columba, Viewpark; St. Gabriel, Viewpark.
   Dean—Rev. Edward Glackin.

7. **Motherwell Deanery:** Cathedral, Motherwell; St. Bernadette, Motherwell; St. Brendan, Motherwell; St. Luke, Motherwell; St. Francis Xavier, Carfin; St. Teresa, Newarthill; St. John Bosco, New Stevenston.
   Dean—Very Rev. George Canon Boyd.

8. **Wishaw Deanery:** St. Isidore, Biggar; St. Athanasius, Carluke; St Mary, Cleland; St. Mary, Lanark; St. Brigid, Newmains; St. Patrick, Shotts; St. Aidan, Wishaw; St. Ignatius, Wishaw; St. Patrick, Wishaw; St. Thomas, Wishaw.
   Dean—Rev. Joseph Clements.

9. **Hamilton Deanery:** Our Lady and St. John, Blackwood; St. Joseph Blantyre; St. John Ogilvie, Blantyre; St. Cuthbert, Burnbank; St. Mary, Hamilton; St. Ninian, Hamilton; Our Lady and St. Anne, Hamilton; St. Paul, Hamilton; St. Peter, Hamilton; St. Mary, Larkhall; St. Patrick, Strathaven.
   Dean—Rev. Thomas O'Hare.

Churches and Clergy of the Diocese

CITY OF MOTHERWELL

OUR LADY OF GOOD AID CATHEDRAL (1875, 1900), Coursington Road.

Very Rev. Noel Provost Carey, *Administrator* (1953)
Rev. Andrew J. Nelson, Ph.B., S.T.L. (1997)

POSTAL ADDRESS: Cathedral House, 31 Coursington Road, MOTHERWELL ML1 1PP. ☎Motherwell (01698) 263045; Fax:01698-258116.
E-mail:Motherwellcathedral@cableinet.co.uk

Sunday Masses: Vigil-Mass, 6.30 p.m.; 10, 11.30 a.m., 6.30 p.m. Evening Service: as announced. Holy Days of Obligation, Masses: Vigil-Mass, 7.30 p.m.; 10, 11.15 a.m., 7.30 p.m. Confessions: Thursday, 8 p.m.; Saturday, 10.30 a.m.; 6 to 6.25 p.m., after Vigil-Mass.
Estimated Catholic population: 1,950.

STRATHCLYDE HOSPITAL, AIRBLES ROAD CENTRE, AND LESLIE HOUSE, ATTENDED FROM OUR LADY OF GOOD AID.
(CATHEDRAL PRIMARY SCHOOL.)

ST. BERNADETTE (1950, 1964), Logans Road.

Very Rev. James J. Canon Ashe (1953)
Rev. Gerard Haddock, Dip. Theol. (1992)

POSTAL ADDRESS: St. Bernadette's, 200 Logans Road, MOTHERWELL ML1 3PH. ☎Motherwell (01698) 263945.

Sunday Masses: Vigil-Mass, 6 p.m., 9.30, 11 a.m., 6 p.m. Holy Days of Obligation, Masses: Vigil-Mass, 7 p.m.; 10 a.m., 7 p.m. Confessions: Thursday, 6.40 to 6.55 p.m., 7.30 p.m.; Saturday,5.30 to 5.55 p.m., after Vigil-Mass.

Estimated Catholic population: 3,000.

CLYDE VIEW SPECIAL SCHOOL AND AVONDALE NURSING HOME ATTENDED FROM ST. BERNADETTE'S .
ST. BERNADETTE'S PRIMARY SCHOOL; (CATHEDRAL PRIMARY SCHOOL).

ST. BRENDAN, Muirhouse (1965, 1968), Muirhouse Road.

Very Rev. George Canon Boyd (1948)

POSTAL ADDRESS: St. Brendan's, 51 Barons Road, MOTHERWELL ML1 2NB.
☎Motherwell (01698) 264448.

Sunday Masses: Vigil-Mass, 6 p.m., 11 a.m. Holy Days of Obligation, Masses: Vigil-Mass, 7.30 p.m.; 10 a.m., 7.30 p.m. Confessions: before and after Services.
Estimated Catholic population: 1,600.

ST. BRENDAN'S PRIMARY SCHOOL; OUR LADY'S HIGH SCHOOL.

ST. LUKE, Braidhurst (1954, 1955), Davaar Drive.

Rev. Daniel Rooney (1972)

Postal address: St. Luke's, Davaar Drive, Braidhurst, MOTHERWELL ML1 3TW. ☎Motherwell (01698) 230402.

Sunday Masses: Vigil-Mass, 5.15 p.m.; 10 a.m., 5.15 p.m. Holy Days of Obligation, Masses: Vigil-Mass, 6.30 p.m.; 10 a.m., 6.30 p.m. Confessions: Saturday, after Vigil-Mass; as requested.
Estimated Catholic population: 600.

ORBISTON NURSING/RESIDENTIAL HOME & DAY CARE CENTRE ATTENDED FROM ST. LUKE'S.
CATHEDRAL PRIMARY SCHOOL.

PARISHES OUTSIDE THE CITY OF MOTHERWELL

The name given last before the name of the Church is the Local Government Authority.

AIRDRIE, North Lanarkshire, St. Andrew (1950, 1954), Whinhall Road.

Rev. Patrick O'Sullivan (1955)
Rev. Stephen Miller, Dip. Theol.*(Hospital Chaplain,*☎ *Airdrie* (01236) 764577) (1993)
Sr. Anne Delaney, *Pastoral Assistant*

POSTAL ADDRESS: St. Andrew's, Whinhall Road, AIRDRIE ML6 0HJ.
☎Airdrie (01236) 763720.

Sunday Masses: Vigil-Mass, 6.30 p.m., 11 a.m., 6.30 p.m. Evening Service: as announced. Holy Days of Obligation, Masses: 10 a.m., 1.00, 7.30 p.m. Confessions: Saturday, after 10 a.m. Mass, 5.30 to 6.15 p.m.
Estimated Catholic population: 2,100.

MONKLANDS GENERAL HOSPITAL (Chaplain: Rev. Stephen Miller, St. Andrew's. Sunday Mass: 4.30 p.m.)
,MAVISBANK SCHOOL FOR HANDICAPPED CHILDREN, ARRAN HOUSE NURSING HOME AND LADY SMITH SHELTERED HOUSING ATTENDED FROM ST. ANDREW'S.
ST. ANDREW'S PRIMARY SCHOOL.

AIRDRIE, North Lanarkshire, St. Edward (1960, 1967), Lady Anne Crescent.

Rev. Robert Kane, Ph.B., S.T.L., M.A (1971)

POSTAL ADDRESS: St. Edward's, Lady Anne Crescent, AIRDRIE ML6 9PZ.
☎Airdrie (01236) 754545.
E-mail: EdwardConf@compuserve.com
Sunday Masses: Vigil-Mass, 6 p.m.; 10 a.m., 12 noon. Holy Days of
Obligation, Masses: Vigil-Mass, 6 p.m.;10 a.m., 1.00, 7.30 p.m.
Confessions: Saturday, after Vigil-Mass .
Estimated Catholic population: 3,000.

WESTER MOFFAT HOSPITAL ATTENDED FROM ST. EDWARD'S.
ST. DOMINIC'S PRIMARY SCHOOL, ST. EDWARD'S PRIMARY SCHOOL.

AIRDRIE, North Lanarkshire, St. Margaret (1836, 1839) Hallcraig Street.

Rev. Brian Logue (1961)
Rev. Kevin Donnelly, Dip.Theol. (1995)
Sr. Mary McKeon, *Pastoral Assistant*

POSTAL ADDRESS: St. Margaret's, 96 Hallcraig Street, AIRDRIE ML6 6AW.
☎Airdrie (01236) 763370.

Sunday Masses: Vigil-Mass,5 p.m.; 10 a.m., 12 noon, 4 p.m. Holy Days
of Obligation, Masses: Vigil-Mass, 7 p.m.; 10 a.m. Confessions: Saturday,
9.30 a.m., after 10 a.m. Mass, after Vigil-Mass.
Estimated Catholic population: 2,200.

ST. ANDREW'S HOSPICE (RELIGIOUS SISTERS OF CHARITY), HENDERSON STREET
AIRDRIE ML6 6DJ. TEL.: AIRDRIE (01236) 766951; FAX: 01236-748786.
BELHAVEN HOUSE, FERGUSSON HOUSE, MEADOWSIDE HOUSE AND SUNART
HOUSE ATTENDED FROM ST. MARGARET'S.
ALEXANDRA PRIMARY SCHOOL, (ST. EDWARD'S PRIMARY SCHOOL, ST. SERF'S
PRIMARY SCHOOL).

AIRDRIE, North Lanarkshire, St. Serf's (1961, 1967), Aitken Street.

Rev. John B. Healy (1954)
Sister Eileen Towey *(Pastoral Assistant)*

POSTAL ADDRESS: St. Serf's, 66 Aitken Street, AIRDRIE ML6 6LT. ☎Airdrie
(01236) 764479.

Sunday Masses: Vigil-Mass, 6 p.m.; 11 a.m. Holy Days of Obligation,
Masses: 10 a.m., 7.30 p.m. Confessions: Saturday, 9.30 a.m., after
Vigil-Mass.
Estimated Catholic population: 3,000.

RAWYARDS HOUSE NURSING HOME (FOR THE ELDERLY) ATTENDED FROM
ST. SERF'S.
ST. SERF 'S PRIMARY SCHOOL.

BAILLIESTON, City of Glasgow, St. Bridget (1880, 1893), Swinton Road.

Right Rev. Mgr. John McIntyre, Ph.L., S.T.L., M.A., Dip.Ed. (1961)
Rev. Francis G. McGachey, S.T.L. (1997)

POSTAL ADDRESS: St. Bridget's, 15 Swinton Road, Baillieston, GLASGOW G69 6DT. ☎0141-771 1058.

Sunday Masses: Vigil-Mass, 6.30 p.m.; 9, 10.30 a.m., 12 noon., 6 p.m. Exposition of the Blessed Sacrament, First Sunday, 12 noon to 5 p.m., with Solemn Sung Evening Prayer and Benediction, or as announced. Holy Days of Obligation, Masses: Vigil-Mass, 7.30 p.m.; 8, 9.30 a.m., 7.30 p.m. Confessions: Saturday, 9 to 9.20 a.m., 5 to 6 p.m; on request. Estimated Catholic population: 4,000. 🦿 Ⓐ

SISTERS OF MERCY, 59 SWINTON AVENUE, BAILLIESTON, GLASGOW G69 6LY. ☎: 0141-573 2728.
GRAMPIAN RESIDENTIAL HOME, LOANCROFT HOME AND SWINTONHILL RESIDENTIAL HOME ATTENDED FROM ST. BRIDGET'S. (MONTHLY MASS AND WEEKLY EUCHARISTIC SERVICE IN ALL HOMES.)
ST. BRIDGET'S PRIMARY SCHOOL; (ST. JOHN OGILVIE PRIMARY SCHOOL, EASTERHOUSE).

BAILLIESTON, City of Glasgow, St. Francis of Assisi (1970, 1973), Crown Street.

Rev. Vivian Hayes (1955)

POSTAL ADDRESS: St. Francis', Crown Street, Baillieston, GLASGOW G69 7XB. ☎0141-773 0084.

Sunday Masses: Vigil-Mass, 6 p.m.; 9.30, 11 a.m., 6 p.m. Evening Service: as announced. Holy Days of Obligation, Masses: Vigil-Mass, 6 p.m.; 10 a.m., 7 p.m. Confessions: Saturday, 10 a.m., after Vigil-Mass to 7.30 p.m. 🦿 ♿
Estimated Catholic population: 1,675.

ST. FRANCIS OF ASSISI PRIMARY SCHOOL.

BARGEDDIE, North Lanarkshire, St. Kevin (1947, 1950), Mainhill Road.

Rev. William Dunnachie, S.T.B., Dip.R.E. (1964)

POSTAL ADDRESS: St. Kevin's, Mainhill Road, Bargeddie, Baillieston, GLASGOW G69 7SS. ☎0141-771 1654.

Sunday Masses: Vigil-Mass, 5.30 p.m.; 10.30 a.m., 5.30 p.m. Holy Days of Obligation, Masses: 9.30 a.m., 7.30 p.m. Confessions: Saturday, after Vigil Mass; on call.
Estimated Catholic population: 800.

DRUMPELIER LODGE (RESIDENTIAL HOME FOR THE ELDERLY) ATTENDED FROM ST. KEVIN'S (MONTHLY MASS AND WEEKLY EUCHARISTIC SERVICE).
ST. KEVIN'S PRIMARY SCHOOL.

BELLSHILL, North Lanarkshire, St. Gerard (1967, 1971), Fleming Road.

Rev. Timothy Brosnan (1957)
Sr. Brigid, S.S.J.A. *(Pastoral Asssitant)*

POSTAL ADDRESS: St. Gerard's, Fleming Road, BELLSHILL ML4 1NF. ☎Bellshill (01698) 843734.

Sunday Masses: Vigil-Mass, 6 p.m.; 11 a.m., 6 p.m. Evening Service: 5 p.m. Holy Days of Obligation, Masses: 9, 11 a.m., 7.30 p.m. Confessions: Thursday, 8 p.m.; Saturday, 10 a.m., 5.15 to 5.45 p.m., after Vigil-Mass to 7.15 p.m. Exposition of the Blessed Sacrament, Monday to Friday, 10 a.m. to 8 p.m.
Estimated Catholic population: 1,740.

ST. GERARD'S PRIMARY SCHOOL.

BELLSHILL, North Lanarkshire, The Sacred Heart (1949 1951), Motherwell Road .

Very Rev. Andrew Canon Reen (1953)
Rev. Charles C. Dornan, B.Ed., S.T.B. (1989)

POSTAL ADDRESS: The Sacred Heart Presbytery, 106 Crossgates, BELLSHILL ML4 2LB. ☎Bellshill (01698) 842709.

Sunday Masses: Vigil-Mass, 6 p.m., 10 a.m., 12 noon, 5 p.m. Evening Service: 6 p.m. Holy Days of Obligation, Masses: 9.30, 11 a.m., 7.30 p.m. Confessions: Thursday, 8 p.m.; Saturday, 10.30 a.m., 5 p.m. Exposition of the Blessed Sacrament, Monday, Tuesday and Wednesday,10.30 a.m. to 9 p.m., Thursday, 7 to 9 p.m.
Estimated Catholic population: 3,800.

SISTERS OF ST. PETER CLAVER, 57 MOTHERWELL ROAD, BELLSHILL ML4 2JA. ☎: BELLSHILL (01698) 747112.
BELLSHILL MATERNITY HOSPITAL ATTENDED FROM SACRED HEART.
SACRED HEART PRIMARY SCHOOL, CARDINAL NEWMAN HIGH SCHOOL.

BELLSHILL, North Lanarkshire, Lithuanian Community, Chaplaincy for

Rev. Joseph McAndrew, S.M.A., *Chaplain* (1960)

POSTAL ADDRESS: St. Casimir, 78 Glencalder Crescent, BELLSHILL ML4 2LU. ☎Bellshill (01698) 746266

Services: Blessed John Duns Scotus, Glasgow: 1st Sunday of the month: Confessions, 1.30 p.m.; Mass, 2 p.m. Holy Family, Mossend: 2nd Sunday of the month: Confessions, 1.30 p.m.; Mass, 2 p.m.; Easter Sunday, 8 a.m.; Carfin, 2nd Sunday of June or as announced.

SCOTTISH LITHUANIAN CULTURAL CENTRE AND SOCIAL CLUB 79A CALDER ROAD, MOSSEND, BELLSHILL ML4 1PX. ☎: BELLSHILL (01698) 745354.

BIGGAR, South Lanarkshire, St. Isidore the Farmer (1937), Coulter Road.

Rev. Michael B. Maher (1968)

POSTAL ADDRESS: St. Isidore's, 6 Coulter Road, BIGGAR ML12 6EP. ☎/ Fax: Biggar (01899) 220189.

Sunday Masses: Vigil-Mass, 5 p.m.; 12 noon. Holy Days of Obligation, Mass: 7.30 p.m. Confessions: at call.
Estimated Catholic population: 230. **A**

FORTH, ST. MARY MAGDALENE, SERVED FROM BIGGAR.
CARSTAIRS STATE HOSPITAL ATTENDED FROM ST. ISIDORE'S.
KELLO HOSPITAL AND ABBEYFIELD NURSING HOME, Biggar, ATTENDED FROM ST. ISIDORE'S.
The Registers of St. Isidore's, Symington (1932-1937) and St. Mary Magdalene, Tarbrax (1917-1923) are deposited at St. Isidore's, Biggar.

BLACKWOOD, South Lanarkshire, Our Lady and St. John (1896, 1880), Carlisle Road.

Very Rev. Patrick J. Canon Moss (1950)

POSTAL ADDRESS: St. John's, Blackwood, Kirkmuirhill, LANARK ML11 9RZ. ☎Lesmahagow (01555) 893459.

Sunday Masses: Vigil-Mass, 6 p.m.; 10 a.m., 6 p.m. Holy Days of Obligation, Masses: 10 a.m., 7.30 p.m. Confessions: Saturday, 5 to 5.50 p.m.; daily, before and after Mass.
Estimated Catholic population: 860.

COALBURN AND LESMAHAGOW SERVED FROM OUR LADY AND ST JOHN'S.
BIRKWOOD HOSPITAL, Lesmahagow, WALLACE HAMILTON HOUSE NURSING HOME AND WATESIDE RETIREMENT HOME ATTENDED FROM BLACKWOOD.
ST. JOHN'S PRIMARY SCHOOL.

BLANTYRE, South Lanarkshire, St. John Ogilvie, High Blantyre (1977, 1979), Broompark Road.

Rev. Dominic M. Towey (1970)

POSTAL ADDRESS: St. John Ogilvie's, Broompark Road, Blantyre, GLASGOW G72 9XD. ☎Blantyre (01698) 828774.
Website:http://www.soft.net.uk/connor/ogilvie.html
Sunday Masses: Vigil-Mass, 6 p.m.; 9 (exc. June, July, August), 11 a.m., 5 p m. Evening Service: as announced. Holy Days of Obligation, Masses: 10 a.m., 7 p.m. Exposition of the Blessed Sacrament in Oratory: Tuesday, 10.30 a.m. to 2 p.m.; Friday, 10.30 a.m. to 8 p.m.; also as announced. Confessions: Saturday, 9.30 to 9.55 a.m. and after Vigil-Mass; other times as announced and requested.
Estimated Catholic population: 1,880.

KIRKTON HOME, AND KIRKCARE HOME ATTENDED FROM ST. JOHN OGILVIE'S.

BLANTYRE, South Lanarkshire, St. Joseph (1877, 1905), Glasgow Road.

Rev. Thomas Brady (1978)
Rev. John M. Irons, B.D (1990)

POSTAL ADDRESS: St. Joseph's, Mayberry Place, Blantyre, GLASGOW G72 9DA. ☎Blantyre (01698) 823896/320055.
E-mail: johnirons@cableinet.co.uk

Sunday Masses: Vigil-Mass, Saturday, 5 p.m.; 9, 10.30 a.m., 12 noon, 5.30 p.m. Holy Days of Obligation, Masses: Vigil-Mass, 7 p.m.; 10 a.m., 1.00, 7 p.m. Confessions: Thursday, 9.30 to 9.55 a.m., 6.30 to 6.55 p.m.; Friday, 9.30 to 9.55 a.m.; Saturday, after Vigil Mass.
Estimated Catholic population: 4,000.

VICTORIA HOUSE, NEW CALDERGLEN HOME AND DEVLIN GROVE ATTENDED FROM ST. JOSEPH'S.
ST. BLANE'S PRIMARY SCHOOL, ST. JOSEPH'S PRIMARY SCHOOL.

BOTHWELL, South Lanarkshire, St. Bride (1910, 1973), Fallside Road.

Right Rev. Mgr. John J. Burns, Ph.L., S.T.L., V.G.. (1956)
Rev. Stephen M.C. Reilly, Ph.L., S.T.L. (1997)

POSTAL ADDRESS: St. Bride's, Fallside Road, Bothwell, GLASGOW G71 8BA.
☎ Bothwell (01698) 852710.

Sunday Masses: Vigil-Mass, 5.30 p.m.; 10 a.m., 12 noon, 6 p.m. Sundays in Advent: Evening Prayer and Benediction, 5.15 p.m. Sundays in Lent: Stations of the Cross and Benediction, 5.15 p.m. Holy Days of Obligation, Masses: Vigil Mass, 7.30 p.m.; 7.30, 9.30 a.m., 7.30 p.m. Exposition of the Blessed Sacrament: Tuesday and Wednesday, 10 a.m. to 8 p.m. Confessions: Saturdays, after 9.30 a.m. Mass, 6.30 to 7 p.m. Estimated Catholic population: 1,900.

FRANCISCANS OF THE IMMACULATE CONCEPTION, FRANCISCAN CONVENT, 7 BLANTYRE MILL ROAD, BOTHWELL, GLASGOW G71 8DE. ☎: BOTHWELL (01698) 852213.
POOR CLARES, POOR CLARE MONASTERY, FALLSIDE ROAD, BOTHWELL, GLASGOW G71 8BA.
KIRKLANDS HOSPITAL, BLAIRSTON NURSING HOME AND SILVERWELLS NURSING HOME ATTENDED FROM ST. BRIDE'S.
ST. BRIDE'S PRIMARY SCHOOL.

BURNBANK, South Lanarkshire, St. Cuthbert (1893, 1908), Glenlee Street.

Rev. John Taylor (1972)
Rev. James O'Kane, S.T.B, J.C.L. (1997)

POSTAL ADDRESS: St. Cuthbert's, 98 High Blantyre Road, Burnbank, HAMILTON ML3 9HW. ☎/Fax: Blantyre (01698) 823105.

Sunday Masses: Vigil-Mass, 6 p.m., 9.30 a.m., 12 noon, 5 p.m. Holy Days of Obligation, Masses: Vigil-Mass, 7 p.m.; 10 a.m., 6, 7 p.m. Confessions: Saturday, after 10 a.m. Mass, after Vigil-Mass; any time, at call. Estimated Cathlic population: 3,000.

UDSTON HOSPITAL AND ABERGLEN RESIDENTIAL RETIREMENT HOME ATTENDED FROM ST. CUTHBERT'S.
ST. CUTHBERT'S PRIMARY SCHOOL; JOHN OGILVIE HIGH SCHOOL; (ST. NINIAN'S PRIMARY SCHOOL).

CADZOW. See HAMILTON, South Lanarkshire, Our Lady and St. Anne, page 352.

CALDERBANK, North Lanarkshire, Corpus Christi (1948, 1952), Crowwood Crescent.

Rev. Paul Morton, Ph.B., S.T.B (1985)

POSTAL ADDRESS: Corpus Christi, Crowwood Crescent, Calderbank, AIRDRIE ML6 9TA. ☎Airdrie (01236) 763670; Fax: 01236-770368. E-mail:cchristi.demon.co.uk

Sunday Masses: Vigil-Mass, 6 p.m.; 9, 11 a.m. Holy Days of Obligation, Masses: 10 a.m., 7 p.m. Confessions: Saturday, after 10 a.m. Mass, after Vigil-Mass.
Estimated Catholic population: 840.

CORPUS CHRISTI PRIMARY SCHOOL.

CALDERCRUIX, North Lanarkshire, St. Mary (1878, 1982), Glen Road.

Rev. Cornelius O'Leary (1962)

POSTAL ADDRESS: St. Mary's, Glen Road, Caldercruix, AIRDRIE ML6 7PZ. ☎Caldercruix (01236) 842220.

Sunday Masses: Vigil-Mass, 5.30 p.m., 11 a.m., 6 p.m. Holy Days of Obligation, Masses: Vigil-Mass, 7 p.m.; 10 a.m., 7 p.m. Confessions: Friday, after 10 a.m. Mass; Saturday, after Vigil-Mass.
Estimated Catholic population: 820.

EASTERCROFT HOUSE ATTENDED FROM ST. MARY'S.
ST. MARY'S PRIMARY SCHOOL.

CAMBUSLANG, South Lanarkshire, St. Bride (1878, 1900), Greenlees Road.

Rev. Thomas Millar (1978)
Rev. John F. Breslin, Ph.L., S.T.L. (1953)

POSTAL ADDRESS: St. Bride's, 21 Greenlees Road, Cambuslang, GLASGOW G72 8JB. ☎ 0141-641 3053; Fax: 0141-641 2828. E-mail: parish@saintbrides.fsnet.co.uk

Sunday Masses: Vigil-Mass, 6 p.m.; 8.30, 10 a.m.,12 noon, 6 p.m. Holy
Days of Obligation, Masses: Vigil-Mass, 7.30 p.m.; 8.30, 10 a.m., 5 p.m.
Confessions: Thursday, 7 to 8 p.m., during Exposition of the Blessed
Sacrament; First Saturday of the month, 10.30 to 11.30 a.m.
Estimated Catholic population: 3,500.

ABBEYFIELD HOME, DUNVEGAN NURSING HOME, GREENCROSS NURSING HOME,
AND GREENLEES NURSING HOME ATTENDED FROM ST. BRIDE'S.
ST. BRIDE'S PRIMARY SCHOOL, Cambuslang; ST. CHARLES' PRIMARY SCHOOL,
Newton.
The Registers of St. Charles', Newton (1894-1997) are deposited at St.
Bride's, Cambuslang.

CARDOWAN, See Stepps, Page 361.

CARFIN, North Lanarkshire, St. Francis Xavier (1862, 1973), Taylor Avenue.

Rev. Joseph Kelly, O.Carm. (1959)
Rev. Andrew Donnelly, O.Carm. (1957)
Rev. Francis McAleese, B.A., B.D., M.Phil., O.Carm. (1997)

POSTAL ADDRESS: St. Francis Xavier's, Taylor Avenue, Carfin,
MOTHERWELL ML1 5AJ. ☎ Motherwell (01698) 263308; Fax:
01698-230988.

E-mail: joeee33@aol.com

Sunday Masses: Vigil-Mass, 6 p.m., 10 a.m., 12 noon. Evening Service:
as announced, Holy Days of Obligation, Masses: 10 a.m., 1.00, 7 p.m,
Confessions: Saturday, 5.15 to 5.45 p.m., after Vigil-Mass.
Estimated Catholic population: 1,700.

CARFIN GROTTO, DEDICATED TO OUR LADY OF LOURDES AND ST. THÉRÈSE.
PILGRIMAGE SERVICE ON SUNDAYS (MAY TO OCTOBER) AT 3 P.M. EXPOSITION OF
THE BLESSED SACRAMENT IN OUR LADY, MAID OF THE SEAS CHAPEL, FROM MAY
TO OCTOBER, AND IN THE PARISH CHURCH FROM OCTOBER TO APRIL.
ARRANGEMENTS FOR GROUP CATERING MAY BE MADE WITH THE PARISH
SECRETARY (01698-263308) OR WITH THE PILGRIMAGE CENTRE (01698-
268941). RETREATS AND CONFERENCE MAY BE ARRANGED THROUGH THE
PILGRIMAGE CENTRE. GROTTO OPEN THROUGHOUT THE YEAR.
OUR LADY AND ST. FRANCIS' PRIMARY SCHOOL.

CARFIN, North Lanarkshire, Holy Ghost Fathers (1973).

Rev. Raymond Barry, C.S.Sp (1959)
Rev. Patrick Gaffney, C.S.Sp. (1963)
Rev. Brian Fulton, C.S.Sp. (1976)

POSTAL ADDRESS: Holy Ghost Fathers, 117 Newarthill Road, Carfin, MOTHERWELL ML1 5AL. ☎ Motherwell (01698) 290831; Fax: 01698-290830; Youth Ministry Team Office: ☎ Motherwell (01698) 297054.

E-mail: hgfcarfin@cableinet.co.uk

CARLUKE, South Lanarkshire, St. Athanasius (1849, 1857), Mount Stewart Street.

Very Rev. Michael A. Canon McCarthy (1953)
Sister Margaret, D.C., *Pastoral Assistant*

POSTAL ADDRESS: St. Athanasius', 21 Mount Stewart Street, CARLUKE ML8 5EB. ☎Carluke (01555) 771250.

Sunday Masses: Vigil-Mass, 6 p.m.; 9, 11.15 a.m. Evening Service: as announced. Holy Days of Obligation, Masses: 10 a.m., 7.30 p.m. Confessions: Every morning, 9.30 to 10 a.m.; Saturday, 5.30 to 6 p.m., after Vigil-Mass to 8 p.m.
Estimated Catholic population: 1,500.

VICTORIA PARK SPECIAL SCHOOL, ROADMEETINGS HOSPITAL, HAZELHEAD NURSING HOME, MILTON GRANGE NURSING HOME, ORCHARD HOUSE AND WOODHURST NURSING HOME ATTENDED FROM ST. ATHANASIUS'.
ST. ATHANASIUS' PRIMARY SCHOOL.

CARSTAIRS, South Lanarkshire, St. Joseph (1851). Served from Lanark.

Sunday Mass: 9.30 a.m.

CHAPELHALL, North Lanarkshire, St. Aloysius (1859, 1894), Main Street.

Rev. Michael Walsh (1959)

POSTAL ADDRESS: St. Aloysius', Main Street, Chapelhall, AIRDRIE ML6 8SF. ☎Airdrie (01236) 763190.

Sunday Masses: Vigil-Mass, 6.30 p.m.; 10 a.m., 12 noon, 5.30 p.m. Holy Days of Obligation, Masses: Vigil-Mass, 7 p.m.; 10 a.m., 7 p.m. Confessions: Monday after 7 p.m. Mass; Saturday, after 10 a.m. Mass, 5.30 to 6.15 p.m., after Vigil-Mass.
Estimated Catholic population: 2,120

PRIMARY SCHOOL.

CLELAND, North Lanarkshire, St. Mary (1874, 1877), Main Street.

Very Rev. Kieran Canon O'Farrell (1950)

POSTAL ADDRESS: St. Mary's, Main Street, Cleland, MOTHERWELL ML1 5QR. ☎Cleland (01698) 860254.

Sunday Masses: Vigil-Mass, 6 p.m.; 9.30, 11.30 a.m. Evening Service: as announced. Holy Days of Obligation, Masses: Vigil-Mass, 7.30 p.m.; 10 a.m., 7.30 p.m. Confessions: Saturday, after 10 a.m. Mass, after Vigil-Mass to 7.30 p.m .
Estimated Catholic population: 1,350.

(also disabled toilet in hall)

CLELAND HOSPITAL ATTENDED FROM ST. MARY'S.
ST. MARY'S PRIMARY SCHOOL.

COALBURN, South Lanarkshire, served from Blackwood.

Special 'bus for 10 a.m. Mass at Blackwood; return after Mass.

COATBRIDGE, North Lanarkshire, St. Augustine, Langloan (1892, 1899), Dundyvan Road .

Rev. James Foley, Ph.L., S.T.L., L.S.S (1955)
Very Rev. Gerald Canon Maher, M.A. (*Retired*) (1945)
Rev. Francis Scally *(Permanent Deacon)* (1999)
Sr. Eileen, *Pastoral Assistant.*

POSTAL ADDRESS: St. Augustine's, 12 Dundyvan Road, Langloan, COATBRIDGE ML5 4DQ. ☎Coatbridge (01236) 423044.

Sunday Masses: Vigil-Mass, 6.30 p.m.; 10 a.m., 12 noon. Evening Service: as announced. Holy Days of Obligation, Masses: Vigil-Mass, 7.30 p.m; 10 a.m., 7.30 p.m. Confessions: Wednesday, after Evening Mass; Saturday, 10.30 a.m., 5 to 6 p.m.
Estimated Catholic Population: 4,000.

DE LA SALLE BROTHERS, 61 BLAIR ROAD, COATBRIDGE ML5 ING. ☎: COATBRIDGE (01236) 432127.
SISTERS OF OUR LADY OF THE MISSIONS, 20A WOOD STREET, COATBRIDGE. ML5 1LX. ☎ 01236-603350.
DEANSTON HOME AND ELLENVALE HOME ATTENDED FROM ST. AUGUSTINE'S.
ST. AUGUSTINE'S PRIMARY SCHOOL; ST. AMBROSE'S HIGH SCHOOL; DRUMPARK SPECIAL SCHOOL.

COATBRIDGE, North Lanarkshire, St. Bartholomew, Townhead (1950, 1953), Teviot Street.

Rev. Hugh P. Kelly (1967)

POSTAL ADDRESS: St. Bartholomew's, 1 Trent Street, COATBRIDGE ML5 2NT. ☎Coatbridge (01236) 421587.

Sunday Masses: Vigil-Mass, 6 p.m.; 10 a.m., 12 noon, 6 p.m. Holy Days of Obligation, Masses: Vigil-Mass 7 p.m., 10 a.m., 7 p.m. Confessions: Saturday, 10.30 a.m., 6.45 to 7.30 p.m.
Estimated Catholic population: 2,400.   🏃 Ⓐ

DEANBANK SPECIAL SCHOOL, ALEXANDER HOSPITAL, BLAIR HOUSE AND LOCHVIEW HOME ATTENDED FROM ST. BARTHOLOMEW'S.
ST. BARTHOLOMEW'S PRIMARY SCHOOL.

COATBRIDGE, North Lanarkshire, St. Bernard, Shawhead (1973, 1974), Hermitage Crescent.

Rev. Damien J. Gilhooley (1968)

POSTAL ADDRESS: St. Bernard's, Hermitage Crescent, Shawhead, COATBRIDGE ML5 4NB. ☎ /Fax: Coatbridge (01236) 422451.
E-mail:st.bernard@virgin.net

Sunday Masses: Vigil-Mass, 6.30 p.m.; 10.30 a.m., 12.15 p.m. Subject to change for June, July and August). Holy Days of Obligation, Masses: 9, 10 a.m., 7.30 p.m. Confessions: daily, 9.30 to 9.55 a.m.; Saturday, after Vigil-Mass.
Estimated Catholic population: 1,500.   🏃 Ⓐ

ST. BERNARD'S PRIMARY SCHOOL.

COATBRIDGE, North Lanarkshire, Holy Trinity and All Saints, Coatdyke (1902, 1977), Muiryhall Street.

Rev. Colin T. Hughes B.Ed. (1986)

POSTAL ADDRESS: Holy Trinity and All Saints', 293 Muiryhall Street, COATBRIDGE ML5 3RZ. ☎Coatbridge (01236) 441110.

Sunday Masses: Vigil-Mass, 5 p.m.; 10.30 a.m., 5.30 p.m. Holy Days of Obligation, Masses: Vigil-Mass, 7.30 p.m.; 9.30 a.m., 7.30 p.m. Confessions: Saturday, 10 a.m., after Vigil-Mass.
Estimated Catholic population: 1,000.   🏃

MONKLANDS DISTRICT GENERAL HOSPITAL. CHAPLAIN: REV. STEPHEN MILLER, ST. ANDREW'S, AIRDRIE. ☎: 01236-763720. SUNDAY MASS 4.30 P.M.
(ST. PATRICK'S PRIMARY SCHOOL; ALEXANDRA PRIMARY SCHOOL, Airdrie)

COATBRIDGE, North Lanarkshire, St. James the Greater, Kirkshaws (1956, 1961), Woodhall Avenue.

Rev. John Kelly (1964)

POSTAL ADDRESS: St. James', 232 Woodhall Avenue, COATBRIDGE ML5 5DF. ☎ Coatbridge (01236) 422233.

Sunday Masses: Vigil-Mass, 6 p.m.; 9.30, 11.30 a.m. Holy Days of Obligation, Masses: Vigil-Mass, 7.30 p.m.; 9.45 a.m., 7.30 p.m. Confessions: daily, 9.15 to 9.30 a.m.; Thursday, 8 p.m.; Saturday, 5 to 5.30 p.m.
Estimated Catholic population: 4,600.

COATHILL HOSPITAL ATTENDED FROM ST. JAMES'.
ST. JAMES' PRIMARY SCHOOL; ST. TIMOTHY'S PRIMARY SCHOOL.

COATBRIDGE, North Lanarkshire, St. Mary, Whifflet (1874, 1893), Hozier Street.

Rev. Raymond Dempsey, M.A (1984)

POSTAL ADDRESS: St. Mary's, Hozier Street, Whifflet, COATBRIDGE ML5 4DB. ☎ Coatbridge (01236) 423550.
E-mail: stmary_coatbridge@compuserve.com

Sunday Masses: Vigil-Mass, 5.15 p.m.; 9.30, 11.30 a.m. Evening Service: as announced. Holy Days of Obligation, Masses: 10 a.m., 1.00, 7 p.m. Confessions: Wednesday, after 10 a.m. Mass; Saturday, 6 p.m.
Estimated Catholic population: 2,200.

CENTENARY HOUSE NUSING HOME AND DUNDYVAN GARDENS (RRESIDENTIAL CENTRE) ATENDED FROM ST.MARY'S.
ST. MARY'S PRIMARY SCHOOL; COLUMBA HIGH SCHOOL.

COATBRIDGE, North Lanarkshire, St. Monica, Old Monkland (1950, 1957), Sharp Avenue.

Rev. John B. Farrell, B.D., B.Ed. (1987)
Rev. Kenneth J. Campbell (1991)
Sr. Kathleen Owens, R.N.D.M., *Pastoral Assistant.*

POSTAL ADDRESS: St. Monica's, Sharp Avenue, Old Monkland, COATBRIDGE ML5 5RP. ☎ Coatbridge (01236) 421750.

Sunday Masses: Vigil-Mass, 6.30 p.m.; 10 a.m., 12 noon, 6.30 p.m. Holy Days of Obligation, Masses: Vigil-Mass, 7.30 p.m.; 8.15, 10 a.m., 7.30 p.m. Confessions: Saturday, 9.30 to 9.50 a.m., 5.30 to 6.15 p.m.
Estimated Catholic population: 4,000.

ST. MONICA'S PRIMARY SCHOOL; (ST. JAMES' PRIMARY SCHOOL).

COATBRIDGE, North Lanarkshire, St. Patrick (1845, 1896), Main Street.

Rev. Eamonn J. Sweeney (1969)
Sr. Moira Duffy, R.S.M., *Pastoral Assistant*

POSTAL ADDRESS: St. Patrick's, 1 St. John Street, COATBRIDGE ML5 3HB.
☎Coatbridge (01236) 606808.

Sunday Masses: Vigil-Mass, 6 p.m., 10 a.m., 12 noon, 6 p.m. Evening Service as announced. Holy Days of Obligation, Masses: Vigil-Mass, 7 p.m., 10 a.m., 1.00, 5.30 p.m. Exposition of the Blessed Sacrament, Monday to Saturday, 10.30 a.m. to 4.30 p.m. Confessions: Thursday, Friday, Saturday, 10.30 a.m.; Friday, 12 noon to 1 p.m.; Saturday, 5 to 5.45 p.m.
Estimated Catholic population: 3,000.

DUNBETH LODGE ATTENDED FROM ST. PATRICK'S.
ST. PATRICK'S PRIMARY SCHOOL; ST. PATRICK'S HIGH SCHOOL; (ST. STEPHEN'S PRIMARY SCHOOL).

COATBRIDGE North Lanarkshire, St. Stephen, Sikeside (1973, 1976), Paddock Street.

Rev. Isaac McLaren (1960)
Sr. Frances Reilly, O.C.V., *Pastoral Assistant*

POSTAL ADDRESS: St. Stephen's, Paddock Street, Sikeside, COATBRIDGE ML5 4PG. ☎ Coatbridge (01236) 420585.

Sunday Masses: Vigil-Mass, 5.30 p.m., 10 a.m., 12 noon, 6 p.m. Holy Days of Obligation, Masses: Vigil-Mass, 7 p.m.; 10 a.m.; 7 p.m. Confessions: Tuesday, 2.30 to 3.30 p.m., 7 to 8 p.m.
Estimated Catholic population: 1,850.

MARY OF HOPE COMMUNITY, (MIXED LAY AND RELIGIOUS COMMUNITY), C/O SR. FRANCES REILLY, 4 BELLVUE WAY, FARRIERS WAY, COATBRIDGE ML5 4FE. ☎ CONTACT PRESBYTERY.
ST. STEPHEN'S PRIMARY SCHOOL.

COATBRIDGE, North Lanarkshire, Xaverian Missionary Fathers, Whifflet (1958).

Rev. Thomas Welsh, S.X., *Co-ordinator* (1977)
Rev. William Hattie, S.X., S.T.B., M.A (1980)
Rev. Emilio Paloschi, S.X (1961)
Rev. Kevin Ryan, S.X., S.T.B., M.A. (1979)
Rev. Paul Zanon, S.X (1939)

POSTAL ADDRESS: St. Francis Xavier Mission Centre, Calder Avenue, COATBRIDGE ML5 4JS. ☎: Coatbridge (01236) 606364. Fax: Coatbridge (01236) 606365.
E-mail: xaverians@cablenet.co.uk

CRAIGEND and GARTHAMLOCK, City of Glasgow, St. Dominic and St. Mungo (united 1989).
St. Dominic, (1972, 1974) Mossvale Road.
St. Mungo, (1954, 1956) Tillycairn Drive.

Parish Team:
Rev. Thomas F. Magill, Ph.D. (1976)

POSTAL ADDRESS: St. Dominic's, 247 Mossvale Road, Craigend, GLASGOW G33 5QS. ☎0141-573 1260.

Sister Gertrude, O.S.F. *(Parish Assistant)*

POSTAL ADDRESS: St. Mungo's, 133 Tillycairn Drive, Garthamlock, GLASGOW G33 5HS. ☎0141-774 2233.

Sunday Masses: Vigil-Mass, 5.30 p.m. (St. Dominic's); 10 a.m. (St. Dominic's); 11.30 a.m. (St. Mungo's). Holy Days of Obligation: Vigil-Mass, 7 p.m. (St. Dominic's); 9.30 a.m. (St. Dominic's), 7 p.m. (St. Mungo's). Confessions: Saturday (St. Dominic's) after Vigil-Mass. Estimated Catholic population: 2,000.　　　　　　　　　　　　**A**

WOODCROFT AND CROFTCOIGN SPECIAL SCHOOLS AND CHEVIOT HOUSE, MOSSVALE ROAD, ATTENDED FROM ST DOMINIC'S.
ST. ROSE OF LIMA PRIMARY SCHOOL

DOUGLAS VILLAGE, South Lanarkshire, St. Mary, Springhill Road. Served from Lanark.

Sunday Mass: Saturday, 5.30 p.m. Other Services by arrangement.

EASTERHOUSE, City of Glasgow, St. Benedict and St. Clare (under Joint Pastoral Team, 1996).

POSTAL ADDRESS: (Pastoral Team): St. Clare's, 18 Drumlanrig Avenue, GLASGOW G34 0JA. ☎0141-771 3740.

Priest members of the team as under.
Sister members:
Sister Marie Byrne, D.C.
Sister Elizabeth Callaghan, D.C.
Sister Eileen McGarry, F.M.A.
Sister Kay Young, F.M.A.

St. Benedict (1959, 1965), Westerhouse Road.

Rev. Bernard Parkes, S.D.B., B.A., C.Q.S.W (1974)
Rev. Robert Gardner, S.D.B., B.A. (1991)

POSTAL ADDRESS: St. Benedict's, 755 Westerhouse Road, GLASGOW G34 9RP. ☎ 0141-771 1991; Fax: 0141-781 0538.

Sunday times are subject to revision. Sunday Masses: Vigil-Mass, 6 p.m.; 11 a.m. Holy Days of Obligation, Masses: 10 a.m., 7.30 p.m. Confessions: Saturday, 10.30 p.m., 5.30 p.m., after Vigil-Mass; at call. Estimated Catholic population: 1,500.

ESKDALE OLD FOLK'S HOME, ATTENDED FROM ST. BENEDICT'S.
ST. BENEDICT'S PRIMARY SCHOOL.

St. Clare (1959, 1965), Drumlanrig Avenue.

Rev. James McGarry, S.D.B., B.D., L.R.A.M., D.S.W., C.Q.S.W.
(*Team Leader*) (1975))
Rev .Brian McGraw, S.D.B., B.Ed. (1985)

POSTAL ADDRESS: St. Clare's, 18 Drumlanrig Avenue, GLASGOW G34 0JA. ☎ 0141-771 3740; Fax: 0141-781 0538.
Service times are subject to revision. Sunday Masses: Vigil-Mass, 6 p.m.; 11 a.m., 6 p.m. Holy Days of Obligation, Masses: 9.30 a.m., 7.30 p.m. Confessions: Saturday, 5.30 p.m.
Estimated Catholic population: 1,200.

EAST KILBRIDE, South Lanarkshire, St. Bride (1946, 1964), Whitemoss Avenue.

Rev. Michael Ryan (1959)
Rev. Michael Brown (1998)

POSTAL ADDRESS: St. Bride's Church, Whitemoss Avenue, East Kilbride, GLASGOW G74 1NN. ☎East Kilbride (01355) 220005.

Sunday Masses: Vigil-Mass, 6 p.m.; 9, 10.30 a.m., 12 noon, 6 p.m. Evening Service: as announced. Holy Days of Obligation, Masses: Vigil-Mass, 7.30 p.m.; 8, 10 a.m., 1.00, 7.30 p.m. Confessions: Saturday, after morning Mass to 11 a.m., after Vigil-Mass to 7.30 p.m.; Thursday, 8 p.m.;on request.
Estimated Catholic population: 4,000.

EAST KILBRIDE, South Lanarkshire, St. Leonard (1966, 1970), St. Leonards Road.

Rev. Michael MacNamee (1959)
Sr. M. Sophia, *Pastoral Assistant*

POSTAL ADDRESS: St. Leonard's, St. Leonards Road, East Kilbride, GLASGOW G74 3YA. ☎ East Kilbride (01355) 247471.

Sunday Masses: Vigil Mass, 6p.m.; 10a.m., 12 noon, 5.15p.m. Holy Days of Obligation, Masses: Vigil-Mass, 7.30 p.m.; 10 a.m., 6, 7.30 p.m. Confessions: Monday to Saturday, after 10 a.m. Mass; Thursday, after evening Mass; Saturday, 5.30 to 5.50 p.m. and after Vigil-Mass.
Estimated Catholic population: 3,000.

EAST KILBRIDE, South Lanarkshire, Our Lady of Lourdes. Westwood (1958, 1963), Murray Road.

Rev. William Nolan, S.T.L. (1977)
Rev. Alexander Stewart, Dip.Theol. (1994)
Rev. Francis D. King, B.D. *(Hospital Chaplain)* (1995)

POSTAL ADDRESS: Our Lady of Lourdes', 30 Canberra Drive, East Kilbride, GLASGOW G75 8DG. ☎East Kilbride (01355) 224511; Fax: 01355-265810.
E-mail: ourladyoflourdeschurch@compuserve.com
Website:http/ourworld.compuserve.com/homepages/ourladyoflourdes church

Sunday Masses: Vigil-Mass, 6 p.m.; 9, 10.30 a.m., 12 noon. Holy Days of Obligation, Masses: Vigil-Mass, 7.30p.m.; 8.15, 10a.m., 6p.m. Confessions: Saturday, 10.30 a.m., 5.15 to 5.45 p.m., after Vigil-Mass Estimated Catholic population: 5,600.

SISTERS OF ST. COLUMBAN, 209 QUEBEC DRIVE, WESTWOOD, EAST KILBRIDE, GLASGOW G75 8BB. ☎: EAST KILBRIDE (01355) 238312.
HAIRMYRES HOSPITAL: CHAPLAIN: REV. FRANCIS D. KING.
BELMONT HOME, CANBERRA HOUSE, STRATHCONA HOUSE AND WESTWOOD HOUSE ATTENDED FROM OUR LADY OF LOURDES.
OUR LADY OF LOURDES PRIMARY SCHOOL; ST. LOUISE'S PRIMARY SCHOOL.

EAST KILBRIDE, South Lanarkshire, St. Vincent de Paul, Greenhills (1974, 1979), Tinto Way.

Rev. Richard J. Rodgers (1960)
Rev. Dominic Quinn, Ph.B., S.T.L. (1988)

POSTAL ADDRESS: St. Vincent de Paul's, Tinto Way, Greenhills, East Kilbride, GLASGOW G75 9DQ. ☎East Kilbride (01355) 243619.

Sunday Masses: Vigil-Mass, 6 p.m.; 10, 11.30 a.m., 6 p.m. (Summer Mass times announved locally.) Holy Days of Obligation, Masses: Vigil-Mass, 7.30 p.m.; 10 a.m., 7.30 p.m. Confessions: Thursday, after 7.30 p.m. Mass; Saturday, after 9.30 a.m. Mass, 5.15 to 5.45 p.m., after Vigil-Mass. Estimated Catholic population: 3,970.   Ⓐ

ST. VINCENT DE PAUL'S PRIMARY SCHOOL; ST. ANDREW'S HIGH SCHOOL;
(ST. LOUISE'S PRIMARY SCHOOL).

FORTH, South Lanarkshire, St. Mary Magdalene (1970, 1992), Hailstonegreen. Served from Biggar.

Sunday Mass: 10 a.m. Holy Days of Obligation, Vigil-Mass, previous evening, 7 p.m. Confessions: at call.
Estimated Catholic population: 170. &

GARTHAMLOCK, City of Glasgow, St. Mungo see CRAIGEND and GARTHAMLOCK page 347. Served from Craigend.

GLENBOIG (Coatbridge), North Lanarkshire, Our Lady and St. Joseph (1880, 1974), South Medrox Street.

Rev. James Naughton (1965)

POSTAL ADDRESS: Our Lady and St. Joseph's, South Medrox Street, Glenboig, COATBRIDGE ML5 2RU. ☎Glenboig (01236) 872608.

Sunday Masses: Vigil-Mass, 5.30 p.m.; 9, 11.30 a.m. Evening Service, 5.30 p.m. as announced. Holy Days of Obligation, Masses: Vigil-Mass, 6.30 p.m.; 10 a.m., 7.30 p.m. Confessions: Thursday, Friday and Saturday, 10.30 a.m.; Thursday, after 7.30 p.m. Mass; Saturday, 5 to 5.25 p.m., 6.15 to 6.45 p.m.
Estimated Catholic population: 1,200. &

OUR LADY AND ST. JOSEPH'S PRIMARY SCHOOL.

GREENGAIRS, North Lanarkshire, St. Dominic (1893). Served from Plains.

Sunday Mass: 10 a.m. Holy Days of Obligation, Mass: 7 p.m. Confessions, Friday, 7.30 p.m.

HALFWAY (Cambuslang), South Lanarkshire, St. Cadoc (1949, 1955), Wellside Drive.

Right Rev. Mgr. Thomas A. Connelly (*Press and Media Relations Officer, Bishops' Conference;* Fax/☎0141-641 2244) (1962)
Rev. Thomas W. Doyle, B.D (1992)

POSTAL ADDRESS: St. Cadoc's, Rosebank Drive, Halfway, Cambuslang, GLASGOW G72 8TD. ☎0141-641 3669.

Sunday Masses: Vigil-Mass, 5.30 p.m.; 10 a.m., 12 noon. Holy Days of Obligation, Masses: 8.30, 9.30 a.m., 7.15 p.m Confessions: Monday to Saturday, 9.30 to 9.50 a.m.; Saturday, 5 to 5.30 p.m
Estimated Catholic population: 2,000. 🔊 Ⓐ

ST. CADOC'S PRIMARY SCHOOL; (ST. CHARLES' PRIMARY SCHOOL, NEWTON).

HAMILTON, South Lanarkshire, St. Mary (1843, 1846), Cadzow Street.

Right Rev. Mgr. Alexander Devanny, V.G (1959)
Rev. Francis Darroch (*Retired*) (1956)
Rev. Joseph Dowds *(Permanent Deacon)* (1999)

POSTAL ADDRESS: St. Mary's, 120 Cadzow Street, HAMILTON ML3 6HX.
☎Hamilton (01698) 423552.

Sunday Masses: Vigil-Mass, 6.30 p.m.; 10, 11.30 a.m., 6.30 p.m. Holy
Days of Obligation, Masses: Vigil-Mass, 7 p.m.; 10 a.m., 12.30, 7 p.m.
Confessions: First Friday, before and after 7 p.m. Mass; Saturday, after
9.30 a.m. Mass, 5 to 5.30 p.m., after Vigil-Mass if required.
Exposition of the Blessed Sacrament, weekdays, 12 noon to 2 p.m.
Estimated Catholic population: 1,850.

AVON NURSING HOME, DOUGLAS VIEW NURSING HOME, GREENBANK NURSING
HOME, LORNE BANK NURSING HOME, AND MAY PARK HOME, ATTENDED FROM
ST. MARY'S.
ST. MARY'S PRIMARY SCHOOL; HOLY CROSS HIGH SCHOOL.

HAMILTON, South Lanarkshire, St. Ninian, Hillhouse (1955, 1958), Hillhouse Road.

Rev. Gerard Bogan (1985)
POSTAL ADDRESS: St. Ninian's Presbytery, 34 St. Ninians Road, Hillhouse,
HAMILTON ML3 9TS. ☎ /Fax: Blantyre (01698) 823638.
Web Site: http://come.to/st_ninians

Sunday Masses: Vigil-Mass, 6 p.m., 10 a.m., 12 noon, 6 p.m. Holy Days
of Obligation, Masses: Vigil-Mass, 7 p.m. 9.30 a.m., 7 p.m. Confessions:
Saturday, 9.15 to 9.45 a.m., 7 to 7.30 p.m.; any time on request.
Estimated Catholic population: 2,700.

COMELYBANK CENTRE AND MILLAR PARK ATTENDED FROM ST. NINIAN'S.
ST. NINIAN'S PRIMARY SCHOOL.

HAMILTON, South Lanarkshire, Our Lady and St. Anne, Cadzow (1883, 1933), Hall Street.

Rev. Thomas O'Hare (1959)
Rev. Ivan R. Boyle, M.A., B.Sc., B.D. (1994)

POSTAL ADDRESS: Our Lady and St. Anne's, Jack Street, HAMILTON ML3
7QP. ☎Hamilton (01698) 423044.

Sunday Masses: Vigil-Mass, 6 p.m.; 9, 10.30 a.m., 12 noon, 6 p.m. Evening Service: 4 p.m. Holy Days of Obligation, Masses: Vigil-Mass, 8 p.m.; 7, 9.30, 11 a.m., 6.30 p.m. Confessions: Thursday, 7 to 7.30 p.m.; Saturday, 9.30 to 10 a.m., 5 to 6 p.m., after Vigil-Mass.
Estimated Catholic population: 4,150.

SISTERS OF ST. JOSEPH OF PEACE, 37 HUTCHISON STREET, HAMILTON ML3 7LQ. ☎: HAMILTON (01698) 286822.
ABERCORN NURSING HOME AND DEERPARK HOME ATTENDED FROM OUR LADY AND ST. ANNE'S.
ST. ANNE'S PRIMARY SCHOOL; ST. ELIZABETH'S PRIMARY SCHOOL.

HAMILTON, South Lanarkshire, St. Paul, Whitehill (1954, 1955), Backmuir Road.

Rev. Damian M. Murphy, Ph.B., S.T.L (1976)

POSTAL ADDRESS: St. Paul's, Backmuir Road, Whitehill, HAMILTON ML3 0PX. ☎ /Fax: Hamilton (01698) 424542.

Sunday Masses: Vigil-Mass, 6 p.m.; 10.30 a.m. Holy Days of Obligation, Masses: 9.30 a.m., 7 p.m. Confessions: daily, 9.15 a.m; Saturday, 6.30 p.m..
Estimated Catholic population: 550.

ST. PAUL'S PRIMARY SCHOOL.

HAMILTON, South Lanarkshire, St. Peter, Laighstonehall (1953, 1981), Buchanan Crescent.

Rev. Leo Muldoon (1964)

POSTAL ADDRESS: St. Peter's, 2 Buchanan Crescent, HAMILTON ML3 8LL. ☎ /Fax: Hamilton (01698) 424721.

Sunday Masses: Vigil-Mass, 6 p.m.; 10.30 a.m., 12 noon, 6 p.m. Evening Service: as announced. Holy Days of Obligation, Masses: Vigil-Mass, 7.30 p.m.; 9, 10a.m., 7.30p.m. Confessions: daily, after 10 a.m. Mass; Saturday, 5.30 to 5.55 p.m., 7 to 7.30 p.m. Exposition of the Blessed Sacrament: Wednesday, 10.30 a.m.to 7.30 p.m.; Saturday, 5.30 to 7.30 p.m.
Estimated Catholic population: 3,200.

ST. MARK 'S PRIMARY SCHOOL; ST. PETER'S PRIMARY SCHOOL.

HARTHILL, North Lanarkshire, St. Catherine of Siena (1924, 1925), Westcraigs Road.

Rev. James Small (1960)

POSTAL ADDRESS: St. Catherine's, Westcraigs Road, Harthill, SHOTTS ML7 5SW. ☎Harthill (01501) 751589.

Sunday Mass: 10.30 a.m. Holy Days of Obligation, Masses: 9 a.m., 7 p.m. Confessions, Saturday, 8 to 8.45 p.m.
Estimated Catholic population: 700 (including Salsburgh)

SALSBURGH, ATTENDED FROM ST. CATHERINE'S.

HOLYTOWN, North Lanarkshire, Christ the King (1975), Main Street.

Rev. Humphrey O'Mahony (1961)

POSTAL ADDRESS: Christ the King, 170 Main Street, Holytown, MOTHERWELL ML1 4TJ. ☎Holytown (01698) 732352.

Sunday Masses: Vigil-Mass, 6.30 p.m.; 10, 11.45 a.m. Holy Days of Obligation, Masses: Vigil-Mass, 7 p.m.; 9.30, 11 a.m., 5 p.m. Confessions: Saturday, 5.30 to 6.15 p.m. and after Vigil-Mass.
Estimated Catholic population: 1,700.

CHRIST THE KNG PRIMARY SCHOOL.

LANARK, South Lanarkshire, St. Mary (1859, 1910), Bannatyne Street.

Very Rev. Francis MacMorrow, C.M., M.A., *Superior* (1950)
Rev. Brian Mullan, C.M., B.A (1954)
Rev. Patrick Hughes, C.M (1957)
Rev. John Hewson, C.M., (1961)

POSTAL ADDRESS: St. Mary's, 70 Bannatyne Street, LANARK ML11 7JS. ☎Lanark (01555) 662234.

Sunday Masses: Vigil-Mass 6.30 p.m., 9.30, 11 a.m., 6.30 p.m. Holy Days of Obligation, Masses: Vigil-Mass: 7.30 p.m.; 8, 10 a.m., 7.30 p.m. Confessions: Wednesday, 7.50 p.m. Saturday, after 9.30 a.m. Mass, 5 to 5.30 p.m., 7 to 7.30 p.m.
Estimated Catholic population: 1,280.

CARSTAIRS AND DOUGLAS SERVED FROM ST. MARY'S.
DAUGHTERS OF CHARITY: ST. CATHERINE'S, 68 BANNATYNE STREET, LANARK ML11 7JS. ☎ LANARK (01555) 661671.

Sᴛ. Mᴀʀʏ's Hᴏsᴘɪᴛᴀʟ, (Dᴀᴜɢʜᴛᴇʀs ᴏғ Cʜᴀʀɪᴛʏ), Cᴀʀsᴛᴀɪʀs Rᴏᴀᴅ, Lᴀɴᴀʀᴋ ML11 7JU. ☎: Lᴀɴᴀʀᴋ (01555) 662393.
Bᴇʟʟꜰɪᴇʟᴅ Hᴏᴍᴇ; McCʟʏᴍᴏɴᴛ Hᴏᴜsᴇ; Cʀᴏssʟᴀᴡ Hᴏᴜsᴇ Nᴜʀsɪɴɢ Hᴏᴍᴇ; Sᴛᴀɴᴍᴏʀᴇ Hᴏᴜsᴇ ꜰᴏʀ Cᴀʀᴇ ᴏꜰ Sᴘᴀsᴛɪᴄ Cʜɪʟᴅʀᴇɴ; Rɪᴅɢᴇᴍᴏᴜɴᴛ Sᴘᴇᴄɪᴀʟ Sᴄʜᴏᴏʟ; Lᴏᴄᴋʜᴀʀᴛ Hᴏsᴘɪᴛᴀʟ; Sᴛ. Mᴀʀʏ's Hᴏsᴘɪᴛᴀʟ, Lanark; Mᴏɴᴛᴇɪᴛʜ Hᴏᴜsᴇ Nᴜʀsɪɴɢ Hᴏᴍᴇ, Carstairs, ᴀɴᴅ Lᴀᴅʏ Hᴏᴍᴇ Cᴏᴛᴛᴀɢᴇ Hᴏsᴘɪᴛᴀʟ, Douglas, ᴀᴛᴛᴇɴᴅᴇᴅ ꜰʀᴏᴍ Sᴛ. Mᴀʀʏ's .
Sᴛ. Mᴀʀʏ's Pʀɪᴍᴀʀʏ Sᴄʜᴏᴏʟ.
Aᴘᴘʟɪᴄᴀᴛɪᴏɴs ꜰᴏʀ Mɪssɪᴏɴs ᴀɴᴅ Rᴇᴛʀᴇᴀᴛs sʜᴏᴜʟᴅ ʙᴇ ᴍᴀᴅᴇ ᴛᴏ Vᴇʀʏ Rᴇᴠ. Sᴜᴘᴇʀɪᴏʀ, C.M.

LARKHALL, South Lanarkshire, St. Mary (1872, 1905), Raploch Road.

Very Rev. Henry A. Canon McGinn, J.P (1946)

Pᴏsᴛᴀʟ ᴀᴅᴅʀᴇss: St. Mary's, Raploch Road, Lᴀʀᴋʜᴀʟʟ ML9 1AN. ☎ Larkhall (01698) 882564.

Sunday Masses: Vigil-Mass, 6.30 p.m.; 8, 10.45 a.m., 4.30 p.m. (November to February) or 6 p.m. (March to November). Evening Service: 4 p.m. (March to November). Holy Days of Obligation, Masses: Vigil-Mass, 7.30 p.m.; 8 a.m., 2 (school), 7.30 p.m. Confessions: weekdays, before and after Mass; Saturday, before and after 10 a.m. Mass, 6 to 6.25 p.m., 7.15 to 7.30 p.m.; eves of First Fridays, 12.20 to 1.20 p.m. (mainly for school children).
Estimated Catholic population: 1,200.

Bᴀʟʟᴀɴᴛɪɴᴇ Hᴏᴜsᴇ, Bʀᴀᴇ Hᴏᴜsᴇ Nᴜʀsɪɴɢ Hᴏᴍᴇ, Cʟɪɴᴛᴏɴ Hᴏᴜsᴇ, Mᴀᴛᴛʜᴇᴡ McWʜɪʀᴛᴇʀ Oʟᴅ Pᴇᴏᴘʟᴇ's Hᴏᴍᴇ, Dᴏᴄᴛᴏʀ Pᴀʀᴋᴇʀ Oʟᴅ Pᴇᴏᴘʟᴇ's Hᴏᴍᴇ, ᴀɴᴅ Sᴇꜰᴛᴏɴ Pᴀʀᴋ Oʟᴅ Pᴇᴏᴘʟᴇ's Hᴏᴍᴇ, ᴀᴛᴛᴇɴᴅᴇᴅ ꜰʀᴏᴍ Sᴛ. Mᴀʀʏ's. Pʀɪᴍᴀʀʏ Sᴄʜᴏᴏʟ.

LESMAHAGOW, South Lanarkshire, served from Blackwood.

Special 'bus from Coalburn to Blackwood for 10 a.m. Mass and return stops at Lesmahagow each way.

MOODIESBURN, North Lanarkshire, St. Michael (1960, 1965), Glenmanor Avenue.

Rev. Michael Briody (1977)

POSTAL ADDRESS: St. Michael's, Glenmanor Avenue, Moodiesburn, Chryston, GLASGOW G69 0DL. ☎Glenboig (01236) 872537.

Sunday Masses: Vigil-Mass, 6.30 p.m., 11 a.m., 6 p.m. Holy Days of Obligation, Masses: announced locally. Confessions: Thursday, 8 p.m.; Saturday, 10.20 a.m.
Estimated Catholic population: 2,900.

ST. MICHAEL'S PRIMARY SCHOOL.

MOSSEND, North Lanarkshire, Holy Family (1868, 1884) Calder Road.

Rev. James A. Grant, S.T.B (1983)
Pastoral assistants:
Sr. Margaret, S.S.J.A.
Sr. Canisius, S.S.J.A.
Sr. Catherine, S.S.J.A.

POSTAL ADDRESS: Holy Family, 57 Hope Street, Mossend, BELLSHILL ML4 1QA. ☎Bellshill (01698) 843165.

Sunday Masses: Vigil-Mass, 6p.m., 10 a.m., 12 noon. Evening service: as announced. Holy Days of Obligation, Masses: 10 a.m., 7.30 p.m. Confessions, during Exposition of the Blessed Sacrament: First Saturday of the month, 10 a.m. to 12 noon; every Thursday, 7 to 8 p.m.
Estimated Catholic population: 1,850.

SISTERS OF ST. JOSEPH OF ANNECY, 14A CLYDESDALE ROAD, MOSSEND, BELLSHILL ML4 2QB. ☎ BELLSHILL (01698) 844992.
HATTON LEA NURSING HOME ATTENDED FROM HOLY FAMILY.
HOLY FAMILY PRIMARY SCHOOL.

MUIRHEAD (Chryston), North Lanarkshire, St. Barbara (1947, 1956), Elmira Road.

Rev. William O'Sullivan (1957)

POSTAL ADDRESS: St. Barbara's, Elmira Road, Muirhead, GLASGOW G69 9EJ. ☎0141-779 2286.

Sunday Masses: Vigil-Mass, 6.30 p.m.; 10 a.m., 12 noon. Evening Service: 6 p.m. Holy Days of Obligation, Masses: Vigil-Mass, 7.30 p.m.; 10 a.m., 7.30 p.m. Confessions: Saturday, before and after 10 a.m. Mass, 5.45 p.m. to Vigil-Mass, after Vigil-Mass to 8 p.m.
Estimated Catholic population: 1,400.

CHILTERNS HOME ATTENDED FROM MUIRHEAD.
ST. BARBARA'S PRIMARY SCHOOL.

NEWARTHILL, North Lanarkshire, St. Teresa (1956, 1960), Benford Avenue.

Rev. Christopher G. Taylor, S.T.B. (1977)

POSTAL ADDRESS: St. Teresa's, Benford Avenue, Newarthill, MOTHERWELl ML1 5BE. ☎ Holytown (01698) 832920.

Sunday Masses: 10 a.m., 12 noon, 6.30 p.m. Holy Days of Obligation, Masses: 7, 9.30 a.m., 7.30 p.m. Confessions: as anounced; on request. Estimated Catholic population: 2,500.

ST. TERESA'S PRIMARY SCHOOL.

NEWMAINS, North Lanarkshire, St. Brigid (1871, 1896, 1933), Westwood Road.

Rev. Joseph Brannigan (1978)
Sr. Maria Goretti, O.S.F. *Pastoral Assistant*

POSTAL ADDRESS: St. Brigid's, 5 Westwood Road, Newmains, WISHAW ML2 9DA. ☎Cambusnethan (01698) 297037; Fax: 01698-297038 (Hall Tel: 01698-292164).
E-mail:brigidnew@aol.com

Sunday Masses: Vigil-Mass, 5.30 p.m.; 9.30 a.m., 12 noon. Holy Days of Obligation, Masses: Vigil-Mass, 7.30 p.m.; 10 a.m., 7.30 p.m. Confessions: Thursday, 6.30 to 7.30 p.m.; on request. Estimated Catholic population: 1,800.

MURDOSTOUN CASTLE NURSING HOME ATTENDED FROM ST. BRIGID'S.
ST. BRIGID'S PRIMARY SCHOOL.

NEWMAINS, North Lanarkshire, Pastoral Centre (1986), Bonkle Road.

Rev. Henry O'Brien, S.T.D., *Director* (1981)
Rev. James Gerard Higgins, *Assistant Director* (1990)
Miss Helen Ward, *Assistant to Director.*
Kieran McQuaid, M.A., PGC.CYS., *Youth Development Officer*
In residence:
Rev. James Duddy, *Chaplain to H.M. Prison Shotts* (1977)
Rev. Thomas G. Devine (1977)
SPRED office (☎ Cambusbethan (01698-384208))

POSTAL ADDRESS: Pastoral Centre, 50 Bonkle Road, Newmains, WISHAW ML2 9AP. ☎ Cambusnethan (01698) 385397; Fax: 01698-381924.

THE RETREAT CONFERENCE CENTRE OFFERS FACILITIES FOR SCHOOL, PARISH AND OTHER ORGANISATIONS. FURTHER DETAILS, PLEASE CONTACT THE CENTRE.

NEW STEVENSTON, North Lanarkshire, St. John Bosco (1946, 1959), Jerviston Street.

Very Rev. Niall Canon Hayes (1949)

POSTAL ADDRESS: St. John Bosco's, 91 Jerviston Street, New Stevenston, MOTHERWELL ML1 4JS. ☎Holytown (01698) 832316.

Sunday Masses: Vigil-Mass, Saturday, 6.15 p.m.; 10 a.m., 12 noon. Evening Service, 6.15 p.m. Holy Days of Obligation, Masses: 9, 10.30 a.m., 7 p.m. Confessions: Saturday, 10 a.m., 5 to 6 p.m., after Vigil-Mass. Estimated Catholic population: 1,500.

ST. PATRICK'S PRIMARY SCHOOL; TAYLOR HIGH SCHOOL.

PLAINS, North Lanarkshire, St. David of Scotland (1900, 1994), Meadowhead Road.

Rev. Thomas Trench (1967)
Rev. Michael Gallagher, S.P.S (1955)

POSTAL ADDRESS: St. David's, Meadowhead Road, Plains, AIRDRIE ML6 7JF. ☎Airdrie (01236) 763226.

Sunday Masses: Vigil-Mass, 6 p.m.; 12 noon, 6 p.m. (Also 10 a.m., in St. Dominic's, Greengairs). Evening Service: as announced. Holy Days of Obligation, Masses: Vigil-Mass, 7.30 p.m.; 10, a.m., 7.30 p.m. (Also 7 p.m., in St. Dominic's, Greengairs). Confessions: Thursday, 8 p.m.; Saturday, 10.30 a.m., 5.15 to 5.45 p.m. (Also, Friday, 7.30 p.m., in St. Dominic's, Greengairs).
Estimated Catholic population: 1,850.

ST. DOMINIC'S, CREENGAIRS (1893), SERVED FROM ST. DAVID'S.
MONKLAND OLD FOLK'S HOME, ATTENDED FROM ST. DAVID'S.
ST. PHILIP'S RESIDENTIAL SCHOOL, "BEECHWOOD", MAIN STREET, PLAINS, AIRDRIE ML6 7SF. ☎ AIRDRIE (01236) 765407. SERVED FROM ST. DAVID'S.
ST. DAVID'S PRIMARY SCHOOL.

RUTHERGLEN, South Lanarkshire, St. Anthony (1965 1970), Mar Gardens.

Rev. Henry J. Allison (1958)
Rev. James G. Nicol, Ph.B., S.T.B., J.C.L. (1978)

POSTAL ADDRESS: St. Anthony's, Mar Gardens, Springhall, Rutherglen, GLASGOW G73 5JE. ☎0141-634 4909.

Sunday Masses: Vigil-Mass, 6.30 p.m.; 9.30, 11.30 a.m., 6 p.m. Holy Days of Obligation, Masses: Vigil-Mass, 7.30 p.m.; 10 a.m., 7.30 p.m. Confessions: Saturday, 9.30 to 9.55 a.m., 5.30 to 6.25 p.m., after Vigil-Mass.
Estimated Catholic population: 2,350.

CATHKIN HOUSE NURSING HOME ATTENDED FROM ST. ANTHONY'S.
ST. ANTHONY'S PRIMARY SCHOOL.

RUTHERGLEN, South Lanarkshire, St. Columbkille (1851, 1940), Main Street.

Rev. Thomas Gibbons (1954)
Rev. Patrick Hennessy, B.A. (1969)
Rev. Stephen Rooney, Dip. Phil., Dip. Theol. (1998)

POSTAL ADDRESS: St. Columbkille's, 2 Kirkwood Street, Rutherglen, GLASGOW G73 2SL. ☎ 0141-647 6034; Fax: 0141-647 9484..

Sunday Masses: Vigil-Mass, 5.30 p.m.; 9, 10.30 a.m., 12 noon, 6 p.m.
Holy Days of Obligation, Masses: Vigil-Mass 7 p.m.; 10 a.m., 1.00, 7 p.m.
Confessions: Monday to Saturday, 9.30 a.m.; Saturday, 5 to 5.30 p.m.
Exposition of the Blessed Sacrament: Monday to Friday, 10.30 a.m. to 1 p.m.
Estimated Catholic population: 5,000.

ABBEYFIELD HOME, ROGER PARK NURSING HOME, ROWANTREE NURSING HOME, DAVID WALKER HOUSE AND RUTHERGLEN SPECIAL NEEDS HIGH SCHOOL ATTENDED FROM ST. COLUMBKILLE'S.
TRINITY HIGH SCHOOL; ST. COLUMBKILLE'S PRIMARY SCHOOL.

RUTHERGLEN, South Lanarkshire, St. Mark, Burnside (1956, 1961), Fernhill Road.

Rev. James O'Hara (1968)

POSTAL ADDRESS: St. Mark's, Fernhill Road, Rutherglen, GLASGOW G73 4DA. ☎0141-634 3053.

Sunday Masses: Vigil-Mass, 6.30 p.m., 11 a.m. Holy Days of Obligation, Masses: 9.30 a.m., 7 p.m. Confessions: Saturday, 10 a.m., after Vigil-Mass.
Estimated Catholic population: 2,000.

FERNHILL SCHOOL, FERNBRAE AVENUE, RUTHERGLEN, GLASGOW G73 4SG. ☎ 0141-634 2674.
'DUNCRAGGAN ' RESIDENTIAL HOME attended from ST. MARK'S.
ST. MARK'S PRIMARY SCHOOL.

RUTHERGLEN, City of Glasgow, Missionaries of Africa (The White Fathers) (1953).

Very Rev. Christopher Wallbank, M.Afr., *Superior* (1974)
Rev. James Barry, M.Afr (1943)
Rev. Patrick Boyd, M.Afr. (1948)
Rev. Herbert Herrity, M.Afr. (1954)
Bro. Ray Legget, M.Afr.
Bro. Eugene Leonard, M.Afr.
Bro. John Murphy, M.Afr.
Also in Residence (Retired):
Rev. Thomas McIlveney, M.Afr (1941)
Rev. John McNulty, M.Afr (1942)
Rev. Thomas Conway,. M.Afr. (1948)

POSTAL ADDRESS: St. Joseph's, 9 Milrig Road, Rutherglen, GLASGOW G73 2NG. ☎ 0141-613 0209; Fax: 0141-647 5321.

SALSBURGH, North Lanarkshire, The Sacred Heart, Main Street, served from Harthill.

Sunday Masses: Vigil-Mass, 6.30 p.m.; 12 noon. Holy Days of Obligation:Vigil-Mass, 7 p.m.; ll a.m. Confessions: Saturday, 6 to 6.25 p.m.

(ST. ALOYSIUS' PRIMARY SCHOOL, CHAPELHALL).

SHOTTS, Motherwell, St. Patrick (1868, 1905), Station Road.

Rev. Brian Lamb, Ph.B., S.T.L. (1988)

POSTAL ADDRESS: St. Patrick's, 84 Station Road, SHOTTS ML7 4BJ. ☎Shotts (01501) 821838.

Sunday Masses: Vigil-Mass, 6.30 p.m.; 10.45 a.m., 6 p.m. Holy Days of Obligation, Masses: 10 a.m., 7.30 p.m. Confessions:Friday, 5.30 to 6 p.m.; Saturday after 9.30 a.m. Mass, 5.45 to 6.15 p.m.
Estimated Catholic population: 2,800.

HARTWOOD HILL HOSPITAL (SUNDAY MASS, 10 A.M.), HERBISON HOUSE AND ROSEHALL MANOR NURSING HOME ATTENDED FROM ST. PATRICK'S.
ST. PATRICK'S PRIMARY SCHOOL.

STEPPS, North Lanarkshire, St. Joseph (1875), Cardowan Road.

Rev. Dominic Douglas, Ph.B., S.T.L. (1984)

POSTAL ADDRESS: St. Joseph's, Cardowan Road, Stepps, GLASGOW G33 6AA. ☎/Fax: 0141-779 2001.

E-mail: stjoseph@ukgateway.net *and* savio@ukgateway.net

Sunday Masses: Vigil-Mass, 5.30 p.m.; 9, 11.30 a.m., 5 p.m. Holy Days of Obligation, Masses: Vigil Mass, 7.30 p.m.; 9.30 a.m., 7.30 p.m. Confessions: Wednesday, after evening Mass, Saturday, after Masses. Estimated Catholic population: 2,000. 🅰

ST. JOSEPH'S PRRMARY SCHOOL.

STONEHOUSE, South Lanarkshire, served from Strathaven.

Sunday Mass (at Mass Centre, Wellbrae): 6 p.m. (November to April, 3 p.m.). Holy Days of Obligation, Vigil-Mass, 7.30 p.m. Confessions: Wednesday, after 10 a.m. Mass; on request.

STRATHAVEN, South Lanarkshire, St. Patrick (1859, 1901), Stonehouse Road.

Rev. Vincent G. Lockhart, M.Sc., M.Th. (1983)

POSTAL ADDRESS: St. Patrick's, 52 Stonehouse Road, STRATHAVEN ML10 6LF. ☎ Strathaven (01357) 520104.

E-mail: stpatricks.strathaven@virgin.net

Sunday Masses: Vigil-Mass, 6 p.m.; 9, 11 a.m. Holy Days of Obligation, Masses: 10 a.m., 7.30 p.m. Confessions: Saturday, after 10 a.m. Mass, 5.15 to 5.45 p.m.; on request. Estimated Catholic population: 1,300. 🤸 🅰

STONEHOUSE SERVED FROM ST. PATRICK'S. FOR MASS TIMES, SEE PRECEDING ENTRY.

STONEHOUSE HOSPITAL, ABBEYFIELD NURSING HOME, AVON PARK NURSING HOME, BURNVIEW NURSING HOME, COLISDENE NURSING HOME, STOBIESIDE NURSING HOME, Strathaven, AVONHAUGH NURSING HOME, CANDERAVON NURSING HOME AND KIRKDENE NURSING HOME, Stonehouse, ATTENDED FROM ST. PATRICK'S.

ST. PATRICK'S PRIMARY SCHOOL.

UDDINGSTON, South Lanarkshire, St. John the Baptist (1883, 1987), Lower Millgate.

Rev. Robert Curley (1962)

POSTAL ADDRESS: St. John the .Baptist's, 136 Lower Millgate, Uddingston, GLASGOW G71 7AH. ☎ Uddingston (01698) 813156.

Sunday Masses: Vigil-Mass, 6 p.m.; 10 a.m., 12 noon, 6 p.m. Holy Days of Obligation, Masses: Vigil-Mass, 6.30 p.m.; 8, 10 a.m., 6.30 p.m. Confessions: After weekday Masses, on request; Saturday, after both Masses.
Estimated Catholic population: 3,600.   🎵 Ⓐ

ST. JOHN THE BAPTIST'S PRIMARY SCHOOL.

VIEWPARK, North Lanarkshire, St. Columba (1939), Old Edinburgh Road.

Rev. Edward Glackin, (1958)

POSTAL ADDRESS: St. Columba's, 693 Old Edinburgh Road, Viewpark, Uddingston, GLASGOW G71 6HF. ☎ Uddingston (01698) 813495.

Sunday Masses: Vigil-Mass, 6 p.m.; 9, 10.45 a.m., 12.30, 6.30 p.m. Holy Days of Obligation, Masses: Vigil-Mass, 6 p.m.; 7, 10 a.m., 7.30 p.m. Confessions: Wednesday, 8 p.m.; Saturday, before and after 10 a.m. Mass, after Vigil-Mass.   Ⓐ
Estimated Catholic population: 3,700.

ROSE PARK NURSING HOME, VIEWPARK OCCUPATIONAL CENTRE AND VIEWPARK OLD FOLK'S HOME ATTENDED FROM ST. COLUMBA'S.
ST. COLUMBA'S PRIMARY SCHOOL.

VIEWPARK, North Lanarkshire, St. Gabriel (1976, 1977), Cedar Drive.

Rev. James Morris, B. Phil., S.T.B., S.T.L.(Mag.) (1973)

POSTAL ADDRESS: St, Gabriel's, 1 Cedar Drive, Viewpark, Uddingston, GLASGOW G71 5LF. ☎/Fax: Uddingston (01698) 817609.

Sunday Masses: Vigil-Mass, 5.30 p.m.; 8 a.m.; 11 a.m. (with signing for the deaf); 5.30 p.m. Holy Days of Obligation, Masses: Vigil-Mass, 7 p.m.; 7, 9.30 a.m., 9 p.m. Confessions: Saturday, 9 to 10.30 a.m., 6.15 to 7 p.m.
Estimated Catholic population: 1,700.   🎵 Ⓐ

ST. GABRIEL'S PRIMARY SCHOOL; (ST. COLUMBA'S PRIMARY SCHOOL).

WILSONTOWN, See Forth, Page 351.

WISHAW, North Lanarkshire, St. Aidan (1960, 1966) Coltness Road.

Rev. Joseph Clements (1962)
Rev. Charles J. O'Farrell, B.Sc., S.T.B. (1991)

POSTAL ADDRESS: St. Aidan's, 298 Coltness Road, WISHAW ML2 7EX.
☎ Cambusnethan (01698) 384730.

Sunday Masses: Vigil-Mass, 6 p.m.; 10 a.m., 12 noon, 6 p.m. Holy Days of Obligation, Masses: Vigil-Mass, 7.30 p.m.; 10 a.m., 7.30 p.m. Confessions: Saturday, after all Masses.
Estimated Catholic population: 2,000.

FIR PARK SPECIAL SCHOOL ATTENDED FROM ST. AIDAN'S.
LAW HOSPITAL. CHAPLAIN: REV. CHARLES J. O'FARRELL, ST. AIDAN'S.
ST. AIDAN'S HIGH SCHOOL; ST. AIDAN'S PRIMARY SCHOOL.

WISHAW, North Lanarkshire, St. Ignatius (1859, 1865), Young Street.

Right Rev. Mgr. Michael Conway, B.A., M.Sc., (1963)

POSTAL ADDRESS: St. Ignatius', 74 Young Street, WISHAW ML2 8HS.
☎Wishaw (01698) 372058.

Sunday Masses: Vigil-Mass, 5.30 p.m.; 10.15 a.m., 12 noon, 6 p.m. Evening Service, as announced. Holy Days of Obligation, Masses: Vigil-Mass 6.30 p.m.; 9.30 a.m., 7.30 p.m. Confessions: Saturday; 9.30 to 9.55 a.m., after 10 a.m., after Vigil-Mass.
Estimated Catholic population: 2,500.

CANONESSES OF ST. AUGUSTINE, 19 STEWARTON TERRACE, WISHAW ML2 8AJ.
☎ WISHAW (01698) 372278.
HELPERS OF THE HOLY SOULS, OUR LADY OF PROVIDENCE, 8 CAMPBELL STREET, WISHAW ML2 8HT. ☎ WISHAW (01698) 358656.
MEDICAL MISSIONARIES OF MARY, 350 KIRK ROAD, WISHAW ML2 8LH.
☎ WISHAW (01698) 381305.
BELHAVEN HOUSE, HEATHER PARK NURSING HOME, KIRKNOWE NURSING HOME, MCALPINE COURT AND THORNHILL HOUSE ATTENDED FROM ST. IGNATIUS'.
ST.IGNATIUS'PRIMARY SCHOOL.; (ST. AIDAN'S PRIMARY SCHOOL; ST. MATTHEW'S PRIMARY SCHOOL).

WISHAW North Lanarkshire, St. Patrick, Shieldmuir (1891, 1898), Shieldmuir Street, Craigneuk.

Rev. Gerard Chromy (1976)

Postal address: St. Patrick's, 71 Shieldmuir Street, WISHAW ML2 7TH.
☎ Wishaw (01698) 351921.

Sunday Masses: Vigil-Mass, 6.30 p.m.; 10 a.m., 12 noon. Evening Service, as announced. Holy Days of Obligation, Masses: Vigil-Mass, 7 p.m.; 10 a.m., 7 p.m. Confessions: Saturday, after 10 a.m. Mass, 6 to 6.20 p.m., after Vigil-Mass.
Estimated Catholic population: 1,750.

ST. MATTHEW'S PRIMARY SCHOOL; (ST. BRENDAN'S PRIMARY SCHOOL).

WISHAW, North Lanarkshire, St. Thomas (1957, 1962), Caledonia Road.

Very Rev. Patrick J. Canon O'Hare (1953)
Rev. Kevin M. McGoldrick, B.D. (1999)

POSTAL ADDRESS: St. Thomas', 12 Tarbert Avenue, WISHAW ML2 0JH.
☎Wishaw (01698) 372775.

Sunday Masses: Vigil-Mass, 6 p.m.; 9.45, 11.45 a.m. Holy Days of Obligation, Masses: Vigil-Mass, 7.15 p.m.; 9.45 a.m., 7.15 p.m. Confessions: Thursday, 7.45 p.m.; Saturday, 10.15 a.m., 6.45 p.m.
Estimated Catholic population: 3,550.

ST. THOMAS' PRIMARY SCHOOL.

RETIRED CLERGY OF THE DIOCESE

Very Rev. Thomas Canon Barry, St. Joseph's, 14 Cumnock Road, Robroyston, GLASGOW G33 1QT. ☎0141-558 5114

Rev. Aidan D'Arcy, 2 Knightswood, Santry, Dublin 9, Ireland. ☎(00 353) 18428283.

Rev. Francis Darroch, St. Mary's, 120 Cadzow Road, HAMILTON ML3 6HX, ☎(01698) 423552.

Rev. John J. Delany, 23 Blairbeth Road, Burnside, Rutherglen, GLASGOW G73 4JF. ☎0141-634 4029.

Very Rev. Herbert Canon Flack, c/o Diocesan Office, Coursington Road, MOTHERWELL ML1 1PP. ☎(01698) 269114.

Very Rev. John Canon Gallacher, Nazareth House, 1647 Paisley Road West, GLASGOW G52 3QT. ☎0141-882 9375.

Rev. John F. Givens, 15 Wellview Drive, MOTHERWELL ML1 3ET. ☎(01698) 263687.

Very Rev. Denis Canon Keane, St. Martin's, Burgathia, Roscarbery, Co. Cork, Ireland. Tel.: (00353)023-48737.

Very Rev. Anthony Canon Kilcoyne, St. Joseph's, 14 Cumnock Road, Robroyston, GLASGOW G33 1QT. ☎0141-558 5114

Very Rev. Gerald Canon Maher, St. Augustine's, 12 Dundyvan Road, Langloan, COATBRIDGE ML5 4DQ. ☎Coatbridge (01236) 423044.

Very Rev. Patrick Canon McGovern, Flat 2/1, 43 Mansionhouse Gardens, GLASGOW G41 3DP. ☎ 0141-649 8666.

Rev. John McMurray, 1/13 Saunders Street, EDINBURGH EH3 6TQ

Rev. Martin O'Grady, Carrigoran House, Newmarket-on-Fergus, Co. Clare, Ireland. ☎ 061368 100.

Rev. Martin O'Keeffe, 3 Sarazen Court, Knightsridge, LIVINGSTON EH54 8SW.

Rev. Sean O'Shea, Castletownbere, Co. Cork, Ireland.

Rev. Walter Scott, 128 Crawford Street, MOTHERWELL ML1 3BN.

Rev. Hugh Sheridan, 2 Toberdoney Fold, Kilrea, Co. Derry, Northern Ireland BT51 5QS.

Rev. William P. Sproule, 41 Maghernageeragh Road, Castlederg, Co. Tyrone, N. Ireland. ☎016626-71673.

Rev. Patrick Walsh, 7 Henderson Road, TROON KA10 6NB.

Rev. John Ward, St. Joseph's Centre, Crinken Lane, Shankill, Co. Dublin.

Rev. William White, c/o Diocesan Centre, Coursington Road, MOTHERWELL ML1 1PP. ☎(01698) 269114.

Very Rev. Alphonsus Canon Woods, 9 Coltpark Avenue, Bishopbriggs, GLASGOW G64 2AT. ☎ 0141-772 1185.

Rev. Deacon James Douglas, 6 Barriedale Avenue, HAMILTON ML3 9DB.

SCHOOL CHAPLAINS

St. Margaret's High School, Airdrie	Rev. Kevin Donnelly.
Cardinal Newman High School, Bellshill	Rev. Stephen Reilly.
John Ogilvie High School, Burnbank	Rev. Ivan Boyle.
Trinity High School, Cambuslang	Rev. Thomas Doyle.
Columba High School,Coatbridge	Rev. Kenneth Campbell.
St. Ambrose's High School, Coatbridge	Rev. Francis McGachey.
St. Patrick's High School, Coatbridge	Rev. Colin Hughes.
St. Andrew's High School, East Kilbride	Rev. Alexander Stewart.
St. Bride's High School, East Kilbride	Rev. Michael Brown.
Holy Cross High School,Hamilton	Rev. James O'Kane.
Our Lady's High School, Motherwell	Rev. Andrew Nelson.
Taylor High School, New Stevenston	Rev. Gerard Higgins.
Fernhill High School,Rutherglen	Rev. Dominic Quinn.
St. Aidan's High School, Wishaw	Rev. Kevin McGoldrick

INSTITUTES OF CONSECRATED LIFE
AND
SOCIETIES OF APOSTOLIC LIFE
MEN
CARMELITES (1998)

St. Francis Xavier's, Taylor Avenue, Carfin, MOTHERWELL ML1 5AJ.
☎ Motherwell (01698) 263308; Fax:(01698) 230998.

HOLY GHOST FATHERS (1973)

Holy Ghost Fathers, 117 Newarthill Road, Carfin, MOTHERWELL, Lanarkshire ML1 5AL. ☎ Motherwell (01698) 290831; Fax: 01698-290830.

MISSIONARIES OF AFRICA (1953) (The White Fathers)

St. Joseph's, 9 Milrig Road, Rutherglen, GLASGOW G73 2NG. ☎ 0141-647 3800/613 0209; Fax: 0141-647 5321.

SALESIANS (1988)

St. Benedict's, 755 Westerhouse Road, GLASGOW G34 9RP. ☎ 0141-771 1991, Fax: 0141-781 0538.
St. Clare's, 18 Drumlanrig Avenue, GLASGOW G34 0JA. ☎ 0141-771 3740.

VINCENTIANS (1859)

St. Mary's, 70 Bannatyne Street, LANARK ML11 7JS. ☎ Lanark (01555) 662234.

XAVERIAN FATHERS (1958)

St. Francis Xavier Mission Centre, Calder Avenue, COATBRIDGE ML5 4JS. ☎ Coatbridge (01236) 606364. Fax: 01236- 606365.

DE LA SALLE BROTHERS (1983)

61 Blair Road, COATBRIDGE ML5 1NG. ☎ Coatbridge (01236) 432127;Fax: 01236-421425.

WOMEN

CANONESSES OF ST. AUGUSTINE (1989)

New Horizons Community Project, 18/19 Stewarton Terrace, WISHAW ML2 8AJ.☎ Wishaw (01698) 372278.

DAUGHTERS OF CHARITY OF ST. VINCENT DE PAUL (1863)

St. Catherine's Convent, 68 Bannatyne Street, LANARK ML11 7JS. ☎ Lanark (01555) 661671.

(1872) St. Mary's Hospital, Carstairs Road, LANARK ML11 7JU. ☎ Lanark (01555) 662393; Fax: 01555-664166.

(1989) Daughters of Charity, 4 Lochdochart Path, GLASGOW G34 0PX. ☎ 0141-771 1750.

DAUGHTERS OF MARY HELP OF CHRISTIANS
(SALESIAN SISTERS) (1992)

751 Westerhouse Road, GLASGOW G34 9RP. ☎ 0141-773 3101.

FRANCISCANS OF THE IMMACULATE CONCEPTION (1878)

(1878) Franciscan Convent, 7 Blantyre Mill Road, Bothwell, GLASGOW G71 8DE. ☎ Bothwell (01698) 852213.

(1976) Franciscan Convent, Innocents' House, 17 Viewpark Road, MOTHERWELL ML1 3ER. ☎ Motherwell (01698) 275273.

(1985) Franciscan Convent, 41 Parkhall Street, The Village East Kilbride, GLASGOW G74 4JT. ☎ East Kilbride (01355) 220438.

(1989) St. Mungo's, 133 Tillycairn Drive, Garthamlock, GLASGOW G33 5HS. ☎ 0141-774 2233.

HELPERS OF THE HOLY SOULS (1948)

(1986) Convent of the Helpers, 11 Park Road, HAMILTON ML3 6PD. ☎ Hamilton (01698) 423307.
(1988) Our Lady of Providence, 8 Campbell Street, WISHAW ML2 8HT. ☎ Wishaw (01698) 358656.

MARY OF HOPE COMMUNITY (1994)

4 Bellvue Way, Farrier's Way, COATBRIDGE ML5 4FE

MEDICAL MISSIONARIES OF MARY (1998)

350 Kirk Road, WISHAW ML2 8LH. ☎ Wishaw (01698) 381305.

MISSIONARY SISTERS OF ST. COLUMBAN (1977)

209 Quebec Drive, Westwood, East Kilbride, GLASGOW G75 8BB. ☎ East
Kilbride (01355) 238312.

POOR CLARES (1953)

(1973) Monastery of the Immaculate Heart of Mary, Fallside Road,
Bothwell, GLASGOW G71 8BA.

RELIGIOUS SISTERS OF CHARITY (1949)

(1957) St. Andrew's Hospice, Henderson Street, AIRDRIE ML6 6DJ.
☎ Airdrie (01236) 766951; Fax: 01236-748786.

SISTERS OF MERCY (1937)

(1992) 59 Swinton Avenue, Baillieston, GLASGOW G69 6LY. ☎ 0141-573
2728.

SISTERS OF ST. JOSEPH OF ANNECY (1969)

(1985) St. Joseph's Convent, 14a Clydesdale Road, Mossend, BELLSHILL
ML4 2QB. ☎ Bellshill (01698) 844992.

SISTERS OF ST. JOSEPH OF PEACE (1936)

(1983) 37 Hutchison Street, HAMILTON ML3 7LQ. ☎ Hamilton (01698)
286822.

SISTERS OF OUR LADY OF THE MISSIONS (1997)

20A Wood Street, COATBRIDGE ML5 1LX.☎ Coatbridge (01236)603350.

SISTERS OF ST. PETER CLAVER (1985)

57 Motherwell Road, BELLSHILL ML4 2JA. ☎/Fax: Bellshill (01698)
747112.

Diocese of Paisley

FOR THE GOOD OF SOULS

TO LEAD IN LOVE

Bishop of Paisley
Right Rev. John Aloysius Mone

Born at Glasgow, 22nd June, 1929; educated Holyrood Secondary
School, Sulpician seminaries in France of Issy-les-Moulineaux and
Paris, Institut Catholique, Paris (Faculty of Etudes Sociales); ordained
priest at Glasgow, 12th June, 1952; assistant priest, St. Ninian 1952-74,
Our Lady and St. George 1975-79; parish priest, St. Joseph, Tollcross,
1979-84; Scottish national chaplain, Girl Guides, 1971; chairman,
Scottish Catholic International Aid Fund, 1974-75; episcopal vicar,
Marriage, 1981-83; chairman, Glasgow Catholic Marriage Advisory
Council, 1981-83; chairman, Scottish Catholic Marriage Advisory
Council, 1982-84; Director, Ministry to Priests programme, 1982-84;
nominated titular bishop of Abercorn (and auxiliary bishop), 24th
April, 1984, and ordained by Thomas Joseph Winning, archbishop of
Glasgow, in Holy Cross Church, Glasgow 14th May, 1984; translated to
Paisley, 8th March, 1988, assuming government of the diocese, 30th
March, 1988; president & treasurer, Scottish Catholic International Aid
Fund, 1988; president, Justice & Peace (Scotland), 1987; president,
Pastoral and Social Commission, 1996.
Residence: 107 Corsebar Road, PAISLEY PA2 9PY.
☎ 0141-889 7200. Fax: 0141-849 6053.

Bishop Emeritus

Right Rev. Stephen McGill, P.S.S., S.T.L.

Born at Glasgow, 4th January, 1912, educated St. Aloysius' College, Glasgow, Blairs College Aberdeen, Le Grand Seminaire, Coutances; ordained priest at Glasgow, 29th June, 1936; La Solitude de St. Sulpice Paris, 1936; priest of St. Sulpice, July 1937; Institut Catholique Paris (Faculty of Theology) (S.T.L. 1939); on staff of Le Grand Seminaire, Bordeaux, October 1939; Le Grand Seminaire, Aix-en-Provence, January 1940; spiritual director, Blairs College, Aberdeen, 1940-51; rector, Blairs College, 1951-60; honorary canon of Glasgow, 1952; nominated bishop of Argyll and The Isles, 4th April, 1960, and consecrated by Gerald Patrick O'Hara, titular archbishop of Pessinus and apostolic delegate to Great Britain, at Oban, 22nd June, 1960; translated to Paisley, 25th July, 1968; retired, 30th March, 1988.

Residence: 13 Newark Street, GREENOCK PA16 7UH.

☎ Greenock (01475) 783696.

(For Diocesan Pastoral Centre, see below).

I. THE DIOCESAN CURIA

Diocesan Offices,c/o St. Laurence's,
6 Kilmacolm Road, GREENOCK PA15 4XP
☎ 01475-892143 Fax: 01475-892146.
e-mail: Diocese_of_Paisley @ compuserve.com
Website:http//ourworld.compuserve.com/homepages/DioceseofPaisley

VICAR-GENERAL
Right Rev. Mgr. John Cunningham, J.C.D.
St. Patrick's, 5 Orangefield Place, GREENOCK PA15 1YX.
☎/Fax: 01475-731166

MODERATOR OF THE CURIA AND VICAR EPISCOPAL

Rev. Gerard J. Gallagher, Ph.B., S.T.B.,J.C.L.

Holy Family, 2 Parkhill Avenue, PORT GLASGOW PA14 6BT.

☎/Fax: 01475-705585.

The Diocesan offices are open on Tuesdays and Fridays 10 am. to 5 p.m.
All official communications should be addressed to the Diocesan Chancellor.

1. THE DIOCESAN OFFICE

Chancellor:	Very Rev. John G. Canon Cunney.
Diocesan Secretary:	Rev. Gerard J. Gallagher, Ph.B., S.T.B., J.C.L.

**Assistant Diocesan
Secretary:** Rev. James Duggan, Ph.B., S.T.L.
Archivist: Very Rev. Bernard J. Canon Canning,
F.S.A.Scot.

Press Secretary Rev. Daniel McLoughlin, Dip.Theol., M.A.
☎/Fax.: 01475-707033

Office Secretary: Mrs.Elizabeth Reid.
Diocesan Treasurer: Rev. John Tormey, Ph.L., S.T.L.
Finance Manager: Mr. Philip McEachen, B.Sc.Hons., M.Sc.
☎ 014175-892144.

Property Committee Very Rev. Thomas J. Canon Cunningham,
(Secretary): Ph.L., S.T.L.

Registrar for Deceased Right Rev. Mgr. Hugh N. Canon Boyle,
Clergy: Ph.L., S.T.L., F.S.A.Scot.,
The Lindens, Bon Secours Hospital,
36 Mansionhouse Road, GLASGOW G41 3DW
☎ 0141-649 9226.
Youth Officer: Mrs. Christine Riddoch, M.A.Hons.,
Dip.C.G., ☎ 0141-889 2717.

2. LITURGY

Director of Liturgy and Rev. James Duggan, St. Conval's,
Master of Ceremonies: Green Farm Road, Linwood, PAISLEY PA3
3HB. ☎ 01505-323751. Fax: 01505-324445.
e-mail: Dopliturgy @aol.com.

Assistant Master of Rev. Andrew B. Coleman, M.A., B.A.,
Ceremonies: St. Patrick's, 5 Orangefield Place,
GREENOCK PA15 IYX. ☎ 01475-720223.

Director of Liturgical Rev. Alexander Buchanan, Dip.Theol.,
Music: Holy Family, 2 Parkhill Avenue,
PORT GLASGOW PA14 6BT.
☎ 01475-705585.

Director of R.C I.A.: Rev. Brian McGee, Dip.Theol., St, Joseph's,
2 Eaglesham Road, Clarkston, GLASGOW
G76 7BT. ☎/Fax.: 0141-644 2640.

Diocesan Concelebration
Vestments: Miss Philomena Barlow,
                                     Sacristan, St. Mirin's Cathedral
                                     (Sacristy ☎ 0141-887 0891;
                                     11 a.m. to 1 p.m.)

3. PRIESTLY FORMATION

Vocations Director: Rev. James Duggan, St. Conval's,
                                     Green Farm Road, Linwood, PAISLEY PA3
                                     3HB. ☎ 01505-323751. Fax: 01505-324445.
                                     e-mail:Dopvocat@aol.com.
Director of On-Going   Rev. James A. Byers
Formation: St. Laurence's, 6 Kilmacolm Road,
                                     GREENOCK PA15 4XP.
                                     ☎ Greenock (01475) 720760.
Pastoral Care of Newly   Rev. John Tormey.
Ordained   St. Fergus', 35 Blackstoun Road, PAISLEY
                                     PA3 1LU. ☎ 0141-889 5056.

4. EDUCATION: VICAR EPISCOPAL:
Very Rev. William Canon Diamond, M.A.

4.1 Religious Education Advisers
Co-ordinator: Very Rev. William Canon Diamond, M.A.
                                     St. Margaret's, 49 Graham Street,
                                     JOHNSTONE PA5 8RA
                                     ☎ 01505-320198; Fax: 01505-383342
Secondary: Rev. John Bollan, Ph.B., S.T.L.
                                     St. Margaret's, 49 Graham Street,
                                     JOHNSTONE PA5 8RA
                                     ☎ 01505-320198; Fax: 01505-383342
Primary & Special: Sr. Mary Francis Collett,
                                     Pastoral Centre, 13 Newark Street,
                                     GREENOCK PA16 7UH. ☎ 01475-724566.

4.2 Church Representatives on Local Education Authorities
East Renfrewshire: Very Rev. Thomas Canon Cunningham,
                                     St. Cadoc's,24 Fruin Avenue,
                                     Newton Mearns, GLASGOW G67 6HA.
                                     ☎/Fax: 0141-639 1073.
Inverclyde: Rev. Thomas H. Boyle, Scotus College,
                                     2 Chesters Road, Bearsden, GLASGOW
                                     G61 4AG. ☎ 0141-942 8384.
Renfrewshire: Very Rev. William Canon Diamond, M.A. ,
                                     St. Margaret's, 49 Graham Street,
                                     JOHNSTONE PA5 8RA
                                     ☎ 01505-320198; Fax: 01505-383342

4.3 Approval of Catholic Teachers Co-ordinator:
Very Rev. William Canon Diamond, M.A.
St. Margaret's, 49 Graham Street,
JOHNSTONE PA5 8RA
☎ 01505-320198; Fax: 01505-383342

4.4 S.P.R.E.D. (Special Religious Education)
(Faith Development for People with Special Needs)
:
Sr. Margaret Duffy (Director),
S.P.R.E.D. Centre, c/o St. Peter's,
154 Braehead Road PAISLEY PA2 8NG
☎ 0141-884 8866.

5. CHRISTIAN UNITY:
Diocesan Representative
on P.A.C.T.
Sr. Maria McGuire, Daughters of Wisdom,
13 Peter Coats, 31 Calside, PAISLEY PA2 6DB
☎ 0141-848 6854.

Diocesan Representative   Sr. Mary Anthony Coyle, O.S.F.,
on Inverclyde Churches   Franciscan Convent, 54 Newark Street,
Together   GREENOCK PA16 7UN ☎ 01475-726849.
e-mail: Anthony@Fran.com.freeserve.co.uk

6. YOUTH
Youth Officer and   Mrs. Christine Riddoch, Diocesan Offices,
Representative on   St. Laurence's. 6 Kilmacolm Road,
National Youth Secretariat: GREENOCK PA15 4XP.☎ 01475-892145.

Diocesan Youth Chaplain: Rev. Vincent Byrne, B.Sc., St. Andrew's,
Auchmead Road, GREENOCK PA16 0JU.
☎ 01475-631750.

7. MISSIONARY AWARENESS
Director of Pontifical   Very Rev. John Canon McElroy,
Mission Aid Societies: St. Joseph's, 2 Eaglesham Road,
Clarkston, GLASGOW G76 7BT.
☎ 0141-644 2640.

8. JUSTICE AND PEACE
Diocesan Core Group   Rev. John G. Eagers, B.Sc., Ph.B., S.T.L.
Contact: St. Peter's, 154 Braehead Road,
PAISLEY PA2 8NG. ☎ 0141-884 2435.

9. CHILD PROTECTION

Coordinator,

c/o David McCann, National

1/2, 15c Hill Street, GLASGOW G3 6RN.
☎ 0141-572 0253.

10. ST. CONVAL'S CEMETERY

Glasgow Road, Barrhead,
☎ 0141-881 1058.
Administrator: Rev. Desmond Berry,
St. Bernadette's,
Park Drive, ERSKINE PA8 7AE
☎ 0141-812 7018

11.DIOCESAN PASTORAL CENTRE

Pastoral Centre, 13 Newark Street,
GREENOCK PA16 7UH.
☎ (01475) 725161/2

II. CONSULTATIVE BODIES

The College of Consultors Right Rev. Mgr. John Cunningham,
V.G., J.C.D.
Very Rev. John G. Canon Cunney,
Rev. Peter McGarry, S.T.L.,
Rev. John Tormey, Rev. Gerard

J.Gallagher,

Rev. Stephen Baillie, Rev. Vincent Byrne.

The Council of Priests:
Chairman: Rev. Gerard J. Gallagher.
Vice-Chairman: Rev. Michael McMahon, Ph.B., S.T.B.,
L.S.S.
Secretary: Rev. Joseph Burke, St. Charles',
5 Union Street, PAISLEY PA2 6DU.
☎ 0141-889 2614.

III. DIOCESAN COMMISSIONS

Liturgy: Convenor: Rev. James Duggan
Permanent Diaconate: Convenor: Rev. James Cunningham,
Ph.L., S.T.D.
Finance: Convenor: Rev. John Tormey
Social Care: Convenor: Mrs. Jean Urquhart
Adult Education: Convenor: Rev. Gerard J. Gallagher.
Vocations: Convenor: Rev. James Duggan

IV. SCOTTISH NATIONAL TRIBUNAL
(Officials of the Tribunal from the Diocese of Paisley)

Right Rev. Mgr. John Cunningham, J.C.D., V.G.
Very Rev. Thomas J. Canon Cunningham, Ph.L., S.T.L.
Rev. James Cunningham, Ph.L., S.T.L.
Very Rev. Mgr. Thomas J. Monaghan.
Rev. Peter McGarry, S.T.L.
Rev. Gerard J. Gallagher, Ph.B., S.T.B., J.C.L.
Rev. Joseph G. Balmer, B D
Rev. Joseph Burke, Ph.B., S.T.B., J.C.L.

Co-ordinator of **Diocesan Auditors:**	Sr. Mary Anthony Coyle, O.S.F., Franciscan Convent, 54 Newark Street, GREENOCK PA16 7UN. ☎ 01475-726849 Fax: 01475-732679. E-mail: Anthony@fran.con.freeserve.co.uk

V. THE CATHEDRAL CHAPTER
(Erected 8th November 1952)

Provost:	Very Rev. Patrick Crean.
Canons:	Very Rev. Brendan Healy; Very Rev. Thomas Jamieson; Very Rev. Felix McCarney; Very Rev. Thomas Nolan *(Canon Penitentiary);* Very Rev. Joseph Quinn; Very Rev. John G. Cunney; Very Rev. William Diamond; Very Rev. Denis J. Sheahan; Very Rev. Thomas J. Cunningham; Very Rev. John McElroy.
Honorary Canons:	Right Rev. Mgr. Matthew Kinsella; Right Rev. Mgr. Hugh Gallagher; Very Rev. Luke Brady; Very Rev. James F. Murphy; Very Rev. Bernard J. Canning; Very Rev. James Jackson; Very Rev. James Murphy; Very Rev. James J. Sheehan; Very Rev. Thomas Grace; Very Rev. Andrew Reid; Very Rev. Gerard Brennan; Very Rev. James O'Connell.

DEANERIES

1. **St. Mirin.** St. Mirin's, Paisley; St. James', Paisley; St. Charles', Paisley;   St. Peter's, Paisley; St. James', Renfrew; St. Columba's, Renfrew;
   St. John Bosco's, Erskine; St. Bernadette's, Erskine.
   Dean—Rev. Peter McGarry.
   Secretary— Rev. Joseph Burke.

2. **St. Fillan.** St. Mary's, Paisley; St. Fergus', Paisley; St. Paul's, Paisley; St. Conval's, Linwood.
   Dean—Rev. John Tormey
   Secretary—Rev. James Duggan.

3. **St. Mary.** St. Mary's, Greenock; St. Patrick's, Greenock; St. Joseph's   Greenock; St. Andrew's, Greenock; St. Ninian's, Gourock; St.
   Joseph and St. Patrick, Wemyss Bay.
   Dean—Right Rev. Mgr. John Cunningham, V.G.
   Secretary—Rev. Andrew Coleman.

4. **St. Margaret.** St. Margaret's, Johnstone; St. Aidan's Johnstone; St. Anthony's, Johnstone; Christ the King, Howwood; St. Fillan's, Houston; Our Lady of Lourdes, Bishopton; Our Holy Redeemer's, Elderslie; St. Colm's, Kilmacolm.
   Dean—Very Rev. William Canon Diamond.
   Secretary—Rev. Michael McMahon.

5. **St. Ninian.** St. Laurence's, Greenock; St. Mungo's, Greenock, St. John's, Port Glasgow; Holy Family, Port Glasgow; St. Francis', Port

Glasgow.
   Dean—Rev. Gerard J. Gallagher.
   Secretary— Rev. Alex Buchanan.

6. **St. John.** St. John's, Barrhead; St. Bridget's Eaglesham; St. Thomas'   Neilston; St. Joseph's, Clarkston; St. Cadoc's, Newton Mearns.
   Dean—Very Rev. Thomas J. Canon Cunningham
   Secretary—Rev. Douglas Macmillan.

Churches and Clergy of
the Diocese
CITY OF PAISLEY

ST. MIRIN'S CATHEDRAL (1808, 1932), Incle Street.

Very Rev. Gerard Canon Brennan,
Administrator (1958)
Very Rev. Thomas Canon Nolan (1954)
Rev. William Crawford (1974)
Rev. Joseph G. Balmer, B.D. (1991)
Sr. Joy Worrell, *Pastoral Assistant*

Postal address: St. Mirin's Cathedral, Cathedral House, Cathedral Precincts, Incle Street, PAISLEY PA1 1HR. ☎ 0141-889 2404; Fax: 0141-848 5744. (Hall: 0141-848 7180).

Sunday Masses: Vigil-Mass, 6.30 p.m.; 8, 10 a.m., 12 noon, 4 p.m. Holy Days of Obligation, Masses: Vigil-Mass, 7 p.m.; 8, 10 a.m., 1.00 p.m., 7 p.m. Confessions: Thursday, 7 p.m.; Saturday, after 10 a.m. Mass, 5.30 to 6.30 p.m. Exposition of the Blessed Sacrament, Monday to Saturday, 10.30 a.m. to 12.50 p.m.
Estimated Catholic population: 4,500.

FRANCISCAN MISSIONARIES OF MARY CONVENT, 95 GARTMORE ROAD, RALSTON, PAISLEY PA1 3JS. ☎ 0141-889 6679.
JERICHO HOUSE, 26 OAKSHAW STREET EAST, PAISLEY PA7 2DP TEL.: 0141-887 9417
HAWKHEAD HOSPITAL, ABBEY COURT CARE CENTRE, CASTLE HOUSE, GARTHLAND HOUSE, NIGHTINGALE HOUSE, ST. MIRREN'S GRAMPIAN HOUSE, HUNTERHILL TUTORIAL CENTRE AND MARY RUSSELL AND KERSLAND SCHOOLS FOR HANDICAPPED CHILDREN served from St. Mirin's.
ST. CATHERINE'S PRIMARY SCHOOL; ST. JOHN OGILVIE'S PRIMARY SCHOOL; ST. ANDREW'S ACADEMY; EAST LANE NURSERY SCHOOL. (ST. CHARLES' PRIMARY SCHOOL).

ST. CHARLES, Charleston (1897, 1986), Union Street.

Rev. Peter McGarry, Ph.B., S.T.L (1978)
Rev. Joseph Burke, B.A., Ph.B., S.T.B., J.C.L. (1998)
Very Rev. Thomas Canon Grace *(Retired)* (1944)

Postal address: St. Charles', 5 Union Street, PAISLEY PA2 6DU. ☎0141-889 2614.

Sunday Masses: Vigil-Mass, 7 p.m.; 10.30 a.m., 12 noon, 7 p.m. Evening Service: 6 p.m. Holy Days of Obligation, Masses: Vigil-Mass, 7 p.m.; 10 a.m., 7 p.m. Confessions: Thursday, 9.30 to 10 a.m., 6.30 to 7 p.m.; Saturday, 9.30 to 10 a.m., 5.45 to 6.55 p.m.
Estimated Catholic population: 3,000.

DAUGHTERS OF WISDOM (MONTFORT SISTERS), 13 PETER COATS, 31 CALSIDE, PAISLEY PA2 6DB. TEL.: 0141-848 6854.
DYKEBAR HOSPITAL SERVED FROM ST. CHARLES' (SUNDAY MASS, 9.15 A.M.).
ACCORD HOSPICE, ALEXANDRA NURSING HOME, BROADSTONE NURSING HOME, CASTLEHEAD NURSING HOME AND SPIERSFIELD NURSING HOME , SERVED FROM ST. CHARLES'.
ST. CHARLES' PRIMARY SCHOOL.

ST. FERGUS, Ferguslie (1948, 1971), Blackstoun Road.

Rev. John Tormey, Ph.L., S.T.L (1981)
Rev. Maurice Callaghan, Ph.B., S.T.B. (1993)
Sr. Breda Byrne, *Parish Sister*
Postal address: St. Fergus', 35 Blackstoun Road, PAISLEY PA3 1LU. ☎ 0141-889 5056; Fax: 0141-887 7144.
E-mail: johnsfpa@aol.com

Sunday Masses: Vigil-Mass, 6 p.m., 11 a.m., 6 p.m. Evening Prayer and Benediction, 5 p.m. Holy Days of Obligation Masses: Vigil-Mass, 7 p.m.;10 a.m., 7 p.m. Confessions: Thursday, 6.30 to 6.55 p.m.; Saturday, 9.30 to 9.55a.m., 5.15 to 5.55 p.m.

Estimated Catholic population: 1,200.

(also disabled toilet in Hall).

LITTLE SISTERS OF THE ASSUMPTION, OGILVIE HOUSE, 51 BLACKSTOUN ROAD, PAISLEY PA3 7NE. ☎ 0141-889 0207.
SALESIAN SISTERS, 143/145 GLENCOATS CRESCENT, PAISLEY PA3 7RT. ☎ 0141-887 3074.
UNIVERSITY OF PAISLEY: CHAPLAIN: REV. JOHN G. EAGERS, B.SC., PH.B., S.T.L., ST. PETER'S.
ST. FERGUS' PRIMARY SCHOOL.

ST. JAMES, North End (1948, 1957), Greenock Road.

Sr. Eileen Glancy, D.C. *(Parish Director)*
Sr. Mary McGinty, D.C. *(Pastoral Assistant)*
Sr. Margaret Brady, D.C.
Sr. Kathleen Hogg, D.C.
Sr. Agnes McQuillan, D.C.
Postal address: St. James', 50 Greenock Road, PAISLEY PA3 2LE. ☎0141-889 5347.
E-mail: paisleydc@aol.com

Sunday Mass: 11 a.m. Holy Days of Obligation, Masses: 9.30 a.m., 7 p.m.
Confessions: Saturday, 10 a.m. to 10.30 a.m., Sunday 10.30 to 11 a.m.

Estimated Catholic population: 780.

DAUGHTERS OF CHARITY OF ST. VINCENT DE PAUL, ST. JAMES' 50 GREENOCK ROAD, PAISLEY PA3 2LE. Tel.: 0141-889 5347.
SPRINGBANK ROAD SHELTERED HOUSING COMPLEX ATTENDED FROM ST. JAMES'.
ST. JAMES' PRIMARY SCHOOL.

ST. MARY, West End (1876, 1891), George Street.

Rev. Charles Cavanagh, M.A (1963)

Postal address: St. Mary's, 163 George Street, PAISLEY PA1 2UN.
☎ 0141-889 2602; Fax: 0141-849 6756.
E-mail:stmaryspaisley.freeserve.co.uk

Sunday Masses: Vigil-Mass, 7 p.m.; 9.30, 11 a.m. Holy Days of
Obligation, Masses: Vigil-Mass, 7 p.m.; 9.30 a.m. Confessions: Saturday,
after 9.30 a.m.Mass, 6.15 to 6.45 p.m.; on request.

Estimated Catholic population: 2,600.

FAITHFUL COMPANIONS OF JESUS, ST. MARGARET'S CONVENT, 34 RICCARTSBAR AVENUE, PAISLEY PA2 6BG. ☎ 0141-889 2496.
CORMIE HOUSE, GLENIFFER HOME, NEWARK HOUSE AND MOREDUN NURSING HOME ATTENDED FROM ST. MARY'S.
ROYAL ALEXANDRA HOSPITAL: (CHAPLAINCY ☎ 0141-580 4573) AND PAISLEY MATERNITY HOSPITAL ATTENDED FROM ST. PETER''S, GLENBURN (☎ 0141-884 2435).CHAPLAINS: REV. IAN G. STEVENSON AND REV. JOHN G. EAGERS, ST. PETER'S.
ST. MARY'S PRIMARY SCHOOL; ST. MIRIN'S HIGH SCHOOL; (ST. PAUL'S PRIMARY SCHOOL).

ST. PAUL, Foxbar (1960, 1964), Brediland Road.

Rev. William R. Harkins (1960)
Very Rev. Patrick Provost Crean (1950)

Postal address: St. Paul's, 118 Brediland Road, PAISLEY PA2 0HE.
☎ Brediland (01505) 813103.

Sunday Masses: Vigil-Mass, 6.30 p.m., 10 a.m., 12 noon. Holy Days of
Obligation, Masses: 10 a.m., 6.30 p.m. Confessions: daily (incl.
Saturday), 9.30 a.m.; Saturday, 6 p.m.
Estimated Catholic population: 940.

ST. PAUL'S PRIMARY SCHOOL.

ST. PETER, Glenburn (1954, 1958), Braehead Road.

Rev. John G.Eagers, B.Sc., Ph.B., S.T.L. (1990)
Rev. Ian Stevenson, B.D., L.H.C.I.M.A., Dip. Couns., Dip.Sup. (1995)

Postal address: St. Peter's, 154 Braehead Road, PAISLEY PA2 8NG.
☎ 0141-884 2435.

Sunday Masses: Vigil-Mass, 6.30 p.m.; 10 a.m., 12 noon. Holy Days of
Obligation, Masses: Vigil-Mass, 6.30 p.m.; 10 a.m., 6.30 p.m.
Confessions: Saturday, after 10 a.m. Mass, 5.30 to 6.25 p.m., after
Vigil-Mass.
Estimated Catholic population: 2,000.

BRAEMOUNT NURSING HOME, GRAMPIAN NURSING HOME AND STANLEY PARK
RESIDENTIAL HOME ATTENDED FROM ST. PETER'S.
ROYAL ALEXANDRA HOSPITAL: (CHAPLAINCY ☎ 0141-580 4573) AND PAISLEY
MATERNITY HOSPITAL ATTENDED FROM ST. PETER"S, GLENBURN (☎ 0141-884
2435).CHAPLAINS: REV. IAN G. STEVENSON AND REV. JOHN G. EAGERS, ST.
PETER'S.
ST. PETER'S PRIMARY SCHOOL.

PARISHES OUTSIDE THE CITY OF PAISLEY
*The name given last before the name of the Church
is the Local Authority.*

BARRHEAD, East Renfrewshire, St. John (1841, 1961), Darnley Road.

Rev. Stephen Baillie (1990)
Rev. Andrew Karwemera (1963)
Rev. Douglas Macmillan, Dip.Phil., Dip.Theol. (1999) ▬
Sr. Patricia McKenna, *Pastoral Assistant*

Postal address: St. John's, Aurs Road, Barrhead, GLASGOW G78 2RW.
☎0141-876 1553; Fax:0141-881 1788.

Sunday Masses: Vigil-Mass, 6.30 p.m.; 10 a.m., 12 noon, 6.30 p.m. Holy
Days of Obligation, Masses: Vigil-Mass, 7 p.m.; 8, 10 a.m., 7 p.m.
Confessions: Saturday, 10.30 a.m., 5.30 to 6.30 p.m. Exposition of the
Blessed Sacrament in Oratory, Monday to Friday, 10.30 a.m. to 10 p.m.

Estimated Catholic population: 5,300.

HOSPITALLER ORDER OF ST. JOHN OF GOD, COMMUNITY HOUSE, ST. MARY'S,
HEYS STREET, BARRHEAD, GLASGOW G78 2SL. ☎/FAX: 0141-876 1950.
SISTERS OF THE CHRISTIAN RETREAT, "STELLA MARIS", 5 LOWNDES STREET,
BARRHEAD, GLASGOW G78 2QX. ☎ 0141-881 5024.
SISTERS OF THE SACRED HEARTS OF JESUS AND MARY, 42 BURNBANK DRIVE,
BARRHEAD, GLASGOW G78 2ER. ☎ 0141-876 1046.
FIRS HOUSE NURSING HOME, MILLVIEW HOUSE NURSING HOME AND
NORWOOD HOUSE NURSING HOME ATTENDED FROM ST. JOHN'S.
ST. JOHN'S PRIMARY SCHOOL; ST MARK'S PRIMARY ; ST. LUKE'S HIGH SCHOOL

BARRHEAD, East Renfrewshire, Montfort House of Prayer (1961), Darnley Road.

Rev. James Cree, S.M.M (1990)
Rev. Donald Macdonald, S.M.M. (1961)
Rev. James Murray, S.M.M. (1966)
Bro. Louis-Marie Rothwell, S.M.M.

Postal address: Montfort House of Prayer, Darnley Road, Barrhead, GLASGOW G78 1TA. ☎ 0141-881 1440; Fax: 0141-880 5154.

Applications for day and evening retreats and days of recollection and all other enquiries should be made to the Secretary.

BISHOPTON, Renfrewshire, Our Lady of Lourdes (1946 1926), Old Greenock Road.

Rev. Michael McMahon, K.H.S., Ph.B., S.T.B., L.S.S. (1985)
Postal address: Our Lady of Lourdes, 66 Old Greenock Road, BISHOPTON PA7 5BE. ☎/Fax: Bishopton (01505) 862471.
E-mail: mike@scotus.demon.co.uk

Sunday Masses: 9, 11 a.m., 6.30 p.m. Holy Days of Obligation, Masses: 10 a.m., 7 p.m. Confessions: before and after Mass, Saturday and Thursday; any time on request.
Estimated Catholic population;600.

GOOD SHEPHERD CENTRE, GREENOCK ROAD, BISHOPTON PA7 5PF. TEL.: BISHOPTON (01505) 862814.
CORA FOUNDATION CORA HOUSE, GREENOCK ROAD, BISHOPTON PA7 5PW. TEL.: BISHOPTON (01505) 863697.
AILSA LODGE RESIDENTIAL HOME ATTENDED FROM OUR LADY OF LOURDES.
(ST. JOHN BOSCO'S PRIMARY SCHOOL, ERSKINE).

CLARKSTON, East Renfrewshire, St. Joseph (1880, 1971), Eaglesham Road.

Rev. Brian McGee, Dip.Theol. (1989)
Very Rev. John Canon McElroy (1956)

Postal address: St. Joseph's, 2 Eaglesham Road, Clarkston, GLASGOW G76 7BT. ☎/Fax: 0141-644 2640.

Sunday Masses: Vigil-Mass, 6 p.m.; 8.30, 10 a.m., 12 noon, 6 p.m. Holy Days of Obligation, Masses: Vigil-Mass, 7 p.m.; 10 a.m., 7 p.m. Confessions: Saturday, 10.30 to 11 a.m., 7 to 7.30 p.m.
Estimated Catholic population: 4,200.

BONNYTON HOUSE, Busby, SHELTERED HOUSING, Carmunnock, EASTWOOD
COURT NURSING HOME, GLENLEA HOME, WILLIAMWOOD HOUSE AND ISOBEL
MAIR SPECIAL NEEDS SCHOOL ATTENDED FROM ST. JOSEPH'S.
ST. JOSEPH'S PRIMARY SCHOOL; (OUR LADY OF THE MISSIONS PRIMARY
SCHOOL).

EAGLESHAM, East Renfrewshire, St. Bridget (1856, 1858), behind 12 Polnoon Street.

Very Rev. Thomas Canon Jamieson (1954)

Postal address: "Mayfield", 12 Polnoon Street, Eaglesham, GLASGOW
G76 0BH. ☎ Eaglesham (01355)303298.

Sunday Masses: Vigil-Mass, 6 p.m.; 11 a.m., Holy Days of Obligation,
Masses: Vigil-Mass, 7 p.m.; 10 a.m. Confessions: Saturday, after morning
Mass, before Vigil-Mass.
Estimated Ctholic population: 545*   Ⓐ

ELDERSLIE, Renfrewshire, Our Holy Redeemer (1969, 1971), Barclay Avenue.

Rev. Neil Duffin (1958)

Postal address: "Airlie," 6 Barclay Avenue, Elderslie, JOHNSTONE PA5
9DX. ☎ Johnstone (01505) 323104.

Sunday Mass: 10 a.m. Holy Days of Obligation, Mass: 10 a.m.
Confessions: Thursday, after evening Mass; Saturday, 10.30 a.m.;
Sunday, 9.30 to 9.50 a.m.
Estimated Catholic population: 820.

ELDERSLIE HOSPITAL FOR HANDICAPPED CHILDREN. AND WALLACE COURT
ATTENDED FROM OUR HOLY REDEEMER'S.
(ST. ANTHONY'S PRIMARY SCHOOL, JOHNSTONE)

ERSKINE, Renfrewshire, St. Bernadette, Park Mains (1983,1987), Park Drive.

Rev. Desmond J. Berry (1976)

Postal address: St. Bernadette's, Park Drive, ERSKINE PA8 7AE.
☎ 0141-812 7018.

Sunday Masses: 11 a.m., 6 p.m. Holy Days of Obligation, Masses: 10
a.m., 7 p.m. Confessions: Saturday, after 10.30 a.m. Mass, 7 to 7.30 p.m.
Estimated Catholic population: 1,250.   ♫ ♿

SISTERS OF NOTRE DAME, 154 MAINS HILL, ERSKINE PA8 7JE. ☎ 0141-812
6164.
ST. ANNE'S PRIMARY SCHOOL.

ERSKINE, Renfrewshire, St. John Bosco (1974, 1979), Barwood Road.

Rev. John H. Fitzsimmons, Ph.L., S.T.L., L.S.S (1963)

Postal address: St. John Bosco's Presbytery, Barwood Road, ERSKINE PA8 6AB. ☎ 0141-812 2571.

Sunday Masses: Vigil-Mass, 6.30 p.m.; 10 a.m., 12 noon. Evening Service; as announced. Holy Days of Obligation, Masses: Vigil-Mass, 7 p.m., 10 a.m., 7 p.m. Confessions: Saturday, 10.30 a.m., 6 p.m., after Vigil-Mass; any other time on request.
Estimated Catholic population: 1,000.

ST. JOHN BOSCO'S PRIMARY SCHOOL.

GOUROCK, Inverclyde, St. Ninian (1896, 1880, 1982), Royal Street.

Very Rev. Mgr. Thomas J. Monaghan (1969)

Postal address: St. Ninian's, 18 Royal Street, GOUROCK PA19 1PN. ☎ Gourock (01475) 632078; Fax: 01475-631984.
E-mail: t.monaghan@lineone.net or st.ninians@lineone.net
Website:http//website.lineone.net/~st.ninians

Sunday Masses: Vigil-Mass, 5.30 p.m.; 9.30, 11.30 a.m. Holy Days of Obligation, Masses: 10 a.m., 7p.m. Confessions. Saturday, 10.30 a.m., 4.45 to 5.15 p.m.

Estimated Catholic population: 2,500.

KEMPOCK HOUSE AND QUEEN'S RESIDENTIAL HOME ATTENDED FROM ST. NINIAN'S.
ST. NINIAN'S PRIMARY SCHOOL; ST. COLUMBA'S HIGH SCHOOL.

GREENOCK, Inverclyde, St. Andrew, Larkfield (1951,1968), Auchmead Road.

Rev. Gerard Oliver Freney (1986)
Rev. Benedict O'Keeffe, M.Agr.Sc (1960)
Rev. Vincent J. Byrne, B.Sc. (1994)
Sr. Sheila Buckley, *Pastoral Assistant*

Postal address: St. Andrew's, Auchmead Road, Larkfield, GREENOCK PA16 0JU. ☎ Gourock (01475) 631750.

Sunday Masses: Vigil-Mass, 6 p.m.; 10, 11.30 a.m., 6 p.m. Holy Days of Obligation, Masses: Vigil-Mass, 6.30 p.m., 8, 10 a.m., 6.30 p.m. Confessions: Monday to Friday, 9.45 a.m., 6.15 p.m.; Saturday, 10.30 to 11 a.m., 5 to 6 p.m., after Vigil-Mass.
Estimated Catholic population: 4,200

INVERCLYDE ROYAL HOSPITAL (INCLUDING POLICE MORTUARY), GLENBURN SPECIAL SCHOOL, LARKFIELD SCHOOL FOR THE DEAF AND INVERCLYDE NURSES' TEACHING COLLEGE ATTENDED FROM ST. ANDREW'S.
H.M.P. GATESIDE. CHAPLAINS: REV. GERALD OLIVER FRENEY, REV. VINCENT BYRNE, ST. ANDREW'S.
SACRED HEART PRIMARY SCHOOL; ST. GABRIEL'S PRIMARY SCHOOL.

GREENOCK, Inverclyde, St. Joseph (1947, 1953), Bow Road.

Rev. Gerard McNellis (1987)
Very Rev. Felix Canon McCarney (1954)

Postal address: St. Joseph's, Bow Road, GREENOCK PA16 7DY. ☎ Greenock (01475) 720789.

Sunday Masses: Vigil-Mass, 6 p.m.; 11 a.m., 6 p.m. Holy Days of Obligation, Masses: Vigil-Mass, 6 p.m., 10 a.m., 7 p.m. Confessions: Thursday, 7.30 p.m., Saturday, 10.30 to 11 a.m., 5 to 6 p.m., after Vigil-Mass.; on request.
Estimated Catholic population: 3,700.

ST. JOSEPH'S PRIMARY SCHOOL; HOLY CROSS PRIMARY SCHOOL; ST. COLUMBA'S HIGH SCHOOL.

GREENOCK, Inverclyde, St. Laurence (1855, 1954), Kilmacolm Road.

Rev. James A. Byers (1971)

Postal address: St. Laurence's, 6 Kilmacolm Road, GREENOCK PA15 4XP. ☎ Greenock (01475) 720760; Fax: 01475-732595.

Sunday Masses: Vigil-Mass, 6 p.m.; 10 a.m., 12 noon. Holy Days of Obligation, Masses: Vigil-Mass, 7p.m.; 10 a.m., 7 p.m. Confessions: Thursday, 6.30 to 6.50 p.m.; Saturday, 9.30 to 9.50 a.m., 5 to 5.40 p.m. Estimated Ctholic population: 2,300.

HILLEND HOUSE (FOR ELDERLY PEOPLE), EAST CRAWFORD STREET, ATTENDED FROM ST. LAURENCE'S.
ST. KENNETH'S PRIMARY SCHOOL; ST. LAURENCE'S PRIMARY SCHOOL.

GREENOCK, Inverclyde, St. Mary (1816, 1862), Patrick Street.

Rev. Andrew Carroll (1974)
Very Rev. Andrew Canon Reid *(Retired, Tel.: 01475-731823)* (1951)
Sr. Thérèse Clary, *Pastoral Assistant*

Postal address: St. Mary's Rectory, 14 Patrick Street, GREENOCK PA16 8NA. ☎ Greenock (01475) 721084; Fax: 01475-731975.

Sunday Masses: Vigil-Mass, 6.30 p.m.; 10 a.m., 12 noon. Holy Days of Obligation, Masses: Vigil-Mass, 6.30 p.m.; 10 a.m., 6.30 p.m. Confessions: Saturday, 10.30 to 11 a.m., 5.30 to 6.15 p.m., after Vigil-Mass.
Estimated Catholic population: 2,350.

FRANCISCAN CONVENT, 54 NEWARK STREET, GREENOCK PA16 7UN. ☎ GREENOCK (01475) 726849; FAX: 01475-732679.
E-MAIL: ANTHONY@FRAN.CON.FREESERVE.CO.UK.
LITTLE SISTERS OF THE POOR, 44 UNION STREET, GREENOCK PA16 8DP. TEL.: GREENOCK (01475) 722465. CHAPLAIN: VERY REV. DENIS J. CANON SHEAHAN (1955). TEL.: 01475-722465/888660.
MARINERS' HOME, BAGATELLE NURSING HOME, BALCLUTHA NURSING HOME AND BELLAIRE NURSING HOME, AND THE WATT COLLEGE, ATTENDED FROM ST. MARY'S.
ST. MARY'S PRIMARY SCHOOL.

GREENOCK, Inverclyde, St. Mungo (1934, 1935), Port Glasgow Road.

Rev. Peter McCahill (1964)

Postal address: St. Mungo's, Gibshill Road, GREENOCK PA15 2UP. ☎Port Glasgow (01475) 741187.

Sunday Masses: Vigil-Mass, 6 p.m.; 10, 11.30 a.m., 6 p.m. Holy Days of Obligation, Masses: Vigil-Mass, 6 p.m.; 10 a.m., 7 p.m. Confessions: Thursday, 6.30 to 7 p.m.; Saturday, 10.30 a.m., 5 to 6 p.m., after Vigil-Mass.
Estimated Catholic population: 2,000.

JERICHO HOUSE (HOSTEL FOR HOMELESS MEN), 14-20 SHANKLAND ROAD, GREENOCK PA15 2NE. TEL.: PORT GLASGOW (01474) 741950.
ST. MUNGO'S PRIMARY SCHOOL; (ST. KENNETH'S PRIMARY SCHOOL)..

GREENOCK, Inverclyde, St. Patrick (1924, 1935), Orangefield Place.

Right Rev. Mgr. John Cunningham, J.C.D., V.G. (1961)
Rev. Andrew B. Coleman, M.A., B.D. (1991)

Postal address: St. Patrick's, 5 Orangefield Place, GREENOCK PA15 IYZ. ☎Greenock (01475) 720223. Fax: 01475-731166.
E-mail: Andrew@st_patricks.freeserve.co.uk

Sunday Masses: Vigil-Mass, 7 p.m.; 8, 10, 11.30 a.m., 7 p.m. Holy Days of Obligation, Masses: Vigil-Mass, 7 p.m.; 8, 10 a.m., 7 p.m. Confessions: Thursday, after evening Mass; Saturday, 9.30 to 10 a.m., 10.30 to 11 a.m., 5.30 to 7 p.m.
Estimated Catholic population: 3,800.

HOUSTON, Renfrewshire, St. Fillan (1841), Main Street.

Rev. John Doherty (1962)
Sr. Marian Murtagh, O.L.M., *Pastoral Assistant.*
Sr. Mirian Wallace, O.L.M., *Pastoral Assistant*

Postal address: St. Fillan's, 1(b) Main Street, Houston, JOHNSTONE PA6 7EL. ☎ Bridge of Weir (01505) 612046.

Sunday Masses: Vigil-Mass, 6.30 p.m.; 9.30, 11 a.m., Holy Days of Obligation, Masses: Vigil-Mass, 7 p.m.; 10 a.m., 7 p.m. Confessions: Saturday, after morning Mass, 5.45 to 6.15 p.m.
Estimated Catholic population: 1,850.

HOWWOOD, Renfrewshire, Christ the King (1948, 1928), Bowfield Road.

Very Rev. John G. Canon Cunney (1955)

Postal address: Christ the King Presbytery, Bowfield Road, Howwood, JOHNSTONE PA9 1BZ. Tel.: Kilbarchan (01505) 702636; Fax: (01505) 703442.

Sunday Masses:Vigil-Mass, 6p.m.; 9.30 or 11 on alternate Sundays. Exposition of the Blessed Sacrament, Sundays, May to end September, 12 noon to Holy Hour, 4 to 5 p.m. Holy Days of Obligation, Mass: 10 a.m. Confessions: Saturday, after morning Mass, 6.30 to 7 p.m.
Estimated Catholic population: 650.

INCHINNAN, Renfrewshire, served from St. James', Renfrew.

Sunday. Mass at 11 a.m. (except July and August) in Community Centre, Old Greenock Road, Inchinnan.

JOHNSTONE, Renfrewshire, St. Aidan (1960, 1967), Tower Road.

Rev. Patrick Brannan (1969)
Right Rev. Mgr. Neil C. McGrory, J.C.L.
(Retired; ☎ *01505-326228)* (1953)

Postal address: St. Aidan's, Tower Road, JOHNSTONE PA5 0AD.
☎ Johnstone (01505) 320900.
E-mail: PBrannanl@csi.com

Sunday Masses: Vigil-Mass, 6.30 p.m.; 10.30 a.m. Holy Days of Obligation, Masses: 10 a.m., 6.30 p.m. Exposition of the Blessed Sacrament: Monday, after 10 a.m. Mass to 8 p.m.; Thursday, after 10 a.m. Mass to 7 p.m. Confessions: Thursday, after 6 p.m. Devotions; Saturday, after 10 a.m. Mass, 6 to 6.20 p.m., after Vigil-Mass.
Estimated Catholic population: 1,400*   **A**

ADAMS HOUSE ATTENDED FROM ST. AIDAN'S.

JOHNSTONE, Renfrewshire, St. Anthony, Corseford and Spateston (1969, 1973), Hallhill Road.

Rev. Patrick Woods (1953)

Postal address: St. Anthony's, Hallhill Road, JOHNSTONE PA5 0SD.
☎Kilbarchan (01505) 702284.

Sunday Masses: 10 a.m., 12 noon, 6 p.m. Holy Days of Obligation, Masses: 10 a.m., 6 p.m. Confessions: Thursday, after Mass; Saturday, 10.30 to 11 a.m., 6.30 to 7.30 p.m.
Estimated Catholic population: 600.

FORDBANK HOUSE ATTENDED FROM ST. ANTHONY'S.
PRIMARY AND SECONDARY SCHOOLS.

JOHNSTONE, Renfrewshire, St. Margaret (1852,1875), Graham Street.

Very Rev. William Canon Diamond, M.A (1955)
Rev. Joseph G. Alexander (1962)
Rev. John Bollan, Ph.B., S.T.L., P.G.C.E. (1994)

Postal address: St. Margaret's, 49 Graham Street, JOHNSTONE PA5 8RA.
☎ Johnstone (01505) 320198; Fax: 01505-383342.

Sunday Masses: Vigil-Mass, 7.30 p.m.; 9, 10.30 a.m., 12 noon, 6 p.m.
Holy Days of Obligation, Masses: 8, 10 a.m., 7 p.m. Confessions:
Saturday, 9.30 a.m., 6 to 7.15 p.m.
Estimated Catholic population: 3,900.

JOHNSTONE HOSPITAL ATTENDED FROM ST. MARGARET'S.
ST. DAVID'S PRIMARY SCHOOL; ST. MARGARET'S PRIMARY SCHOOL; (ST. ANTHONY'S PRIMARY SCHOOL).

KILMACOLM, Inverclyde, St. Colm's (1995, 1992), Smithy Brae.

Rev. William McDade, Ph.L (1962)
Postal address: The Old Lodge, Cora Campus, Greenock Road,
BISHOPTON PA7 5PF. ☎/Fax: Bishopton (01505) 862255.
E-mail (Church): stcolmchurch@quista.net
       (Personal):wmcdade@quista.net

Sunday Masses: Vigil-Mass, 6 p.m.; 10 a.m. Holy Days of Obligation,
Mass: 7.30 p.m. Confessions: Saturday, 5.40 p.m.; on request.
Estimated Catholic population: 450.

PRINCESS LOUISE SCOTTISH HOSPITAL FOR EX-SERVICEMEN AND WOMEN,
Erskine, ATTENDED FROM KILMACOLM.
(ST. FRANCIS' PRIMARY SCHOOL, PORT GLASGOW).

LINWOOD, Renfrewshire, St. Conval (1898, 1967), Green Farm Road.

Very Rev. Brendan Canon Healy (1954)
Rev. James Duggan, Ph.B., S.T.L. (1992)

Postal address: St. Conval's, Green Farm Road, Linwood, PAISLEY PA3
3HB. ☎ Johnstone (01505) 323751. Fax: 01505-324445.
E-mail: Stconvals@aol.com

Sunday Masses: Vigil-Mass, 6.30 p.m.; 10.30 a.m., 6.30 p.m. Holy Days
of Obligation, Masses: Vigil-Mass, 6.30 p.m.; 9, 10 a.m., 6.30 p.m.
Confessions: Thursday, 8 p.m.; Saturday, 10 to 10.30 a.m., 5.30 to 6.20
p.m., after Vigil-Mass.
Estimated Catholic population: 2,500.   🔧 Ⓐ

CLIPPENS SPECIAL NEEDS SCHOOL ATTENDED FROM ST. CONVAL'S.
OUR LADY OF PEACE PRIMARY SCHOOL; ST. BRENDAN'S HIGH SCHOOL.

LOCHWINNOCH, Renfrewshire, Our Lady of Fatima (1954), High Street. Served from Howwood. Tel.: 01505-702636. Fax: 01505-703442.

Sunday Mass: 9.30 or 11 a.m. on alternate Sundays. Holy Days of
Obligation. Mass: 7 p.m.

NEILSTON, East Renfrewshire, St. Thomas (1861), Main Street.

Very Rev. Bernard J. Canon Canning, F.S.A.Scot (1956)

Postal address: St. Thomas', 70 Main Street, Neilston, GLASGOW G78
3NJ. ☎ 0141-881 1478; Fax: 0141-876 1702.

Sunday Masses: Vigil-Mass, 6 p.m.; 9, 11 a.m. Holy Days of Obligation,
Masses: 8.30, 10.30 a.m., 7 p.m. Confessions: Saturday, 9.30 to 10 a.m.,
10.30 to 11 a.m., 5.30 to 6 p.m., after Vigil-Mass.
Estimated Catholic population: 1,100.   🔧

PRIMARY SCHOOL.

NEWTON MEARNS, East Renfrewshire, St. Cadoc (1966, 1981), Fruin Avenue.

Very Rev. Thomas J. Canon Cunningham, Ph.L., S.T.L (1956)

Postal address: St. Cadoc's, 24 Fruin Avenue, Newton Mearns, GLASGOW
G77 6HA. ☎/Fax: 0141-639 1073.

Sunday Masses: Vigil-Mass, 6.30 p.m.; 10 a.m., 12 noon, 6.30 p.m. Holy
Days of Obligation, Masses: Vigil-Mass, 7 p.m.; 10 a.m., 7 p.m.
Confessions: Saturday, 10.30 to 11 a.m., 7.15 p.m.
Estimated Catholic population: 3,100.   🔧 ♿

MEARNSKIRK HOUSE, ABBEYFIELD HOUSE, CROOKFUR HOMES, FUINARY HOUSE,
ST. JOHN'S (THORNHILL) NURSING HOME AND WELLMEADOW LODGE
ATTENDED FROM ST. CADOC'S.
ST. CADOC'S PRIMARY SCHOOL.

PORT GLASGOW, Inverclyde, St. Francis (1969, 1974), Auchenbothie Road.

Rev. Daniel McLoughlin, Dip.Theol., M.A.
(Diocesan Press Secretary); ☎/Fax: 01475-707033 (1982)
Sr. Margaret Molloy, O.L.M., *Pastoral Assistant*

Postal address: St. Francis', Auchenbothie Road, PORT GLASGOW PA14 6JD. ☎Port Glasgow (01475) 704222; Social Centre (01475) 706033; Fax: 01475-707033.
E-mail: stfrancis@theport.demon.co.uk
Internet site:http://www.theport.demon.co.uk
Sunday Masses: Vigil-Mass, 6 p.m.; 10, 11.30 a.m. Holy Days of Obligation, Masses: Vigil-Mass, 7 p.m.; 9.30 a.m., 7 p.m. Confessions: Thursday, 7.30 p.m.; Saturday, 10 to 10.30 a.m., 5 to 5.45 p.m.
Estimated Catholic population: 3,000.

ST. FRANCIS' PRIMARY SCHOOL; (ST. MICHAEL'S PRIMARY SCHOOL).

PORT GLASGOW, Inverclyde, The Holy Family (1946. 1959), Parkhill Avenue.

Rev. Gerard J. Gallagher, Ph.B., S.T.B., J.C.L (1984)
Rev. Alexander D. Buchanan, Dip. Theol. (1992)

Postal address: Holy Family Presbytery, 2 Parkhill Avenue, PORT GLASGOW PA14 6BT. ☎/Fax: Port Glasgow (01475) 705585.

Sunday Masses: Vigil-Mass, 6.30 p.m.; 10 a.m., 12 noon, 6.30 p.m. Holy Days of Obligation, Masses: Vigil-Mass, 7 p.m.; 10 a.m., 7 p.m. Confessions: Saturday, after 10 a.m. Mass, 5.50 to 6.20 p.m.
Estimated Catholic population: 4,700.

CONVENT OF OUR LADY OF THE MISSIONS, CLUNE HOUSE, CLUNE BRAE, PORT GLASGOW PA14 5SW. TEL.: PORT GLASGOW (01475) 706173.
SISTERS OF THE SACRED HEARTS OF JESUS AND MARY, LORETO HOUSE, NORTHFIELD AVENUE, PORT GLASGOW PA14 6PJ. TEL.: PORT GLASGOW (01475) 705229.
HOLY FAMILY PRIMARY SCHOOL; ST. MICHAEL'S PRIMARY SCHOOL; ST. STEPHEN'S HIGH SCHOOL.

PORT GLASGOW, Inverclyde, St. John the Baptist (1846, 1854), Shore Street.

Rev. David Boyd, M.A. (1985)

Postal address: St. John the Baptist, 23 Shore Street, PORT GLASGOW PA14 5HD. ☎ Port Glasgow (01475) 741139; Fax: 01475-745038.

E-mail: johnthebaptist.portglasgow@btinternet.com

Sunday Masses: Vigil-Mass, 6 p.m.; 11a.m., 4 p.m. Holy Days of Obligation, Masses: Vigil-Mass, 6 p.m.; 9.30 a.m., 6 p.m. Confessions: Saturday, after 10 a.m. Mass, 5 to 5.45 p.m.
Estimated Catholic population: 1,800.

URSULINES OF JESUS, 1 LILYBANK ROAD, PORT GLASGOW PA14 5AN. TEL.: PORT GLASGOW (01475) 711407.
BROADSTONE HOUSING COMPLEX AND MARCHMONT NURSING HOME ATTENDED FROM ST. JOHN THE BAPTIST'S.
ST. JOHN'S PRIMARY SCHOOL; LILYBANK SPECIAL NEEDS SCHOOL;
(ST. MICHAEL'S PRIMARY SCHOOL).

RENFREW, Renfrewshire, St. Columba, (1969, 1974), Campsie Drive.

Rev. Edward D. Cameron (1985)

Postal address: St. Columba's, 35 Campsie Drive, RENFREW PA4 0RB. ☎ 0141-886 2570; Fax: 0141-885 0086; Mobile: 07977585132.

Sunday Masses: Vigil-Mass, 5.30 p.m.; 10 a.m., 12 noon. Holy Days of Obligation, Masses: Vigil-Mass, 7 p.m.; 9.30 a.m. Confessions: Saturday, after morning and Vigil Masses.
Estimated Catholic population: 2,000.

(ST. CATHERINE'S PRIMARY SCHOOL; ST. JAMES'PRIMARY SCHOOL).

RENFREW, Renfrewshire, St. James (1877, 1903), Inchinnan Road.

Rev. James Cunningham, Ph.L., S.T.D (1960)
Rev. Joseph Dow (1973)

Postal address: St. James', Inchinnan Road, RENFREW PA4 8NG.
☎ 0141-886 2022.

Sunday Masses: 8, 10 a.m., 12 noon, 7.15 p.m. Holy Days of Obligation
Masses: 7.30, 9.30, 11 a.m., 8 p.m. Confessions: before all weekday
Masses, Saturday, 10 to 10.30 a.m., 6 to 8 p.m.   **A**
Estimated Catholic population: 2,400.

FRANCISCAN MISSIONARY SISTERS FOR AFRICA, MOREDUN CONVENT,
ALEXANDRA DRIVE, RENFREW PA4 8UB. ☎ 0141-886 2040.
STEWART HOUSE, Renfrew, AND LITTLE INCH NURSING HOME, Inchinnan,
ATTENDED FROM ST. JAMES'.
ST. JAMES' PRIMARY SCHOOL; TRINITY HIGH SCHOOL.

WEMYSS BAY, Inverclyde, St. Joseph and St. Patrick (1971, 1901), Forbes Place.

Very Rev. Joseph Canon Quinn (1954)

Postal address: St. Joseph's, 1 Forbes Place, WEMYSS BAY PA18 6AU.
☎ Wemyss Bay (01475) 520272.

Sunday Masses: Vigil-Mass, 6 p.m.; 10 a.m., 6 p.m. Holy Days of
Obligation, Masses: Vigil-Mass, 6.30p.m.; 10a.m., 6.30p.m. Confessions:
Saturday, 10.30 a.m., 5.30 p.m.
Estimated Catholic population: 690.   ♿
                                                (Toilets in Hall)

INVERKIP HOUSE NURSING HOME AND L.ANGHOUSE RESIDENTIAL HOME,
Inverkip, ATTENDED FROM WEMYSS BAY.
(ST. NINIAN'S PRIMARY SCHOOL, Gourock).

RETIRED PRIESTS OF THE DIOCESE

Rev. Francis Bradley, Dargle Valley Nursing Home, Crookstown, Enniskerry, Co. Wicklow, Ireland.

Very Rev. Luke Canon Brady, 234 Moyville, Rathfarnham, Dublin 16, Ireland.

Right Rev. Mgr. Charles Burns, O.B.E., Palazzo Doria, Via del Plebiscito 107, 00186 Roma, Italy.

Rev. Felix Connelly, 15 Midtown, Dalry, CASTLE DOUGLAS DG7 3UT

Rev. Colm Fox, Narin, Portnoo, Co. Donegal, Ireland.

Right Rev. Mgr. Hugh Canon Gallagher, Nazareth House, 1647 Paisley Road West, GLASGOW G52 3QT. ☎ 0141-810 5906.

Very Rev. Thomas A. Canon Grace, St. Charles', 5 Union Street, PAISLEY PA2 6DU. ☎ 0141-889 2614.

Rev. John Heffernan, The Lodge, Our Lady of Fatima, Oakpark, Tralee, Co. Kerry, Ireland. ☎ 066 7128768.

Very Rev. James Canon Jackson, Nazareth House, 1647 Paisley Road West, GLASGOW G52 3QT

Right Rev. Mgr. Matthew Canon Kinsella, 70 Eldon Street, GREENOCK PA16 8NA. ☎ 01475-727740.

Rev. Joseph Logue, 86 Union Street, GREENOCK PA16 8BE. ☎ 01475-719371.

Right Rev. Mgr. Neil C. McGrory, St. Aidan's, Tower Road, JOHNSTONE PA5 0AD. ☎ 01505-336228.

Very Rev. James F. Canon Murphy, Burlington Villa, Forbes Place, WEMYSS BAY PA18 6BL. ☎ 01475-521394.

Very Rev. James Canon Murphy, 24 Johnstone Terrace, GREENOCK PA16 8BD

Very Rev. James Canon O'Connell, 39 Paisley Road, Barrhead, GLASGOW G78 1HW. ☎ 0141-881 3304.

Very Rev. Andrew Canon Reid, St. Mary's, 14 Patrick Street, GREENOCK PA16 8NA ☎ 01475-731823.

Very Rev. James J. Canon Sheehan, Manorhamilton, Co. Leitrim, Ireland.

Rev. Michael G. Sheridan,Burlington Villa, Forbes Place, WEMYSS BAY PA18 6BL

SCHOOL CHAPLAINS

St. Luke's, Barrhead	Rev. Stephen Baillie.
St. Columba's High, Gourock	Rev. Gerard McNellis.
Notre Dame High, Greenock	Rev. Andrew Coleman.
St. Cuthbert's High, Johnstone	Rev. John Bollan.
St. Brendan's High, Linwood	Rev. James Duggan.
St. Andrew's Academy, Paisley	Rev. Joseph Balmer.
St. Mirin's High, Paisley	Rev. John Tormey.
St. Stephen's High, Port Glasgow	Rev. Alexander Buchanan.
Trinity High, Renfrew	Rev. Edward Cameron.

HOSPITAL CHAPLAINS

Royal Alexandra Hospital, Paisley	Rev. Ian Stevenson
Assistant	Rev. John Eagers
	(St. Peter's, Paisley)
Inverclyde Royal Hospital, Greenock	Rev. Oliver Freney.
	Rev. Vincent Byrne
	Rev. Benedict O'Keeffe
	(St. Andrew's, Greenock)

INSTITUTES OF CONSECRATED LIFE AND SOCIETIES OF APOSTOLIC LIFE

MEN

MONTFORT FATHERS (1961)

Montfort House, Darnley Road, Barrhead, GLASGOW G78 ITA.
☎ 0141-881 1440; Fax: 0141-880 5154.

HOSPITALLER ORDER OF ST. JOHN OF GOD (1999)

St. Mary's Nursing Home, Heys Street, Barrhead, GLASGOW G78 2EN.
☎/Fax: 141-876 1950.
Chaplain: Rev. Robert Moore, O.H.Sac.

JERICHO BENEDICTINES (1980)

Monastery of Jesus, Harelaw Farm, Kilbarchan, JOHNSTONE PA10 2PY.
☎ Bridge of Weir (01505) 614669; Fax: 01505-613008.
Resident Superior: Rev. James Ferguson (1965).

WOMEN

DAUGHTERS OF CHARITY OF ST. VINCENT DE PAUL (1921)

(1997) St. James'. 50 Greenock Road, PAISLEY PA3 2LE. ☎0141-889
5347. E-mail: paisleydc@aol.com

DAUGHTERS OF WISDOM (MONTFORT SISTERS) (1992)
13 Peter Coats, 31 Calside, PAISLEY PA2 6DB. ☎0141-848 6854.

FAITHFUL COMPANIONS OF JESUS (1889)

(1978) St. Margaret's Convent, 34 Riccartsbar Avenue, PAISLEY PA2
6BG. ☎/Fax: 0141-889 2496.

FRANCISCAN MISSIONARIES OF MARY (1997)

95 Gartmore Road, Ralston, PAISLEY PA1 3JS. ☎0141-889 6679.

FRANCISCAN MISSIONARY SISTERS FOR AFRICA (1954)

(1984) Moredun Convent, Alexandra Drive, RENFREW PA4 8UB.
☎ 0141-886 2040; Fax: 0141-886 5030.

FRANCISCANS OF THE IMMACULATE CONCEPTION (1878)

Franciscan Sisters, 54 Newark Street, GREENOCK PA16 7UN. ☎Greenock
(01475) 726849; Fax: 01475-732679.
E-mail: Anthony@fran.con.freeserve.co.uk
(1999)Franciscan Sisters, 14/16 Rowan Street, GREENOCK PA16 7EG

LITTLE SISTERS OF THE ASSUMPTION (1968)

Ogilvie House, 51 Blackstoun Road, Ferguslie Park, PAISLEY PA3 1LU. ☎0141-889 0207.

LITTLE SISTERS OF THE POOR (1884)

Holy Rosary Home, 44 Union Street, GREENOCK PA16 8DP. ☎Greenock (01475) 722465; Fax: 01475-722168.
Chaplain: Very Rev. Denis J. Canon Sheahan (1955). ☎01475-722465/888660.

SALESIAN SISTERS (1969)

Salesian Sisters, 143 Glencoats Crescent, PAISLEY PA3 1RT. ☎0141-887 3074.

SISTERS OF THE CHRISTIAN RETREAT (1989)

(1994) "Stella Maris", 5 Lowndes Street, Barrhead, GLASGOW G78 2QX. ☎ 0141-881 5024.

SISTERS OF NOTRE DAME (1992)

154 Mains Hill, ERSKINE PA8 7JE. ☎0141-812 6164.

SISTERS OF OUR LADY OF THE MISSIONS (1958)

(1980) Convent of Our Lady of the Missions, Clune House, Clune Brae, PORT GLASGOW PA14 5SW. ☎ Port Glasgow (01475) 706173.

(1996) Sisters of Our Lady of the Missions, Flat 24a, Riverside View, Houston Road, BRIDGE OF WEIR PA11 3QP. ☎ 01505-613514.

SISTERS OF THE SACRED HEARTS OF JESUS AND MARY (1911)

(1994) Loreto House, Northfield Avenue, PORT GLASGOW PA14 6PJ. ☎Port Glasgow (01475) 705229.

(1999) 42 Burnbank Drive, Barrhead, GLASGOW G78 2ER. ☎0141-876 1046.

URSULINES OF JESUS (1975)

(1981) Ursuline Convent, 1 Lilybank Road, PORT GLASGOW PA14 5AN. ☎Port Glasgow (01475) 711407.

EDUCATION AND FORMATION
A—Priestly Formation

NATIONAL VOCATIONS OFFICE, 2 Chesters Road, Bearsden, GLASGOW G61 4AG. ☎/Fax: 0141-943 1995. Directors: Rev Stephen Connolly (1987); Rev. Michael Bagan (1978).

THE PONTIFICAL SCOTS COLLEGE, ROME.

1600 - The Pontifical Scots College Rome - 2000
(400th Anniversary Painting (Detail): Patricia Hakim 1999.
Copyright; (Photograph by Rev. Stephen Robson)

The Scots College in Rome was founded by Pope Clement VIII on 5th December, 1600.

Address: Pontificio Collegio Scozzese, Via Cassia 481, 00189 Roma, Italy.

Tel.: + 39 06 3366 8085 (*Staff*);

+ 39 06 3366 8039 (*Students*);

+ 39 06 3366 8001 (*Secretary*).

+ 39 06 3366 8027 (*Scots Pilgrim Centre*)

Fax: +39 06 3365 3387.

E-mail : pontscot@tin.it (*Staff*)

romescot@tin.it (*Students*)

jubilee.rep@libero.it (*Scots Pilgrim Centre*)

Web site: http//digilander.iol.it/scotscollege/

Rector, Very Rev. Christopher McElroy, Ph.B., S.T.L. (1980)
Vice-Rector, Rev. Raymond J. Breslin, Ph.B., S.T.L. (1989)
Spiritual Director, Rev. Stephen Robson, B.Sc., M.Th., C.Biol., M.I.Biol. (1979).

Total number of Seminarians	18
Archdiocese of St. Andrews and Edinburgh	2
Diocese of Aberdeen	2
Diocese of Argyll and The Isles	2
Diocese of Galloway	2
Archdiocese of Glasgow	7
Diocese of Motherwell	1
Diocese of Paisley	2
Total number of Postgraduates	8
Diocese of Motherwell	1
Archdiocese of Arequipa, Peru	1
Archdiocese of Czestochowa, Poland	2
Diocese of Dodoma, Tanzania	1
Diocese of Kibungo, Rwanda	1
Archdiocese of Seoul, South Korea	1
Diocese of Suwon, South Korea	1

THE ROYAL SCOTS COLLEGE, SALAMANCA.—The Scots College in Spain was founded at Madrid in 1627 by Colonel William Semple of Lochwinnoch and, in 1771, it was transferred to Valladolid. The College was transferred to Salamanca in 1988.

Address: Real Colegio de Escoceses, ISPE, Avda. de Champagnat 121-133, 37007 Salamanca, Spain.
Tel.: (00 34)923 25 40 11 (*Rector and Staff*);
      (00 34) 923 23 32 04 (*Students*).
Fax: (00 34) 923 24 26 00.
E-mail:realcolescoceses@planalfa.es

Rector, Very Rev. Mgr. Denis E. Carlin, Ph.B., S.T.L., M.A., J.C.L. (1974)
Vice-Rector, Rev. Thomas J. Shields, Ph.B., S.T.L. (1989)
Spiritual Director, Rev. Joseph Toal, S.T.B. (1980).

Total number of Students in Salamanca	12
Archdiocese of St. Andrews and Edinburgh	2
Diocese of Aberdeen	1
Diocese of Argyll and The Isles	1
Diocese of Dunkeld	1
Diocese of Galloway	2
Archdiocese of Glasgow	2
Diocese of Paisley	1
Diocese of Gibraltar	1
Archdiocese of Birmingham	1*

'Post-graduate Student.

SCOTUS COLLEGE—National Major Seminary, founded in 1993 following a decision of the Bishops' Conference of Scotland taken the previous year, in succession to Chesters College, Bearsden, and Gillis College, Edinburgh. It is under the patronage of Blessed John Duns Scotus. In carrying out the programme of priestly formation, particularly spiritual, human and pastoral formation, Scotus College depends on the assistance of many agencies and groups throughout Scotland. It is affiliated to the Pontifical University of Maynooth and is associated with the University of Glasgow. Under the terms of the affiliation with the Pontifical University of Maynooth courses followed at Scotus College can lead to the award of a Degree of B.D. General, the Diploma in Theology and the Diploma in Philosophy and Arts.

Address: Scotus College, 2 Chesters Road, Bearsden, GLASGOW G61 4AG.
☎ 0141-942 8384 (*General Enquiries and Staff*);
Students: 0141-942 9489 (*Recreation Room*)/8485 (*Garden Block*)/3674 (*West Block*) .
Fax: 0141-943 1767. E-mail: @scotus.demon.co.uk

Rector: Very Rev. Neil Donnachie (1971)
Vice-Rector and Director of Liturgy: Rev. Michael B. Regan, B.A., M.Litt., M.Th., D.E.A. (1982).
Spiritual Director: Rev. Thomas H. Boyle, Dip.Theol. (1986).
Pastoral Director: Rev. Andrew McKenzie, M.A.(1988).
Director of Studies: Rev. Paul Kelly, M.A., D.Phil. (1985).

In Residence
Rev. George Donaldson, Ph.L., S.T.L., Dip.R.E. (1961)

VISITING STAFF
Rev. David Boyd, `M.A. (1985)
Rev. Patrick Boylan, L.S.S. (1977)
Rev. Gerad J. Conroy, Ph.B., S.T.B., L.S.S. (1982).
Rev. John A. Hughes, Ph.B., S.T.L., Sc.P., M.A., Dip.Ed. (1984).
Dr. Elizabeth M. Kearney, M.A., LL.B., B.D., Ph.D.
Rev. John Keenan, LL.B., S.T.B., Ph.L. (1995).
Rev. William McFadden, Ph.B., S.T.L., M.S. (1985)
Dr. Mary McHugh, B.A., M.Litt., Ph.D., F.S.A.Scot., LL.B.
Rev. Michael McMahon, Ph.B., S.T.B., L.S.S. (1985)
Rev. Paul G. Milarvie, Ph.B., S.T.L. (1993)
Sr. Catherine Mulligan, S.N.D., M.A., M.Ed., Dip.Ed.Psych., M.A.C.P.
Ms. Linda O'Kane, B.S., D.C.E., Post. Dip. Couns.Sup.
Rev. Dominic Quinn, Ph.B., S.T.L. (1988).
Prof. Patrick Reilly, M.A., B.Litt.
Rev. Joseph Sullivan, Ph.B., S.T.L.(1985).

Rev. Gerard Tartaglia, Ph.B., S.T.B., J.C.L. (1985)
Ms. Margaret Tomlinson, B.A., L.R.A.M., L.G.S.M., F.E.S.B.
Rev. John Tormey, Ph.L., S.T.L. (1981)
Prof. Peter Walsh, K.C.S.G., M.A., Ph.D., F.R.S.E., D.Litt.

ADMINISTRATORS
Sr. Patricia Cusick, O.L.S.
Mr. James D. McKean, M.A., LL.B.
Sr. Julia Mclaughlin, S.N.D.

PERSONNEL
Miss Sue Jardine

Total number of Seminarians	21
Archdiocese of St. Andrews and Edinburgh	2
Diocese of Aberdeen	3
Diocese of Dunkeld	7
Archdiocese of Glasgow	1
Diocese of Motherwell	4
Diocese of Paisley	4

COLLEGIUM URBANUM DE PROPAGANDA FIDE.—Scots students are to be found in the register of Propaganda College during the seventeenth and eighteenth centuries. In the year 1772 the Cardinal de Bernis founded two bursaries for the Scottish Mission and since then Scots students have regularly been allocated places in this college. There are no Scots students in Propaganda College this year.

FRANCE.—In lieu of the ancient Scots Colleges in Paris (founded 1325) and Douai (founded 1576) suppressed during the French Revolution, the French Government provides bursaries for Scottish Ecclesiastical Students in French Seminaries. There are no Scots ordinands in France this year.

B—Education for Teaching Qualifications

ST. ANDREW'S CAMPUS, UNIVERSITY OF GLASGOW; Address: St. Andrew's Campus, University of Glasgow, Duntocher Road, Bearsden, GLASGOW G61 4QA. ☎ 0141-943 1424

BISHOPRIC OF THE FORCES
Bishop in Ordinary to H.M. Forces
Right Rev. Francis Joseph Walmsley, C.B.E.

Residence: Bishop's Oak, 26 The Crescent, Farnborough Park, Farnborough, Hants. GU14 7AS. ☎ 01252-373699.
Secretary: Rev. Deacon Peter Lattey. *Asst. Secretary:* Mrs. Freda Sheppard.
Financial Secretary: Mr. Matthew Murphy.

ADMINISTRATION
Office: 26 The Crescent, Farnborough, Hants. GU14 7AS.
☎ 01252-349004; Fax: 01252-349006.

VICARS GENERAL
Mgr. Tom Burns, S.M., Q.H.C., V.G., Principal RC Chaplain (RN)
MOD Chaplains (Naval), Room 281, Victory Building, HM Naval Base Portsmouth PO1 3LS. ☎ 01705-727903.
Mgr. Kevin Vasey, O.B.E., V.G., MOD Chaplains (Army), Trenchard Lines, Upavon, Pewsey, Wilts. SN9 6BE. ☎ 01980-615803.
Mgr. Thomas Devany,V.G., Principal RC Chaplain, Chaplaincy Services, HQ PTC, RAF Innsworth, Gloucester GL3 IEZ. ☎ 01452-712612, Ext. 5166.

ECCLESIASTICAL CONSULTANT
Right Rev. Mgr. Ralph Brown, J.C.D., Archbishop's House, Westminster, London SW1P 1QJ. ☎ 0171-828 3255.

CHANCERY
CHANCELLOR: Rev. Deacon Peter Lattey..
VICE CHANCELLOR: Rev. Phelim Roland.

RECORDS
CHAPLAIN i/c RC RECORDS: BFGB, AGPDO, Middle Hill, Aldershot, Hants. GU11 1PP. ☎ 01252-349007; Fax: 01252-349006.
NOTARY: Mrs. M. K. Day.

CHAPLAINS FROM SCOTTISH DIOCESES

Royal Navy:
    Rev Michael Sharkey (Glasgow).
    Rev. Andrew McFadden (Paisley).
Royal Air Force:
    Rev. Alan Wilson, S.T.B. (Galloway)
Royal Army Chaplains Dept:
    Rev. Matthew Despard (Motherwell).
    Rev. Donald Cumming (Glasgow).

DIRECTORY OF CHAPLAINS FOR SCOTLAND

ARBROATH, Angus.
Officiating Chaplain: 56 Dishlandtown Street, ARBROATH DD11 1QU.
(01241-873013).
Church: St. Thomas of Canterbury, Dishlandtown Street, Arbroath.

BENBECULA, Western Isles.
Officiating Chaplain: Griminish, ISLE OF BENBECULA HS7 5QA
(01870-602221)
Church: St. Mary, Benbecula.

COCHRANE—See Rosyth.

DUNBLANE, Stirling.
Officiating Chaplain: St. Clare, Claredon Place, DUNBLANE FK15 9HB
(01786-822146)
Church: School Chapel, QVS Dunblane.

EDINBURGH
Army Chaplain: Served from Catterick (01748-872309).
Church: St. Mark's, Oxgangs Avenue, Edinburgh.

FASLANE, West Dunbartonshire.
R.N. Chaplain: H.M.S. Neptune, Faslane, HELENSBURGH G84 8HL
(01436-674321, Ext. 6216)
Church: St. Peter, H.M.S. Neptune, Faslane.

GLENCORSE, Midlothian
Officiating Chaplain: 56 John Street, PENICUIK EH26 8HL
(01968-673709)
Church: Sacred Heart, John Street, Penicuik.

INVERNESS, Highland.
Officiating Chaplain: St. Columba's, 1 Walker Crescent, Culloden,
INVERNESS IV1 2LZ. (01463-791957).

KINLOSS, Moray. R.A.F. Chaplain St. Mary's, R.A.F. Kinloss, FORRES
IV36 0UH
☎ Forres (01309) 672161, Ext. 7537.
Church: St. Mary, R.A.F. Kinloss.

LEUCHARS, Fife.
Officiating Chaplain St. Fillan's, 20 King Street, NEWPORT-ON-TAY DD6
8BN (01382-542324).
Church: St. Michael, R.A.F. Leuchars.

LOSSIEMOUTH, Moray.
R.A.F. Chaplain: Served from Kinloss. Church: Our Lady, R.A.F.
Lossiemouth.

NEPTUNE, See Garelochhead (page 310.)

PITREAVIE, Fife.
H.O.C., St. John & St. Columba's, 137 Admiralty Road Rosyth, DUNFERMLINE KY11 2QL (01383-412084).
Church: SS. Peter & Paul, H.M.S. Caledonia, Rosyth.

PRESTWICK, South Ayrshire.
Officiating Chaplain: St. Ann's Church, Annbank Road, Mossblown, AYR KA6 5DZ. ☎ 01292-520204.
Church: St. Quivox, St. Quivox Road, Prestwick.

ROSYTH, Fife.
RN Chaplain. H.O.C., St. John & St. Columba, 137 Admiralty Road, Rosyth, DUNFERMLINE KY11 2QL. (01383-412084).
Church: SS. Peter & Paul, H.M.S. Caledonia, Rosyth.

TAIN, Easter Ross, Highland
Officiating Chaplain: St. Vincent, Cameron Road, TAIN   V19 1NN (01862-892592).
Church: St. Vincent, Cameron Road, Tain.

PERSONAL PRELATURE
OF THE HOLY CROSS AND OPUS DEI

Personal Prelatures are juridical structures of a secular character governed by a Prelate and erected by the Holy See to carry out specific pastoral or missionary activities. The general norms on personal Prelatures are contained in the Code of Canon Law—canons 294 to 297. Each has its own statutes approved by the Holy See. Opus Dei is a personal Prelature, international in its scope, which aims to spread throughout all sectors of society a deep awareness of the universal call to sanctity and apostolate in the fulfilment of one's ordinary profession or job. It is formed by a Prelate with his own clergy and by lay people, men and women, who in virtue of
a divine vocation freely join the Prelature.

REGIONAL VICAR FOR GREAT BRITAIN

MGR. NICHOLAS MORRISH, M.A., S.T.D.,
6 Orme Court, LONDON W2 4RL. ☎ 0171-229 7574.
E-Mail:london@opus dei.org

CLERGY WORKING IN SCOTLAND

Rev. Gonzalo Gonzalez, LL.D., D.C.L. (1955)
Rev. Stefan Hnylycia, B.Sc., P.G.C.E. (1986)

Postal address: Dunreath, 231 Nithsdale Road, GLASGOW G41 5HA. ☎ 0141-427 3236; Fax: 0141-427 7547.
Glenalvon (a cultural centre for women whose pastoral care is entrusted to the Opus Dei Prelature), 5 Kirklee Gardens, GLASGOW G12 0SG. ☎/Fax: 0141-339 32

APOSTOLIC EXARCHATE FOR UKRAINIANS IN GREAT BRITAIN

Apostolic Exarch
Right Rev. Michael Kuchmiak, C.Ss.R., D.D.
Titular Bishop of Agathopolis
Address: 22 Binney Street, LONDON W1Y 1YN.
☎ 0171-629 1073

THE CURIA

22 Binney Street, LONDON W1Y 1YN. ☎ 0171-629 1073.
VICAR GENERAL: Very Rev. Bokdan B. Lysykanych, Ph.D., D.Litt.
FINANCIAL SECRETARY: Rev. Stephan Oracz, S.T.D.

EDINBURGH: Our Lady of Pochaev and St. Andrew's Ukrainian Catholic Church, Dalmeny Street (1947, 1965). Rev. Lubomyr Pidluskyj, 6 Mansion House Road, EDINBURGH EH9 1TZ. ☎ 0131-553 7595, 0131-667 5993. Sunday Liturgy of St. John Chrysostom: Saturday, 6 p.m.; 11 a.m. (*sung*). Holy Days of Obligation, Sung Liturgy of St. John Chrysostom, 7.30 p.m. Confessions: Saturdays, 5.30 to 6.30 p.m.; Sundays, 9.30 to 10.30 a.m.

Served from Edinburgh:

ANNAN. St. Columba's Church, Market Street: 3rd Sunday of the month, Liturgy, 7 p.m.

CARLISLE, Ukrainian House, Silloth Street: 1st Sunday of the month, Liturgy, 7 p.m.

DUNDEE, Cathedral: 4th Sunday of the month, Liturgy, 4 p.m.

FALKIRK, St. Martha's Convent, 25 Wellside Place: 2nd Sunday of the month, Liturgy, 3 p.m.

GALASHIELS, St. Andrew's Church, Market Street: 3rd Sunday of the month, Liturgy, 3 p.m.

GLASGOW, Convent of Mercy, Hill Street, Garnethill: 2nd Sunday of the month, Liturgy, 6 p.m.

LOCKERBIE, Ukrainian Chapel, Halmuir Hostel: 1st Sunday of the month, Liturgy, 4 p.m.

NEWCASTLE UPON TYNE, St. Dominic's Church, New Bridge Street, 5th Sunday of the month, Liturgy, 5 p.m.

(On 1st January, 1968, the Chaplaincy for Ukrainian Catholics in Scotland and the North of England became a part of the Ukrainian Exarchate for Great Britain. The estimated Ukrainian population in the South of Scotland and the North of England is 700.)

THE CLERGY OF SCOTLAND

ALPHABETICAL LIST AND ADDRESSES

ARCHBISHOPS AND BISHOPS

CONTI, Right Rev. MARIO JOSEPH, Bishop of Aberdeen; Bishop's House, 3 Queen's Cross, ABERDEEN AB15 4XU. ☎ 01224-319154.

DEVINE, Right Rev. JOSEPH, Bishop of Motherwell; 22 Wellhall Road, HAMILTON ML3 9BG. ☎ 01698-423058.☎ 01698-263715.

LOGAN, Right Rev. VINCENT, Bishop of Dunkeld; Bishop's House, 29 Roseangle, DUNDEE DD1 4LX. ☎ 0182-224327.

McGILL, Right Rev. STEPHEN, P.S.S., Bishop Emeritus of Paisley; 13 Newark Street, GREENOCK PA16 7UH. ☎ 01475-783696.

MONE, Right Rev. JOHN ALOYSIUS, Bishop of Paisley; 107 Corsebar Road, PAISLEY PA2 9PY. ☎ 0141-889 7200.

MURRAY, Right Rev. IAN, Bishop of Argyll and The Isles, Bishop's House,
Esplanade, OBAN PA34 5AB. ☎ 01631-571 395.

O'BRIEN, Most Rev. KEITH PATRICK, Archbishop of St. Andrews and Edinburgh; St. Bennet's, 42 Greenhill Gardens, EDINBURGH EH10 4BJ.
☎ 0131-447 3337.

TAYLOR, Right Rev. MAURICE, Bishop of Galloway; Candida Casa, 8 Corsehill Road, AYR KA7 2ST. ☎ 01292-266750.

WINNING, His Eminence Cardinal THOMAS JOSEPH, Archbishop of Glasgow; 40 Newlands Road, GLASGOW G43 2JD

ABBOTS

DILWORTH, Right Rev. Dom GERARD MARK, O.S.B., M.A., Ph.D., F.R.Hist.Soc., F.S.A.Scot., Abbot Emeritus of Fort Augustus, Titular Abbot of Iona; St. Catherine's Convent of Mercy, 4 Lauriston Gardens, EDINBURGH EH3 9HH.

GILBERT, Right Rev. Dom HUGH, O.S.B., B.A., Abbot of Pluscarden; Pluscarden Abbey, ELGIN IV30 8UA. ☎ 01343-890257.

McGLYNN, Right Rev. Dom DONALD, O.C.R., Abbot of Nunraw; Sancta Maria Abbey, Nunraw, HADDINGTON EH41 4LW. ☎ 01620-830223.

SPENCER Right Rev. Dom ALFRED, O.S.B., Abbot Emeritus of Pluscarden; Pluscarden Abbey, ELGIN IV30 8UA.

PRIESTS, SECULAR AND REGULAR

Names marked with one asterisk are customarily addressed as
Very Reverend.
Names marked with two asterisks are customarily addressed as
Right Reverend.

Addison, Paul M., O.S.M.; St. Vincent de Paul's, Kingsway East, DUNDEE DD4 8AA. ☎ 01382-500446.

Agnew, John; St. John's, 115 Main Street, Fauldhouse, BATHGATE EH47 9BJ. ☎ 01501-770225.

Alexander, Joseph G.; St. Margaret's, 49 Graham Street, JOHNSTONE PA5 8RA.☎01505-320198.

Allen, John M.; St.Anne's, 2 Sweyn Road, THURSO KW14 7NW. ☎ 01847-893196.

Allison, Henry; St. Anthony's, Mar Gardens, Springhall, Rutherglen, GLASGOW G73 5JE.☎0141-634 4909.

*Anderson, William R. T. Canon, M.A., F.T.C.L. Cathedral Clergy House, 20 Huntly Street, ABERDEEN AB10 1SH. ☎01224-640160.

Angelosanto, Aldo, S.T.L.; St. Pius X, Balerno Street, Douglas, DUNDEE DD4 8NP.☎01382-778449.

*Anthony, William Canon (*S. Andrews; Retired*); 3 Craigs Terrace, Rumford, FALKIRK FK2 0SD. ☎01324-717058.

*Armstrong, Raymond, C.M., M.A.; St. Mark's, 80 St. Mark Street, GLASGOW G32 7EA. ☎0141-778 1011.

*Ashe, James J. Canon; St. Bernadette's, 200 Logans Road, MOTHERWELL ML1 3PH. ☎01698-263945.

Asare, Gabriel O., M.A. (*Kumasi, Ghana*); St. Joseph's, 2 Tanfield Walk, ABERDEEN AB24 4AQ. ☎01224-484226.

Austin, Joseph Gyim-; St. Joseph's, 2 Tanfield Walk, ABERDEEN AB24 4AQ.☎01224-484226.

Axe, Anthony, O.P., B.A., M.A.; St. Albert's, 25 George Square, EDINBURGH EH8 9LD. ☎0131-650 0900.

Bacon, Gerard M.; St. Laurence's, 215 Kinfauns Drive, GLASGOW G15 7UD. ☎0141-944 2063.

Bagan, Michael, St. Margaret of Scotland, Drip Road, STIRLING FK9 4UA. ☎01786-474883.

Bailey, Bede, O.P.; St. Albert's, 25 George Square, EDINBURGH EH8 9LD. ☎0131-650 0900.

Baillie, Stephen; ; St. John's, Aurs Road, Barrhead, GLASGOW G78 2RW. ☎ 0141-876 1553.

Balmer, Francis; St. Barnabas',140 Wellshot Road, GLASGOW G32 7BH. ☎0141-778 2861.

Balmer, Joseph G., B.D.; Cathedral Precincts, Incle Street, PAISLEY PA1 1HR. ☎0141-889 2404.

Bancewicz, Anthony; Holy Cross, 113 Dixon Avenue, GLASGOW G42 8ER. ☎0141-423 0105.

Banyard, Peter Granger-, S.J.; St. Aloysius', 10 Woodside Place, GLASGOW G3 7QF. ☎0141-332 3659.

Barclay, Charles; St. John the Baptist's, 37 St. Ninian's Road, EDINBURGH EH12 8AL. ☎0131-334 1693.

Barnes, Gerard F.; St. Anne's, 21 Whitevale Street, GLASGOW G31 1QW. ☎ 0141-554 0285.

Barnett, Francis, S.J.; St. Mary's, 7 Academy Street, NAIRN IV12 4RJ. ☎01667-453323/01309-672306.

Barr, David M.; St. Margaret's, 4 Viewfield Terrace, DUNFERMLINE KY12 7HZ. ☎01383-625611.

Barry, James, M.Afr.; St. Joseph's, 9 Milrig Road, Rutherglen, GLASGOW G73 2NG. ☎0141–647 3806.

**Barry, Mgr. John C., D.C L., M.A.; Our Lady, Star of the Sea, 9 Law Road, NORTH BERWICK EH39 4PN. ☎01620-892195.

Barry, Peter R., B.A., Cert.Ed.; St. Columba's, 12 Culloden Court, Culloden, INVERNESS IV2 7DX. ☎01463-791957.

Barry, Raymond, C.S.Sp.; Holy Ghost Fathers 117 Newarthill Road, Carfin, MOTHERWELL ML1 5AL. ☎ 0198-290831/297054.

*Barry, Thomas Canon (*Motherwell, Retired*); St. Joseph's, 19 Cumnock Road, Robroyston, GLASGOW G33 1QT. ☎0141-558 5114.

Barry, Thomas Noel(*Glasgow, on leave of absence*); c/o Diocesan Office, 196 Clyde Street, GLASGOW G1 4JY

Batchelor, Kenneth S.(*S.Andr, Retired*); Flat 32, 18 Lauder Road, EDINBURGH EH9 2EL. ☎0131-667 9265.

Bath, Jeremy C., M.C.I.B.S., S.T.B.; St. Martin's, High Street, TRANENT EH33 1HJ. ☎ 01875-610232.

Beary, Benedict, O.S.A.; St. Joseph's, 20A Broomhouse Place North, EDINBURGH EH11 3UE. ☎0131-443 3777.

Beattie, Felix, M.A., S.T.L. (*Glasg., Retired*); Nazareth House, 1647 Paisley Road West, GLASGOW G52 3QT.

**Beattie, Mgr. Hugh, M.B.E. (*Motherwell*); 102A Kilnside, Finchamstead, Berkshire RG11 3PH.

Bell, Michael (*S. Andr.*); P.O. Box 717, Cayucos, California 93430, U.S.A.

*Benetti, Antonio, M.C.C.J.; Comboni Missionaries, 138 Carmyle Avenue, GLASGOW G32 8DL. ☎0141-641 4399.

*Bennett, John Canon; St. Albert's, 180 Albert Drive, GLASGOW G41 2NH. ☎0141-429 5287

Berry, Desmond J; St. Bernadette's, Park Drive, ERSKINE PA8 7AE. ☎0141-812 7018.

Birrell, Martin, O.S.B., M.A.; Pluscarden Abbey, ELGIN IV30 8UA.

Bogan, Gerard; St. Ninians', 34 St. Ninian's Road, Hillhouse, HAMILTON ML3 9TS. ☎01698-823638.

Boland, Joseph; St. Matthew's, Grassyards Road, New Farm Loch, KILMARNOCK KA3 7SH. ☎01563-533587.

Boles, John (*Glasg. Retired*); "Woodville' 18 Greenhead Road, DUMBARTON G82 1EL

Bollan, John, Ph.B., S.T.L.; St. Margaret's, 49 Graham Street, JOHNSTONE PA5 8RA. ☎ 01505-320198.

Bonnici,, Keith Paul, O.S.B.; St. Peter & St. Benedict, The Lodge, Glen Doe Road, FORT AUGUSTUS PH32 4BG. ☎01320-366451.

Borland, David M., B.D.; St. Michael's, Treeswoodhead Road, Bellfield, KILMARNOCK KA1 4NX. ☎01563-525993.

*Botter, Constant, S.C.J.; Smithstone House, Dalry Road, KILWINNING KA13 6PL. ☎01294-552515.

Boyce, John, M.A., B.D.; Sacred Hearts, 17 Harbour Street, GIRVAN KA26 9AJ. ☎ 01465-713331.

Boyd, Daniel, L.C.L.; St. Joseph's, 30 Broomhill Road, BONNYBRIDGE FK4 2AN. ☎01324-812417.

Boyd, David, M.A.; St. John the Baptist's, 23 Shore Street, PORT GLASGOW PA14 5HD. ☎ 01475-741139.

*Boyd, George Canon; St. Brendan's, 51 Barons Road, MOTHERWELL ML1 2NB. ☎01698-264448.

**Boyd, Mgr. Joseph V. Canon, V.G.; St. Paul's; 2 Peggieshill Place, Belmont, AYR KA7 3RF. ☎01292-260197.

Boyd, Patrick, M.Afr.; St. Joseph's, 9 Milrig Road, Rutherglen, GLASGOW G73 2NG. ☎0141-647 3806.

Boyd, William; St. Mary's, West Road, IRVINE KA12 8RE. ☎ 01294-279130/272852.

Boylan, Patrick, L.S.S.; St. Margaret's, 16 Clerk Street, LOANHEAD EH20 9DR. ☎0131-440 0412.

*Boyle, Daniel J . Canon, M.A. (*S. Andr., Retired*); 12 Green Road, KINROSS KY13 7TP. ☎01577-862608.

**Boyle, Mgr. Hugh N. Canon, S.T.L., F.S.A.Scot.; The Lindens, Bon Secours Hospital, 36 Mansionhouse Road, GLASGOW G41 3DW. ☎0141-649 9226.

Boyle, Ivan R., B.Sc., M.A., B.D.; St. Anne's, Jack Street, HAMILTON ML3 7QP. ☎01698-423044.

Boyle, James (*Motherwell*), St. Paul's, 16 Birdston Road, Milton of Campsie, GLASGOW G66 8BU. ☎01360-310355.

Boyle, Joseph; St. Philip's, 150 Drumlochy Road, GLASGOW G33 3RF. ☎0141-774 5688.

Boyle, Patrick J., B.D.; St. Flannan's, 79 Hillhead Road, Kirkintilloch GLASGOW G66 2HY. ☎0141-776 2310.

Boyle, Thomas H. *(Paisley)*; Scotus College, 2 Chesters Road, Bearsden GLASGOW G61 4AG. ☎ 0141-942 8384.

Boyle, Victor T., Ph.B., S.T.L. *(Paisley)*; Pontificio Collegio Scozzese, Via Cassia 481, 00189 Roma, Italy. ☎ + 39 6 366 68027.

Bradburn, George C., S.T.L.; St. Michael's, 7 Cardross Road, DUMBARTON G82 4JE. ☎01389-762709.

Bradley, Francis *(Paisley, Retired)*, Dargle Valley Nursing Home, Cookstown Enniskerry, Co. Wicklow, Ireland.

*Bradley, Mgr. Hugh, B.A., Ph.B., S.T.B., L.H.E...; St. Matthew's, 2 South Crosshill Road, Bishopbriggs, GLASGOW G64 2LZ. ☎ 0141-772 1619.

Bradley, Robert, S.T.D. *(Glasgow, Retired)*; Our Lady and St. George's, 50 Sandwood Road, GLASGOW G52 2QE. ☎0141-882 4868.

*Brady, Luke Canon *(Paisley, Retired)*; 234 Moyville, Rathfarnham, Dublin 16, Ireland.

Brady, Thomas; St. Joseph's, Mayberry Place, Blantyre, GLASGOW G72 9DA. ☎ 01698-823896/320055.

Brannan, Christopher, LL.B.; St. Francis', 231 Deeside Gardens, ABERDEEN AB15 7PS.. ☎01224-315893.

*Brannan, John Canon *(Glasgow, Retired)*; Nazareth House, 1647 Paisley Road West, GLASGOW G52 3QT.

Brannan, Patrick; St. Aidan's, Tower Road, JOHNSTONE PA5 0AD. ☎01505-320900.

Brannigan, Joseph; St. Brigid's, 5.Westwood Road, Newmains, WISHAW ML2 9DA. ☎ 01698-297037.

Brassill, Laurence, O.S.A.; St. Joseph's, 20A Broomhouse Place North, EDINBURGH EH11 3UE . ☎ 0131 443 3777.

*Bremner, Alexander Canon, L.C.L.; Holy Spirit, 1 McGrigor Road, St. Ninian's, STIRLING FK7 9BL. ☎ 01786-474277.

*Brennan, Gerard Canon; Cathedral House, Cathedral Precincts, Incle Street, PAISLEY PA1 1HR. ☎0141-889 2404.

**Brennan, Mgr. James K. *(S.Andews., Retired)*; Kilcready, Mullinavat, Waterford, Ireland.

Brennan, William G.; Catholic Church, 1A Milton Place, Pittenweem, ANSTRUTHER KY10 2LR. ☎01333-311262.

Breslin, John F., Ph.L., S.T.L.; St. Bride's, 21 Greenlees Road, Cambuslang, GLASGOW G72 8JB. ☎ 0141-641 3053.

Breslin, Raymond J., Ph.B. S.T.L. *(Motherwell)*; Pontificio Collegio Scozzese, Via Cassia 481, 00189 Roma, Italy. ☎ + 39 06 3366 8085.

Briody, Michael, St. Michael's, Glenmanor Avenue, Moodiesburn, GLASGOW G69 0DL. ☎ 01236-872537.

Broderick, John D. *(Glasgow, Retired)*; Nazareth House, 1647 Paisley Road West, GLASGOW G52 3QT.

Brook, Peter, S.J.; Flat 3, 56 Bentinck Street, GLASGOW G3 7TT.

Brooks, Paul T., Ph.B., S.T.L.;Holy Family and St Ninian's, 20 Union Street, Kirkintilloch, GLASGOW G66 1DH. ☎ 0141-776 1063.

Brosnan, Timothy; St. Gerard's, Fleming Road, BELLSHILL ML4 1NF. ☎ 01698-843734.

Brown, Archibald, S.T.B., B.A.; Our Lady and St. Meddan's, 4 Cessnock Road, TROON KA10 6NJ. ☎ 01292-313541.

Brown, David; St. Ninian's, 5 Baldwin Avenue, GLASGOW G13 2EE. ☎ 0141-959 1308.

Brown, George, O.F.M., M.A.; St Teresa's, 120 Niddrie Mains Road, Craigmillar, EDINBURGH EH16 4EG. ☎ 0131-661 2185.

Brown, Gordon R., M.A., Ph.L. *(S.Andrews, Retired)*; 77A Falcon Avenue, EDINBURGH EH10 4AN. ☎ 0131-447 0545.

Brown, Michael; St. Bride's Church, Whitemoss Avenue, East Kilbride, GLASGOW G74 1NN. ☎ 01355-220005.

Buchanan, Alexander D., Dip.Theol.; Holy Family, 2 Parkhill Avenue, PORT GLASGOW PA14 6BT. ☎ 01475-705585.

Burholt, Symeon, O.S.B., B.A., S.T.B. *(Monk of Pluscarden)*; St.Mary's Monastery, P.O. Box 345, Petersham, Mass. 01366, U.S.A.

Burke, Joseph, B.A., Ph.B., S.T.B.,J.C.L.; St. Charles', 5 Union Street, PAISLEY PA2 6DU. ☎ 0141-889 2614.

Burke, Joseph Noel, S.T.B.; St. Agnes', 694 Balmore Road, GLASGOW G22 6QS. ☎ 0141-336 8175.

Burke, Patrick J., M.Th., S.T.D.; Catholic Presbytery, 52 Quakerfield, Bannockburn, Stirling FK7 8HZ. ☎/Fax: 01786-812249; *(University Chaplaincy)* ☎ 01786-467164.

**Burns, Mgr. Charles, O.B.E.,D.H.E., P.A.Dip., F.S.A., F.,S.A.Scot. *(Paisley)*; Palazzo Doria, Via del Plebiscito 107, 00186 Roma, Italy.

Burns, James A.*(Glasgw, Retired)*; St. Stephen's, 12 Park Road, Dalmuir, CLYDEBANK G81 3LD. ☎ 0141-952 1461.

**Burns, Mgr. John J., Ph.L., S.T.L., V.G.; St. Bride's, Fallside Road, Bothwell, GLASGOW G71 8BA.☎ 01698-852710.

Burns, John J. N.; St. Paul's, 1653 Shettleston Road, GLASGOW G32 9AR. ☎ 0141-778 1014.

Burns, Michael, M.A.; *(S.Andrews, on Further Studies);* St. Mary of the Assumption Rectory, 5 Linden Place, Brookline, Mass. 02146, U.S.A..

Byers, James A.; St. Laurence's, 6 Kilmacolm Road, GREENOCK PA15 4XP. ☎ 01475-720260.

*Byrne, Brian P.Canon; Sacred Heart and St. Anthony's, 2A Wotherspoon Crescent, Armadale, BATHGATE EH48 2JD. ☎ 01505-730261.

Byrne, Vincent J., B.Sc.; St. Andrew's, Auchmead Road, Larkfield, GREENOCK PA16 0JU. ☎ 01475-631750.

Caira, Mark, O.C.R.; Sancta Maria Abbey, Nunraw, HADDINGTON EH41 4LW

Cairns, Joseph; St. Bernadette's, 361 Carntyne Road, GLASGOW G32 6JL. ☎ 0141-778 3060.

Callaghan, John (S. *Andrews, Retired)*; 23A Calder Court, Braehead, STIRLING FK7 7QU. ☎ 01786-465731.

Callaghan, Maurice, Ph.B., S.T.B.;St. Fergus', 35 Blackstoun Road, PAISLEY PA3 1LU. ☎ 0141-889 5056.

Cameron, Allan P.; St. Martin's, 201 Ardencraig Road, GLASGOW G45 0JJ. ☎ 0141-634 2262

Cameron, Edward D.; St. Columba's, Campsie Drive, RENFREW PA4 0RB. ☎ 0141-886 2570.

Campbell, Donald Ewen, S.T.B.; St. Mary's, Bornish, LOCHBOISDALE HS8 5SA. ☎ 01878-710350.

Campbell, G. Stuart, S.T.B.; St. Columba's, 40 Scott's Street, ANNAN DG12 6JG. ☎ 01461-202776.

Campbell, John G.; St. Paul's, 1653 Shettleston Road, GLASGOW G32 9AR. ☎ 0141-778 1014.

Campbell, Kenneth J., St. Monica's, Sharp Avenue, Old Monkland, COATBRIDGE ML5 5RP. ☎ 01236-421750.

Campbell, Michael K., Ph.B., S.T.L.*(Motherwell)*; c/o Diocesan Centre, Coursington Road, MOTHERWELL ML1 1PP. *Tel.;* 01698-269114.

*Canning, Bernard J. Canon, F.S.A.Scot..; St. Thomas', 70 Main Street, Neilston, GLASGOW G78 3NJ. ☎ 0141-881 1478.

Cannon, P. Aidan; St. Agatha's, 160 Methil Brae, Methil, Leven KY8 3LU. ☎ 01333-423803.

Capaldi, Isaias Gerard, S.J.; Sacred Heart, 28 Lauriston Street, EDINBURGH EH3 9DJ. ☎ 0131-229 9104.

Capaldi, Paul; St. Margaret's, Hope View, Loch Road, SOUTH QUEENSFERRY EH30 9LS. ☎ 0131-331 1007.

Carey, Michael; Shrub Cottage, Station Road, Oakley, DUNFERMLINE KY12 9NW. ☎ 01383-850335.

*Carey, Noel Provost; Cathedral House, 31 Coursington Road, MOTHERWELL ML1 1PP. ☎ 01698-263045.

Carey, Terence, O.C.D.; Mount Carmel, 61 Hamilton Avenue, GLASGOW G41 4HA. ☎ 0141-427 0794.

*Carlin, Mgr. Denis E., Ph.B., S.T.L., M.A., J.C.L. *(Paisley);* Real Colegio de Escoseses, Avda. de Champagnat 121-133, 37007 Salamanca, Spain. ☎ (00 34) 923 25 40 11.

Carroll, Andrew; St. Mary's, 14 Patrick Street, GREENOCK PA16 8NA. ☎ 01475-721084.

Carroll, Jeremiah *(Glasgow, Retired);* 7 Lartigue Place, Ballybunion, Co. Kerry, Ireland.

Carroll John J., S.T.B.; St. Joseph's, 14 Fullarton Avenue, GLASGOW G32 8NA. ☎ 011-778 1054.

Casey, John; St. Lucy's, 9 Pine Crescent, Abronhill, Cumbernauld, GLASGOW G67 3BB. ☎ 01236-724894.

Cassidy, Eustace, C.P .;18 Wiltonburn Road, GLASGOW G53 7JF. ☎ 0141-876 1230.

Cassidy, Mark J., Ph.B., S.T.L.; St. Anne's, 100 Dundee Street, CARNOUSTIE DD7 7PH. ☎ 01241-853386.

*Cassidy, Michael J. Canon; St. Margaret Mary's, 87 Boswall Parkway, EDINBURGH EH5 2JQ. ☎ 0131-552 4782.

Cavanagh, Charles, M.A.; St. Mary's, 163 George Street, PAISLEY PA1 2UN. ☎ 0141-889 2602.

Centra, Carlo; St. Gregory's, 136 Kelvindale Road, GLASGOW G20 8DP. ☎ 0141-946 3009.

Chalmers, John, D.C.L.; St. Simon's, 33 Partick Bridge Street, GLASGOW G11 6PQ. ☎ 0141-339 7618.

Chalmers, Stuart P., Ph.B., S.T.L.; St. Mary's, Bridgefield, STONEHAVEN AB39 2JE. ☎ 01569-762433.

Chambers, Allan T.; St. Mary's, 4 West End, WEST CALDER EH55 8EF. ☎ 01506-871240.

Chambers, Martin, S.T.B.: St. John's, Hayocks Road, STEVENSTON KA20 4DE. ☎ 01294-463225.

Chambers, Thomas J., B.A.; Our Lady of Good Counsel, 6 Broompark Circus, GLASGOW G31 2JE ☎ 0141-554 1558.

Christie, James, S.J., Flat 3, 56 Bentinck Street, GLASGOW G3 7TT

Chromy, Gerard; St. Patrick's, 71 Shieldmuir Street, WISHAW ML2 7TH. ☎ 01698-351921.

Clancy, Daniel *(Glasgow, Retired)* Coolydoody, Ballyduff, Co. Waterford, Ireland.

**Clancy, Mgr. James T. Canon, S.T.B., Ph.L., V.G.; St. Andrew's Cathedral House, 90 Dunlop Street, GLASGOW G1 4ER. ☎ 0141-221 3096.

Clancy, Reginald, O.F.M., B.A.(Hons.); St. Teresa's, 120 Niddrie Mains Road, Craigmillar, EDINBURGH EH16 4EG. ☎ 0131-661 2185.

Clarke, Patrick; St. Marie's, 101 Dunnikier Road, KIRKCALDY KY2 5AP. ☎ 01592-592111.

Clarke, William E.; St. Andrew's Cathedral House, 90 Dunlop Street, GLASGOW G1 4ER. ☎ 0141-221 3096.

Clements, Joseph; St. Aidan's, 298 Coltness Road, WISHAW ML2 7EX. ☎ 01698-384730.

Clinton, Peter *(Glasgow, Retired)* Roadside Cottage, Auchenstarry, Kilsyth, GLASGOW G65 0DF. ☎ 01236-821946.

**Coakley, Mgr. Matthew Canon; St. James', 20 Beltrees Road, GLASGOW G53 5TE. ☎ 0141-882 4927.

Cochrane, Stephen J.,B.Sc., M.A., B.D.; St. Paul's; 2 Peggieshill Place, Belmont, AYR KA7 3RF. ☎01292-260197.

*Coia, Romeo Canon, M.A., B.A. *(Glasgow.);* St. Bride's, 9 Muirnwood Place, Monifieth, DUNDEE DD5 4JL. ☎ 01382-534557.

Coleman, Andrew B., M.A., B.D.; St. Patrick's, 5 Orangefield Place, GREENOCK PA15 1YZ. ☎ 01475-720223.

Colford, Noel, Ph.L., S.T.L. *(Glasgow)*; Holy Cross, BRODICK KA27 8AJ. ☎ 01770-302030.

Collins, John A. *(Glasgow, Retired)*; The Presbytery, 1 George Street, MILLPORT KA28 0BG. ☎ 01475-530537.

*Conacher, Giles, O.S.B; Pluscarden Abbey, ELGIN IV30 8UA. ☎ *(Abbey)*: 01343-890257.

Connell, Bernard; Our Lady of Perpetual Succour, 17 Mitre Road, GLASGOW G11 7EF. ☎ 0141-339 1324.

**Connelly, Mgr. Thomas A.; St. Cadoc's, Rosebank Drive, Halfway, Cambuslang, GLASGOW G72 8TD. ☎ 0141-641 3669/2244.

Conniffe, Peter M., O.S.M.; St. Vincent de Paul's, 145 Kingsway East, DUNDEE DD4 8AA. ☎ 01382-500446505835.

Connolly, Felix *(Paisley, Retired)*; 15 Midtown, Dalry, CASTLE DOUGLAS DG7 3UT.

*Connolly, John Joseph Provost; St. Teresa's, 5 Graham Street, DUNDEE DD4 9AB. ☎ 01382-825133.

Connolly, Stephen;St. Andrew's, 29 Roman Road, Bearsden, GLASGOW G61 2SN. ☎ 0141-942 4635.

Conrad, Richard, O.P., M.A., Ph.D.; St. Albert's, 25 George Square, EDINBURGH EH8 9LD. ☎ 0131-650 0900.

Conroy, David A., M.A, M.M.S., I.M.S.Dip.; St. Ninian's Presbytery, Windsor Road, NEWTON STEWART DG8 6HR ☎ 01671-402182/ 01988-500396.

Conroy, Gerard J., Ph.B., S.T.B., L.S.S.;St. Stephen's, 12 Park Road, Dalmuir, CLYDEBANK G81 3LD. ☎ 0141-952 1461.

Conroy, Michael, B.A., M.Sc., M.Th., C.Psychol., Dip.Couns., A.F.B.Ps.S.; Our Lady and St. Helen's, 117 Achray Road, Condorrat, Cumbernauld, GLASGOW G67 4JG. ☎ 01236-731258.

Conroy, Paul M., Ph.L., S.T.L.;Our Lady and St. George's, 50 Sandwood Road, GLASGOW G52 2QE. ☎ 0141-882 4868.

*Conway, Robert Francis, O.F.M., C.Q.S.W;. St. Teresa's 120 Niddrie Mains Road, Craigmillar, EDINBURGH EH16 4EG. ☎ 0131-661 2185.

Conway, John; St. Flannan's, 79 Hillhead Road, Kirkintilloch, GLASGOW G66 2HY. ☎ 0141-776 2310.

**Conway, Mgr. Michael J. B.A., M.Sc.; St. Ignatius' 74 Young Street, WISHAW ML2 8HS. ☎ 01698-372058.

Conway, Thomas, M.Afr.; St. Joseph's, 9 Milrig Road, Rutherglen, GLASGOW G73 2NG. ☎ 0141-647 3806.

*Conway, Mgr. Thomas Kevin Canon *(Galloway, Retired)*; 3 Essex Park Cottages, Kellwood Place, Georgetown, DUMFRIES DG1 4JA. ☎ 01387-267039.

Conway, William, S.T.L., L.S.S.; St. Machan's, Chapel Street, Lennoxtown, GLASGOW G66 7DE. ☎ 01360-310276.

**Copland, Mgr. John E. Provost, V.G.; St. Thomas', Chapel Street, KEITH AB55 3AL. ☎ 01542-882352.

Copsey, Richard, O.Carm.: Elphinstone House, 7 High Street, Old Aberdeen, ABERDEEN AB24 3EE. ☎ 01224-482444.

Cosker, James; Christ the King, 220 Carmunnock Road, GLASGOW G44 5AR.☎ 0141-637 2882.

Courtney, Francis; Our Lady and St. Mark's, Ferry Loan, Bank Street, ALEXANDRIA G83 0UW. ☎ 01389-752091.

Coyle, Joseph, S.T.D.; St. Joseph's, Faifley, CLYDEBANK G81 5EZ. ☎ 01389-872236.

Coyle, Raymond, B.A.; The Presbytery, 3 Union Street, ELLON AB41 9BA. ☎ 01358-721485.

Crawford, William; Cathedral House, Cathedral Precincts, Incle Street, PAISLEY PA1 1HR. ☎0141-889 2404.

*Crean, Patrick Provost; St. Paul's, 118 Brediland Road, PAISLEY PA2 0HE. ☎ 01505-813103.

Creanor, John; Catholic Presbytery, Market Street, GALASHIELS TD1 1BY. ☎ 01896-752328.

Creaven, Fintan, S.J.; St. Aloysius', 10 Woodside Place, GLASGOW G3 7QF. ☎ 0141-332 3039.

Cree, James, S.M.M.; Montfort House, Darnley Road, Barrhead, GLASGOW G78 1TA. ☎ 0141-881 1440.

**Creegan, Mgr. Joseph, B.A., M.Ed., V.G.; Flat 5, The Old Rectory, 61 Main Street, Invergowrie, DUNDEE DD2 5BA. ☎ 01382-561067.

*Crowley, John Canon, Ph.L., S.T.L. *(Galloway, Retired)*; 68 Homemount House, Gogoside Road, LARGS KA30 9LS. ☎ 01475-686991.

Cudlipp, John C. B.D.; Cathedral House, 61 York Place, EDINBURGH EH1 3JD. ☎ 0131-556 1798/0027.

Culley, Alexander J.; Reul-na-Mara, Brandon Street, DUNOON PA23 8BU. ☎ 01369-702125.

Cumming, Donald J., Ph.B., S.T.L. *(Glasgow, Army Chaplain);* c/o MOD Chaplains (Army), Trenchard Lines, Pewsey, Wilts. SN9 6BE.

Cummins, Norbert, O.C.D.; Mount Carmel, 61 Hamilton Avenue, GLASGOW G41 4HA. ☎ 0141-427 0794.

*Cunney, John G. Canon; Christ the King Presbytery, Bowfield Road, Howwood, JOHNSTONE PA9 1BZ. ☎ 01505-702636.

Cunningham, James, Ph.L., S.T.D.; St. James', Inchinnan Road, RENFREW PA4 8NG. ☎ 0141-886 2022.

**Cunningham, Mgr. John, J.C.D., V.G.; St. Patrick's, 5 Orangefield Place, GREENOCK PA15 1YZ. ☎ 01475-720223.

*Cunningham, Thomas J. Canon, Ph.L., S.T.L.; St. Cadoc's, 24 Fruin Avenue, Newton Mearns, GLASGOW G77 6HA. ☎ 0141-639 1073.

Cunningham, Thomas S.*(Glasgow, Retired)*; St. Catherine's, 90 Lamont Road, GLASGOW G21 3PP. ☎ 0141-558 6723.

Curley, Robert; St. John the Baptist's, 136 Lower Millgate, Uddingston, GLASGOW G71 7AH. ☎ 01689-813156.

Currie, David *(Glasgow, Retired);* 19 Risk Street, DUMBARTON G82 1SE.

Currie, Patrick G.; Holy Cross, Croy, Kilsyth, GLASGOW G65 9JG. ☎ 01236-822148.

Cushley, Leo W., Ph.B., S.T.B., S.L.L., J.C.D. *(Motherwell.)*; Apostolic Nunciature in Burundi, c/o Ufficio Corrieri, Secretariat of State, 00120 Vatican City.

Dalrymple, Jock J., M.A., S.T.L.; St. Mary's Presbytery, 35 North Street, Leslie, GLENROTHES KY6 3DJ. ☎ 01592-741963.

D'Arcy, Aidan *(Motherwell, Retired)*; 2 Knightswood, Santry, Dublin 9, Ireland. ☎ (00353) 18428283.

Darroch, Francis F. *(Motherwell, Retired)*; St. Mary's, 120 Cadzow Street, HAMILTON ML3 6HX. ☎ 01698-423552.

Davie, Alex, B.D.; St. Philip's, 83 Kenilworth Rise, Dedridge, LIVINGSTON EH54 6JL. ☎ 01506-414453.

Day, Anthony *(Portsmouth)*;Cathedral House, Corran Esplanade, OBAN PA34 5AB. ☎ 01631-562123.

Debkowski, Anthony, S.A.C.; Garfield, 136 Comely Place, FALKIRK FK1 1QQ. ☎ 01324-621902.

Deegan, Maurus, O.S.B.; Pluscarden Abbey, ELGIN IV30 8UA.

Delany, John J. *(Motherwell, Retired);* 23 Blairbeth Road, Burnside, Rutherglen, GLASGOW G73 4JF. ☎ 0141-634 4029.

De La Torre, Oscar, S.X., M.Div.;St. Vincent de Paul's, 22 Main Street, Thornliebank, GLASGOW G46 7SH. ☎ 0141-638 0750.

Dempsey, Raymond, M.A.; St. Mary's, Hozier Street, Whifflet, COATBRIDGE ML5 4DB. ☎ 01236-423550.

Despard, Matthew F.; *(Motherwell, Army Chaplain)*; c/o MOD Chaplains (Army), Trenchard Lines, Upavon, Pewsey, Wilts SN9 6BE.

**Devanny, Mgr. Alexander, V.G; St. Mary's, 120 Cadzow Street, HAMILTON ML3 6HX. ☎ 01698-423552.

*Devine, Bernard V. Canon; St. Margaret Mary's, 99 Dougrie Road, Glasgow G45 9NT. ☎ 0141-634 6152.

Devine, Thomas G.; c/o Pastoral Centre, 50 Bonkle Road, Newmains, WISHAW ML2 9AP

Devlin, Gerard *(Motherwell)*; St. Mary's University College, Waldegrave Road, Twickenham, Middlesex TW1 4SX.

*Diamond, William Canon, M.A.; St. Margaret's, 49 Graham Street, JOHNSTONE PA5 8RA. ☎ 01505-320198.

*Docherty, Mgr. Henry, Ph.L., S.T.L., M.Litt.., F.S.A.Scot., *(Motherwell)*; General Secretariat, Bishops' Conference of Scotland, 64 Aitken Street, AIRDRIE ML6 6LT. ☎ 01236-764061.

Doherty, Daniel P.; St. Joseph's, East Toll, Cowdenbeath Road, BURNTISLAND KY3 0LJ. ☎ 01592-872207.

Doherty, James *(Glasgow, on Sick Leave)*; 6 Inverewe Avenue, GLASGOW G46 8TA

Doherty, John; St. Fillan's, 1b Main Street, Houston, JOHNSTONE PA6 7EL. ☎ 01505-612046.

Doherty, John *(Motherwell)*; Mariapolis Marilen, 30 Lacote Road, Greendale, Vic 3341, Australia.

Doherty, Joseph, C.Ss.R.; St. Mary's, Hatton Road, Kinnoull, PERTH PH2 7BP. ☎ 01738-624075.

*Doherty, Philip Canon; Our Lady and St. Bride's, 74 Stenhouse Street, COWDENBEATH KY4 9DD. ☎ 01383-510549.

**Donachie, Mgr. Benjamin Canon, M.A., Dip.Ed.; St. Thomas of Canterbury, 29 Dishlandtown Street, ARBROATH DD11 1QU. ☎ 01241-873013.

Donaldson, George, Ph.L., S.T.L., Dip.R.E. *(Motherwell);* Scotus College, 2 Chesters Road, Bearsden, GLASGOW G61 4AG. ☎ 0141-942 8384.

*Donnachie, Neil *(Glasgow)*; Scotus College, 2 Chesters Road, Bearsden, GLASGOW G61 4AG. ☎ 0141-942 8384.

Donnelly, Andrew, O.Carm.; St. Francis Xavier's, Taylor Avenue, Carfin, MOTHERWELL ML1 5AJ. ☎ 01698-263308.

Donnelly, Brian *(Motherwell)*; 2a Sandbank Terrace, Maryhill, GLASGOW G20 0PW. ☎ 0141-945 5305.

Donnelly, Gerald, M.A.; The Presbytery, 1 Sherwood Crescent, LOCKERBIE DG11 2DY. ☎ 01576-202563.

*Donnelly, John Canon *(Galloway, Retired)*; 41 Overmills Road, AYR KA7 3LH. ☎ 01292-285865.

Donnelly, Kevin, Dip.Theol.; St. Margaret's, 96 Hallcraig Street, AIRDRIE ML6 6AW. ☎ 01236-763370.

Donnelly, William B.; St. Andrew's, 29 Roman Road, Bearsden, GLASGOW G61 2SN. ☎ 0141-942 4635.

Donoghue Matthew, M.A. (S. *Andr., Retired)* 9 Fair-a-Far, EDINBURGH EH4 6QB. ☎ 0131-312 6531.

Doogan, Dominic, M.P.S.; St. Mahew's, 'Dunollie', Main Road, Cardross, DUMBARTON G82 5NY. ☎ 01389-841784.

Dooley, Peter, S.D.B.; St. Paul's, 4 Muirhouse Avenue, EDINBURGH EH4 4UB. ☎ 0131-332 3320.

Dornan, Charles C., B.Ed., S.T.B.; Sacred Heart, 106 Crossgates, BELLSHILL ML4 2LB. ☎ 01698-842709.

Dorward, Neil, M.A., B.D.; St. James', 5 High Street, KINROSS KY13 7AW. ☎ 01577-863329.

Douglas, Dominic S., Ph.B., S.T.L.; St. Joseph's Cardowan Road, STEPPS, Glasgow G33 6AA. ☎ 0141-779 2001.

Dow, Joseph; St. James', Inchinnan Road, RENFREW PA4 8NG. ☎ 0141-886 2022.

*Doyle, Alistair M. Canon, B.A., Dip.R.E.; St. Sylvester's, 19 Institution Road, ELGIN IV30 1QT. ☎ 01343-542280.

Doyle, Thomas W., B.D.; St. Cadoc's. Rosebank Drive, Halfway, Cambuslang, GLASGOW G72 8TD. ☎ 0141-641 3669.

Drysdale, Martin, Ph.L., S.T.L.; St. Fillan's, Ford Road, CRIEFF PH7 3HN. ☎ 01764-3269.

Duddy, James; Pastoral Centre, 50 Bonkle Road, Newmains, WISHAW ML2 9AP. ☎ 01698-385397.

Duffin, Charles,M.C.C.J.; Comboni Missionaries, 138 Carmyle Avenue, GLASGOW G32 8DL. ☎ 0141-641 4399.

Duffin, Neil; Our Holy Redeemer's, 6 Barclay Avenue, Elderslie, JOHNSTONE PA5 9DX. ☎ 01505-323104.

**Duffy, Mgr. Anthony L.; St. Cuthbert's, 104 Slateford Road, EDINBURGH EH14 1PT. ☎ 0131-443 1317 (in diocesan office hours: 452 8244).

**Duffy, Mgr. Francis Canon *(Galloway, Retired)*; Nazareth House, Hill Street, KILMARNOCK KA3 1HG. ☎ 01563-537872.

Duffy, Patrick, S.X.; St. Vincent de Paul's, 22 Main Street, Thornliebank, GLASGOW G46 7SH. ☎ 0141-638 0750.

Dugdale, John, S.C.J.; St. John Ogilvie's, Village Centre, Bourtreehill, IRVINE KA11 1JX. ☎ 01294-212587.

Duggan, James, Ph.B., S.T.L.; St. Conval's, Green Farm Road, Linwood, PAISLEY PA3 3HB. ☎ 01505-323751.

Dunn, Gerard, M.B.; St. Columban's, 31 Kingsborough Gardens, GLASGOW G12 9NH ☎ 0141-334 1602.

Dunn, Stephen, B.Sc., B.D.; Immaculate Heart of Mary, 162 Broomfield Road, GLASGOW G21 3UE. ☎ 0141-558 5025.

Dunnachie, William, S.T.B., Dip.R.E.; St. Kevin's, Mainhill Road, Bargeddie, Baillieston, GLASGOW G69 7SS. ☎0141-771 1654.

Dunne, Richard *(Glasgow, Retired)*; Nazareth House, 1647 Paisley Road West, GLASGOW G52 3QT. ☎ 0141-810 4359.

Eagers, John G., B.Sc., Ph.B., S.T.L.; St. Peter's, 154 Braehead Road, PAISLEY PA2 8NG. ☎ 0141-884 2435.

Fallon, Michael; St. Catherine's, 2 Captains Row, EDINBURGH EH16 6QP. ☎ 0131-664 1596.

Farrell, John B., B.D., B.Ed.; St. Monica's, Sharp Avenue, Old Monkland, COATBRIDGE ML5 5RP. ☎ 01236-421750.

Farrington, Michael D., Ph.L., S.T.L.; St. Andrew's, 27 Brooke Street, DUMFRIES DG1 2JL. ☎ 01387-254281.

Ferguson, James (*Paisley*); Monastery of Jesus, Harelaw Farm, Kilbarchan, JOHNSTONE PA10 2PY. ☎ 01505-614669.

Ferrari, James; St. Michael's, 53 Blackness Road, LINLITHGOW EH49 7JA. ☎ 01506-842145.

Finnigan, William F., Dip.Theol.; St. John's, Melville Street, PERTH PH1 5PY. ☎ 01738-622241.

Firth, Kevin, B.A., S.T.L.; Our Lady, Star of the Sea, and St. Drostan's, 73 Commerce Street, FRASERBURGH AB43 9LR. ☎ 01346-518215.

FitzGerald, Sean M.; St. Kessog's, Balloch Road, Balloch, ALEXANDRIA G83 8LQ. ☎ 01389-753080.

**Fitzpatrick, Mgr. Patrick G., S.T.L., L.R.A.M., B.Mus.Sac., L.C.G., B.Mus.Hons., D.C.E.; St. Leo's, 5 Beech Avenue, GLASGOW G41 5BY. ☎ 0141-427 0293.

Fitzsimmons, John H., Ph.L., S.T.L., L.S.S.; St. John Bosco's Presbytery, Barwood Road, ERSKINE PA8 6AB. ☎ 0141-812 2571.

*Flack, Herbert Canon (*Motherwell, Retired*); c/o Diocesan Centre, Coursington Road, MOTHERWELL ML1 1PP. ☎ 01698-269114.

*Flannery, John P. Canon; St. Joseph's, 14 Ballochmyle Street, Catrine MAUCHLINE KA5 6QP. ☎ 01290-551408.

Flynn, Eamonn; Our Lady, Star of the Sea, 10 Ardrossan Road, SALTCOATS KA21 5BW. ☎ 01294-463461.

Flynn, Thomas W., R.G.N.; St. Theresa's, Kilronan Park, 41 Main Street, East Calder, LIVINGSTON EH53 0ES. ☎ 01506-880918.

**Foley, Mgr. Daniel (*S. Andr., Retired*); St. Mary's, 6 Wilkieston Road, Ratho, NEWBRIDGE EH28 8RH. ☎ 0131-333 1051.

Foley, James, Ph.L., S.T.L., L.S.S.; St. Augustine's, 12 Dundyvan Road, Langloan, COATBRIDGE ML5 4DQ. ☎ 01236-423044.

Foley, James; St. Fillan's, 20 King Street, NEWPORT-ON-TAY DD6 8BN. ☎ 01382-542324.

Forrest, Andrew A.; St. Mary's Presbytery, Linlithgow Road, BO'NESS EH51 0DP. ☎ 01506-822339.

Forrester, William, S.J.; Wellcross, 193 Nithsdale Road, GLASGOW G41 5EX ☎ 0141-423 3005.

Fortune, Alan, S.J.; St. Aloysius' 10 Woodside Place, GLASGOW G3 7QF. ☎ 0141-332 3039.

Fox, Colm (*Paisley, Retired*); Narin, Portnoo, Co. Donegal, Ireland.

*Fraser, William Canon; St. Margaret's, Argyll Street, LOCHGILPHEAD PA31 8NE. ☎ 01546-602380.

Freney, Gerard O.; St. Andrew's, Auchmead Road, Larkfield, GREENOCK PA16 0JU. ☎ 01475-631750.

Friel, Daniel, Ph.L., S.T.L. (*Glasgow, Retired*); St. Patrick's, Strathleven Place, DUMBARTON G82 1BA. ☎ 01389-762503.

Friel, Eamon V., Ph.L., S.T.L., B.A.(Hons.); St. Mary's, 89 Abercromby Street, GLASGOW G40 2DQ. ☎ 0141-554 0872.

*Friel, James Canon; St. Mary's. Poldrate, HADDINGTON EH41 4DA. ☎ 01620-822138.

Friel, Paul, B.D.; Our Lady of Lourdes, 51 Lourdes Avenue, GLASGOW G52 3QU. ☎ 0141-882 1024.

Friel, Terence (*Glasgow*); 66 Ardencaple Quadrant, HELENSBURGH G84 8DR

Fulton, Brian, C.S.Sp.; Holy Ghost Fathers 117 Newarthill Road, Carfin, MOTHERWELL ML1 5AL. ☎ 01698-290831/297054.

Gaffney, Patrick, C.S.Sp.; Holy Ghost Fathers 117 Newarthill Road, Carfin, MOTHERWELL ML1 5AL. ☎ 0198-290831/297054.

*Galbraith,John Angus Canon, B.A.; St. Peter's, Daliburgh, LOCHBOISDALE HS8 5SS. ☎ 01878-700305.

*Gallacher, John F. Canon (*Motherwell, Retired*), Nazareth House, 1647 Paisley Road West, GLASGOW G52 3QT. ☎ 0141-882 9375.

*Gallacher, Peter Canon, M.A., Dip.Ed. (*S. Andrews, Retired*); 45 Gilmore Place, EDINBURGH EH3 9NG. ☎ 0131-229 5672.

Gallacher, Peter M., Ph.B., S.T.L., S.L.L.; Christ the King, 220 Carmunnock Rad, GLASGOW G44 5AP.☎ 0141-637 2882.

Gallagher, Dermot, C.P.; St. Mungo's Retreat, 52 Parson Street, GLASGOW G4 0RX. ☎ 0141-552 1823.

Gallagher, Francis; St. Alphonsus', 18 Stevenson Street, GLASGOW G40 2ST. ☎ 0141-552 0519.

Gallagher, Gerard J., Ph.B., S.T.B., J.C.L.; Holy Family, 2 Parkhill Avenue, PORT GLASGOW PA14 6BT. *Tel.*: 01475-705585 .

**Gallagher, Mgr. Hugh Canon (*Paisley, Retired*); Nazareth House, 1647 Paisley Road West, GLASGOW G52 3QT.

Gallagher, Michael, S.P.S.; St. David's, Meadowhead Road, Plains, AIRDRIE ML6 7JF. ☎ 01236-763226.

Gallagher, Neil; St. Fergus', Gallowshade, FORFAR DD8 1NG. *Tel.*: 01307-462104.

**Gallagher, Mgr. Owen; St. Ninian's, 5 Baldwin Avenue, GLASGOW G13 2EE. ☎ 0141-959 1308.

*Gallagher, Padraig, C.Ss.R.; St. Mary's, Hatton Road, Kinnoull, PERTH PH2 7BP. ☎ 01738-624075.

Galt, Ronald, M.A., B.D.(*Glasgow*): c/o Diocesan Office, 196 Clyde Street, GLASGOW G1 4JY

Gannon,John F., B.D. (*Glasgow, on further studies)*; Plater College, Pullens Lane, Oxford OX3 0DT

Gardner, Albert J.; St. Kessog's, 4 Campsie Dene Road, Blanefield, GLASGOW G63 9BN. ☎ 01360-770300.

Gardner, Robert, S.D.B., B.A.; St. Benedict's, 755 Westerhouse Road, GLASGOW G31 9RP. ☎ 0141-771 1991.

Gaskell, Austin, O.P., M.A., M.Ed.; St. Mary's, BEAULY IV4 7AU. ☎ 01463-782232.

*Gemmell, David R., M.Th.; Cathedral House, 61 York Place, EDINBURGH EH1 3JD. ☎ 0131-556 1798/0027.

Gibbons, Thomas; St. Columbkille's, 2 Kirkwood Street, Rutherglen, GLASGOW G73 2SL. ☎ 0141-647 6034.

Gilfedder, Christopher; St. Gabriel's, 83 Merrylee Road, GLASGOW G43 2QY. ☎ 0141-637 4138.

Gilfedder, Francis H. (*Glasgow, Retired*); c/o Irvine, 30 Canal Street, RENFREW PA4 8QD.

Gilhooley, Damien J.; St. Bernard's, Hermitage Crescent, Shawhead, COATBRIDGE ML5 4NB. ☎ 01236-422451.

Gilhooley, Stephen A.; Our Lady's, 222 Lanark Road West, CURRIE EH14 5NW. ☎ 0131-449 2372.

Gillespie, George F., Ph.L., S.T.B.; Our Lady of Perpetual Succour, 17 Mitre Road, GLASGOW G11 7EF. ☎ 0141-334 5330.

**Gilmartin, Mgr. John; Our Lady of Lourdes, 51 Lourdes Avenue, GLASGOW G52 3QU. ☎ 0141-882 1024.

Givens, John Francis (*Motherwell, Retired*); 15 Wellview Drive, MOTHERWELL ML1 3ET. ☎ 01698-263687.

Glackin, Edward; St. Columba's, 693 Old Edinburgh Road, Viewpark, Uddingston, GLASGOW G71 6HF. ☎ 01698-813495.

*Glancey, Lawrence A. Canon, Ph.L., M.A. (*S. Andr., Retired*); St. Andrew's, 77 Belford Road, EDINBURGH EH4 3DS. ☎ 0131-332 6925.

Glancy, Leo; Christ the King, Bowhouse Road, GRANGEMOUTH FK3 0HB. ☎ 01324-484974.

*Glen, Thomas Canon (*Glasgow, Retired*); Nazareth House, 1647 Paisley Road West, GLASGOW G52 3QT.

Golden, Colin K., Dip. Theol.; St. John's, Melville Street, PERTH PH1 5PY. ☎ 01738-622241.

Golden, Kevin J.; Our Lady of Sorrows, Finlarig Terrace, Fintry, DUNDEE DD4 9JF. ☎ 01382-502068.

Gonzalez, Gonzalo, LL.D., D.C.L.; Dunreath, 123 Nithsdale Road, GLASGOW G41 5HA. ☎ 0141-427 3236.

*Gordon, Hugh F. Canon (*S. Andrews, Retired*); 45 Gilmore Place, EDINBURGH EH3 9NG. ☎ 0131-228 9084.

Gowans, Brian; St. Mary's, 15 Upper Bridge Street, STIRLING FK8 1ES. ☎ 01786-473749.

*Grace, Thomas A. Canon (*Paisley., Retired*); St. Charles', 5 Union Street, PAISLEY PA2 6DU. ☎ 0141-889 2614.

Grady, Patrick (*Aberdeen, Retired*); c/o Bishop's House, 3 Queen's Cross, ABERDEEN AB15 4XU.

**Grady, Mgr. Patrick J. Canon, Prot.Ap., B.A.; (*S.Andrews, Retired*) 47 Gilmore Place, EDINBURGH EH3 9NG. ☎ 0131-221 1646.

Grant, James A., S.T.B.; Holy Family, 57 Hope Street, Mossend, BELLSHILL ML4 1QA. ☎ 01698-843165.

Gray, Stuart F., B.D.; The Presbytery, Main Street, Glencraig, LOCHGELLY KY5 8AL. ☎ 01592-860225.

Greenan, Thomas, S.T.B. (*S. Andr.*); Apartado 2866, Centre de Gobierno, San Salvador, El Salvador.

*Grennan, John, O.C.D.; Mount Carmel, 61 Hamilton Avenue, GLASGOW G41 4HA. ☎ 0141-427 0794.

Grugan, Aelred, O.S.B.(*Monk of Fort Augustus*); Catholic Chapel of St. Philip Howard, Glenridding, Penrith, Cumbria CA11 0PG. ☎ 017684-82212.

Hackett, Paul, S.J.; Our Holy Redeemer's, 71 Kenneth Street, STORNOWAY HS1 2DS. ☎ 01851-702070.

Haddock, Gerard, Dip.Theol.; St. Bernadette's, 200 Logans Road, MOTHERWELL ML1 3PH. ☎ 01698-263945.

Hall, Peter, O.F.M.; Bl. John Duns Scotus, 270 Ballater Street, Glasgow G5 0YT. ☎ 0141-429 0740.

Halloran, Brian M., B.D., M.Phil., Ph.D.; St. James', 17 The Scores, ST. ANDREWS KY16 9AR. ☎ 01334-472856.

Hamill, Gerard, M.H.M.; St. Joseph's House, 30 Lourdes Avenue, GLASGOW G52 3QU. ☎ 0141-883 0139.

Hand, Gerard R., S.T.L.; St. Patrick's, 30 Low Craigends, Kilsyth, GLASGOW G65 0PF. ☎ 01236-822136.

*Hanlon, Thomas Provost, L.S.S., S.T.L., Ph.L.; St. Anthony's, Rumford, FALKIRK FK2 0SB. ☎ 01324-715650.

Hannah, Stephen;Holy Cross, 113 Dixon Avenue, GLASGOW G42 8ER. ☎ 0141-423 0105.

Hardy, Benedict, O.S.B., B.A., B.A.Div.; Pluscarden Abbey, ELGIN IV30 8UA.

Harkins, William R.; St. Paul's, 118 Brediland Road, PAISLEY PA2 0HE. ☎ 01505-813103.

Harrison, Peter, S.J.; Wellcross, 193 Nithsdale Road, GLASGOW G41 5EX ☎ 0141-423 3005.

**Hart, Mgr. Daniel J. C., Ph.L., S.T.L., M.A., Dip.Ed.; St. Helen's, 165 Camphill Avenue, GLASGOW G41 3DR. ☎ 0141-632 2626.

Harty, John, S.T.B.; St. Leonard's Presbytery, St. Leonard's Place, DUNDEE DD3 9HD. ☎ 01382-858151/810739.

Hassay, Gerard P., S.J.; St. Aloysius', 10 Woodside Place, GLASGOW G3 7QF. ☎ 0141-332 3039.

Hastings, Philip (*Glasgow, Retired*): St. Joseph's, 19 Cumnock Road, Robroyston, Glasgow G33 1QT.

Hattie, William, S.X., S.T.B., M.A.; Xaverian Mission Centre, Calder Avenue, COATBRIDGE ML5 4JS. ☎ 01236-606364.

Hayes, James; St. Cuthbert's Presbytery, 28 Dailly Road, MAYBOLE KA19 7AU. ☎ 01655-882145.

Hayes, James, S.J.; St. Margaret's, 87 St. Olaf Street, LERWICK ZE1 0ES. ☎ 01595-692233.

*Hayes, Niall Canon; St. John Bosco's; 91 Jerviston Street, New Stevenston, MOTHERWELL ML1 4JS. ☎ 01698-832316.

Hayes, Vivian; St. Francis', Crown Street, Baillieston, GLASGOW G69 7XB. ☎ 0141-773 0084.

*Healy, Brendan Canon; St. Conval's, Green Farm Road, Linwood, PAISLEY PA3 3HB. ☎ 01505-323751.

Healy, Dermot J. (*Glasgow, on foreign missions*); c/o Society of St. James the Apostle, 24 Clark Street, Boston,Mass. 02109, U.S.A.

Healy, John B.; St. Serf's, 66 Aitken Street, AIRDRIE ML6 6LT. ☎ 01236-764479.

*Healy, Liam Canon; St. David's, 41 Eskbank Road, DALKEITH EH22 3BH. ☎ 0131-663 4286.

*Heaps, Christopher, S.D.B.; St. Paul's, 4 Muirhouse Avenue, EDINBURGH EH4 4UB. ☎ 0131-332 3320.

Heenan, Christopher, B.D.; St. Pius', Brodick Road, KIRKCALDY KY2 6EY. *Tel.*: 01592-261901.

Heffernan, John (*Paisley, Retired*); The Lodge, Our Lady of Fatima, Oakpark, Tralee, Co. Kerry, Ireland. ☎ 066 7128768.

Hendrie, Robert, Ph.L., S.T.L.; St. Luke's, Garngrew Road, Haggs, Banknock,BONNYBRIDGE FK4 1HP. ☎ 01324-840368.

*Hendry, Charles Canon; St. John's, Melville Street, PERTH PH1 5PY. ☎ 01738-622241.

**Hendry, Mgr. Ronald J. K. Canon, J.P. (*Argyll, Retired*); Nazareth House, 34 Claremont Street, ABERDEEN AB10 6RA.

Hendry, Thomas John; St. Teresa's, 86 Saracen Street, GLASGOW G22 5AD. ☎ 0141-336 8212.

Hennessy, Patrick, B.A.; St. Columbkille's, 2 Kirkwood Street, Rutherglen, GLASGOW G73 2SL. ☎ 0141-647 6034.

Hennessy, Thomas; St. Mary Magdalene's, 16 Milton Crescent, EDINBURGH EH15 3PF. ☎ 0131-669 3611.

*Henretty, Michael Canon; St. Maria Goretti's, 259 Bellrock Street, GLASGOW G33 3LN. ☎ 0141-774 4151.

Henry, David John; Our Lady and St. Margaret's, 48 Bridgend, DUNS TD11 3EX. ☎ 01361-883714.

Herrity, Herbert, M.Afr.; St. Joseph's, 9 Milrig Road, Rutherglen, GLASGOW G73 2NG. ☎0141-647 3806.

Hewson, John, C.M.;St. Mary's, 70 Bannatyne Street, LANARK ML11 7JS. ☎ 01555-662234.

Higgins, Edward J. (*Glasgow, Retired*); 8 Inverewe Avenue, Deaconsbank, GLASGOW G46 8TA. ☎ 0141-638 5624.

Higgins, James G.; Pastoral Centre, 50 Bonkle Road, Newmains, WISHAW ML2 9AP. ☎ 01698-385397.

High, James H., M.A.; St. Margaret's, Market Street, MONTROSE DD10 8NB. ☎ 01674-672208.

Hill, Gerard C., Ph.L., S.T.L., M.A.; St. Augustine's, 393 Ashgill Road, GLASGOW G22 7HN.☎ 0141-772 1905.

Hill, Robert J., B.Sc., Cert.Ed.; Turnbull Hall, 15 Southpark Terrace, GLASGOW G12 8LG. ☎ 0141-339 4315.

Hnylycia, Stefan, B.Sc., P.G.C.E.; Dunreath, 231 Nithsdale Road, GLASGOW G41 5HA. ☎ 0141-427 3236.

Hodgson, Nicholas C., Ph.B., S.T.L., J.C.L.; St. Kentigern's, 26 Parkgrove Avenue, EDINBURGH EH4 7QR. ☎ 0131-336 4984.

Holloran, Thomas; Holy Cross, 113 Dixon Avenue, GLASGOW G42 8ER. ☎ 0141-423 0105.

*Holmes, Joseph, M.H.M.; St. Joseph's House, 30 Lourdes Avenue, GLASGOW G52 3QU. ☎ 0141-883 0139.

Holuka, Ryszard, S.T.L., M.A.; St. Alexander's, 100 Stirling Street, DENNY FK6 6DL. ☎ 01324-823310.

Hood, Thomas, O.C.R.; Sancta Maria Abbey, Nunraw, HADDINGTON EH41 4LW.

Hosie, Andrew (*Glasgow*); c/o Diocesan Ofice, 196 Clyde Street, GLASGOW G1 4JY

Hourigan, Augustine, C.P.; St. Mungo's Retreat, 52 Parson Street, GLASGOW G4 0RX. ☎ 0141-552 1823.

Hughes, Colin T., B.Ed.; Holy Trinity and All Saints', 293 Muiryhall Street, COATBRIDGE ML5 3RZ. ☎ 01236-441110.

Hughes, John A., M.A., Dip.Ed., Ph.B., S.T.L., Sc.P.; Chaplain's Residence, St. Andrew's Campus, University of Glasgow, Duntocher Road, Bearsden, GLASGOW G61 4QA. ☎ 0141-942 7719.

Hughes, Patrick, C.M.; St. Mary's, 70 Bannatyne Street, LANARK ML11 7JS. ☎ 01555-662234.

Hughes, Simon A., B.Mus.(Hons.), B.D.; St. Francis Xavier's, 1 Hope Street, FALKIRK FK1 5AT. ☎ 01324-623567.

Hurley, Denis A.; Holy Family and St Ninian's, 20 Union Street, Kirkintilloch, GLASGOW G66 1DH. ☎ 0141-776 1063.

Hurley, Hubert, C.P.; St. Mungo's Retreat, 52 Parson Street, GLASGOW G4 0RX. ☎ 0141-552 1823.

Hurley, Thomas; St. Jude's, 159 Pendeen Road, Barlanark, GLASGOW G33 4SH. ☎ 0141-771 5004.

Hutson, Michael, Dip.T.Mus., Dip.R.C.R.E., B.D.; Church House, Morar, MALLAIG PH40 4PB. ☎ 01687-462201.

Hutton, Douglas (*S.Andrews, Retired*); St.Andrew's, 77 Belford Road, EDINBURGH EH4 3DS. ☎ 0131-332 2958.

Irons, John M., B.D.; St. Joseph's, Mayberry Place, Blantyre, GLASGOW G72 9DA. ☎ 01698-23896/320055.

*****Jackson,** James Canon (*Paisley, Retired*), Nazareth House, 1647 Paisley Road West, GLASGOW G52 3QT.

Jaconelli, Francis {*Glasgow., Retired*); 17 Baronscourt Road, PAISLEY PA1 2TW. *TEL.:* 0141-889 6793.

Jaconelli, Raymond, O.C.R.; Sancta Maria Abbey, Nunraw, HADDINGTON EH41 4LW. ☎ 01620-830223/830228.

*Jamieson, Thomas Canon; St. Bridget's, 12 Polnoon Street, Eaglesham, GLASGOW G76 0BH. ☎ 01355-303298.

Johnson, Peter, S.D.B.; St. Paul's, 4 Muirhouse Avenue, EDINBURGH EH4 4UB. ☎ 0131-332 3320/315 2571.

Johnston, Michael H., S.L.L. (*S. Andrews*); Pontificio Ateneo S. Anselmo, Piazza Cavalieri di Malta 5, 00153 Roma, Italy.

Johnston, Roderick H., S.T.B.; St. John's, St. John's Road, Caol, FORT WILLILAM PH33 7PR. ☎ 01397-700622

*Judge, Stephen Canon, B.D., M.Th.; St. Margaret's, 149 Main Street, Davidson's Mains, EDINBURGH EH4 5AQ. ☎ 0131-336 1083.

Kaim, Andrzej, S.A.C.; St. Aidan's, Gattonside, MELROSE TD6 9NW.

Kane, Charles, St. Louise's, 4 Inverewe Avenue, Deaconsbank, GLASGOW G46 8TA. ☎ 0141-638 4709.

Kane Robert, Ph.B., S.T.L., M.A.; St. Edward's, Lady Anne Crescent, AIRDRIE ML6 9PZ. ☎ 01236-754545.

Karwemera, Andrew; St. John's, Aurs Road, Barrhead, GLASGOW G78 2RW. ☎ 0141-876 1553.

Kay, David, S.J.; St. Lawrence's, 21 Castle Street, DINGWALL IV15 9HU. *Tel.*: 01349-863143.

*Keane, Denis Canon; (*Motherwell, Retired*); St. Martin's, Burgathia, Roscarbery, Co. Cork, Ireland. ☎ *(00353)* 023-48737.

Kearns, Hugh (*Glasgow, Retired*); Sr. Margaret's Hospice, East Barns Street, CLYDEBANK G81 1EG.

Kearns, Thomas, O.P.; St. Albert's, 25 George Square, EDINBURGH EH8 9LD. ☎ 0131-650 0900.

Keating, Michael (*Glasgow, Retired*); c/o Ferry, Sheskinbeg, Derrybeg, Letterkenny, Co. Donegal, Ireland. ☎ Eire (00353) 75-44102.

Keegans, Patrick, S.T.B.; St. Margaret's, 27 John Street, AYR KA8 0BS. *Tel.*. 01292-263488.

Keenan, John; Christ the King, 220 Carmunnock Road, GLASGOW G44 5AP. ☎ 0141-637 2882.

Keenan, Joseph; St. Peter's, 46 Hyndland Street, GLASGOW G11 5PS. ☎ 0141-576 1378.

*Keevins, Frank, C.P.; St. Gabriel's, West Loan, PRESTONPANS EH32 9JX. ☎ 01875-810052.

Kelly, Edward; St. Anthony's, 62 Langlands Road, GLASGOW G51 3BD. ☎ 0141-445 1416.

Kelly, Hugh P.; St. Bartholomew's, 1 Trent Street, COATBRIDGE ML5 2NT. ☎ 01236-421587.

Kelly, John, St. James', 232 Woodhall Avenue, COATBRIDGE ML5 5DF. ☎ 01236-422233.

Kelly, Joseph, O.Carm.;St. Francis Xavier's, Taylor Avenue, Carfin, MOTHERWELL ML1 5AJ. ☎ 01698-263308.

Kelly, Martin J. (*Motherwell*); Iglesia Nistra Sra de Fatima, El Enpalma, Padres de Santiago Apostol, Casilla 5823, Guayaquil, Ecuador.

Kelly, Patrick (*S. Andrews, Retired*); 2 Durham Terrace, New Mills, DUNFERMLINE KY12 8SZ.

*Kelly, Patrick J. Canon; Holy Name, 200 Hillside Road, GLASGOW G43 1BU. ☎ 0141-649 9668.

Kelly, Paul, M.A., D.Phil.(*St. Andrews and Edinburgh*);Scotus College, 2 Chesters Road, Bearsden, GLASGOW G61 4AG. ☎ 0141-942 8384.

Kelly, Peter, Dip. Theol., Dip.Phil./Arts; Our Lady of the Waves,Westgate, DUNBAR EG42 1JL. ☎ 01368-862701.

Kennedy, Francis, Ph.L., S.T.L. (*Glasgow*); c/o Obispado, Pasaje Catedral 1750, 7600 Mar del Plata, Argentina.

Kennedy, Patrick, M.A. (*Argyll, Retired*); Nazareth House, 1647 Paisley Road West, GLASGOW G52 3QT.

**Kennedy, Mgr. Stephen Canon (*Galloway, Retired*); 15 Dalmellington Road, AYR KA7 3TH. ☎ 01292-286001.

Keogh, Terence Williams-, O.M.I.;St. Mary, Star of the Sea, 106 Constitution Street, Leith, Edinburgh EH6 6AW. ☎ 0131-554 2482/467 7449.

Kerr, Fergus, O.P., M.A., S.T.M., D.D.; St. Albert's, 25 George Square, EDINBURGH EH8 9LD. ☎ 0131-650 0900.

Kerr, Francis; St. Peter's, 77 Falcon Avenue, Morningside, EDINBURGH EH10 4AN. ☎ 0131-447 2502.

Kerr, John, M.A. (*Galloway, Retired*); Candida Casa, 8 Corsehill Road, Ayr KA7 2ST.

Kerr, Philip J., Ph.B., S.T.L.; St. Francis Xavier's, 1 Hope Street, FALKIRK FK1 5AT. ☎ 01324-623567.

Keyes, Oliver, C.Ss.R.; St. Mary's, Hatton Road, Kinnoull, PERTH PH2 7BP. ☎ 01738-624075.

Kilbride, Thomas, M.A., S.T.B.; St. Andrew's Cathedral House, 90 Dunlop Street, GLASGOW G1 4ER. ☎ 0141-221 3096.

*Kilcoyne, Anthony Canon (*Motherwell, Retired*); St. Joseph's, 14 Cumnock Road, Robroyston, GLASGOW G33 1QT. ☎ 0141-558 5114.

Kilpatrick, Arthur J. (*Paisley, long-term Sick Leave*); Flat 26, Maclehose Court, 1 Eldon Street, GREENOCK PA16 7UG. ☎ 01475-787969.

King, Francis D., B.D.; Our Lady of Lourdes, 30 Canberra Drive, East Kilbride, GLASGOW G75 8DG. ☎ 01355-224511.

Kingham, Andrew J., B.D. *(St. Andrews and Edinburgh, on Further Studies)*;Les Missionnaires Oblats de Marie Imaculée, Edifice Deschatelets, 175 Rue Main, Ottawa, Canada K1S 1C3.

**Kinsella, Mgr. Matthew Canon (*Paisley, Retired*); 70 Eldon Street, GREENOCK PA16 8NA. ☎ 01475-727740.

Kinsler, John; Our Lady of Perpetual Succour, 2 Crummock Street, BEITH KA15 2BD. ☎ 01505-502392.

Kirby, James (*Glasgow, Sick leave*); St. Joseph's, 14 Cumnock Road, Robroyston, GLASGOW G33 1QT.

*Klein, Augustine Canon (*Dunkeld, Retired*); Wellburn Home, 118 Liff Road, Lochee, DUNDEE DD2 2QT.

Kozminski, Andrzey, S.A.C.; Cathedral House, 61 York Place, EDINBURGH EH1 3JD. ☎ 0131-556 1798/0027.

Lafferty, James; Our Lady of Loreto, 707 Dumbarton Road, Dalmuir, CLYDEBANK G81 4HD. ☎ 0141-952 9795.

Lamb, Brian J., Ph.B., S.T.L.; St. Patrick's, 84 Station Road, SHOTTS ML7 4BJ. ☎ 01501-821838.

Latham, Stephen, B.Sc., M.A., B.D., Dip.Ed.; St. Joseph's, Lewis Street, STRANRAER DG9 7AL. ☎ 01776-703125.

Lavery, Terence, S.D.B.; St. Paul's, 4 Muirhouse Avenue, EDINBURGH EH4 4UB. ☎ 0131-332 3320.

Lawlor, James M., M.A.(Oxon.); Our Lady of Fatima, 75 Millerfield Road, GLASGOW G40 4RP. ☎ 0141-554 5008..

**Lawson, Mgr. Alistair, B.A., V.G.; St. Mary's, 9 Livery Street, BATHGATE EH48 4HS. ☎ 01506-655766.

Lawson, Patrick J.; St. Winin's, St. Winning's Lane, KILWINNING KA13 6EP. ☎ 01294-55227.

Lea, Michael, B.A. (*Argyll, Retired*); Emmaus, I Hillside Avenue, KINGUSSIE PH21 1PA. ☎ 01540-661649.

Lekawa, Marian A., S.A.C.; Polish Catholic Mission in Scotland, 4 Park Grove Terrace, GLASGOW G3 7SD. ☎ 0141-339 9163.

Lennon, Peter; Immaculate Heart of Mary, 162 Broomfield Road, GLASGOW G21 3UE. ☎ 0141-558 5025.

Lewandowski, Pius Boleslaw, O.F.M.; 33 Baldovan Terrace, DUNDEE DD4 6NH.

Lindsay, Edward (*Glasgow, Retired*); St. Joseph's, 14 Cumnock Road Robroyston, Glasgow G33 1QT.

Livingstone, Gerald A., B.D.; St. Duthac's, Bundalloch Road, Dornie, KYLE IV40 8EL. ☎ 01599-585229.

Lochrie, Laurence, S.J.; Mount Carmel, Sandyhill Road, BANFF AB45 1BE. ☎ 01261-812204.

Lockhart, Vincent G.; St. Patrick's, 52 Stonehouse Road, STRATHAVEN ML10 6LF. ☎ 01357-520104.

Lodge, Benedict, C.P.; Our Lady of the Rosary and St. Columba, Newtonmore Road, KINGUSSIE PH21 1HF. ☎ 01540-661322.

Logue, Brian; St. Margaret's, 96 Hallcraig Street, AIRDRIE ML6 6AW. ☎ 01236-763370.

Logue, Joseph (*Paisley, Retired*); 86 Union Street, GREENOCK PA15 8BE. ☎ 01475-719371.

Loughlin, John (*Glasgow, Retired*); St. Joseph's, 14 Cumnock Road, Robroyston, GLASGOW G33 1QT.

*Loughlin Rupert Canon; St. Bride's, Rie-Achan Road, PITLOCHRY PH16 5AL. ☎ 01796-472174.

Lowrie,Hugh,S.T.B.; c/oArchdiocesan Office, 196 Clyde Street,GLASGOW G1 4JY

Lynch, Michael; St. Peter's, 1 South Crescent Road, ARDROSSAN KA22 8DU. ☎ 01294-464063.

Lyons, John, B.D.; Our Lady of the Assumption, 493 Bilsland Drive, GLASGOW G20 9JN. ☎ 0141-946 2683.

McAleese, Francis, O.Carm., B.A., B.D., M.Phil.; St. Francis Xavier's, Taylor Avenue, Carfin, MOTHERWELL ML1 5AJ. ☎ 01698-263308.

McAlinden, Paul;Our Lady and St. George's, 50 Sandwood Road, GLASGOW G52 2QE. ☎ 0141-882 4868.

*McAllister, John Canon; St. Peter-in-Chains, 28 Hope Street, INVERKEITHING KY11 1LW. ☎ 01383-413195.

McAndrew, Joseph, S.M.A.; St. Casimir, 78 Glencalder Crescent, BELLSHILL ML4 2LU. ☎ 01698-746266/745354.

McAtamney, Hugh Vincent, S.J.; St. Aloysius' 10 Woodside Place, GLASGOW G3 7QF.☎ 0141-332 3039.

MacAulay, John P., S.T.B., J.C.L.; c/o Diocesan Office, St.Columba's Cathedral, Corran Esplanade, OBAN PA34 5AB

McAuley, John, S.T.B.; St. Philomena's, 1255 Royston Road, GLASGOW G33 1EH. ☎ 0141-770 4237.

McAuley, Joseph L., LL.B., Ph.B., S.T.L.; St. Bernard's, 18 Wiltonburn Road, GLASGOW G53 7JF. ☎ 0141-876 9012.

McAuley, Roderick M.; St. Kieran's, 6 St. John Street, CAMPBELTOWN PA28 6BQ. ☎ 01586-552160.

McAvoy, Hugh, C.P.;St. Gabriel's, West Loan, PRESTONPANS EH32 9JX. ☎ 01875-810052.

*McBride, Kenneth Canon; Cathedral House, 150 Nethergate, DUNDEE DD1 4EA. ☎ (*Cathedral*) 01382-225228; (*University Chaplaincy*) 01382-223755.

McBride, Peter; St. Thomas', 826 Cumbernauld Road, GLASGOW G33 2EE. ☎ 0141-770 4057.

McCabe, Patrick Joseph, B.A. (*Galloway, on sick leave*); c/o Candida Casa, 8 Corsehill Road, AYR KA7 2ST.

*McCafferty, George Canon (*Galloway, Retired*); 18 Solway Place, TROON KA10 7EJ. ☎ 01292-314989.

McCafferty, Peter; (*Glasgow, Retired*); 182 King's Park Road, GLASGOW G44 4SU.☎0141-649 3880.

McCaffrey, Kenneth J., Dip.Theol., Dip.Ed.; St. Mungo's, 25 Mar Street, ALLOA FK10 1HR. ☎ 01259-212486.

McCahill, Peter; St. Mungo's, Gibshill Road, GREENOCK PA15 2UP. ☎ 01475-741187

McCann, Robert; St. Constantine's, 54 Uist Street, GLASGOW G51 3XW. ☎ 0141-445 1434.

McCann Thomas, B.Sc. (*Galloway, Retired*); 25 Monro Avenue, DUMFRIES DG1 4YH. ☎ 01387-251611.

*McCarney, Felix Canon; St. Joseph's, Bow Road, GREENOCK PA16 7DY. ☎ 01475-720789.

McCarthy, Anthony; Our Lady of Good Counsel, 29 Westfield Road, Broughty Ferry, DUNDEE DD5 1ED. ☎ 01382-778750.

*McCarthy, Michael A. Canon; St. Athanasius', 21 Mount Stewart Street, CARLUKE ML8 5EB. ☎ 01555-771250.

*McClorry, Brian, S.J.; Wellcross, 193 Nithsdale Road, GLASGOW G41 5EX ☎ 0141-423 3005.

McConville, Timothy (*S. Andrews*); Apartado 2866, Centro de Gobierno, San Salvador, El Salvador, Central America.

McCruden, James R., M.A., Dip.Ed.; St. Joseph's, 2A Ancaster Square, CALLANDER FK17 8ED. ☎ 01877-330702.

*McCullagh, Michael C. Canon (*S.Andr., Retired*); St. Anne's Convent, Windsor Gardens, MUSSELBURGH EH21 7LP. ☎ 0131-653 2725.

McCulloch, Derick W.B., B.D., B.A., M.A., S.T.L.; St. Nathalan's, 48 Golf Road, BALLATER AB35 5RS. ☎ 01339-756043.

McDade, William (*St. Colm's, Kilmacolm*); The Old Lodge, Cora Campus, Greenock Road, BISHOPTON PA7 5PF. ☎ 01505-862255.

MacDonald, Angus; St. Roch's, 311 Roystonhill, GLASGOW G21 2HN. ☎ 0141-552 2945.

*MacDonald, Bernard G. Canon; St. Mary's, 22A South Street, FOCHABERS IV32 7ED. ☎ 01343-820285.

Macdonald, Donald, S.M.M.; Montfort House, Darnley Road, Barrhead, GLASGOW G78 1TA. ☎ 0141-881 1440.

MacDonald, James A.; Our Lady of Lourdes, 30 Bathgate Road, Blackburn, BATHGATE EH47 7LF. ☎ 01506-652957.

*Macdonald, John Angus Canon, S.T.B., M.A., M.Litt.; St. Mary's, Belford Road, FORT WILLIAM PH33 6BT. ☎ 01397-702174.

*MacDonald, Michael J., Ph.B., S.T.L.,;Cathedral House, Corran Esplanade, Oban PA34 5AB. ☎ 01631-562123.

*McDonald, Robert A. Canon; St. Mary's, Huntly Street, Inverness IV3 5PR. ☎ 01403-233519.

**Macdonald, Mgr. Roderick Provost, S.T.L.., V.G.; St. Mun's, Ballachulish PA39 4JG. ☎ 01855-811203.

*McElroy, Christopher J. Ph.B., S.T.L., (*Glasgow*); Pontificio Collegio Scozzese, Via Cassia 481, 00189 Roma, Italy. ☎ +39 06 3366 8085.

*McElroy, John Canon; St. Joseph's, 2 Eaglesham Road, Clarkston, Glasgow G76 7BT. ☎ 0141-644 2640.

McElwee, Charles J.; St. Eunan's, 2 Gilmour Street, Clydebank G81 2BW. ☎ 0141-952 1108.

McFadden, Andrew, Ph.B., S.T.L.(*Paisley, R.N. Chaplain*); c/o Principal RC Chaplain (RN), MOD Chaplains (Naval), Room 281, Victory Building, HM Naval Base, Portsmouth PO1 3LS

MacFadden, Charles, S.T.L. (*Glasgow, Retired*); 31 Muirpark Drive, Bishopbriggs, Glasgow G64 1RD

McFadden, Patrick J., B.A. (*S. Andrews., Retired*); 16 Townparks, Convoy, Lifford, Co. Donegal, Ireland.

McFadden, William R., Ph.B., S.T.L., M.S.; St. John's, 92 Glaisnock Street, Cumnock KA18 1JU. ☎ 01290-421031.

McGachey, Francis G., S.T.L.; St. Bridget's, 15 Swinton Road, Baillieston, Glasgow G69 6DT. ☎ 0141-771 1058.

McGarrigle, George (*Glasgow, Retired*); Flat 1/2, 2 Gadsburn Court, Glasgow G21 3LS. ☎ 0141-557 5270.

McGarrity, Neil A. M., Dip.Theol.; St. Mary's, Chapel Road, Duntocher, Clydebank G81 6DL. ☎ 01389-873280.

*McGarry, Alexander Canon; St. Brigid's, 30 Newton Street, Kilbirnie KA25 6HW. ☎ 01505-682215.

McGarry, James, S.D.B., B.D., L.R.A.M., D.S.W., C.Q.S.W.; St. Clare's, 18 Drumlanrig Avenue, Glasgow G34 0JA. ☎ 0141-771 3740.

McGarry, Peter, Ph.B., S.T.L.; St. Charles', 5 Union Street, Paisley PA2 6DU. ☎ 0141-889 2614.

McGeady, William J.; St. John Vianney's, 40 Fernieside Gardens, Gilmerton, Edinburgh EH17 7HN. ☎ 0131-658 1793/664 4349.

McGee, Brian, Dip.Theol.; St. Joseph's, 2 Eaglesham Road, Clarkston, Glasgow G76 7BT. ☎ 0141-644 2640.

**McGee, Mgr. Eugene (*Glasgow, Retired*); Gleneagles Court, 3e Hilton Road, Bishopbriggs, Glasgow G64 3DZ. ☎ 0141-772 2761.

*McGee, John A., S.T.L.; Cathedral House, 27 Dalmilling Crescent, Ayr KA8 0QL. ☎ 01292-265716.

McGhee, Edward, M.Ed.; St. Brendan's, 63 Corrie Crescent, Saltcoats KA21 6JN. ☎ 01294-463843.

McGinley, John G.; Sacred Heart, 50 Old Dalmarnock Road, Glasgow G40 4AU. ☎ 0141-554 0806.

McGinley, William; St. Conval's, 21 Hapland Road, Glasgow G53 5NT. ☎ 0141-882 5265.

*McGinn, Henry A. Canon, J.P.; St. Mary's, Raploch Road, LARKHALL ML9 1AN. *Tel.*. 01698-882564.

*McGinness, Samuel Canon; St. Bride's, 9 Hunterston Road, WEST KILBRIDE KA23 9EX. *Tel./Fax:* 01294-823188.

McGinty, Desmond J., B.A.; St. Patrick's, 252 Dumbarton Road, Old Kilpatrick, GLASGOW G60 5LJ. ☎ 01389-873044.

McGoldrick, Kevin M., B.D.; St. Thomas', 12 Tarbert Avenue, WISHAW ML2 0JH. ☎ 01698-372775.

*McGovern, Patrick B. Canon *(Motherwell, Retired)*; Flat 2/1, 43 Mansionhouse Gardens, Langside, GLASGOW G41 3DP. ☎ 0141-649 8666.

McGrath, Brian, O.F.M.; Bl. John Duns Scotus, 270 Ballater Street, GLASGOW G5 0YT. ☎ 0141-429 0740.

McGrath, Colman F., Ph.L.;Sacred Heart Church, Kyle Road, Kildrum, Cumbernauld, GLASGOW G67 2DY. ☎ 01236-721387.

McGrath, John: St. Constantine's, 54 Uist Street, GLASGOW G51 3XW. ☎ 0141-445 1434.

McGrath, Stephen, O.F.M.; St. Patrick's, 5 South Grey's Close, 40 High Street, Edinburgh EH1 1TQ. ☎ 0131-556 1973.

McGraw, Brian, S.D.B., B.Ed.; St. Clare's, 18 Drumlanrig Avenue, GLASGOW G34 0JA. ☎ 0141-771 3740.

McGread, Justinian, C.P.; 4 Southbrae Drive, GLASGOW G13 1PX. ☎ 0141-576 8766.

*McGread, Thomas Joseph Canon *(Galloway, Retired)*; 4 Southbrae Drive, GLASGOW G13 1PX. ☎ 0141-576 8766.

McGrorry, John J. Ph.B., S.T.L., M.A.; St. Joseph's, 3 Buchanan Street, Milngavie, GLASGOW G62 8DZ. ☎0141-956 1400.

**McGrory, Mgr. Neil C., J.C.L., *(Paisley, Retired)*; St. Aidan's, Tower Road, JOHNSTONE PA5 0AD. ☎ 01505-326228.

McGuire, Desmond, O.F.M.; St. Teresa's, 120 Niddrie Mains Road, Craigmillar, EDINBURGH EH16 4EG. ☎ 0131-661 2185.

McGuire, John *(Glasgow)*; Paróquia Nossa Senhora da Penha, Caixa Postal 1012, 18147-000 Araçariguama, São Paulo, Brazil. ☎ 00 55 11 498-1322.

*McGuire Patrick N., S.M.A., S.T.B., F.C.C.A.; S.M.A. Fathers, St. Theresa's, Abbey House, Claredon Place, DUNBLANE FK15 9HB. ☎ 01786-824002.

McHugh, John J. (*S. Andrews, Retired*), St. Joseph's, Crinken Lane, Shankill, Co. Dublin, Ireland.

McIlveney, Thomas, M.Afr.; St. Joseph's, 9 Milrig Road, Rutherglen, GLASGOW G73 2NG. ☎ 0141-647 3806.

**McInally, Mgr. Hugh Francis Canon, J.P., C.A., Ph.B., S.T.B., V.G.; St. Mary's Rectory, 22 Powrie Place, DUNDEE DD1 2PQ. ☎ 01382-226384.

McInally, Patrick J., S.T.B., Dip.Lit.; St. Columba's, Ashlar Lane, CUPAR KY15 4AN. tel.: 01334-653000.

MacInnes, Colin, S.T.B. *(Argyll)*; Parroquia San Jose Obrero, Comite del Pueblo, Casilla 17-11-06553, Quito, Ecuador.

**MacInnes, Mgr. Ewen Canon *(Argyll, Retired)*; Nazareth House, 1647 Paisley Road West, GLASGOW G52 3QT.

McInnes, John E., B.D.; St. Luke's, 2A Stone Place, Mayfield, DALKEITH EH22 5PG. ☎ 0131-663 1476.

**McIntyre, Mgr. John, Ph.L., S.T.L., M.A., Dip.Ed.; St. Bridget's, 15 Swinton Road, Baillieston, GLASGOW G69 6DT. ☎ 0141-771 1058.

McIntyre, Joseph; St. Peter's, 9 Forman Road, LEVEN KY8 4HH. ☎ 01333-425627.

MacKay, Donald J., S.T.B.; Star of the Sea, CASTLEBAY HS9 5XD. ☎ 01871-810267.

**McKay, Mgr. Gerard, M.A., Ph.B., S.T.B., J.C.D. (*Argyll*); Via Aurelia 172, 00189 Roma, Italy.

McKay, Harry, Ph.L.; St. Joseph's Presbytery, Broomlands Road, South Carbrain, Cumbernauld, GLASGOW G67 2PT. ☎ 01236-722897.

McKelvie, Peter C.; St. Saviour's, 39 Merryland Street, GLASGOW G51 2QG. ☎ 0141-445 1166.

McKenna, Dennis (*Dunkeld*); c/o Bishop's House, 29 Roseangle, DUNDEE DD1 4LX.

McKenzie, Alfred, Ph.B., S.T.L.; St. Michael's, 7 Cardross Road, DUMBARTOn G82 4JE. ☎01389-762709.

McKenzie, Andrew, M.A.(*Glasgow*);Scotus College, 2 Chesters Road, Bearsden, GLASGOW G61 4AG. ☎ 0141-942 8384.

*McKillop, Robert Andrew, O.S.B., M.B.E., M.A.; St. Joseph's Convent, Wellburn Home, 118 Liff Road, Lochee, DUNDEE DD2 3QT

**MacKinnon Mgr. Donald W., B.A., V.G.; St. Mary's, ARISAIG PH39 4NH. ☎ 01687-450223.

Mackinnon, John P.;St. Mary's, Griminish, ISLE OF BENBECULA HS7 5QA. ☎ Benbecula (01870) 602221.

McLaren, Isaac; St. Stephen's, Paddock Street, Sikeside, COATBRIDGE ML5 4PG. ☎ 01236-420585.

McLaughlan, Kenneth B., Ph.L., B.D. (*Galloway*); Kaiserswortherstrasse 211, 40474 Dusseldorf 30, Germany.

McLaughlin, Angus, O.P., B.A.; Blackfriars, 36 Queen's Drive, GLASGOW G42 8DD ☎ 0141-423 2971 *also* Priest's House, Mingarry, ACHARACLE PH36 4JX. ☎ 01967-431251.

McLaughlin, Henry, S.T.L. (*S. Andrews*); Apartado Postal 212, San Cristobal de las Casas, Chiapas CP29200, Mexico.

McLean, Brian F., Ph.B., S.T.B., J.C.L.; St. Serf's, 14 Chapel Street, Highvalleyfield, DUNFERMLINE KY12 8SJ. ☎ 01383-880366.

McLean, John, B.A., M.Sc., A.T.I.; St. Ann's, 27 Annbank Road, Mossblown, AYR KA6 5DZ. ☎ 01292-520204.

MacLellan, Alistair D., (*Glasgow*); St. John's Parish, 20 Coral Street, East Frankston 3199, Victoria, Australia.

MacLellan, Malcolm J.; St. Michael's, Eriskay, LOCHBOISDALE HS8 5JL. ☎ 01878-720201.

McLellan, William; St. John's Presbytery, St. John's Way, Main Street, Twechar, Kilsyth, GLASGOW G65 9TA. ☎ 01236-822263.

McLoughlin, Daniel J., Dip.Theol., M.A.; St. Francis', Auchenbothie Road, PORT GLASGOW PA14 6JD. ☎ 01475-704222/707033.

McMahon, James A., M.A. (*S. Andrews, Retired*); 45 Gilmore Place, EDINBURGH EH3 9NG. ☎ 0131-229 5171.

McMahon, Joseph, B.A.; Sacred Heart, 1 Drummond Place, GRANGEMOUTH FK3 9JA. ☎ 01324-482253.

McMahon, Lawrence; St. Robert's, 310 Peat Road, GLASGOW G53 6SA. ☎ 0141-881 1137.

McMahon, Michael M., Ph.B., S.T.B., L.S.S.; Our Lady of Lourdes, 66 Old Greenock Road, BISHOPTON PA7 5BE. ☎ 01505-862471.

McMahon, William; St. Ninian's, 5 Baldwin Avenue,GLASGOW G13 2EE.☎ 0141-959 1308.

McManus, James, C.Ss.R.; St. Mary's, Hatton Road, Kinnoull, PERTH PH2 7BP. ☎ 01738-624075.

McManus, Matthew Francis; St. Winin's, St. Winning's Lane, KILWINNING KA13 6EP. ☎ 01294-552276/832181.

*MacMaster, Iain Canon; St. Andrew's, Columshill Street, ROTHESAY PA20 0HX. ☎ 01700-502047.

**McMeel, Mgr. John J. *(S. Andr., Retired);* Mulrany, Brighton Road, CUPAR KY15 5DH.

Macmillan, Douglas C., Dip.Phil., Dip. Theol.; ; St. John's, Aurs Road, Barrhead, GLASGOW G78 2RW. ☎ 0141-876 1553.

*MacMorrow, Francis, C.M., M.A.; St. Mary's, 70 Bannatyne Street, LANARK. ML11 7JS. ☎ 01555-662234.

McMullan, Joseph; Priest's House, 17 Newbigging, MUSSELBURGH EH21 7AJ. ☎ 0131-665 2137.

McMurray, John *(Motherwell, Retired);* 1/13 Saunders Street, EDINBURGH EH3 6TQ.

**McNally, Mgr. Anthony Canon, V.G.; St. Columba's, 9 Upper Gray Street, EDINBURGH EH9 1SN. ☎ 0131-667 1605.

McNally, Luke, O.C.R.; Sancta Maria Abbey, Nunraw, HADDINGTON EH41 4LW.

MacNamee, Michael; St. Leonard's, St. Leonard's Road, East Kilbride, GLASGOW G74 3YA. ☎ 01355-247471.

McNaught, Edward Brian, S.T.B., B.A.; St. Brendan's, 187 Kelso Street, GLASGOW G13 4BH. ☎ 0141-952 1471.

*McNaughton, Declan;St. Columban's, 31 Kingsborough Gardens, GLASGOW G12 9NH. ☎ 0141-334 1602.

*McNay, John Canon *(S. Andr., Retired)*; 31 Station Road, Oakley, DUNFERMLINE KY12 9RJ. ☎ 01383-852372.

MacNeil, James L., Ph.B., S.T.D. *(Argyll)*; 2 Caird Drive, GLASGOW G11 5DS.

MacNeil, Roderick J.; St. Michael's, Ardkenneth, Iochdar, LOCHBOISDALE HS8 5RD. ☎ 01870-610243.

*MacNeill, Calum Canon, B.A., S.T.L. *(Argyll, Retired)*; c/o Diocesan Office, St.Columba's Cathedral, Corran Esplanade, OBAN PA34 5AB

McNellis, Gerard; St. Joseph's, Bow Road, GREENOCK PA16 7DY. ☎ 01475-720789.

McNulty, John, M.Afr.; St. Joseph's, 9 Milrig Road, Rutherglen, GLASGOW G73 2NG. ☎ 0141–647 3806.

McNulty, Joseph; St. Paul's, 1213 Dumbarton Road, Glasgow G14 9UP. ☎ 0141-950 2488.

McNulty, Michael T. (*S. Andr., Retired*); Sligo Road, West End, Bundoran, Co. Donegal, Ireland.

McNulty, Thomas; Sacred Heart, 56 John Street, PENICUIK EH22 8HL. ☎ 01968-673709.

McPartlin, Francis; St. Gildas', Rosneath, HELENSBURGH G84 0RJ. ☎ 01436-831357.

McQuade, John, S.J.; Sacred Heart, 28 Lauriston Street, EDINBURGH EH3 9DJ. ☎ 0131-229 9104.

*MacQueen, Angus J. Canon; St. Barr's, Northbay, CASTLEBAY HS9 5YQ. ☎ 01871-890228.

**McShane, Mgr. James Canon, K.C.H.S., S.T.L., L.S.S.; St. Margaret's, Sinclair Street, CLYDEBANK G81 1AE. ☎ 0141-952 9508.

McShane, Joseph (*Argyll, Retired*), c/o Margaret McShane, Beltrees, Linwood Road, PAISLEY PA1 2TL.

McSorley, Patrick; St. Quivox, 34 St. Quivox Road, PRESTWICK KA9 1LU. ☎ 01292-478068.

McWilliams, Martin, B.D.; St. Leonard's Presbytery, St. Leonard's Place, DUNDEE DD3 9HD. ☎ 01382-858151/810739.

Mackle, Joseph, Dip.Theol.; St. Gabriel's, 83 Merrylee Road, GLASGOW G43 2QY.☎ 0141-637 4138.

Magee, Gerard; St. Paul's, 53 Galston Road, Hurlford, KILMARNOCK KA1 5HT. ☎ 01563-525963.

**Magee, Peter G., Ph.B., S.T.L., J.C.L, (*Galloway*); Mission Permanente du Saint Siege, 16 Chemin du Vengeron, C.P.28, CH-1292 Chambésy, Geneva, Switzerland.

Magill, Gerard, S.T.L. (*Motherwell*); St Louis University, The Department of Theological Studies, 3634 Lindell Blvd., St. Louis, MO63108-3395, U.S.A.

Magill, Thomas F., Ph.B., S.T.B., L.S.S.; St. Dominic's, 247 Mossvale Road, Craigend, GLASGOW G33 5QS. ☎ 0141-573 1260.

Maguinness, Gerard H., Ph.B., S.T.L. (*Motherwell, on further studies*); Pontificio Collegio Scozzese, Via Cassia 481, 00189 Roma, Italy. ☎ + 39 06 3366 8085.

**Maguire, Mgr. Desmond; St. Patrick's Presbytery, Strathleven Place, DUMBARTON G82 1BA. ☎ 01389-762503.

*Maher, Gerald Canon, M.A. (*Motherwell, Retired*); St. Augustine's, 12 Dundyvan Road, Langloan, COATBRIDGE ML5 4DQ. ☎ 01236-423044.

Maher, James, S.D.B.; St. Paul's, 4 Muirhouse Avenue, EDINBURGH EH4 4UB. ☎ 0131-332 3320.

Maher, Michael B.; St. Isidore's, 6 Coulter Road, BIGGAR ML12 6EP. ☎ 01899-220189.

*Mahoney, Jack, S.J.;Sacred Heart, 28 Lauriston Street, EDINBURGH EH3 9DJ. ☎ 0131-229 9821.

*Malaney, Hugh Canon; St. Vincent's, Cameron Road, TAIN IV19 1NN. ☎ 01862-892592.

*Mallon, Francis Canon; St. Bartholomew's, 32 Croftfoot Drive, GLASGOW G45 0NG. ☎ 0141-634 2051.

Maloney, Michael, B.D.; St. Dominic's, 21 Kirriemuir Road, Woodhill, Bishopbriggs, GLASGOW G64 1DL. ☎ 0141-762 1154.

Mancini, Ralph *(Galloway, Retired)*; 1 Oakfield Drive, Georgetown, DUMFRIES DG1 4PD. ☎ 01387-263047.

Mann, Andrew, B.A., S.T.B.; Sacred Heart, 15 Grampian Road, Torry, ABERDEEN AB11 8ED. ☎ 01224-878489.

Manning, John (*Glasgow, Retired*); Genazzano, Cahergal Gardens, Ballyvolane Road, Cork, Ireland.

Mannion, Thomas G. (*Glasgow, Retired*); 48 Greenock Road, PAISLEY PA3 2LB.

Markus, Gilbert, O.P., B.A., B.D., M.Th., S.T.L.; Blackfriars, 36 Queen's Drive, GLASGOW G42 8DD. ☎ 0141-423 2971/553 4144.

*Marley, Euan, O.P.; St. Albert's, 25 George Square, EDINBURGH EH8 9LD. *TEL.:* 0131-650 0900.

*Marshall, Gordian, O.P., B.Ed.; Blackfriars, 36 Queen's Drive, GLASGOW G42 8DD. ☎ 0141-423 2971.

Martin, Aidan, Ph.B., S.T.B.; St. Catherine's, 90 Lamont Road, Glasgow G21 3PP. ☎ 0141-558 6723.

Martin, James; Our Holy Redeemer's, South Bank Street, CLYDEBANK G81 1PH. ☎ 0141-952 1293.

*Martin, Niall; St. Patrick's, Buchlyvie, STIRLING FK8 3PB. ☎ 01360-850274.

*Mathews, Eugene Canon, J.C.L.; Sacred Hearts, 17 Harbour Street, GIRVAN KA26 9AJ. ☎ 01465-713331.

Meagher, Francis *(Glasgow, Retired)*;Flat 6, Clifford Court, 271 Nithsdale Road, GLASGOW G41 5LS

*Meechan, Michael Canon, S.T.L. (*Glasgow, Retired*); St. Peter's Presbytery, Howatshaws Road, DUMBARTON G82 3DR. ☎ 01389-764131.

Milarvie, Paul G., Ph.B., S.T.L.; Our Lady and St. Helen's, 117 Achray Road, Condorrat, Cumbernauld, GLASGOW G67 4JG. ☎ 01236-731258.

Millar, Thomas; St. Bride's, 21 Greenlees Road, Cambuslang, GLASGOW G72 8JB. ☎ 0141-641 3053.

Miller, Stephen, Dip.Theol.; St. Andrew's, Whinhall Road, AIRDRIE ML6 0HJ. ☎ 01236-763720/764755.

Mills, Joseph; Corpus Christi, 42 Lincoln Avenue, GLASGOW G13 3RG. ☎ 0141-954 3777.

Milton, Michael J.; St. Ninian's, Dickson Avenue, DUNDEE DD2 4DA. ☎ 01382-669966.

Mitchell Alexander J.; St. Mark's, Oxgangs Avenue, EDINBURGH EH13 9HX. ☎ 0131-441 3915.

Monaghan, Andrew; M.Th.; St. Mary's, 48 Main Street, PATHHEAD EH37 5QB. ☎ 01875-320266.

*Monaghan, Mgr. Thomas J.; St. Ninian's, 18 Royal Street, GOUROCK PA19 1PN. ☎ 01475-632078.

Monaghan, William A.; St. Martin's, 201 Ardencraig Road, GLASGOW G45 0JJ. ☎ 0141-634 2262.

Mone, William; Immaculate Conception, 2049 Maryhill Road, GLASGOW G20 0AA. ☎ 0141-946 2071.

*Mooney, Michael Canon (*Glasgow, Retired*), St. Michael's, 1350 Gallowgate GLASGOW G31 4DJ. ☎ 0l4l-554 0530.

Moore, Francis Paul Gabriel, B.A., A.T.C.L. (*Galloway.,retired*); 40 Woodcroft Avenue, LARGS KA30 9EW. ☎ Largs (01475) 673177.

*Moran, Peter A. Canon, Ph.L., S.T.L., M.A., M.Ed., L.T.C.L.; Catholic Church, 116 North Street, INVERURIE AB51 4TL. ☎ 01467-620319.

Morgan, George (*Glasgow, Retired*); c/o St. Saviour's, 39 Merryland Street, GLASGOW G57 2QG. ☎ 0141-445 1166.

**Morgan, Mgr. Vaughan F.J., C.B.E. (*St. Andrews.*); The Oratory School, Woodcote, Reading, Berkshire RG8 0PJ.

Morris, James, B.Phil., S.T.B., S.T.L. (Mag); St. Gabriel's, 1 Cedar Drive, Viewpark, Uddingston, GLASGOW G71 5LF. ☎ 01698-817609.

Morris, Mark, Dip.Theol.; Corpus Christi, 42 Lincoln Avenue, Glasgow G13 3RG. ☎ 0141-954 3777.

Morrison, John A.; Immaculate Conception, 2 Old Bongate, JEDBURGH TD8 6DR. ☎ 01835-862426.

Morrow, James, Ph.L., S.T.L., M.A. (*Paisley*) Humanae Vitae House, Chapel Brae, Braemar, BALLATER AB35 5YT. ☎ 013387-41380.

Morton, Paul, Ph.B., S.T.B.; Corpus Christi, Crowwood Crescent, Calderbank, AIRDRIE ML6 9TA. ☎ 01236-763670.

*Moss, Patrick J. Canon; St. John's, Blackwood, Kirkmuirhill, LANARK ML11 9RZ. ☎ 01555-893459.

Muchall, Gordon, LL.B., N.P.; St. Andrew's, 126 Victoria Street, Craigshill, LIVINGSTON EH54 5BJ. ☎ 01506-432141.

Muldoon, John (*Glasgow, Retired*); St. Joseph's, 14 Cumnock Road, Robroyston, GLASGOW G33 1QT

Muldoon, Leo; St. Peter's, 2 Buchanan Crescent, HAMILTON ML3 8LL. ☎ 01698-424721.

Mulholland, John, B.D.;St. Thomas', 826 Cumbernauld Road, GLASGOW G33 2EE. ☎ 0141-770 4057.

Mulholland, Steven P., M.A., S.T.L.; St. Mungo's, 25 Mar Street, ALLOA FK10 1HR. ☎ 01259-212486.

Mullan, Brian, C.M., B.A.; St. Mary's, 70 Bannatyne Street, LANARK ML11 7JS. ☎ 01555-662234.

Mullen, Ian; St. Clement's, Craigowan Road, DUNDEE DD2 4NJ. ☎ 01382-621658.

Mullen, Thomas; Our Lady of Lourdes, 67 Aberdour Road, DUNFERMLINE KY11 4QZ. ☎ 01383-722202.

Murphy, Damian M., Ph.B., S.T.L.; St. Paul's, Backmuir Road, Whitehill, HAMILTON ML3 0PX. ☎ 01698-424542.

Murphy, Francis (*Glasgow, Retired*); 88 Slieve Rua Drive, Stillorgan, Blackrock, Co. Dublin, Ireland.

*Murphy, James F. Canon (*Paisley, Retired*); Burlington Villa, Forbes Place, WEMYSS BAY PA18 6BL. . ☎ 01475-521394.

*Murphy, James Canon (*Paisley, Retired*); 24 Johnstone Terrace, GREENOCK PA16 8BD.

Murphy, John, M.A.;Mount Carmel, Kirkton Road, Onthank, KILMARNOCK KA3 2DF. ☎ 01563-523822..

Murphy, Joseph (*Glasgow, Retired*); Ballydesmond, Mallow, Co. Cork, Ireland.

Murphy Peter; St. Monica's, 171 Castlebay Street, GLASGOW G22 7NE. ☎ 0141-772 4348.

Murphy, Stephen, O.C.R.; Sancta Maria Abbey, Nunraw, HADDINGTON EH41 4LW.

*Murphy, Thomas J. Provost; Our Lady of Lourdes and St. Patrick's, 35 Sorn Road, Auchinleck, CUMNOCK KA18 2HR. ☎ 01290-421521.

*Murphy, Thomas Canon (*Glasgow, Retired*); Immaculate Conception, 2049 Maryhill Road, GLASGOW G20 0AA. ☎ 0141-946 2071.

Murray, James, S.M.M.;Montfort House, Darnley Road, Barrhead, GLASGOW G78 1TA. ☎ 0141-881 1440.

Murray, Noel, B.Th.; St. Aloysius', 10 Hillkirk Street, GLASGOW G21 1TH. ☎ 0141-558 5495.

Murray, Paul G., B.Sc., Ph.B., S.T.L.; St. Bartholomew's, 32 Croftfoot Drive, GLASGOW G45 0NG. ☎ 0141-634 2051.

**Murray, Mgr. Thomas Canon, S.T.L. (*Glasgow, Retired*); 7 Moore Drive, South Colgrain, Helensburgh G84 7LE. ☎ 01436-676531.

Murtagh, Brendan J., B.A.; Our Lady and St. Mark's, Ferry Loan, Bank Street, ALEXANDRIA G83 0UW. ☎ 01389-752091.

Naughton, James; Our Lady and St. Joseph's, South Medrox Street, Glenboig, COATBRIDGE ML5 2RU. ☎ 01236-872608.

Nelson, Andrew J., Ph.B., S.T.L.; Cathedral House, 31 Coursington Road, MOTHERWELL ML1 1PP. ☎ 01698-263045.

Nicol, James G., Ph.B., S.T.B., J.C.L.; St. Anthony's, Mar Gardens, Springhall, Rutherglen,GLASGOW G73 5JE.☎0141-634 4909.

*Nolan, Thomas Canon; Cathedral House, Cathedral Precincts, Incle Street, PAISLEY PA1 1HR. ☎0141-889 2404.

Nolan, William, S.T.L.; Our Lady of Lourdes, 30 Canberra Drive, East Kilbride, GLASGOW G75 8DG. ☎ 01355-224511.

Norman, Leonard, O.C.R., B.Sc.; Sancta Maria Abbey, Nunraw, HADDINGTON EH41 4LW.

Nugent, Gerard; St. Patrick's, 137 William Street, GLASGOW G3 8UR.☎ 0141-221 3579.

Nugent, Kenneth, S.J.; Catholic Presbytery, Main Street, KIRKWALL KW15 1BU. ☎ 01856-872462.

***O'Brien**, Eamon Canon (*S.Andr., Retired*); St. Andrew's, 77 Belford Road, Edinburgh EH4 3DS. ☎ 0131-343 1217.

O'Brien, Gerard, C.P.; 159 Warriston Street, Glasgow G33 2LA

O'Brien, Henry, S.T.D.; Pastoral Centre, 50 Bonkle Road, Newmains, WISHAW ML2 9AP. ☎ 01698-385397.

O'Brien, Thomas, M.H.M., B.D., Ph.L.; St. Joseph's House, 30 Lourdes Avenue, GLASGOW G52 3QU. ☎ 0141-883 0139.

O'Connell, Con, O.F.M.; St. Patrick's, 5 South Grey's Close, 40 High Street, EDINBURGH EH1 1TQ. ☎ 0131-556 1973.

*O'Connell, James Canon (*Paisley, Retired*); 39 Paisley Road, Barrhead, GLASGOW G78 1HW. . ☎ 0141-881 3304.

O'Connor, Bernard, O.S.A.; SS. Peter and Paul, 29 Byron Street, DUNDEE DD3 6QN. ☎ 01382-825067.

*O'Connor, Michael Canon (*S. Andrews, Retired*); General Hospital, Skibbereen, Co. Cork. Ireland.

O'Connor, Michael, O.M.I.; St. John Ogilvie's, 159 Sighthill Drive, EDINBURGH EH11 4PY.☎ 0131-453 5035.

*O'Donnell, Hugh Canon; St. Mary's, 150 Shawhill Road, GLASGOW G43 1SY. ☎ 0141-632 1726.

O'Donnell, Neil, B.A., B.D., Dip.Ed., Dip.R.E.; St. Andrew's & St. Cuthbert's, High Street, KIRKCUDBRIGHT DG6 4JW. ☎01557-330687.

O'Dowd, Sean, B.A.; St. Patrick's, Buchlyvie, STIRLING FK8 3PB. *Tel.*: 01360-850274.

O'Dwyer, Noel, O.F.M.; Bl. John Duns Scotus, 270 Ballater Street, GLASGOW G5 0YT. ☎ 0141-429 0740.

O'Farrell, Charles J., B.Sc., S.T.B.; St. Aidan's 298 Coltness Road, WISHAW ML2 7EX. ☎ 01698-384730.

*O'Farrell, John Canon, O.B.E., R.D., J.P.; Immaculate Conception, 41 High Street, Lochee, DUNDEE DD2 3AP. ☎ 01382-611282.

O'Farrell, Kieran Canon; St. Mary's, Main Street, Cleland, MOTHERWELL ML1 5QR. ☎ 01698-860254.

**O'Farrell,Mgr.Peter, B.Th.; St. Matthew's, 2 South Crosshill Road, Bishopbriggs, GLASGOW G64 2LZ. ☎ 0141-772 1619.

O'Flynn, Jeremiah Canon, Ph.L., *(Glasgow, Retired)*; 24 Benvoirlich Estate, Cork, Ireland.

O'Gorman, Benedict *(Galloway)*; c/o Candida Casa, 8 Corsehill Road, AYR KA7 2ST.

O'Grady, Martin *(Motherwell, Retired);* Carrigoran House, Newmarket-on-Fergus, Co. Clare, Ireland. ☎ 061368-100.

O'Hagan, John; St. Joachim's, 102 Inzievar Terrace, Carmyle, GLASGOW G32 8JT. ☎ 0141-641 1517.

O'Hara, James; St. Mark's, Fernhill Road, Rutherglen, GLASGOW G73 4DA. ☎ 0141-634 3053.

*O'Hare, Patrick J. Canon; St. Thomas', 12 Tarbert Avenue, WISHAW ML2 0JH. ☎ 01698-372775.

O'Hare, Thomas; St. Anne's, Jack Street, HAMILTON ML3 7QP. ☎ 01698-423044.

O'Kane, James, S.T.B., J.C.L.; St. Cuthbert's, 98 High Blantyre Road, Burnbank, HAMILTON ML3 9HW. ☎ 01698-823105.

O'Kane, John, C.P.; St. Mungo's Retreat, 52 Parson Street, GLASGOW G4 0RX. ☎ 0141-552 1823.

O'Keeffe, Benedict, M.Agr.Sc.: St. Andrew's, Auchmead Road, Larkfield, GREENOCK PA16 0JU. ☎ 01475-631750.

O'Keeffe, Martin *(Motherwell, Retired);* 3 Sarazen Court, Knightsridge, LIVINGSTON EH54 8SW.

O'Keeffe, Michael *(Glasgow, Retired);* Derryvillane, Mitchelstown, Co. Cork, Ireland.

O'Leary, Cornelius F.; St. Mary's, Glen Road, Caldercruix, AIRDRIE ML6 7PZ. ☎ 01236-842220.

O'Leary, Michael *(Motherwell)*; c/o Diocesan Office, Coursington Road, MOTHERWELL ML1 1PP.

O'Mahony, Humphrey; Christ the King, 170 Main Street, Holytown, MOTHERWELL ML1 4TJ. ☎ 01698-732352.

Ommer, Francis Gilmour, M.R.C.V.S. *(Galloway, Retired)*; 464 Downall Green, North Ashton, WIGAN WN4 0NA. ☎ 01942-721712.

O'Neill, James Vincent, S.J.; Sacred Heart, 28 Lauriston Street, EDINBURGH EH3 9DJ. ☎ 0131-229 9104.

O'Neill, Sean *(Glasgow, Retired)*; I Earn Road, TROON KA10 7DS. ☎ 01292-318913.

O'Reilly, James E. *(Glasgow, Retired)*;Flat 2, Clifford Court, 271 Nithsdale Road, GLASGOW G41 5LS. ☎ 0141-419 0844.

O'Riordan, Jeremiah *(Motherwell, Sick leave)*; c/o Diocesan Centre, Coursington Road, MOTHERWELL ML1 1PP.

O'Rourke Francis; St. Michael's, 1350 Gallowgate, GLASGOW G31 4DJ. ☎ 0141-554 0530.

O'Rourke, Thomas; St. Peter's Presbytery, Howatshaws Road, DUMBARTON G82 3DR. ☎ 01389-764131.

**Osborne, Mgr. Patrick; Sacred Heart Church, Kyle Road, Kildrum, Cumbernauld, GLASGOW G67 2DY. ☎ 01236-721387

O'Shea, Sean *(Motherwell, Retired)*; West End, Castletownbere, Co. Cork, Ireland.

*O'Sullivan, Basil Canon, J.C.L.; St. Clare, Claredon Place, DUNBLANE FK15 9HB. ☎ 01786-822146.

O'Sullivan, Eugene; St. Francis', Tullideph Road, DUNDEE DD2 2PN. ☎ 01382-668007.

O'Sullivan, Patrick; St. Andrew's, Whinhall Road, AIRDRIE ML6 0HJ. ☎ 01236-763720.

O'Sullivan, William; St. Barbara's, Elmira Road, Muirhead, GLASGOW G69 9EJ. ☎ 0141-779 2286.

Owens, Kenneth J., B.Sc., Ph.B., S.T.L., M.P.S.; St. John Vianney's, 40 Fernieside Gardens, Gilmerton, EDINBURGH EH17 7HN. ☎ 0131-658 1793/664 4349.

Paloschi, Emilio, S.X.; Xaverian Mission Centre, Calder Avenue, COATBRIDGE ML5 4JS.

Parkes, Bernard, S.D.B., B.A., C.Q.S.W.; St. Benedict's, 755 Westerhouse Road, GLASGOW G34 9RP. ☎ 0141-771 1991.

Parkinson, Henry, B.A., H.Dip.Ed. *(Glasgow, Retired)*; 25F Skaterigg Gardens, Glasgow G13 1ST. ☎ 0141-954 2877.

Parsons, Anthony, O.C.D.; Mount Carmel, 61 Hamilton Avenue, GLASGOW G41 4HA. ☎ 0141-427 0794.

Peat, James, B.D.; SS. John Cantius and Nicholas, 34 West Main Street, BROXBURN EH52 5RJ. ☎ 01506-852040.

Pidluskyj, Lubomyr; 6 Mansion House Road, EDINBURGH EH9 1TŽ. ☎ 0131-553 7595/667 5993.

Poland, Martin D.; St. Sophia's, Bentinck Street, GALSTON KA4 8HT. ☎ 01563-820339.

Pollock, Robert O.P., B.A. M.A., Ph.D.; Blackfriars, 36 Queen's Drive, GLASGOW G42 8DD. ☎ 0141-423 2971.

Portelli, Joseph; St. Mary's, Bowmont Street, KELSO TD5 7DZ. ☎ 01573-224725.

Porter, Adrian, S.J.; Flat 3, 56 Bentinck Street, GLASGOW G3 7TT.

Postlethwaite, Basil, B.A. (S. Andrews); Casa Parroquial, Dulce Nombre de Maria, Dept. de Chalatenango, El Salvador.

Power, Denis A. (Motherwell, Retired); St. Joseph's Centre, Crinken Lanc, Shankill, Co. Dublin, Ireland.

Prior, Gerard; St. Peter's, 9 Carmondean Centre, Carmondean, LIVINGSTON EH54 8PT. ☎ 01506-438787.

Purcell, Leonard A.; St. Peter's, 46 Hyndland Street, GLASGOW G11 5PS. ☎ 0141-576 1378; Minicom (Voice and Text): 0141-357 5772.

Purcell, Michael, Ph.L., M.A., Ph.D., Drs.; St. Mary of the Angels, 100 Glasgow Road, Camelon, FALKIRK FK1 4HJ. ☎ 01324-620138.

Puton, Tadeusz Adam, S.A.C.; 1 Barony Place, EDINBURGH EH3 6PB. ☎ 0131-558 3726.

*Quinlan, Denis F. Canon; St. Joseph's, 15A Hill Street, KILMARNOCK KA3 1HA. ☎ 01563-521832.

**Quinlan, Mgr. Martin Provost (Glasgow, Retired); Nazareth House, 1647 Paisley Road West, GLASGOW G52 3QT.

Quinlan, Sean, O.S.A.; SS. Peter and Paul, 29 Byron Street, DUNDEE DD3 6QN. ☎ 01382-825067.

Quinn, Dominic, Ph.B., S.T.L.; St. Vincent de Paul's, Tinto Way, Greenhills, East Kilbride, GLASGOW G75 9DQ. ☎ 01355-243619.

Quinn, James, S.J.; Sacred Heart, 28 Lauriston Street, EDINBURGH EH3 9DJ.☎ 0131-229 9104.

*Quinn, Joseph Canon; St. Joseph's, 1 Forbes Place, WEMYSS BAY PA18 6AU. ☎ 01475-520272.

*Rae, James Canon; St. John's, 3 Sandford Gardens, EDINBURGH EH15 1LP. ☎ 0131-669 5447.

Randall, Peter, S.J.;Sacred Heart, 28 Lauriston Street, EDINBURGH EH3 9DJ. ☎ 0131-229 9821.

Randolph, Hugh, O.C.R.; Sancta Maria Abbey, Nunraw, HADDINGTON EH41 4LW.

Ratcliffe, Gerard, C.Ss.R.; Wellburn Cottage, 120 Liff Road, Lochee, DUNDEE DD2 2QT.☎ 01382-622212.

Rawlings, Frederick (Glasgow., Retired); Tig na Sagart, Portnoo, Co Donegal, Ireland.

*Reen, Andrew Canon; Sacred Heart, 106 Crossgates, BELLSHILL ML4 2LB. ☎ 01698-842709.

Regan, Michael B., B.A., M.Litt., M.Th., D.E.A. (St. Andrews and Edinburgh); Scotus College, 2 Chesters Road, Bearsden, GLASGOW G61 4AG. ☎ 0141-942 8384.

*Reid, Andrew Canon *(Paisley, Retired)*; St. Mary's, 14 Patrick Street, GREENOCK PA16 8NA. ☎ 01475-731823.

Reid, John, O.S.A., S.T.L.; St. Joseph's, 20A Broomhouse Place North, EDINBURGH EH11 3UE . ☎ 0131 443 3777.

Reihill, Seamus, B.A.; St. Patrick's, Buchlyvie, STIRLING FK8 3PB. ☎ 01360-850274.

Reilly, Brian C., M.A., S.T.B., L.S.S.; St. Brigid's, 12 Prospecthill Crescent, GLASGOW G42 0JN. ☎ 0141-647 3585.

Reilly, James V. *(Glasgow, Retired)*; 3 Ardenvohr, Main Road, Cardross, DUMBARTON G82 5JX. ☎ 01389-841194.

Reilly, Patrick T.; c/o Diocesan Office,c/o St. Lawrence's, 6 Kilmacolm Road, GREENOCK PA15 4XP

Reilly, Stephen M.C., Ph.B., S.T.L.; St. Bride's, Fallside Road, Bothwell, GLASGOW G71 8BA. ☎ 01698-852710.

Rhatigan, Thomas, M.A.*(S.Andrews, Retired)*; St. Philomena's, Niddry Road, Winchburgh, BROXBURN EH52 6RY. ☎ 01506-891310.

Richardson, Anselm M, O.S.M.; St. Vincent de Paul's, 145 Kingsway East, DUNDEE DD4 8AA. ☎ 01382-500446.

Richardson, Niven, M.A., B.D. *(Motherwell)*; c/o Diocesan Centre, Coursington Road, MOTHERWELL ML1 1PP.

Roberts, John; Flat 7, Maryville Flats, 14 Cumnock Road, Robroyston, GLASGOW G33 1QT. ☎ 0141-558 2185.

Robinson, Benedict; *(St. Andrews, Retired);* Jericho House, 14 Shankland Road, GREENOCK PA15 2NE

Robinson, John G.; St. Joseph's, 17 Rosetta Road, PEEBLES EH45 8JU. ☎ 01721-720865.

Robson, Stephen, B.Sc., M.Th., C.Biol., M.I.Biol.*(S.Andrews)*; Pontificio Collegio Scozzese, Via Cassia 481, 00189 Roma, Italy. ☎ + 39 06 3366 8085.

Rodgers, George; SS. Mary and David, 15 Buccleuch Street, HAWICK TD9 0HH. ☎ 01450-372037.

Rodgers, Richard J.; St. Vincent de Paul's, Tinto Way, Greenhills, East Kilbride, GLASGOW G75 9DQ. ☎ 01355-243619.

*Rogerson, John Canon *(S. Andrews, Retired)*; The Hermitage, 115 Whitehouse Loan, EDINBURGh EH9 1BB. ☎ 0131-447 9740.

Rooney, Daniel; St. Luke's, Davaar Drive, Braidhurst, MOTHERWELL ML1 3TW. ☎ 01698-230402.

Rooney, Jim, Dip.Theol.; St. Pius X, 4 Bayfield Terrace, GLASGOW G15 7EJ. ☎ 0141-944 2044.

Rooney, Stephen, Dip. Theol.; St. Columbkille's, 2 Kirkwood Street, Rutherglen, GLASGOW G73 2SL. ☎ 0141-647 6034..

*Rossi, Mgr. Gaetano Canon *(Glasgow, Retired)*; 16 Heriot Crescent, Bishopbriggs, GLASGOW G64 3NG. ☎ 0141-772 7989.

*Rourke, Patrick J. Canon *(S.Andrews, Retired)*; Climber Hall, Kells, Co. Meath, Ireland.

*Rowan, Nicholas Canon; St. Brigid's, 12 Prospecthill Crescent, GLASGOW G42 0JN. ☎ 0141-647 3585.

**Ryan, Mgr. James, M.R.Ed.; St. Peter's, 46 Hyndland Street, GLASGOW G11 5PS. ☎ 0141-576 1378.

Ryan, Kevin, S.X., S.T.B., M.A.; Xaverian Mission Centre, Calder Avenue, COATBRIDGE ML5 4JS. ☎ 01236-606364.

Ryan, Michael; St. Bride's Church, Whitemoss Avenue, East Kilbride, GLASGOW G74 1NN. ☎ 01355-220005.

Sarelo, Zbigniew; St. Francis Xavier's, 1 Hope Street, FALKIRK FK1 5AT. ☎ 01324-623567.

Savage, Mark, O.S.B., LL.B.; Pluscarden Abbey, ELGIN IV30 8UA.

Savage, Michael *(on Sabbatical)*; St. Pius X, 4 Bayfield Terrace, GLASGOW G15 7EJ. ☎ 0141-944 2044.

Scally, John, B.D.; St. John and St. Columba's, 137 Admiralty Road, Rosyth, DUNFERMLINE KY11 2QL. ☎ 01383-412084.

Scott, Walter, M.A., LL.B., S.T.L. *(Motherwell, Retired)*; 128 Crawford Street, MOTHERWELL ML1 3BN.

Seed, Michael Benedict, O.S.B., S.T.L., B.Sc.; The Bungalow, Gower Street, BRORA KW9 6PU. ☎ 01408-621388.

Senespleda, Joseph, S.J.; Sacred Heart, 28 Lauriston Street, EDINBURGH EH3 9DJ. ☎ 0131-229 9104.

Shankland, David *(Paisley)*; 9913 Abfaltersbach 24, Austria.

Sharkey, Michael *(Glasgow, R.N. Chaplain)*; c/o Principal R.C. Chaplain (R.N.), MOD Chaplains (Naval), Room 281, Victory Building, H.M. Naval Base, Portsmouth PO1 3LS.

Sharkey, Stephen, B.D. Dip.Ph.;St. Andrew's, 27 Brooke Street, DUMFRIES DG1 2JL. ☎ 01387-254281.

Sharp, James *(Paisley)*; Padres de San Columbano, Casilla 787, Arica, Chile.

Sharp, Neil *(Paisley.)*; Padres de San Columbano, Casilla 787, Arica, Chile.

*Sheahan, Denis J.Canon; Holy Rosary Home, 44 Union Street, GREENOCK PA16 8NA. ☎ 01475-722465/888660.

Sheary, John, S.T.L.; St. Ronan's, Ladyton Estate, Bonhill, ALEXANDRIA G83 9EA. ☎ 01389-759457.

*Sheehan, James J. Canon *(Paisley., Retired);* Manorhamilton, Co. Leitrim, Ireland.

*Sheehan, Malachy, O.M.I.; St. Mary, Star of the Sea, 106 Constitution Street, Leith, EDINBURGH EH6 6AW. ☎ 0131-554 2482/467 7449.

Sheridan, Hugh *(Motherwell, Retired)*; 2 Toberdoney Fold, Kilrea, Co. Derry, Northern Ireland BT51 5QS.

**Sheridan, Mgr. John; St. Paul's, 1213 Dumbarton Road, GLASGOW G14 9UP. ☎ 0141-950 2488.

Sheridan, Michael G. *(Paisley, Retired);* Burlington Villa, Forbes Place, WEMYSS BAY PA18 6BL

Sherry, Michael, O.C.R.; Sancta Maria Abbey, Nunraw, HADDINGTON EH41 4LW.

Shields, Thomas J., Ph.B., S.T.L. *(Dunkeld);* Real Colegio de Escoceses, Avda. de Champagnat 121-133, 37007 Salamanca, Spain. ☎ (00 34) 923 25 40 11.

*Simcox, James Canon, B.A.; St. Martin's, 331 Main Street, Renton, DUMBARTON G82 4PZ. ☎ 01389-752089.

**Simpson, Mgr. Daniel P. (S. *Andrews, Retired*); The Hermitage, 115 Whitehouse Loan, EDINBURGH EH9 1BB. ☎ 0131-447 6210.

Skelley, Charles Stewart, S.J.; St. Joseph's House, 43 Gilmore Place, EDINBURGH EH3 9NG. ☎ 0131-229 5672.

Slavin, William J., C.Psychol.; St. Charles', 1 Kelvinside Gardens, GLASGOW G20 6BG. ☎ 0141-946 7622.

Sloan, Michael; St. Ninian's, 232 Marionville Road, EDINBURGH EH7 6BE.. ☎ 0131-661 2867.

Small, James; St. Catherine's, Westcraigs Road, Harthill, SHOTTS ML7 5SW. ☎ 01501 -751589.

Smith, Brendan *(Motherwell, on sick leave)*; Littlebridge, Moneymore, Co. Derry, N. Ireland.

Smith, James; St. Joseph's, 49 Raeburn Crescent, Whitburn, BATHGATE EH47 8HQ. ☎ 01501-740348.

**Smith, Mgr. Peter, J.C.L.; St. Conval's, 21 Hapland Road, GLASGOW G53 5NT. ☎ 0141-810 4976..

*Smyth, Kevin A. Canon *(Dunkeld, Retired)*; Crossroads Cottage, Leitfie, Meigle, BLAIRGOWRIE PH11 8NZ. ☎ 018284-338.

*Somers, Richard Canon, B.A. (S. *Andr., Retired)*; Carrigetna, Kilmoganny, Co Kilkenny, Ireland.

Spencer, Michael H., S.J.; Wellcross, 193 Nithsdale Road, GLASGOW G41 5EX ☎ 0141-423 3005.

*Spencer. Paul Francis, C.P.; St. Mungo's Retreat, 52 Parson Street, GLASGOW G4 0RX. ☎ 0141-552 1823.

Sproule, William P. *(Motherwell, Retired);* 41 Maghernageer Road, Castlederg, Co. Tyrone, N. Ireland. *Tel.*: 01662-6 71673.

*Sreenan, Hugh J. Canon; St. Stephen's, 8 Bank Street, BLAIRGOWRIE PH10 6DE. ☎ 01250-872171.

*Stanley, Charles T. Canon; Our Lady of Aberdeen, 70 Cairngorm Crescent, ABERDEEN AB12 5BR. ☎ 01224-876704.

Stevenson, Ian, B.D., L.H.C.I.M.A., Dip.Couns., Dip.Sup.; St. Peter's, 154 Braehead Road, PAISLEY PA2 8NG. ☎ 0141-884 2435.

Stewart, Alexander, Dip.Theol; Our Lady of Lourdes, 30 Canberra Drive, East Kilbride, GLASGOW G75 8DG. ☎ 01355-224511.

Stewart, Colin M., Ph.D., M.Ed.., S.T.B.; St. Michael's, Main Street, Tomintoul, BALLINDALLOCH AB37 9EX. ☎ 01807-580226.

*Stone, Duncan Canon *(Aberdeen, Retired)*; 9 Cathedral Square, FORTROSE IV10 8TB. ☎ 01381-621088.

Strachan, Alexander, B.D.; St. Margaret Mary's, 99 Dougrie Road, GLASGOW G45 9NT. ☎ 0141-634 6152.

Sullivan, Joseph E., Ph.B., S.T.L ;Our Lady of Lourdes, 51 Lourdes Avenue, GLASGOW G52 3QU. ☎ 0141-882 1024.

Suszko, George, S.A.C.; St. Columba's, 143 Marina Road, Boghall, BATHGATE EH48 1RS. ☎ Bathgate (01506)653955.

Swanston, Prof. Hamish, Obl.C.Ss.R.; St. Mary's, Hatton Road, Kinnoull, PERTH PH2 7BP. ☎ 01736-624075.

Sweeney, Anthony; St. Benedict's, 60 Drumchapel Road, GLASGOW G15 6QE. ☎ 0141-944 1767.

Sweeney, Eamonn J.; St. Patrick's, 1 St. John Street, COATBRIDGE ML5 3HB. ☎ 01236-606808.

Sweeney James, C.P.; 45 Queen Mary Avenue, GLASGOW G42 8DS. ☎ 0141-423 0051.

Sweeney, Peter; St. John Ogilvie's, 97 Wellhouse Crescent, GLASGOW G33 4HF. ☎ 0141-771 3125.

Symon, John Canon, M.A., Ph.L., S.T.L. *(Aberdeen, Retired)*; Nazareth House, 34 Claremont Street, ABERDEEN AB10 6RA. ☎ 01224-582091.

*Szuberlak, Boleslaw Canon *(Retired)*; 40 Broughton Road, EDINBURGH EH7 4ED. *TEL.:* 0131-556 4142.

Tabone, Loreto; St. Mary's, 15 Upper Bridge Street, STIRLING FK8 1ES. ☎ 01786-473749.

Tartaglia, Gerard, Ph.B., S.T.B., J.C.L.; St. Mary's, 150 Shawhill Road, GLASGOW G43 1SY. ☎ 0141-632 1726.

Tartaglia, Philip, Ph.B., S.T.D.; St. Mary's, Chapel Road, Duntocher, CLYDEBANK G81 6DL. ☎ 01389-873280.

Taylor, Christopher G., S.T.B.; St. Teresa's, Benford Avenue, Newarthill, MOTHERWELL ML1 5BE. ☎ 01698-832920.

Taylor, John; St. Cuthbert's, 98 High Blantyre Road, Burnbank, HAMILTON ML3 9HW. ☎ 01698-823105.

Tedeschi, Sabatino; St. Charles', 1 Kelvinside Gardens, GLASGOW G20 6BG. ☎ 0141-946 2769.

*Terry, Joseph Canon *(Argyll, Retired)*; c/o Diocesan Office, St. Columba's Cathedral, Corran Esplanade, OBAN PA34 5AB

Thompson, George, M.A., Dip.Ed.; St. Peter's, Craignair Street, DALBEATTIE DG5 4AX. *TEL.:* 01556-610358.

Thomson, James *(Motherwell)*; St. Columba's, Corsee Cottage, 5 High Street, BANCHORY AB31 5RP. ☎ 01330-822835.

Timoney, Bartholomew, O.F.M., L.R.A.M., A.R.C.M.; St. Patrick's, 5 South Grey's Close, 40 High Street, EDINBURGH EH1 1TQ. ☎ 0131-556 1973.

Toal, Joseph, S.T.B. *(Argyll and The Isles);* Real Colegio de Escoceses, Avda. de Champagnat 121-133, 37007 Salamanca, Spain. ☎ (00 34) 923 25 40 11.

Tobin, Patrick *(Glasgow, Retired)*; Castletown, Killeagh, Co. Cork, Ireland. ☎ 00353 21 668304.

*Tobin, William Canon *(Glasgow, Retired)*; 98 Balmuildy Road, Bishopbriggs, GLASGOW G64 3EP.

Tolan, Andrew; St. Dominic's, 21 Kirriemuir Road, Woodhill, Bishopbriggs, GLASGOW G64 1DL. ☎ 0141-762 1154.

Toner, Gerald A., S.M.A., M.A.; St. Theresa's, Abbey House, Claredon Place, DUNBLANE FK15 9HB. ☎ 01786-824002.

Tormey, John, Ph.L., S.T.L.; St. Fergus', 35 Blackstoun Road, PAISLEY PA3 1LU. ☎ 0141-889 5056.

Torrens, Alberic, O.F.M.; St. Patrick's, 5 South Gray's Close, 40 High Street, EDINBURGH EH1 1TQ. ☎ 0131-556 1973.

*Tortolano, Godfrey, O.F.M.; St. Patrick's, 5 South Gray's Close, 40 High Street, EDINBURGH EH1 1TQ. ☎ 0131-556 1973.

Tosh, Alistair G.; St. Mary's, 28 Greenock Road, LARGS KA30 8NE. ☎ 01475-672324.

Towey, Dominic M.; St. John Ogilvie's, Broompark Road, Blantyre, GLASGOW G72 9XD. ☎ 01698-828774.

Toy, Daniel *(Glasgow, Retired)*; 93 Holmscroft Street, GREENOCK PA15 4DP

Tracey, David; Our Lady and St. Margaret's, 20 Marine Gardens, GLASGOW G51 1HH. ☎0141-427 7505.

Tracey, James G.; Holy Cross, 11 Bangholm Loan, EDINBURGH EH5 3AH. ☎ 0131-552 3957.

Trainer, David; St. Columba's,74 Hopehill Road,GLASGOW G20 7HH. ☎ 0141-332 4530.

Traynor, Edward P., Ph.B., S.T.B., Lic.Psych., J.P.; St. Peter's, BUCKIE AB56 1QN. ☎ 01542-832196.

Trench, Thomas; St. David's, Meadowhead Road, Plains, AIRDRIE ML6 7JF ☎ 01236-763226.

**Tweedie, Mgr. John *(S.Andrews, Retired);* Flat 50, Springbank Gardens, FALKIRK FK2 7DF. ☎ 01324-639928.

Twist, John,S.J.; St. Aloysius' 10 Woodside Place, GLASGOW G3 7QF. ☎ 0141-332 3039.

*Urquhart, John Canon; St. Bernadette's, 323 Main Street, LARBERT FK5 4EU. ☎ 01324-553250.

Vesey, Edward *(Glasg.)*; Parroquia Santa Marianita, Casilla 5823, Guayaquil, Ecuador.

Waite, David, O.Carm.: Elphinstone House, 7 High Street, Old Aberdeen, ABERDEEN AB24 3EE. ☎ 01224-482444.

Wallace, David J., Ph.B., S.T.L.;St. Patrick's Presbytery, Strathleven Place, DUMBARTOn G82 1BA. ☎ 01389-762503.

Wallace, James; St. Bernadette's, Baingle Brae, Tullibody, ALLOA FK10 2SG. ☎ 01259-213274.

*Wallbank, Christopher, M.Afr., Th.L.; St. Joseph's, 9 Milrig Road, Rutherglen, GLASGOW G73 2NG. ☎0141–647 3806/613 0209..

*Walls, Andrew M.; St. Vincent de Paul's, 145 Kingsway East, DUNDEE DD4 8AA. ☎ 01382-500446.

*Walls, John Canon, S.T.L.; St. Teresa's, Glasgow Road, DUMFRIES DG2 9DE. ☎ 01387-252603.

Walls, Roland C., M.A.; 23 Manse Road, ROSLIN EH25 9LF.

Walls, Ronald J., M.A., Dip.Ed. *(Aberdeen, Retired)*; 54 Aird Street, Portsoy, BANFF AB45 2RB. ☎ 01261-842950.

Walsh, Anthony *(Glasgow, Retired)*; 3 Warren Street, GLASGOW G42 8AQ. ☎ 0141-423 4607.

Walsh, Donald, O.F.M.; Bl. John Duns Scotus, 270 Ballater Street, GLASGOW G5 0YT. ☎ 0141-429 0740.

Walsh, James B. (S *Andrews.,Retired)*; Sancta Maria, Ballyness, Falcarragh, Letterkenny, Co. Donegal, Ireland.

Walsh, James L., S.T.D.; St. Basil's College, 95 St. Joseph Street, Toronto. M5S 2R9, Canada.

Walsh, John *(Galloway, Retired)*; 31 Mansfield Road, PRESTWICK KA9 2DN. ☎ 01292-476179.

Walsh, Joseph, S.T.L.; Our Lady of Consolation, 113 Dixon Avenue, GLASGOW G42 8EL. ☎ 0141-423 5188.

Walsh, Joseph, M.H.M.; Nazareth House, 13 Hillhead, BONNYRIGG EH19 2JF. ☎ 0131-654 2513.

Walsh, Michael (S. *Andrews)*; The Presbytery, Mountcollins, Abbeyfeale, Co. Limerick, Ireland.

Walsh, Michael; St. Aloysius', Main Street, Chapelhall, AIRDRIE ML6 8SF ☎ 01236-763190.

Walsh, Michael J., S.M.A., M.A., Dip.Ed.; S.M.A. Fathers, St. Theresa's, Abbey House, Claredon Place, DUNBLANE FK15 9HB. ☎ 01786-824002.

Walsh, Patrick *(Motherwell, Retired)*; 7 Henderson Road, TROON KA10 6NB.☎01292-315407.

Walsh, Philip M., O.S.M.; St. Vincent de Paul's, Kingsway East, DUNDEE DD4 8AA. ☎ 01382-500446.

Ward, David Francis, F.S.A.Scot.; Our Lady of Lourdes, 42 Struan Road, Letham, PERTH PH1 2JP. ☎ 01738-623902.

Ward, John F, B.A.; 'Dunavard', Station Road, Garelochhead, HELENSBURGH G84 0DB. ☎ 01436-810498.

Ward, John L. *(Motherwell, Retired)*; St. Joseph's Centre, Crinken Lane, Shankill, Co. Dublin, Ireland.

**Ward, Mgr. Maurice, Ph.L., S.T.L.; St. Joseph's, 41 Lomond Street, HELENSBURGH G84 7ET. ☎ 01436-672463.

Warner, Camillus, O.S.B.; Pluscarden Abbey, ELGIN IV30 8UA.

Warren, Martin Troubridge-, O.C.R.; Sancta Maria Abbey, Nunraw, HADDINGTON EH41 4LW.

Welsh, Francis (S. *Andrews, Retired)*; c/o Whyte, 241 Muiryhall Street, COATBRIDGE ML5 3NR.

Welsh, Thomas, S.X.; Xaverian Mission Centre, Calder Avenue, COATBRIDGE ML5 4JS. ☎ 01236-606364.

Whelan, Seamus, B.A.; St. Patrick's, Buchlyvie, STIRLING FK8 3PB. ☎ 01360-850274.

White, Hugh G., S.T.L., L.S.S.; St. Matthew's, 36 Carnethie Street, ROSEWELL EH24 9AT. ☎ 0131-440 2150.

White, Thomas P., Ph.B., S.T.B.; St. Maria Goretti's, 259 Bellrock Street, GLASGOW G33 3LN. ☎ 0141-774 4151.

White, William *(Motherwell, Retired);* c/o Diocesan Centre, Coursington Road, MOTHERWELL ML1 1PP. *Tel.;* 01698-269114.

Whitehead, Gerard Maurus, O.S.B.; Nazareth House, 34 Claremont Street, ABERDEEN AB10 6RA.

Wilson, Alan, S.T.B. *(Galloway, R.A.F. Chaplain)*; c/o Principal Chaplain, Chaplaincy Services, HQ PTC, R.A.F. Innsworth, Gloucester GL3 1EZ.

*Wilson Ian, O.S.A.; SS. Peter and Paul, 29 Byron Street, DUNDEE DD3 6QN. ☎ 01382-825067.

Wolstenholme, Anthony, M.C.C.J.; Comboni Missionaries, 138 Carmyle Avenue, Carmyle, GLASGOW G32 8DL. ☎ 0141-641 4399.

Woodford, Michael, Ph.B., S.T.B., Dip.Past.Theol.; All Saints', 567 Broomfield Road, GLASGOW G21 3HW. ☎ 0141-558 7824.

*Woods, Alphonsus Canon *(Motherwell, Retired)*; 9 Coltpark Avenue, Bishopbriggs, GLASGOW G64 2AT. ☎ 0141-772 1185.

**Woods, Mgr. John Noel, M.P.S.; St. Joseph's, 14 Fullarton Avenue, GLASGOW G32 8NA. ☎ 0141-778 1054.

Woods, Patrick; St. Anthony's, Hallhill Road, JOHNSTONE PA5 0SD. ☎ 01505-702284.

**Wynne, Mgr. Thomas, B.D.; St. Margaret's, ROY BRIDGE PH31 4AE. ☎ 01398-712238.

Zanon, Paul, S.X.; Xaverian Mission Centre, Calder Avenue, COATBRIDGE ML5 4JS. ☎ 01236-606364.

PERMANENT DEACONS

Cafferty, Michael; c/o St. Mungo's, 25 Mar Street, ALLOA FK10 1HR.

Cameron, George *(Aberdeen)*; 400 East Monroe Street, Phoenix, Arizona, 85004-2376, U.S.A.

Campbell, John, Dip.Tech.Ed., H.N.C., F.T.C.; c/o St. Mary's Rectory, 22 Powrie Place, DUNDEE DD1 2PQ.

Clark, Thomas; c/o St. Francis', Tullideph Road, DUNDEE DD2 2PN.

Connelly, David; 7 Balhousie Street, PERTH PH1 5HJ.

Cooke, Jacques, C.Eng., M.I.Chem.E.; 42 Kenneth Street, INVERNESS IV3 5DH. ☎ 01463-230670.

Cousins, Anthony, M.A., Dip.Ed.; c/o St. Stephen's, 8 Bank Street, BLAIRGOWRIE PH10 6DE. ☎ 01250-872171.

Douglas, Dr. James *(Motherwell, Retired)*; 7 Barriedale Avenue, HAMILTON ML3 9DB.

Dowds, Joseph 7 Glenfalloch, East Kilbride, GLASGOW G74 2JL

Forsyth, David; c/o St. Bride's, 80 High Street, Monifieth, DUNDEE DD5 4AG.

Futers, John, Corpus Christi, 16 Dunvegan Avenue, Portlethen, ABERDEEN AB12 4NE.

Fyffe, David, Dip.Com., B.A.; c/o St. Leonard and St. Fergus, St. Leonard's Place, DUNDEE DD3 9HD.

Gordon, Ian, M.A.; c/o St. Fergus', Gallowshade, FORFAR DD8 1NG.

Joss, William H.; Cathedral Clergy House, 20 Huntly Street, ABERDEEN AB10 1SH.

Kilkerr, Brian, K.C.H.S., A.B.I.I.B.A.; 'Maranatha', 43 Valentine Drive, Danestone, ABERDEEN AB22 8YF. ☎ 01224-826555.

Lippok, Paul; St. Vincent's, Cameron Road, TAIN IV19 1NN.

McAviney, John, C.Q.S.W.; c/o St. Mungo's, 25 Mar Street, ALLOA FK10 1HR.

McEwan, John, S.F.O.; 25 Townlands Park, CROMARTY IV11 8YY. ☎ 01381-600281.

McFarlane, David H., B.Sc., B.Comm.; c/o St. Patrick's, 3 Maitland Street, DUNDEE DD4 6RW.

MacFarlane, Duncan; The Old Schoolhouse, 103 High Street, SELKIRK TD7 4JX. ☎ 01750-21779.

Mackinnon, Angus *(Dunkeld)*; 27 Easton Road, BATHGATE EH48 2AX. ☎ 01506-654109.

Scally, Francis; 4 Woodlands Place, COATBRIDGE ML5 1LD. ☎ 01236-422577.

Woodside, John, M.I.S.M.; Trinity, 43 Charleston Crescent, Cove, ABERDEEN AB12 3DZ ☎ (Blairs Parish): 01224-869424.

SPECIALISED MINISTRIES

PASTORAL CARE OF H.M. PENAL ESTABLISHMENTS

Catholic Members of Joint Prison Chaplaincies Board
Rev. Kenneth J. McCaffrey (Dunkeld, Convenor) (☎01259-212486).
Rev. Brian Gowans (St. Mary 's, 15 Upper Bridge Street, STIRLING FK8
1ES (*ex officio*) (☎01786-473749).
Vacant.

National Chaplain and Advisor in Religion
Rev. Brian Gowans, Scottish Prison Service, Calton House, 5 Redheughs
Rigg, EDINBURGH EH12 9HW. ☎ 0131-244 4104.

Archdiocese of St. Andrews and Edinburgh:
H.M. Prison Edinburgh
Rev. Ben Beary, O.S.A., St. Joseph's, Sighthill (☎0131-443 3777).
Sr. Mary Roach, 38/5/6 Niddrie Mains Terrace, EDINBURGH EH16 4QU.
(☎ 0131-669 7558).
H.M. Young Offenders Institution Polmont
Rev. Brian Gowans,St. Mary 's, 15 Upper Bridge Street, STIRLING FK8
1ES(☎01786-473749).
H.M Institution Cornton Vale, Stirling
Vacant.
Sr. Monica Neilson, Good Shepherd Sisters, Baillieston (☎ 0141-771
8477).

Diocese of Aberdeen:
H M. Prison Craiginches, Aberdeen
Rev. Andrew Mann, Sacred Heart (☎ 01224-878489)
H.M. Prison Porterfield, Inverness
Rev. Deacon John McEwan, St. Ninian's, Inverness (☎ 01463-232136)
H.M. Prison Peterhead
Rev. Raymond Coyle, Ellon (☎ 01358-721485)

Diocese of Dunkeld:
H.M. Prison Perth
 Rev. Neil Dorward,, St. James', Kinross (☎ 01577-863329).
 Rev. Deacon David Connelly, Perth (☎ 01738-449072).
H.M. Prison Friarton
 Rev. Deacon David Connelly , Perth(☎ 01738-449072).
H.M. Prison, Glenochil
 Rev. Kenneth J. McCaffrey, St. Mungo's, Alloa (☎ 01259-212486).
H. M. Young Offenders Institution Glenochil
 Rev. James Wallace, Tullibody (☎ 01259-213274).
H.M. Prison, Castle Huntly
 Rev. Eugene O'Sullivan, St. Francis', Dundee (☎ 01382-688007)
H M. Prison Noranside, Fern, Forfar
 Rev. Neil Gallagher, Forfar; (☎ 01307-462104)

Diocese of Galloway:
H.M. Prison Penninghame, Newton Stewart
 Rev. David A. Conroy, Our Lady and St. Ninian's (☎ 01671-402182).
H M. Young Offenders Institution, Dumfries
 Very Rev. John Canon Walls, St. Teresa's, Dumfries (☎ 01387-252603).

Archdiocese of Glasgow
H.M. Prison Barlinnie
 Rev. Stephen Connolly, St. Andrew's, Bearsden (☎ 0141-942 4635).
 Rev. Robert Hill, Turnbull Hall, University of Glasgow (☎ 0141-339 4315).
 Rev. Patrick Boyle, St. Flannan's, Kirkintilloch, (☎ 0141-776 2310).
H. M. Prison Low Moss
 Rev. Peter Murphy, St. Monica's, Milton (☎ 0141-772 4348).
 Sr. Margaret Brady, Daughters of Charity (☎ 0141-889 5347).

Diocese of Motherwell:
H.M. Remand Institution Longriggend
 Bro. Levinus Lawlor.
H M. Prison Shotts
 Rev. James Duddy, Pastoral Centre, Newmains (☎ 01698-385397).
H.M. Prison Dungavel, Strathaven, and National Induction Centre, Shotts.
 Rev. Brian Donnelly, 2A Sandbank Terrace, Maryhill, GLASGOW G20 0PW (☎ 0141-945 5305).

Diocese of Paisley:
H.M. Prison, Greenock
 Rev. Oliver Freney, St. Andrew's, Greenock (☎ 01475-631750).
 Rev. Vincent J. Byrne, St. Andrew's, Greenock (☎ 01475-631750.

HOPE—For the support of Offenders, Prisoners and their Families.
Development Officer: David Connelly, 18 Stevenson Street, GLASGOW G40 2ST (☎ 0141-553 2545).

Employment Project: Contact—Joseph O'Neil (☎ 0141-552 0229).
Women's Support Project: Contact—Sr. Monica Neilson. (☎0141-552 0229).
Accommodation Project: Contact—Steve Olney (☎ 0131-447 7165).
Perth Prison Visitors' Centre: Contact—Gill Paterson (☎ 01738-625470).

HOPE Support Groups
East Kilbride: Josephine Jordan (☎ 01355-229311).
Bellshill: Ann Hunter, 59 Portland Place, Hamilton (☎ 01698-283 499).
Glasgow: Betty Sermanni, 12 Kilmailing Road, Glasgow (☎ 0141-637 6763).
Edinburgh: Kate Gill (☎ 0131-667 1888).
Aberdeen: Rev. Andrew Mann (☎ 01224-878489).
Falkirk: Pauline Neilson (☎ 01234-622413).
Stirling: Eileen Vintnis (☎ 01786-464156).
Greenock: Rev. Stephen Baillie (☎ 01475-720223).

PASTORAL CARE OF LINGUISTIC GROUPS IN SCOTLAND

CHAPLAIN FOR FRENCH-SPEAKING CATHOLICS (ABERDEEN AREA)

Very Rev. Peter A. Canon Moran, Catholic Church, 116 North Street, INVERURIE AB51 4TL. ☎ Inverurie (01467) 620319.
Mass at St. Francis', Mannofield (p.143) each month during school year.

CHAPLAINCY FOR GERMAN-SPEAKING CATHOLICS:

German-Speaking Catholic Centre: Ardmory, 30 Langside Drive, GLASGOW G43 2QQ. ☎ 0141-637 3316.

CHAPLAIN FOR LITHUANIANS:

Chaplain: Rev. Juozas Andrusius (Joseph McAndrew), S.M.A., St Casimir, 78 Glencalder Crescent, BELLSHILL ML4 2LU. Tel: Bellshill (01698) 746266, or Scottish Lithuanian Social Club, 79a Calder Road, Mossend, BELLSHILL ML4 IPX. ☎ Bellshill (01698) 745354.

CHAPLAINS FOR POLES:

Office of the Polish Catholic Mission in Scotland, 4 Park Grove Terrace, GLASGOW G3 7SD. ☎ 0141-339 9163.

Rev. Antoni Debkowski, S.A.C., Garfleld, 136 Comely Place, FALKIRK FK1 1QQ. ☎ Falkirk (01324) 621902.
Falkirk, St. Francis Xavier, Hope Street: Mass, every Sunday, 1 p.m.
Perth, St. John the Baptist, 20 Melville Street: Mass third Sunday of every month, 3 p.m.
Alloa, St. Mungo, 25 Mar Street: Mass fourth Sunday of every month, 11.15 a.m.

Rev. Marian Lekawa, S.A.C., 4 Parkgrove Terrace, GLASGOW G3 7SD. ☎ 0141-339 9163.
Glasgow, St. Simon's, 33 Partick Bridge Street: Mass every Sunday, 11 a.m.
Dundee, St. Andrew's Cathedral, 150 Nethergate: Mass first Sunday of every month, 2 p.m.
Aberdeen, St. Peter's, 3 Chapel Court, Justice Street: Mass, last Sunday of every other month, 5.30 p.m.

Rev. Tadeusz Puton, S.A.C., I Barony Place, EDINBURGH EH3 6PB. ☎ 0131-558 3726.
Edinburgh, St. Anne's, Oratory, 9 Randolph Place: Mass every Sunday, 10.45 a.m.
Kirkcaldy, St. Marie's, 101 Dunnikier Road: Mass second and fourth Sunday of every month, 1 p.m.
Galashiels, Our Lady, Market Street: Mass, third Sunday of every month, 1.45p.m.

ORDINATIONS - 1999

I - PRIESTHOOD

DIOCESE OF ARGYLL AND THE ISLES

Rev. John Paul Mackinnon, S.T.B., was born at Daliburgh, South Uist, on 14th July, 1974, and had his secular education at Daliburgh and Liniclate Secondary School. He preapared for the priesthood at the Royal Scots College, Salamanca, Spain, taking his degree of S.T.B. from the Pontifical University of Salamanca. He was ordained priest by the Most Reverend Keith Patrick O'Brien, Archbishop of St. Andrews and Edinburgh and Administrator Apostolic of Argyll and The Isles, in St. Peter's Church, Daliburgh, on 24th June, 1999. Father Mackinnon is now temporary administrator of St. Mary's, Benbecula.

DIOCESE OF GALLOWAY

Rev. Stephen Sharkey, B.D., was born at Parkhead, Glasgow, on 2nd February, 1969, and had his secondary education at St. Andrew's Secondary School, Glasgow. After working as an engineer in the telecommunications industry, he prepared for the priesthood at the National Seminary of Scotus College, Bearsden, taking his degree of B.D. from the Pontifical University of Maynooth. He was ordained priest by the Right Reverend Maurice Taylor, Bishop of Galloway, in St. Michael's Church, Parkhead, Glasgow, on 25th June, 1999. Father Sharkey is now assistant at St. Andrew's, Dumfries.

ARCHDIOCESE OF GLASGOW

Rev. John McGrath, S.T.B., was born at Helensburgh, on 6th September, 1965, and attended St. Parick's High School, Dumbarton. He prepared for the priesthood at the Royal Scots College, Salamanca, Spain, taking his degree of S.T.B. at the Pontifical University of Salamanca, spending a further year taking a post-graduate Diploma at the Pontifical University of Maynooth. He was ordained to the priesthood by His Eminence Thomas Joseph Cardinal Winning, Archbishop of Glasgow, in St. Joseph's Church, Helensburgh, on 4th July, 1999. Father McGrath is now assistant at St. Constantine's, Govan.

Rev. William McMahon was born in Glasgow on 19th December, 1962, and attended St. Columba of Iona Secondary School, Cowcaddens. He prepared for the priesthood at the Royal Scots College, Salamanca, Spain. He was ordained priest by the Cardinal Archbishop of Glasgow in St. Augustine's Church, Milton, on 29th June, 1999. Father McMahon is now assistant at St. Ninian's, Knightswood.

Rev. John Mulholland, B.D., was born in Paisley on 25th September, 1960, and attended Lourdes Secondary School, Cardonald. He prepared for the priesthood at Scotus College, Bearsden, taking his degree of B.D. from the Pontifical University of Maynooth. He received the priesthood at the hands of Cardinal Thomas J. Winning, Archbishop of Glasgow, in St. Conval's Church, Pollok, on 24th June, 1999. Father Mulholland is now assistant at St. Thomas', Riddrie.

Rev. David John Wallace, Ph.B., S.T.L., was born in Bellshill, Lanarkshire, on 19th February, 1974. He attended Our Lady's High School, Cumbernauld. He prepared for the priesthood at the Pontifical Scots College, Rome, taking his degrees of Ph.B. and S.T.B. at the Pontifical Gregorian University, Rome, and the degree of S.T.L. at the Pontifical Athenaeum of St. Anselm, Rome. He was ordained to the priesthood by His Eminence Thomas Joseph Cardinal Winning, Archbishop of Glasgow, in the Church of Our Lady and St. Helen, Condorrat, on 27th June, 1999. Father Wallace is now assistant at St. Patrick's, Dumbarton.

Rev. Thomas Peter White, Ph.B., S.T.B., was born in Glasgow on 28th February, 1975, and attended Holy Cross High School, Hamilton. He prepared for the priesthood at the Pontifical Scots College, Rome, and took his degrees of Ph.B. and S.T.B. at the Pontifical Gregorian University, Rome. He was ordained priest by the Cardinal Archbishop of Glasgow in St. Joachim's Church, Carmyle, on 3rd July, 1999. Father White is now assistant at St. Maria Goretti's, Cranhill.

DIOCESE OF MOTHERWELL

Rev. Kevin Michael McGoldrick, B.D., was born in Glasgow on 24th August, 1967, and attended Trinity High School, Rutherglen. He prepared for the priesthood at the National Seminary of Scotus College, Bearsden, taking his B.D. from the Pontifical University of Maynooth. He was ordained priest by the Right Reverend Joseph Devine, Bishop of Motherwell in St. Columbkille's Church, Rutherglen. Father McGoldrick is now assistant at St. Thomas', Wishaw.

DIOCESE OF PAISLEY

Rev. Douglas Charles Macmillan, Dip.Phil., Dip.Theol., was born in Glasgow on 1st August, 1953, and had his secondary education in St. Aloysius' College, Glasgow. After leaving school, he undertook a career in banking with the Royal Bank of Scotland. He prepared for the priesthood at Chesters and Scotus Colleges, Bearsden, taking his Diplomas in Philosophy and Theology from the Pontifical University of Maynooth. He was ordained priest by the Right Reverend John A. Mone, Bishop of Paisley, in St. Aidan's Church, Johnstone, on 17th April, 1999. After a temporary appointment at Holy Family, Port Glasgow, Father Macmillan is now an assistant at St. John's, Barrhead.

II – PERMANENT DIACONATE

DIOCESE OF DUNKELD

Rev. Angus Mackinnon was born in Armadale, West Lothian, on 20th March, 1931. After his secondary education at St. Mary's Senior Secondary School, Bathgate, he was a police officer, a production controller and computer operations manager. He is married with two sons and a daughter, all of whom are married. He was ordained deacon by the Right Reverend Vincent Logan, Bishop of Dunkeld, in St. John's Church, Perth, on 6th March, 1999. Deacon Mackinnon is to carry out a full-time ministry in the Diocese of Dunkeld, and after a temporary appointment in Perth is awaiting a further appointment.

DIOCESE OF MOTHERWELL

Rev. Joseph Dowds was born in Govan on 9th October, 1948, and attended St. Gerard's Secondary School, Govan. On leaving school, he entered the Civil Service, being appointed to the Inland Revenue, in which he is now an Inspector of Taxes. He is married with an adult daughter and son. He had his formation for ordination following the diaconal programme, first during the year at St. Mary's, Blairs, until its final closure in 1996 and thereafter at St. Mary's, Kinnoull. He was ordained deacon by the Right Reverend Joseph Devine, Bishop of Motherwell, in St. Mary's Church, Hamilton, on 25th March, 1999. Deacon Dowds, while still continuing his professional work with the Inland Revenue, carries out a part-time ministry as pastoral assistant at St. Mary's, Hamilton.

Rev. Francis Scally was born in Baillieston on 3rd May, 1933, and had his education at St. Bridget's School, Baillieston. After leaving school, he took his City and Guilds Certificate in upholstery, and was a Master Upholsterer. From 1981 to 1993, he was Supreme Secretary of the Knights of St. Columba. Married, he has a son and three daughters, all of whom are married. He was ordained deacon by Bishop Devine of Motherwell in the Cathedral Church of Our Lady of Good Aid, Motherwell, on 4th November, 1999. Deacon Scally exercises a full time ministry in St. Augustine's, Langloan, Coatbridge.

OBITUARIES 1998-99

Very Rev. John Canon Duffy – 21st November, 1998

John Duffy was born in Calderbank on 21st May, 1920, and attended St. Aloysius' Primary School in Chapelhall from the age of 5 until he entered St. Mary's College, Blairs, the National Minor Seminary, in 1934, remaining there until he began his studies in philosophy and theology at St. Peter's College, Bearsden, in 1939.

He was ordained to the priesthood in St. Andrew's Cathedral, Glasgow, on 29th June, 1946.

Although the probable division of the Archdiocese of Glasgow was already being talked about at that time, it had not yet been finally decided on, so, although the young Father Duffy was a Lanarkshire man, he was appointed to a curacy in the city of Glasgow, at St. Philomena's, Provanmill, where he remained two years until 1948, when he was transferred to the parish of St. Mary Immaculate, Pollokshaws. In 1950 he was transferred to St. Ninian's, Knightswood, where again he remained two years before again being transferred, this time to St. Michael's, Parkhead.

After a further two years, he volunteered for service as a chaplain in the Royal Air Force, and remained in the Service until 1973, when he became parish priest of Our Lady, Star of the Sea, Garelochhead. While there, in 1990 he was appointed a Canon of the Chapter of the Metropolitan Cathedral Church of St. Andrew.

Turning 75, he retired to Clynder in 1995, but some time before his death, his health deteriorated and he had to enter St. Margaret's Hospice, Clydebank, where his last days were made comfortable by the devoted attentions of the Religious Sisters of Charity. He died there on 21st November, 1998.

The Funeral Mass was offered in St. Margaret's Church, Clydebank, on 25th November following, the principal celebrant being His Eminence the Cardinal Archbishop of Glasgow, who was accompanied by a goodly number of priests, and which was attended by many faithful from Garelochhead and other parishes in which the late Canon had served.

May he rest in peace.

Rev. John J. McCabe – 3rd December, 1998

John James McCabe was born in Abercrombie Street, Calton on 11th May 1931, the only son of John and Ruby McCabe and brother to his two older sisters, Mary and Ruby. The family soon moved to Riddrie and for his childhood John was a member of St. Thomas's parish, a parish which in its day was considered a "nursery for the priesthood." His primary education was in the local St. Thomas's school and St. Aloysius' College and in 1947 he went to Blairs College, Aberdeen to complete his secondary education.

In 1951 he was chosen to be one of the small band of students to go the Royal Scots College, Valladolid, which had reopened the previous year after being closed since the Civil war. Life was not easy so soon after the turmoil of war and it is to the credit of the students and staff that the College survived its perilous restart and ultimately flourished. It was in Spain that John began his love affair with all things Spanish, the food, the language, the scenery and the people. Many friendships were made among his classmates at the Seminary which were to last a lifetime. Because the students got home only once in three years there were opportunities to explore the vast country and meet the people. Indeed the students had to spend part of their summer holidays teaching English to Spanish seminarians, one reason perhaps for the preponderance of the Glasgow accent in Spain.

John was ordained In the College Chapel on 6th April 1957 by Bishop William Hart of Dunkeld, a former student of the College. It was a proud day for his parents and family who had travelled from Scotland for the occasion, the climax of many years of prayer and support for their son, so far away. The Church in Glasgow owes a debt of gratitude particularly to John McCabe senior for not only giving his son to the priesthood but also for the financial support many a cleric and charity received through him in his capacity as a senior manager in Green's Playhouse.

In June 1957 the newly ordained priest returned to Scotland and after a summer placement in Our Holy Redeemer's, Clydebank, he was appointed to the Immaculate Conception, Maryhill, where he would spend the next 16 years under the tutelage of the lovable Canon Pat Torley. A new church was in the process of being built in Maryhill Road so there was all the excitement and hassle such a project brings. The parish was long established with its own traditions and these were carried on into the new church to blend in with the liturgical reforms of the Second Vatican Council.

John was by nature a very intense individual who drove himself hard in whatever task he undertook, whether it was parish visitation, youth clubs, or parish sodalities. He had an extraordinary memory for faces and years later would remember parishioners from his early days when he met them in different circumstances. His devotion to the sick was always foremost in his ministry wherever he went. But his intense nature along with a craving for cigarettes were to cause him health problems which were with him for the rest of his days.

In 1973 John was sent to Helenburgh as assistant and here he was responsible for the renovation of the parish hall. He was involved in the community as a member of the steering committee for the Community

Council and was on the board of St. Andrew's List D School, Shandon. During this time his mother became seriously ill with a stroke and was confined to hospital for the rest of her days. The road between Glasgow and Helensburgh often saw John's car "in flight" between hospital and parish. There was the added sorrow of his father predeceasing his mother after years of daily visits to her bedside.

1976 saw John in Christ the King parish followed in 1981 with two years in St. Maria Goretti's, Cranhill, where he celebrated his Silver Jubilee as a priest. The Church filled with parishioners and friends was a testament to the love and esteem in which he was held by so many. Though his two sisters were married and far away from home John was never short of friends and he always remained loyal to them down through the years.

In 1983 he became administrator of Our Lady and St. Margaret's, Kinning Park, a mother parish of the Archdiocese which had fallen on hard times due to the decline in population. The Pugin church had to be demolished but John organised the parish to adapt the hall and create a chapel which would serve the needs of the people. His skills as an organiser in such matters brought about an invitation to join the Fabric and Planning board of the Archdiocese, of which he ultimately became Vicar Episcopal. His planning skills were put to use in his next parish, St. Joseph's, Cumbernauld, (1985) where he remodelled the sanctuary and increased the living space in the parish house. His final appointment was to Our Lady of Lourdes, Cardonald, in 1988, very fitting for someone who had had a great devotion to the Mother of God and her Rosary. He accompanied Bishop Renfrew each year on the October Rosary pilgrimage to Lourdes and after the Bishop's death, himself took on the leading of the pilgrimage. Even though his health gave cause for concern once again he threw himself into Parish life beautifying the Church, upgrading the hall, and supervising the purchase of a new church organ and still visiting the sick and the children in the schools.

In October 1995 on his doctor's advice he retired from active ministry to Moodiesburn, where family and friends were made most welcome in his home. But each weekend he would assist in any parish which called on his services and it was his delight to offer the Holy Mass for the people, and not have to worry about parish administration. Concern for others' needs still played a part in his life and right to the end he was visiting the sick at home or in hospital when he discovered their need.

John's death on 3rd December 1998 came suddenly but not as a surprise to those who knew and loved him for he had really burned himself out with the labours of the years. After the Funeral Mass in Our Lady of Lourdes he was buried in the Priests' Plot, Dalbeth, a cemetery he knew well from his frequent visits to his parents' grave and where he had recently concelebrated the annual Mass for those buried in that cemetery. With all the faithful departed may he now rest in peace.   *(Contributed)*

Very Rev. John A. Canon Sheridan – 16th January, 1999

Canon John A. Sheridan, retired Parish Priest of St. Margaret's, Airdrie, died in the Victoria Infirmary, Glasgow, on 16th January, 1999, in the 93rd year of his age and the 68th of his priesthood. At the Funeral Mass in Christ the King, King's Park, Glasgow, on 21st January following, which was concelebrated by a large number of priests from his own diocese of Motherwell and elsewhere, prior to interment in the Priests' Plot in St. Patrick's Cemetery, New Stevenston, the principal celebrant was the Right Reverend Joseph Devine, Bishop of Motherwell, who delivered the following homily:

I last saw Canon John Sheridan on Wednesday, in the Victoria Infirmary, to which he had been admitted only a couple of hours earlier from Bon Secours Hospital where he had been for a few days for respite care. Despite my anxiety about his condition, the young doctor caring for him, a girl whom I had confirmed in St. Margaret's some 12 years ago, assured me that there was no immediate cause for alarm, as the trouble facing the Canon was little more than a respiratory condition, complicated by something about which she was uncertain as he was heavily sedated. But when I heard from Mgr. Devanny, who visited the Canon that same evening, that he had not recovered consciousness, I felt sure that whatever that complication was, it was more likely than not to be lethal, not due to any intuition on my part. It was based on knowledge, knowledge supplied by the Canon himself only a couple of weeks earlier, when Mgr. Devanny and Frank Cassidy visited him over the Christmas season. On leaving, the Canon said, "I don't think that it will be long now". Ever true to his nickname as the efficient Baxter, Canon Sheridan, like the polymath that he ever was, proved to be a better diagnostician of his own impending death than the best of the recent graduates in medicine from Glasgow University. In a sense, we would not have wanted it to have been otherwise. In death, as in life, Canon Sheridan dictated the analysis, getting the forecast of his own death right, even as he got nearly all things in life correct. Correct is the word to describe him. He was simply a correct kind of person in everything.

He was born on 1st October, 1906, in Manchester. Hence the slightly English accent that never left him. However, that apart, his journey to the priesthood followed the traditional pattern of hundreds of young Scottish boys of that time, being a student in Blairs from 1922-25, before going to the Scots College in Rome in 1925, from which he was ordained to the priesthood on 26th July, in 1931, in the lovely Church of St. Ignatius, in the city centre. His outstanding academic brilliance ensured that he would remain there for the next 2 years, to gain his doctorate in philosophy and theology, in his remarkable thesis on the hylomorphism of Roger Bacon, a thesis that he wrote in Latin, just to prove that he could do it. I have never known a Scottish priest to imitate his example. No wonder that he was the sole Magister Aggregatus that our nation has ever had, at least to the best of my knowledge.

He remained in the Scots College in Rome for a further 5 years, from 1933 to 1938, as first tutor then Vice-Rector to Mgr. Clapperton. I never heard him speak of those years for the Canon was the most reticent of men. But I suspect that the Canon was a brilliant tutor to the students of that era, irrespective of subject material, for he was as close as I ever met to being an accomplished scholar across all the major academic disciplines.

On returning home in 1938, he spent the next 3 years at St. Edmund's College in the University of Cambridge, before going to Blairs from 1941 to 50, teaching all manner of things - not least philosophy subjects, especially cosmology and theodicy, for part of that time, in the war years, when Blairs became a senior and junior seminary for a time. Prior to leaving Blairs, he became its headmaster, not its Rector, from 46 to 49, a role for which he was so well suited. He was a brilliant teacher, an academic to the manor born. He was also a different kind of academic, as he combined extraordinary academic talent with wonderful practical skills. It was with regard to the latter that I first became aware of him in 1949, the year that I entered Blairs. That awareness was in regard to sledges, of all things. I wondered as a small boy about the huge and impressive sledge used by the students of the day, on the runs down the slope in front of the College. I wondered more about the names on the sledges, printed above the runners. All were named after Greek mathematicians and philosophers. Only years later, did I discover that Canon Sheridan had made them. This practical skill was never to desert him, as a maker of toys in his retirement years.

I am indebted to Canon George Boyd for the following further insight into the Canon's remarkable gifts. He once entered a snooker competition open to the staff and all the philosophy students, a competition which he won at the first time of asking. After its outcome, he mused aloud that maybe he should try to learn how to play that game.

On returning to the relatively new Diocese of Motherwell in 1950, he served for a year in St. Margaret's in Airdrie, then doing the same in St. Joseph's, Blantyre. He became parish priest of the old parish of St. Charles', Newton, from 1952-1955, at which point he became parish priest of St. Bridget's in Baillieston, from 1955 to 1961. I suspect he was very happy there, certainly the most productive part of his pastoral ministry as a priest. Our own chancellor, Mr. Frank Cassidy, recalls a homily that the Canon gave on the feast of the Epiphany, at a Holy Hour on that day, which was staggering for all who heard him on the kaleidoscopic landscape that he opened up on the significance of that feast. But that was Canon Sheridan, a preacher who would never have thought for a moment that his listeners were not on his wavelength. In a sense, it was a courtesy to his congregation, that he ever thought that what was so clear to him would have been less clear to them.

Then in 1961, a surprising turn of events was to occur, when he accepted an invitation to become a professor of theology in St. Joseph's College, in Edmonton, Alberta, in Canada. He remained there for the next 6 years, years that co-incided with the period of preparation and celebration of the Second Vatican Council. But that period of the life of the Church was not entirely a happy experience for the Canon. Ever an academic and a scholastic academic at that, he sensed that the new approaches adopted by the Council had reduced his shelf life to a perilous degree. He knew that within academic circles in seminaries his days were numbered. The rising importance of Scripture, the lessening of the importance of philosophy and the new emphasis on liturgy and the importance of the vernacular in the sacred sciences meant that so much with which he was so familiar had run its course. Sadly, I think that he began to see himself as yesterday's man, in the new order that had occupied centre stage. I do not say this lightly. I take my signal from the fact that he never concelebrated at any Mass in the post-conciliar era. His reason for so doing was unique, as it was metaphysically impossible for concelebrants to pronounce the words of consecration simultaneously!

I can still see him, during my years in Motherwell, coming to many Diocesan events, in the robe of a Canon, never as a concelebrant. I was ever pleased to see him so, for the Canon was so proud of being a priest of this Diocese and a member of the Chapter of Canons, a role that he exercised actively from his appointment to the Chapter in 1969, two years after being appointed as parish priest of St. Margaret's, Airdrie, in 1967, a role that he enjoyed for the next 10 years, until his retirement from the active ministry in 1977, some 22 years ago.

John Sheridan was ever a gentleman in everything that he did, courteous and kindly to a fault in all his dealings with people. He was also an intensely shy man, a priest ever so content with his own company, a very skilled musician who delighted in all manner of academic pursuits. But casual conversation was not his strength. Instead, reticence was. I well recall a lunch which I hosted for him in 1991, in the Diocesan Office, at the time of his diamond jubilee of ordination. With him were a couple of priests who had served with him in earlier times. The Canon hugely enjoyed that occasion. But I remember that both of his former assistants told me at the end of the lunch that they had heard him say more in a couple of hours at that lunch than he had ever spoken over the 5 years when they were his assistants. No doubt exaggeration has a place here. Canon Sheridan ever knew well how to deploy one word when many another would have used a hundred or thousand words.

His long years of retirement were immensely happy years for him, here in the parish of Christ the King. The supporting evidence for this is overwhelming. For starters, it was his wish to be buried from this Church, a church were he supplied a Sunday Mass for almost all of the past 22 years.

Cardinal Winning, to whom I am indebted for being here last night at the reception of the Canon's mortal remains, has a lovely story about his first parish priest, the late Mgr Alex Hamilton, in the parish of St. Mary's in Hamilton, suggesting to him that he ought to try to preach above the head of the congregation about once a month, just to show that he could do it. That was effortless for John Sheridan, even if he was ever unaware that this was the case.

But it reaped immense side benefits for many young people of this area. Their parents well recognised the immense intellect of the Canon. For year after year, he coached so many young people through Higher Maths exams, as well as just about higher anything else, so broad was his talent. Nor was that talent solely intellectual. He continued to be a wonderful toy maker to many of the grandchildren of his friends.

What a life he had, a life that I want to put in context in the light of the readings for his funeral Mass. The first speaks of a rich banquet on God's holy mountain for all who are his friends. Just about the last thing that I would ever think of Canon Sheridan was that he was a bon viveur. Quite the reverse. He was ever a man of simple tastes. That is why I chose that first reading. If ever a man deserved to be seated at a rich banquet forever it is John Sheridan. If nothing else, I am sure that he will enjoy that novelty eternally.

Our second reading speaks of the influence that we have on one another in life. Here I am thinking of the people who should be grateful to Canon Sheridan for his being part of their lives, generations of students for the priesthood in Rome and Blairs, people in the parishes where he served and so many of the young people of this parish whom he helped reach tertiary education.

But the Gospel for today is not so much for the Canon as all of us, in the light of the life that he led. Line after line, we can see the qualities that marked his life, qualities such as simplicity of lifestyle, meekness of manner, gentleness in relationships, purity of being, service of all or anyone without the thought of price. When you add to that his steadfastness in priestly service and unfailing commitment to all that the Church ever asked of him, can anyone doubt but that the Lord would have welcomed him home last Wednesday? Without doubt, the priorities of his life serve as an example to all of us.

I do not think that I ever met anyone who did not like John Sheridan. Of course, most of his contemporaries have long pre-deceased him, men like

Mgr. Gerry Rogers and Mgr. John Conroy, both former Vicars General of Motherwell Diocese, both kind of giants in their day, but giants of a different kind. The more I think of Canon John Sheridan, the more comes to my mind the old cliche that we will not see his like again. However, in our lifetime, that is almost certainly going to be true. John Sheridan was quite unique, a priest of whom Motherwell Diocese is immensely proud.

Eternal rest grant unto him O Lord, and let perpetual light shine upon him. May he rest in peace. Amen.

CONCLUSION. As we come to the Final Commendation and Farewell, I renew all the condolences that I offered at the opening of this Mass to the Canon's relatives and his friends. In addition, I thank all those who were good to him and who cared for him in this parish, at Bon Secours Hospital and the Victoria Infirmary. Assuredly, that is what he would have wanted me to do in his name. But even more, or so I suspect, for the Canon was an old fashioned kind of priest in the best sense of that phrase, he would want me to ask you to pray for his eternal happiness. That I do, in the sure knowledge that this will be so. Finally, my thanks to all of you for coming here today as a fitting way to honour his memory. He would have been delighted that so many took the trouble to do so.

Very Rev. Thomas Canon Meikleham – 16th January, 1999

By birth Thomas Meikleham was a Devonian, being born in Plymouth on 29th September, 1908. His education, however, took place in Scotland, first of all in Lawside Academy, Dundee, from 1913to 1922, then in St. Mungo's Academy, Glasgow until 1924, when he entered the National Minor Seminary, St. Mary's College, Blairs, where he remained until 1928, when he entered St. Peter's College, Bearsden, the Senior Seminary of the Archdiocese of Glasgow, to prepare for the priesthood. He was ordained priest in St. Andrew's Cathedral, Glasgow on 29th June, 1934.

His first appointment as a priest was as a curate in St. Palladius', Dalry, still (and for another fourteen years) part of the Archdiocese of Glasgow. He remained there until 1945, when he was transferred to the important parish of St. Mary Immaculate, Pollokshaws, where he remained until 1949. In that year, he was appointed to succeed the late Mgr. (later Bishop) James Ward, as Chaplain to Notre Dame Training College, where he remained for ten years until he was appointed parish priest of St. Brendan's, Yoker. For much of this period, he acted as Chaplain to the Lawyer's Guild, specifically from 1946 to 1963. Not only that, he served as the first Chairman of St. Margaret of Scotland Adoption Society from 1954 to 1967, laying the foundations for so much sterling work in that field which others were able to build on after him. After eight years at the Western edge of the city, he was given the charge of St. Aloysius', Springburn, at a time when the future of many of the inner city districts and the communities who lived there was beginning to become very uncertain.

After eleven years, in 1978, he was appointed parish priest of the rural parish of St. John of the Cross, Twechar, where he suffered the trauma of being attacked and robbed in his own presbytery. It was while he was in Twechar that he was appointed to the Chapter of the Metropolitan Cathedral Church of St. Andrew, a position which he retained until his death.

Age finally caught up with him in 1990, when, aged 82, he retired to spend his declining years with the Little Sisters of the Poor at their new Home in Robroyston, where he benefitted from the devoted care given to him. His health finally deteriorating, he entered Stobhill Hospital, where he died on 16th January, 1999.

His obsequies were conducted in the Chapel of St. Joseph's Home, the Vigil being conducted by his cousin, Canon Thomas Grace of the Diocese of Paisley, while the principal celebrant of the funeral Mass was His Eminence the Cardinal Archbishop of Glasgow.

May he rest in peace.

Very Rev. George Canon Fryer – 20th January, 1999

Canon George Fryer, retired Parish Priest of Our Lady and St. Joseph's, Glenboig, died in Altnagevin Hospital, Derry, Northern Ireland, on 20th January, 1999, in the 81st year of his age and the 56th of his priesthood. The Funeral Mass was concelebrated in the Church of Our Lady of Lourdes, Steelstown, Derry, on 23rd January following, the principal celebrant being the Right Reverend Joseph Devine, Bishop of Motherwell, who was accompanied by the Most Reverend Francis Logan, Auxiliary Bishop of Derry. Interment followed in the Priests' Plot of St. Mary's Cemetery, Buncrana, Co. Donegal. On 27th January, a Requiem Mass was celebrated in Glenboig, at which the principal celebrant was Bishop Devine, who delivered the following homily:

After a very contented decade of retirement in Derry, where Canon Fryer enjoyed good health for nearly all of that time, with sadness I learned of his death last Wednesday afternoon. He had been admitted to hospital on the previous evening as a precaution. There he died, on the following afternoon, due to in internal haemorrhage only 4 days after the death of a former member of our Diocesan Chapter, Canon John Sheridan.

If 1999 has started sadly for us, with the deaths of two well respected priests of the Diocese, perhaps we will be spared further sad news as the year unfolds. But that sadness is on our part. Assuredly, 1999 ushered in a wonderful home-coming for both of them, to that homeland to which each of us is called from the day of our baptism. In the case of Canon Fryer, it was a lengthy journey in human terms, as he was born on 21st May, 1918, shortly before the conclusion of the first world war, in Clydebank, a town that was to know very difficult times in the second world war. After his primary education, he went to St. Patrick's High School in Dumbarton, at that point one of the only two Catholic High Schools in the county of Dunbartonshire, then going to the old senior seminary in Bearsden, from which he was ordained on 3rd October, 1943, by Bishop Campbell of Argyll and The Isles, as the Archbishop of Glasgow of the day was very ill and would die within a couple of months of George's ordination.

The first 25 years of the Canon's life were circumscribed by a tension that few of us now know. Born into an era when the devastation of the first world war exacted a huge toll on our country, growing up at a time when life was hard for people, due to the economic depression that characterised much of life in the 20's and 30's, his must have been a fairly grim time in which to be a child or a young adult.

With the late 30's, when he became a senior seminarian, while on the surface things were getting better, the air was full of rumours of war on the horizon. Of course, it happened. The events around us profoundly affect our lives. Given the circumstances of our late Canon's life, from his birth to the date of his ordination, I cannot begin to imagine the effect of all this on him. With all the others of his own generation, he had not been given the best possible introduction to life.

However, in George's case, two immensely important advantages helped him meet the future with confidence. The first was his family, a great aid to him as a child and a young man. The second was the faith that they gave him, a faith that was supremely important to him all the days of his life. That faith transcended all the negative signals that the world was giving him. That faith was his supreme value in his work as a priest. That was how I ever saw him, a man of faith in all that he did.

That ministry lasted for some 45 years, an honourable length of service for anyone to be able to give. He would have longed to have served further, had it not been for failing eyesight and an acute arthritic condition. But that is to rush the story of his life. That life, in terms of pastoral ministry, was quite evenly spread in five parishes, the first of which was St. Bridget's in Baillieston. He was very happy there, working with the young people of the day and developing his love for music and singing. He was there from 1943 to 1951, in effect resulting in him becoming a priest of Motherwell Diocese in 1948, as Baillieston is allied to Lanarkshire rather than Glasgow.

In 1951 he moved to the Cathedral parish in Motherwell, an appointment that he was to relish for the following 8 years, for it gave him increased scope for his musical talents, with a fine Cathedral choir at his disposal. He would also enjoy, for much of that time, a great parish priest, the Vicar General of the day, Mgr. Gerry Rogers, who left at the same time as George's going to Carluke, even as Mgr. Rogers was about to leave for Rome to become a judge of the Sacred Roman Rota. A fellow assistant priest of the time was Cardinal Winning, Archbishop of Glasgow. Another was Mgr. Burns.

Perhaps it was as parish priest of Carluke, a pleasant little town of the day, that he would have enjoyed most as a priest. The Catholic population of the day was 800. St. Athanasius' in Carluke is one of our oldest parishes, formed in the 1850's due to the presence of Irish navigators, building the road and rail networks from Glasgow to England. He spent the next 6 years there, from 1959 to 1965. That relatively relaxed kind of setting, allowed him to undertake a wider role, as a school examiner and a member of the national committee to produce a new national hymn book to meet the new needs facing the Church, a task that was to occupy him in the early years that he spent in his next appointment. I am sure that he was sorry to leave Carluke, as it is one of the nicest parishes in our Diocese, centred on the old fruit growing area of Lanarkshire.

In 1965, he moved to St. Andrew's in Airdrie, an entirely different kind of setting from much that he had previously known, an urban housing scheme in north Airdrie, marked by all the difficulties, socially, economically and humanly, that have ever marked such a development. Those would have been hard years for him in the parish where he was to serve longest, some 17 years, from 1965 to 1982. He did a good job there, against considerable odds. He brought his skills to bear in his work of making the new approaches of the Second Vatican Council a reality. In addition, he established a parish identity for the people there, since nearly all of them had come from different areas of Airdrie, a new community with so much debt to pay for the new Church and hall. It is to his credit that he left the parish priest who followed him in credit.

In 1982 he came here, to Our Lady and St. Joseph's, Glenboig, a fine old parish, traditional in style, a fact that I am sure that he would have much appreciated. The next year I came to Motherwell. Only then did I begin to know him personally, when he was already an old age pensioner, as he was 65 at that time. It gave me much pleasure to install him a Canon of the Diocesan Chapter a few years later.

With the onset of the late 1980's, his failing eyesight and his increasing difficulties in physically meeting the demands of his office as a parish priest, were of concern to him. Rather diffidently, in the light of his service to the Diocese, I suggested to him that he should retire. He saw the merit of that suggestion and retired from the active ministry 11 years ago, in 1988, retiring to be with his brother in Derry. He greatly enjoyed being there with his family, at least for part of that time, until the death of his brother a few years ago. I am so grateful to Mgr. Devanny for visiting him regularly over the past few years and always finding him so contented. So it was a surprise to me and all of us that the end came so suddenly last Wednesday.

Due to the fact that his funeral was last Saturday, it meant that, apart from Mgr. Devanny and myself, no other priest from our Diocese was able to be there, except for Fr. Willie Sproule and Fr. Colum Morris. Hence the significance of tonight, an opportunity to celebrate this memorial Mass for him, for clergy and people alike.

In the context of the readings for this Mass, I am sure that the Canon would have much enjoyed our choice of the first reading, that rich banquet prepared by the Lord for all his faithful servants, especially if the Lord would have allowed Canon George to be the one to select the wines for the different courses! Our second reading, that in regard to the effect that we have in life upon others is still more telling. Canon Fryer was a most accomplished priest, a very gifted musician and choir master, until old age and arthritis robbed him of his ability to play both of those roles. That was a great loss to him and the Church at large. He accepted that loss without complaint.

I will remember him best as fighter against losing so much that was of importance to him, his talents and abilities. In a sense, he reminds me of a great film, the one about Arnhem, the bridge that was ever too far. He put up such a fight to struggle against great odds as the years took their toll on him. He never wanted to retire from being a priest engaged in the active ministry.

Then, in retirement, the Lord surprised him most of all, with a wonderfully contented decade of joy with his family and new friends in Derry. As Mgr. Devanny said last Friday evening, at the reception of his mortal remains, George even managed to pick up the traces of a Derry accent in the final years of his life. To his nephew Brian and Sadie his wife, here with us from Derry, I offer our condolences, even as with them we remember the life and ministry of Canon George Fryer with appreciation and much affection.

Eternal rest grant to him, O Lord, and let perpetual light shine upon him. May he rest in peace. Amen.

Very Rev. Michael J. Canon Jackson — 2nd February, 1999

Canon Michael Jackson, retired parish priest of Sacred Heart, Penicuik, died in Nazareth House, Lasswade, on Candlemas Day, 2nd February, 1999, in the 81st year of his age and the 56th of his priesthood. At his Funeral Mass on 4th February following, the following homily was delivered by Canon Daniel J. Boyle, retired parish priest of Rosyth.

I would give much, my dear friends, to have ready and to hand an appropriate poetic quotation with which to begin this tribute to Canon Jackson. HE would have had one, I am quite sure! All who knew him would recognise his trademark : a quotation, a smile and his own particular, special laugh. Today though, : No quotation, No smile, No special laugh. And here is our first lesson ! We meet to do honour to his human remains, to that Temple, wherein dwelt the Holy Spirit. But we know that here lies only the shell, while Michael, the true Michael, the real Michael, the person lives on in the presence of God, now that he has "shuffled off his mortal coil."

Father Jackson was born in Ireland nearly 81 years ago and after completing his studies in All Hallows College, Dublin, he was ordained to the Priesthood in 1943 and came to serve in our Archdiocese right away. His 56 years of ministry began in St. Mary's, Bathgate and then, over the years, he came to know so much of our Archdiocese. Think of the map of the Archdiocese! He ministered in West Lothian, Stirlingshire, Edinburgh City, Fife, the Borders until in 1967 he was appointed Parish Priest here in Penicuik. He remained in charge of this Parish until he was forced by illness to retire some short time ago.

Though his experience in the Ministry was varied in kind and in place, there runs through it a theme, a sense of almost fierce dedication, a dedication which might seem to some people today a bit "old fashioned", a dedication which welled up from the very heart of the vocation to which he felt himself to have been called by God.

Right to the end, he was "the dedicated Shepherd" of the flock entrusted to him by God, the true priest, who never failed to ensure that his people were able to assist at the Most Holy Sacrifice of the Mass every single day and enjoy at all times the Graces of the Sacraments. Even from his sickbed, while he was still in hospital, it was his great pre-occupation; that it should be so. This was his ideal. This was why he had been ordained as priest and to that ideal he remained faithful to the point that latterly he did not even take a holiday.

The picture that Jesus paints of the "good and Faithful" shepherd is not the fancy, romantic picture that artist like to make of it. For Jesus, as He sees its, the Good Shepherd must be ready "to lay down his life for his flock". I can remember very clearly how Canon Jackson, even in the latter days of his illness, driven by his sense of care for his flock and out of devotion for The Sacred Heart of Jesus, the patron of his parish, discharged himself from hospital, in order to bring Holy Communion to the sick and the housebound of the parish on the First Friday of the Month and that personally! Rash? Yes ! Risky in view of hi¢ sickness? Yes! But how gloriously worthy of a true and faithful shepherd and pastor of the flock;!

He was also a very practical man. I can well remember how, when, during the short period when our ministries coincided in Bathgate, a time, just after the war, when things were scarce, he had an eye for a bargain and for an opportunity. He made sure that what was needed, happened. His ability in things material can be seen wherever he was in charge, in the part he played in the Committees of the Archdiocese and, above all, we need look no further than here in Penicuik. "Si monunentum quaeris, circumspice".

His nature was such that he readily made friends and that in all spheres of life. Such too was his readiness to help that he endeared himself to many not just of his own parishioners but to many further afield.

So it is that we have come from many parts and for many reasons to pay this tribute to a good friend and to a faithful priest. Surely the presence here today of the good nuns of Nazareth House, of the Nursing Staff of the Western General Hospital, to whom we offer our thanks for the care they gave the Canon, and the presence too of the officers, N.C.Os. and Other ranks from the Barracks, whom he served for many years, all bear witness to that friendship.

And now we pray to God that He overlook any imperfection in him, such as our fallible human nature inevitably brings. May God welcome him into His Kingdom of Glory to share in and, maybe, add to the happiness of the Saints in Heaven.

I am sure that the Canon would not wish this tribute to be too long and I am also very sure that some of you who knew the Canon well must be wondering why, until now, no mention has been made of his fascination with motor cars. No tribute would be complete without such a mention.

You may have been a bit confused by that first reading, of how it found its place here in a Requiem Mass. I think that it is very appropriate here.

In the Second Book of Kings, Elijah and Elisha approach the River Jordan. Elijah rolls up his cloak and strikes the waters to give them passage. As they go on Elisha asks of Elijah that he be given a double portion of Elijah's Prophetic powers, a request to which the prophet agrees, on the condition that, when Elijah himself is taken up, Elisha sees him going. You remember what happens. A Fiery Chariot, drawn by flaming horses [4 h.p.?], rushes between them and Elijah is taken up to heaven. As he goes, Elisha cried out (I use an older translation) : My Father! My Father! Israel's Chariot and its Charioteer!"And the cloak, symbol of Elijah's prophetic power, falls to earth for Elisha to pick up.

I offer this to you as a parable in the context of the Canon's death, of his love for cars, and for the problem that the death of the Canon brings with it. Who will accept to pick up HIS Mantle and follow in his ministry? I throw this out, as a challenge, especially to any young man here! Who will come forward to serve like the Canon and fill his place?

Towards the last days of his life, the Canon seemed rather fixed on the coming Feast of the Presentation of Our Blessed Lord and the Purification of Our Blessed Lady. Was this a wonderful presentiment of the actual day of his death ?

"Now, Lord, You can dismiss Your servant in peace, just as You promised; for my eyes have seen the salvation which You have preparted for all nations to see; a light to enlighten the pagans and the Glory of Your people, Israel."

So now, a Fiery Chariot will carry the Canon's body to Ireland there to rest with the other members of his family.

As he goes, our prayers go with him, with our deepest sympathy and our prayers for his family and friends, and with our prayers, our thanks for having allowed us to know him and for allowing him to give these 56 years of service to the Archdiocese.

And in our prayers for the Happy Repose of the Canon we add our prayers for those so many good priests who came from Ireland to help spread the Gospel here in Scotland.

And now, Please 'please' do allow me one more quotation. It could not finish other-wise :

"Good night, sweet Prince ! And may flights of angels sing thee to thy rest!"

Eternal rest grant unto him, O Lord..........

Rev. James Keegan –3rd March, 1999

Father James Joseph Keegan, retired Parish Priest of St. Patrick's, Strathaven, died on 3rd March, 1999, travelling between Lanark and Carluke on his way to Ireland, in the 72nd year of his age and the 47th of his priesthood. At the Funeral Mass in St. Patrick's, Shieldmuir, on 9th March following, prior to interment in St. Mary's Cemetery, Lanark, the following homily was delivered by the Right Reverend Joseph Devine, Bishop of Motherwell, who was the principal celebrant:

In 22 years as a bishop, I have never before celebrated a Requiem Mass for 3 priests within 3 weeks. Canon John Sheridan died on 16th January. Canon George Fryer died a week later. Only a week ago, our brother in the priesthood, Fr. James Keegan died. All 3 were retired priests of our Diocese, Canon Sheridan for some 22 years, Canon Fryer for 11years and Fr. Keegan for the past 6 years.

The year before a new millennium and the great jubilee of the year 2000 has been a sad start for us, with the deaths of three retired priests almost before 1999 has had a month to run its course In Fr. Jim Keegan's case, his death came unexpectedly, on a train journey from Lanark, en route to the airport, for a holiday with his family in Ireland. Ile died as the train reached Carluke, from where he was reclaimed by us for his funeral here in St. Patrick's, Shieldmuir, where he served as an assistant priest and as a parish priest in earlier times. But that is to rush the story of his life in the active ministry of the priesthood. Like all good stories, let me start at its beginning

Fr. James Keegan was born on 19th April, 1927, in Carrigtwohill, Co. Cork. After primary school, he then went to St Colman's, Fermoy, for his secondary education, before entering the senior seminary of St. Patrick's, Carlow, from where he was ordained for the Diocese of Motherwell on 8th June, 1952.

On arriving in Scotland, he served an initial summer appointment in the old parish of St. Margaret's Airdrie, before going to Longriggend for the next six years He much enjoyed his years of service in the north east sector of the Diocese, where he made friends for the rest of his life, before going to St. Columba in Viewpark, from 1958 to 1960. That was also a happy time for him, continuing to made good friends, who would be his friends until the end of his life. It was also a good time for the Catholic community in Lanarkshire, due to better living conditions and the rising fortunes of a football team in the east end of Glasgow, with 5 of its 11 players from this county, even if Fr. James would have been unaware of that fact. He was never affected by the football mania that is part of the culture of the West of Scotland. His own interests were rather more sophisticated, with a bent towards another kind of turf, as well as fondness for reading, not least the Summa Theologica of St. Thomas Aquinas.

After his time in Viewpark, he spent the next 9 years here, St. Patrick's, Shieldmuir, a parish that had produced so many vocations both to the priesthood and religious life in the previous 30 years. Those were years that were to become dominant in the life of the Catholic Church worldwide, the time of the Second Vatican Council and its immediate aftermath. Perhaps it was not his favourite council, as Jim was a very traditional kind of priest, someone for whom change tended to be a threat rather than an opportunity. Whatever the case, he gave of his best here, in a very changed kind of world, to his manner of thinking, religiously and morally, the swinging 60's.

We next find him in Whifflet, for a year, from 1969 to 1970, before becoming parish priest of St. Luke's in Motherwell. I suspect that he must have looked back on that year with some amusement, under the quite unique Fr. Ian McLaughlin, a man of distinctive abilities, not least with a tin whistle in a pulpit, whose sense of time for the celebration of a Sunday Mass bordered on the exceptional!

In 1970, with Cardinal Winning's appointment to be the first "officialis" of the new Scottish National Matrimonial Tribunal, there was a vacancy in the quite new parish of St. Luke's, in the Forgewood area of Motherwell. Bishop Thomson asked Father Keegan to fill the vacancy. He had a hard act to follow. If I had been given such an assignment, I wonder if I could have done better, as Cardinal Winning is a hard act for anyone to follow. Fr. Keegan was there for the next 7 years, from 1970 to 1977. It was while he was there that he began to suspect that his own health was suspect and that he was perhaps not destined to see through the biblical three score and ten years that was once seen as an average life span. Bishop Thomson was also aware of this and assigned him to the more rural setting of St. Patrick's in Strathaven, where he was to be for the following decade.

It was only when I came to the Diocese in 1983 that I began to know him personally. I recall with affection my visits to that parish in the mid 80's. At that point, it was my impression that his earlier forebodings about his health had vanished and that he was ready for a greater challenge. I appointed him as parish priest here in 1987, a task that he was happy to undertake, not least as a whole host of major jubilees were soon to follow, the centenary of the parish's foundation, being the first of these. He entered into this with great enthusiasm, not least in his desire to upgrade the interior of the church building, which he achieved with considerable success. I remember that centenary, on St. Patrick's day, 1991. It was the first of five or six occasions since that day when Cardinal Winning was the principal concelebrant for the Mass of the Solemn Dedication of St. Patrick's church.

But soon thereafter, he began to suspect that serious health difficulties were going to beset him. As a result, he felt that he had to retire from the active ministry, which he did the following year, retiring to Lanark to spend the days of his retirement.

However, a surprising turn of events was to take place a year or so later, when James began a very active apostolate on behalf of the Church in Need as the Scottish leader of that most worthy cause. For the better part of the next 3 years, he was to be found in many a parish in the central belt making an appeal for that charity and raising many a thousand pounds for the purposes of that charity. In addition, when free to do so, he was more than willing to undertake supply work, at weekends or longer, in different parishes of the Diocese, virtually until he died.

But the toll on his health began to tell and he had to resign from his work for Aid to the Church in Need just over a year ago, although he was still willing to do supplies in our parishes until recently, even as recently as a fortnight or so before he died. I suspect his ability to find a supplementary

form of service for the past 6 years or so must have given him immense
pleasure and satisfaction. In effect, it meant that, like so many priests in
Scotland over the course of this century, he died with his boots on, in a
manner of speaking.

In the context of the readings for his Requiem Mass, how will we remember
him? James was of delicate build and health, someone ever in need of that
rich banquet on God's holy mountain to which all his faithful servants have
a gilt-edged invitation. That is what we all receive through the sacraments of
initiation, baptism, the eucharist and confirmation. James was one of the
anointed of the Lord, as a priest of the New Testament he deeply appreciated
that vocation although he was to live out the major years of his priesthood in
a period of immense change in the Church. He would have chosen, if given
the chance, to have been born earlier rather than later, as that would have
been easier for him, in the years of his active ministry

But retirement brought great blessings for him, not least on his work for
the Church in Need. He devoted his energy, time and talents to working for
the oppressed in the countries of Eastern Europe, people who had been
oppressed for generations by the godless creed of communism. Now we pray
that if he is in need, we will meet that need by our prayers for him. He asks
no more of us, nor no less.

Therefore, with faith and confidence we pray:- "Eternal rest grant unto
him, O Lord. Let perpetual light shine upon him. May he rest in peace"
Amen.

Very Rev. Charles Canon Brodie, T.D. — 15th March, 1999

*Canon Charles Brodie, parish priest of St. John the Baptist's, Fauldhouse, died on
15th March, 1999, in the 80th year of his age and the 53rd of his priesthood. At his
Funeral Mass in St. John the Baptist's on Friday, 19th March following, the following
homily was delivered by Father John Robinson, parish priest of Peebles:*

In the first place I say thanks to Canon Brodie for trusting me to be his
executor in succession to his very good friend, Laurence, Canon Davidson.

I should also say that last night, among his papers I discovered that he
wished no panygeric preached!

So aware of his interest in words and their meanings, I checked the
Dictionary.

Provided I don't speak too highly of him, nor praise him overmuch I would
hope to show adequate respect for a good friend's wishes.

Secondly, in carrying out his wishes I am most grateful for the help of Mrs

Agnes Gorrie, his Sister, Mgr Alistair Lawson of Bathgate, Fr Allan Chambers, Dean of West Lothian, and people of the parish.

As we gather to celebrate our salvation in Christ, as we enter into the Holy of Holies with Jesus our Great High Priest, we give thanks to God for the Life and Work of Charles Canon Brodie, we pray that he may enjoy the remission of all his sins, and ask comfort and consolation for his relatives and friends and for the people of the parish in the face of his sudden death.

Charles was born at Comely Bank, Edinburgh May 16th 1919 - younger son of James Thomas Brodie and Mary Elizabeth McBain, and was baptised in St Andrew's Ravelston. The family then moved to North Berwick by way of Aberlady.

If any of the many girls who admired this handsome young man at school and in the parish had succeeded in their plans for his future - then we would not be here today and we would not have had almost 53 years of priestly service from him in this Diocese. He was the first young man in 60 years from his parish to study for the Priesthood .

When asked,as a boy, I think by Archbishop McDonald what he was going to be - he said he wanted to be a priest, but would be Bishop first!

His formal preparation for the Priesthood took place at Campion House, Osterley, Oscott, Birmingham, and Blairs College, Aberdeen.

He has ministered to the people of God in this Diocese since his Ordination in the Cathedral on July 25th 1946 in St Andrews, Fife; St Mary and St David, Hawick; Holy Cross, Edinburgh; St Machan's, Lennoxtown; St Mary's, Leslie; Our Lady and St Andrew's, Galashiels; and in this parish of St John The Baptist for the past 13 years.

In addition to parish duties in the early years of his ministry he also worked as a Chaplain to the Territorial Army 8th/9th Battalion Royal Scots with the rank of Major and earned the Territorial Decoration. He did tell me he enjoyed that work, though it was some time before his family discovered the honour paid to him. He was a man who didn't like fuss, and kept a humble silence concerning his gifts and achievements. I didn't discover till Monday that he played the violin - so we missed out on a possible double act in the Borders!

In the second reading we hear St Paul speak of his responsibilities as a Preacher of the Word and dealing with those who criticised him. For sure with Charlie there would be no watering down of the Word of God nor of the Teaching of the Church founded on that Word - fidelity to such can as we know be costly - and at times Charlie's understanding of what was required of him in these matters along with a natural shyness could make him seem distant and unfeeling, but there was love and gentleness there, also warmth.

Perhaps at Osterley, where much was made of the English martyrs, he was influenced by the spirit at work in Edmund Campion who if I remember correctly addressed Queen Elizabeth as follows regarding the Catholic Mission; "The enterprise is begun, it is of God, and cannot be withstood". She was not amused, as anyone listening to the current Radio 4 series "This Sceptred Isle" would appreciate.

As a Preacher of the Word he sought to keep himself up to date as regards Scripture and Theology as his library indicates.

When I was asked in 1981 to go to Galashiels Parish as Assistant and be Chaplain to St Mary's, Balnakiel - I hesitated - having some sense (from where I don't know) that this might be a difficult posting.

Around the time of appointment I had taken part in the Parish Renewal week for Priests at St Mary's, Kinnoull and you might say was full of it. I didn't think Charlie was too enamoured of what I tried to share (even that word was a problem then) Acknowledging the gifts recognised in each other and anointing each other with the oil of Gladness wasn't quite his scene Saying sorry to the parish in a formal way for shortcomings in ministry was not on either! Not because he was unaware of such he would have no problem acknowledging that he was an earthenware vessel - but not in that way.

I realised quickly that I had to make a difficult decision. He could be formidable in debate Like his shooting his aim was sure, and he knew what to use for bait Was I to contend with him/confront him on Pastoral and Theological matters or seek to develop a human and working relationship, letting these other matters important as they were and are, take care of themselves. I chose the latter, and I am happy that I did. And in our working out of that relationship together we were both helped by the Sisters at Balnakiel.

Such relationship contributed much to our Parish preparation for the Papal Visit in 1982, and in subsequent years preparing the parish for Holy Week and Easter - his gentle hints that we ought not to be doing our own thing in Balnakiel (with insufficient servers just the Sisters!) -meant we joined forces liturgically and musically for the benefit of the whole Parish - and he was delighted at the response.

He also trained me in appreciation of higher things - like roofs, gutters, tiles, slates, dry rot, etc. etc. - and I'm still learning

I know from Galashiels and from this parish that he tried to treat everyone the same, he had no favourites. I know, too, that people appreciated the time he gave them and the way in which he listened. And I sense here very deep affection for the Canon affection he had too for all whom he served. It seems to me on reflection that after ploughing the difficult furrow of a far flung Border Parish with a small percentage of Catholics, his move here brought him much Pastoral satisfaction. No doubt his patience in Pastoral Ministry was developed along with that required by his expertise in shooting and fishing.

So we give thanks to the Lord for landing a good catch for the People of God in Charlie; for his willingness to be hooked by the Grace of God; for his preaching of the Word welcome or un-welcome; for all his efforts to follow and serve His Lord and master to the end - Now that his work is done may he enjoy eternal rest. And may we show our appreciation of him not just in our prayers for him but in continued faithfulness to our Mission as Church in the World; eager to hand on the Good News; and to better understand it; taking on responsibility for ministry in the Church;

binding up broken hearts; proclaiming liberty to captives; giving for ashes a garland, for mourning robe the oil of gladness - and in preparing for the Jubilee 2000 proclaiming a year of favour from the Lord.

To the God who gave Charles to his family and to the family of the Church, be all glory honour and power for ever and ever. Amen.

Rev. Neil F. McDaid, A.M.I.E.E. – 25th April, 1999

Neil Francis McDaid, a nephew of the Jesuit Fathers William and Joseph Dempsey, was born in Maryhill in the North-West of Glasgow,on 18th November, 1920, and attended St. Charles'Primary School, before transferring to St. Mungo's Academy, which he left in 1938 with his Higher Leaving Certificate. He attended the Royal Technical College, Glasgow, from time to time between 1939 and 1958, at different times gaining initial and further qualifications for his chosen (and successful) career in the engineering side of Post Office Telephones.

However, he felt the call to the priesthood and entered St. Peter's College, Cardross, for studies in philosophy and theology. He was ordained priest by Archbishop Campbell of Glasgow in St. Andrew's Cathedral, Glasgow, on 29th June, 1963.

After ordination, his first appointment was as assistant priest at St. Maria Goretti's parish in the Cranhill district of the East End of Glasgow. While there, he served for some time as a member of the Catholic Youth Training Committee. In 1971, he was transferred to Yoker, where he served as assistant priest in St. Brendan's Parish for three years, before being transferred to Dennistoun as assistant priest in Our Lady of Good Counsel parish.

His last appointment, in 1978, was as assistant priest in St. Brigid's, Toryglen, where he remained until he retired in 1987. He spent the first years of his retirement in Cardonald, living with a sister, but after her death, his health was such that he had eventually to take up residence in Nazareth House, where he died on 25th April, 1999.

His Funeral took place from Our Lady of Lourdes Church, Cardonald, on 29th April following.

May he rest in peace.

Rev. Denis A. Power –28th April, 1999

Father Denis A. Power, retired Parish Priest of St. Catherine's, Harthill, died in St. Joseph's Centre, Shankill, Dublin, on 28th April, 1999, in the 73rd year of his age and the 48th of his priesthood. His Funeral Mass was celebrated in the Holy Rosary Church, Murroe, Co. Limerick, prior to interment in the family plot in Abbington, Co. Limerick.   At a Requiem Mass in St. Teresa's, Newarthill., on 5th May following, the Right Reverend Joseph Devine, Bishop of Motherwell, delivered the following homily:

After many months of being close to death, it was with sadness but no surprise that we learned of the death of Fr. Denis Power last Wednesday evening, 28th April. The surprise was that he managed to fight on for so long against seemingly impossible odds. Yet that was a very real part of his nature, to do his best to combat frailty, even death itself. In the light of our faith, death was not the victor here. Life was the victor, that eternal life to which Denis was called from the day of his baptism.

Denis Power was born on 17th April, 1926, in Abbington, County Limerick, some 9 years after his brother Father Joseph Power, who died in Glasgow in April, 1965. Like Joseph before him, Denis received his secondary education with the Christian Brothers in Limerick, before entering St Patrick's College, Thurles, in 1945, from which he was ordained for the Diocese of Motherwell on 10th June, 1951.

His initial pastoral appointment was to St. Augustine's, Coatbridge, from 1951-54, before moving to the Cathedral for the next five years. In these early years, two of his exceptional talents began to blossom. The first was a musical talent, being able to play all manner of musical instruments, especially the piano and the violin. The second was a considerable manual dexterity in handicraft work. I never knew any priest who had such an extensive collection of tools.

In 1959 he moved to St. Cadoc's, Halfway for a couple of years, before going to St. Cuthbert's, Burnbank, from 1961-64. However it was on moving to St Monica's in Coatbridge in early 1965 the tragedy struck, with the quite unexpected death of his brother, Fr. Joseph Power, on 13th April of that year. A bit of the light went out for Denis, a light that would never burn in him so strongly thereafter.

In 1968 he was appointed assistant priest of St. Serf's, Airdrie and in 1972 he became parish priest of St. Serf's, a role that he was to fulfil for the next 11 years, easily his longest pastoral appointment. He much enjoyed that role. The parish had only been founded some 7 years earlier and the church opened the year prior to his arrival. That parish serves a large urban community and he had the task of building up its identity as well as removing its substantial debt to the Diocese. In both of these tasks he enjoyed considerable success.

In fact, it was there that I met him for the first time, in 1981, when deputising for Bishop Thomson, at a Confirmation Mass, I can recall him then being animated in conversation, but of frail appearance. Especially I remember that his colour did not look healthy.

Two years later, within a couple of months of my arrival in Motherwell, Fr. Power collapsed. A complete rest and rehabilitation was needed. He was anaemic and had suffered damage to his general health to such a degree that it was uncertain that he would be able to continue in the pastoral ministry. However, he took charge of the situation with great courage and worked unremittingly at bringing about a complete recovery.

He spent the autumn, winter and spring of 1983-84 in Dublin in a strict health rehabilitation programme largely conducted under his own direction with a bit of medical support. So successful was that programme that he returned in the summer of 1984 and I was delighted to offer him the parish of St Teresa's, Newarthill.

Over the next 6 years or so, he continued to give good service to that parish and the Diocese. I saw him many times in those years. His major difficulty was a growing loss of hearing, combined with the fact he was embarrassed about wearing a hearing aid. With the coming of the 1990's, he saw that he was beginning to withdraw into himself and was finding it ever harder to cope with pastoral demands

In 1992, I raised with him the thought that perhaps he should give some thought to retiring, as he was then over 65 and his general health was declining. Ever a man to resist things getting the better of him, he responded with the suggestion that perhaps a small parish would suit him best at that point, as it was at that point that I had begun to alert the clergy that the Diocese would find it increasingly difficult to staff its parishes. Conscious of that situation, Denis did his best to help, even for a little time and I continue to be grateful to him for that generosity of spirit.

In October, 1992 he went to St. Catherine's. Harthill. However that winter of 1992 was one of the worst in living memory. It further depleted his reserves of energy. As a result, his final full year in the active ministry was an ever uphill battle against the inevitable. To his own regret, but to no one's surprise, he retired in 1994, going to Dublin and residential care, in the light of his overall condition.

The past 5 years were hard years for him, years of pain and increasing ill-health. If not in a position for much of that time to appreciate the splendid care which he was receiving, the Diocese is deeply in the debt of all those who cared for him during a long human purgatory of illness. Well, he is beyond all pain now, all the burdens of life and suffering.

How will we best remember him? Perhaps the readings for this Mass give us some pointers. Denis Power knew a great deal of tragedy, pain and suffering in his life, the counter to which the Lord provides for all his faithful people on the mountain, his holy mountain, where he has provided a rich banquet and a veil to screen all who are there against future pain and suffering, a place where mourning and death shall be no more. Fr. Denis Power surely qualifies for such a destiny. That vision from the book of Revelations is a great promise to all of those who have endured much hardship, but who die in the Lord, the Lord who will give them rest after their work, as their good deeds will go with them.

But it is the Gospel that gives us the surest direction of all, the final moments of the life of the Lord, his death on the cross and his burial. But death was not the victor here, or if it was, it was only for three days. Death is our common lot. There is no escaping it. But we are a people made for life, not death, that eternal life for which death is but a stepping stone.

Although not the mildest or meekest of personalities, Denis Power had little or no interest in wealth or power. He had a clear sense of justice and was opposed to all who would victimise the oppressed. He greatly prized being a priest and knew that he had a vocation to that way of life. Any other form of living would have been quite unimaginable for him. He was also courageous about admitting to his own shortcomings and would have wished to have made more of his life than he did. All of us can say the same.

Finally, I commend his soul to the Lord whom he sought to serve, even as I give my condolences on his loss to his relatives and friends in those parishes where he served in days gone by. With confidence we pray:

"Eternal rest grant unto hm, O Lord, and let perpetual light shine upon him. May he rest in peace". Amen.

Rev. Michael J. Devane — 26th May, 1999

Father Michael Devane, retired founder parish priest of St. Pius X, Kirkcaldy, died in Cameron Hospital, Methil, on 26th May, 1999, in the 82nd year of his age and the 58th of his priesthood. At his Funeral Mass in St. Pius X on Monday, 31st May following, the folowing homily was delivered by Father Patrick Clarke, parish priest of St. Marie's, Kirkcaldy:

Michael John Devane was born at Castlepollard, Co West Meath in Ireland on 8 July 1917, the only son of James Devane and Catherine Kelly. He was brought up in a house full of women: his mother and 9 sisters (his father - a policeman in the Royal Irish Constabulary having died when Michael was about 10 years old).

His Primary Education was completed in Magherafelt, Co Derry, where the family finally settled. From there Michael went on to St Patrick's Junior

Seminary in Armagh to study for the priesthood. His senior seminary training lay in the hands of the Vincentian Fathers of All Hallows College, Dublin, where he was ordained priest on 22 June 1941, at the express invitation of the late Archbishop Andrew Joseph McDonald OSB - for the Archdiocese of St Andrews and Edinburgh. Michael's sole ambition then and, indeed throughout his entire life was to be a good priest and give his life in the service of God and God's people. His first appointment was to St Alexander's in Denny, where he happily served under Father Francis P O'Brien until the latter's death in December 1947. It was in Denny, as he frequently reminded us, that he 'was learned to speak proper'. Coincidentally, having started his life in this diocese under the parish priest of Denny, Father O'Brien, Michael completed that life under a parish priest from Denny, Father Chris Heenan, the present parish priest of St Pius, here in Kirkcaldy. Michael was helped to settle in at Denny both by the warm welcome he received from Father O'Brien and the people of Denny and by the presence of the curate in the neighbouring parish of St Joseph's, Bonnybridge - his classmate and friend - Father Pat Rourke (one of the very few remaining survivors of the class of 41) and happily here with us today.

Early in 1948, Michael was transferred to St Cuthbert's in the Slateford area of the City of Edinburgh under Monsignor Peter Connolly. Having been blissfully happy in Denny, he didn't greatly appreciate the life of the city-slicker. He yearned to return to his beloved Stirlingshire; a wish that was fulfilled in 1952 (3 December) when, having thanked him for "the grand work you've done in St Cuthbert's", Archbishop Gordon Joseph Gray appointed Michael to serve under Canon William McCabe of St Machan's, Lennoxtown, but with particular responsibility for St Kessog's, Blanefield. There he had pastoral care of a number of villages and small hamlets, including Blanefield itself, Balfron and Buchlyvie - as well as the major neurosurgical unit of Killearn Hospital (not to mention what he described as 'his policies' of the Campsie Hills, Ben Lomond and the eastern shore of Loch Lomond - all of which he insisted required frequent pastoral visitation).

It was at this time that Miss Mary Reynolds - who has served in St Alexander's, Denny during the earlier years - returned to duty to act as Michael's housekeeper. She accompanied him to St Pius', Kirkcaldy in 1964 when he was appointed parish priest in his own right of this new parish, which had just been detached from the mother parish of St Marie's under Canon Joseph Byrne. He officially took up his appointment on 11 September that year, initially setting up house in the temporary presbytery of 2 Turnberry Drive, whilst waiting for the present presbytery in Brodick Road to be built. Things were tough in those early days, but with Miss Reynolds' loyal support, the companionship of his beloved cocker spaniel, Roma, both of whom had accompanied him from Blanefield and, of course, with the generous help of enthusiastic and welcoming parishioners, Michael built up Canon Byrne's foundations to establish the viable and active community of faith that today is St Pius' parish.

I had known Michael well as a friend and colleague when we were stationed in Stirlingshire in the early 60's and I kept in touch with him after he and his great friends, Father John Kerrisk and Father Gerard McGarry were transferred to Fife. Their premature deaths were a great blow to Michael and to Miss Reynolds. On my appointment to St Patrick's, Lochgelly in 1986, I looked forward to renewing our close friendship. In fact, I was greatly surprised that Michael and Mary were not standing on the doorstep on my arrival in Lochgelly, so I phoned early the next day to ask why. I was informed that Michael had been taken ill and admitted to the Victoria Hospital. That afternoon he took his first stroke while I was at his bedside. Although he eventually made an excellent recovery from the effects of that stroke, two years later he suffered a massive haemorrhage and it was clear that it would be very difficult for him to return to the onerous task of administering a parish. It was decided that retirement would be in the best interests of both Michael and Miss Reynolds, so we began to look at suitable properties in the town - as Michael was adamant that they both wished to remain resident in the locality, where they had been made so welcome and happy for almost 25 years. Fortunately, the local authority provided a small retirement flat for the two of them to rent in the Blackcraigs area of the town.

It was then that Michael began what he often jokingly referred to as 'the best years of his life'. Freed from all the hassle and administrative burden of pastoral work, he yet made himself freely available to help out in the local parishes and especially in the Carmelite Convent at Dysart, where he proved to be a most popular confessor and pastor, both with the Community and the lay congregation. He was proud of the fact that, as a curate in Denny all those years earlier, he had officiated at the marriage of the parents of the present Mother Prioress, Sister Francis ODC. He had great affection for his little charge - as they had for him - and he will be sadly missed.

By 1990 Miss Reynold's health had deteriorated to such an extent that she required to be closer to members of her own family and so she retired to Armadale where she stayed with her niece, Katie, until moving into a local nursing home where constant care could be provided. Her death just two years ago yesterday, ie on 30 May 1997, though a happy release for Mary, was a great loss to Michael who loyally and frequently visited her - even after she was no longer able to converse with him, or eventually even recognise him. Following Mary's death, he restricted his driving to short local journeys in and around Kirkcaldy.

He was immensely grateful to Mrs Muriel Garrett for her constant care for him both in his flat in Blackcraigs and, when on the occasions when he was unwell, in the Garrett family home. The ferry trip and the drive home to Magherafelt were by now beyond him, so he saw less and less of his family. However, he still endeavoured to keep in regular touch with them by phone - especially with his surviving sisters, Bridie, Eileen, Anna and Kathleen (Sister Martina) as well as his identical twin nephews, Peter and

Paul Henry, priests in Geneva and Orlando respectively. He thoroughly enjoyed the final family gathering which he attended in London last year for the Diamond Jubilee of his sister Kathleen's Religious Profession.

Michael was an avid reader, especially of the classics and rejoiced to quote from Shakespeare, Dickens, P G Wodehouse and such like; he used to cut out and preserve interesting articles that he had read so that he could share his enjoyment with others. Over the years he and Miss Reynolds travelled extensively throughout Scotland on their days off. In latter years, as I got the chance to visit remote parts of my own country which I had never previously visited and enthused over their beauty, I was gently reminded by himself that this wandering Irishman and his housekeeper had been there, done that, and bought the souvenirs, years beforehand! In fact, there's hardly a nook or cranny of this country they had not visited.

Latterly, he kept himself fit by making a daily circumnavigation of Beveridge Park whenever weather permitted. Just as he had become a well-kent face in the parish of St Pius' and throughout the streets of Templehall, so he became well-kent amongst the regulars in the Park, canine as well as human! Michael had a wonderful sense of humour and over the years we enjoyed many a laugh together. He was always neat and tidy, punctilious in all he did and wrote, dignified and reverent in his celebration of the liturgy; he was never rushed, for he was always punctual and arrived in plenty of time for the various church services. Most of all he was a devout and devoted priest, who answered the call of God to come to this country as a missionary, served God's people well and unfailingly tended to their spiritual needs. Undoubtedly, his standards were high, both for himself as well as for others. His life of prayer centred around his daily celebration of Mass and recitation of the Divine Office and the Rosary.

After a relatively short illness, he died in the Cameron Hospital, Windygates in the early hours of last Wednesday morning, 26 May 1999. May God reward him for his loyal and faithful service in the Church his Master founded, by welcoming him into the joys of the Kingdom prepared for him since the foundation of the world. May he rest in peace.

Very Rev. John J. Canon O'Brien – 30th May, 1999

Within view of the well known and beautiful Galway Bay Fr. John O'Brien was born in the City of Galway on Nov. 25 1924, the only child of James and Josephine O'Brien. From his earliest days Galway with all its beauty and its culture was his first love. Every week without failure he received and read all the local Galway newspapers from cover to cover. He followed in great detail all the happenings and events, including street fights and pub fights around his native county. He personally knew and met nearly all the players on the Galway Gaelic football team especially those involved in winning the All-Ireland McKenna Cup Final in 1998

After that great achievement he invited them over and entertained them in Glasgow ensuring first that they attended Holy Mass in his own parish Church as it happened to be a Sunday. This was indicative of the man's generosity and faith.

John's father was a policeman in the R.I.C. (the force that existed in Ireland before the Treaty in 1921). He always had a great love and respect for the police wherever he met them; so much so that he often said had he not become a priest he would have joined the Garda Siochana following in his father's footsteps. But God had destined him for a higher calling. After leaving Woodquay, Galway City, John and his parents moved to Ballyglunin, Tuam, Co Galway,to begin his primary education, then on to St Mary's Secondary School, Galway. Having completed his education there, John, for the first time left his native county to begin his Ecclesiastical education in St Peter's College, Wexford, in preparation for his ordination to the Priesthood on June 4th 1950. He was ordained a priest for the Archdiocese of Glasgow by Bishop James Staunton of the diocese of Ferns.

His first appointment as assistant priest was to the parish of St. Joseph's, Tollcross, where he ministered for seventeen years. He is fondly remembered there to this day as a good priest who preached the Word of God, administered the Sacraments and visited the parishioners frequently in their homes. He took an active part in the popular parish events of the time; badminton and tennis, etc. It was later he graduated to the golf course, where he had many ups and downs; more head-ups than down.

After many happy years in St. Joseph's he was appointed to the Immaculate Heart of Mary parish in Balornock; while there he was also chaplain to Stobhill Hospital. Moving to a new parish is no easy matter for any priest especially when he has been there for such a long time as John was in St. Joseph's, Tollcross, but as usual he took it all in his easy going stride. Then on to St Luke's, (now Bl. John Duns Scotus) Ballater St., before being promoted to parish priest in St Mary's, Calton, succeeding Mgr. Michael Ward, V.G. another Galway man, who had just retired.

Finally he moved in 1978 to be the parish priest of his beloved Parish, Our Lady of Consolation, Govanhill. John was a special genius for friendships, he made friends easily, as he loved a good 'crac,' where time stood still, the company being good and plenty of cigarettes available. In circumstances such as these he was in his element talking into the wee sma' hours.

His motto in life could have been 'manana' or when God made time he made plenty of it'. He is now with God where time is no more. "As for man, his days are like grass: he flowers like the flower of the field; the wind blows and he is gone."

John was a very happy man in his new parish, consisting, as he often said, 'of best people in the world from Donegal to Bengal.' He was made very welcome come by all the community.

Fr. John spoke Irish Gaelic fluently; consequently he was very much in tune and at home with the people he served so well. Although he was on very friendly terms with the Pakistani community he never really mastered the Asian dialects.

He was an avid reader. Not only did he read well into the night but with an almost photographic memory he could retain what he read. One would have to be very sure of one's facts and dates before attempting to contradict him. Yet he was a great confidant, friend and a wonderful conversationalist.

As well as being very committed to his pastoral work he also organised a 'soup kitchen' for the needy in his area. He loved and cared very much for the poor. There was a constant stream to his chapel house door looking for help. He never turned anyone way. A mug of tea and a sandwich was always available. He could nevertheless spot easily and quickly the character who tried to con him. In addition to his parish work he was a member of the Archdiocesan Finance Committee. His talents and good judgement were very much appreciated in such important matters.

In recognition for his great work in the Archdiocese and in his present parish of Our Lady of Consolation, the Cardinal Archbishop invited him to occupy a stall in the Cathedral Chapter. This he accepted with humility as an honour not in any self-esteem but as a tribute to the faith and loyalty of the good people of his parish.

It was on Sunday 30th May 1999 that the news began to emerge that Father John O'Brien had died. His family was devastated, his parishioners were shocked, his fellow priests saddened. Although he had been ill for some time, his sudden death was completely unexpected. He was 'waked' in Our Lady of Consolation side-chapel until the Funeral Mass on Monday June 7th. This Mass was attended by his family, a large number of priests from within and outwith the diocese, many nuns and of course hundreds of mourning parishioners and many other people from parishes in which he served so well in former years. The principal concelebrant at the Mass was Cardinal Winning. Later that day Fr. John's remains were flown to his native Galway, stopping for a short while in the Bon Secours Hospital Chapel where it remained before being taken on to the parish church in Ballyglunin. The Requiem Mass was concelebrated by a good number of priests from Scotland and Ireland and in the presence of a crowded church. The principal celebrant was the parish priest Father Joe O'Brien. Cardinal Winning was represented by Canon Patrick J. Kelly.

Afterwards Fr. John's remains were taken to the parish cemetery in Abbeyknocmoy to be buried in the family grave. A well kept and serene little cemetery it is, contiguous to the ruins of the Old Abbey founded by the Cistercians in the 12th century: later to be occupied by the Franciscans. There Fr. John and all the monks separated greatly by time but now near to each other in death will await the Resurrection and hear the words of our Divine Saviour "Well done good and faithful servants." May he rest in peace in that "holy ground".

(Contributed)

Right Rev. Mgr. John Hanrahan – 1st June, 1999

John Hanrahan, was born on All Saints Day in the Holy Year of 1925, in Corofin, Co. Clare, Ireland, and had his early education in the local primary school, from 1931to1939, when he went to St. Flannan's College, Ennis. He studied for the priesthood at All Hallows College, Dublin, and was ordained priest there for the Archdiocese of Glasgow on 18th June, 1950, by Bishop Michael O'Reilly of St. George's, Newfoundland.

On coming to Scotland that Summer, he was appointed to Holy Cross, Croy, as an assistant priest. It has to be said that, however deep his devotion to Our Lady may have been before, his time in Croy certainly made him a staunch and life-long client of Our Lady of Lourdes, for at that period devotion to the Mother of God under that beloved title was very strong in the village which had the reputation of being all but totally Catholic in its population. This aspect of his spirituality was to stand him in very good stead in later life.

After seventeen years in Croy, he came into the city to be assistant at Christ the King, King's Park, but after a year, in 1968, he returned to the country, or at least to a less urban situation, as assistant priest in St. Mary's, Duntocher, where he remained until 1974, when he was appointed parish priest of St. Helen's, Langside. It was during his eleven years there that he began to suffer from the cancer which was to destroy so much of his jaw, but still he managed to survive and steadfastly to carry out his devoted work as a priest, there and in Holy Cross, Crosshill, where he was appointed parish priest in succession to the late Mgr. John Gillespie, in 1984. During his years in St. Helen's and Holy Cross, he acted as Confessor to the nuns of the Carmelite Monastery at Langside. While in Holy Cross, he was Dean of St. John's Deanery and after the re-organisation of the deaneries, of the Govanhill-Laurieston Deanery. It was while he was parish priest of Holy Cross that he was honoured, in 1993, by being named a Prelate of Honour to His Holiness.

In 1995, he surrendered the burden and responsibility of administering a parish to be able to give more time to direct contact with the faithful, and moved to Cardonald to be an assistant priest in the parish of Our Lady of Lourdes, indeed a very appropriate choice, considering his own devotion to Our Lady under that title, to whose shrine he was such a constant visitor.

He himself gave constant thanks for her intercession which led to his being spared so long, and recovering so often from the continuing depredations of the illness which had afflicted him for so many years. It was said, and one may believe with truth, that if any man had endured his Purgatory in this life it was John Hanrahan.

Finally, shortly before his death, his health had deteriorated so much that he had to enter St. Francis' Nursing Home in Govan, and there he died on 1st June, 1999.

The funeral took place from the Church of Our Lady of Lourdes, on 8th June, the principal celebrant was His Eminence the Cardinal Archbishop of Glasgow, who was joined by a great number of priests, and by an overflow congregation. Interment followed in Corofin.

May he rest in peace.

Very Rev. John Canon Gowans — 15th July, 1999

Canon John Gowans, retired parish priest of The Holy Family, Mastrick, Aberdeen, died on 15th July, 1999, on board the Eurostar train between Paris and London, while returning from Lourdes to his retirement home in Troon, in the 77th year of his age and the 47th of his priesthood. At his Funeral Mass in the Church of Our Lady and St. Meddan, Troon, on Friday, 23rd July following, the following homily was delivered by the Right Reverend Mario J. Conti, Bishop of Aberdeen:

"These things will I remember as I pour out my soul:

How I would lead the rejoicing crowd into the House of God" (Psalm 41: 5)

Canon John was born at Dennistoun, Glasgow 7th October 1922 and was educated at St. Mungo's Academy, after which he attended the Royal Technical College in Glasgow, subsequently working as a chemist at Glasgow Gas Works before doing National Service in the RAF and serving in India.

After a short time in his old job he went to St. Peter's College, Cardross to study for the priesthood and was ordained in St. Andrew's Cathedral on June 29' 1953 by the Archbishop of Glasgow. Thereafter he was appointed to St. John's, Portugal Street, Glasgow, followed by a curacy at St. Patrick's, Dumbarton, where he served until he was appointed to St. Brendan's, Yoker in 1974. In 1976 he went to Aberdeen where he spent the rest of his life apart from the last two years, when, in failing health, he lived in retirement in the home of his sister-in-law in Troon.

In the Liturgy of the Word, during the course of Mass, the Responsorial Psalm acts as a sort of bridge, connecting the readings of the Old and New Testaments. I would like you to think of it now in that way as we gather from the readings thoughts apt for the occasion.

Today's psalm is a pilgrim's psalm. The pilgrim likens himself to the deer "that yearns for running streams" - he is yearning for God. "When can I enter and see" he asks "the face of God?"

Even when he is at rest his memory is of pilgrimage: "These things will I remember as I pour out my soul; how I would lead the rejoicing crowd into the House of God".

Our song then is the song of the pilgrim. He is on the move, "thirsting for God". The image is, of course, suited to that of our deceased colleague, Canon John Gowans. If, towards the end of his life, he was invested as an honorary chaplain to the shrine of Our Lady of Lourdes, it was in acknowledgement of the fact that for 38 years he led annual pilgrimages to the shrine of Our Lady, the Immaculate One - to the running streams where he found refreshment. Even after returning from such a pilgrimage, he would go on holiday and instinctively return, now no longer as a leader, but as a humble devotee of Our Lady, to the cave by the flowing river.

To say that John was out of sympathy with his times, would be an understatement. He saw all too readily the corrosion that was taking place in our society. He ached with concern for the young. He feared the "time of great distress" foreseen by the prophet Daniel (our first reading). He warned of"shame and everlasting disgrace". Not everyone liked his underlining of the reality of evil and of hell, but John was an unashamedly conservative Catholic - in the best sense of the word (and certainly not in a political sense!). Once he hit upon a bright idea which attracted attention not only from the young people of his parish, but also from the Catholic press he established among the young the idea of a sin bin, into which they would throw all that was unworthy of the Lord.

His interest in the young stemmed perhaps from the time when as a priest at St. Patrick's, Dumbarton, he served on the Board of Managers of St. Andrew's Approved School, Shandon, and on the sub-area Education Committee. Each year he would take groups of young lads to Aberdeen where he had the admiration and support of the Sisters of Nazareth. This, incidentally, was his introduction to the Diocese of Aberdeen, where in 1976 he was permitted by the Archbishop of Glasgow to accept a temporary appointment. The following year he was appointed parish priest of Mastrick where he remained until his retirement in 1997. During that time he made application for incardination into the diocese, an application which was generally welcomed, and he was incardinated as a priest of the diocese in October 1981. Five years later he became a member of the Cathedral Chapter, and shortly afterwards was appointed Spiritual Director of the Provincial Council of St. Vincent de Paul, where his sympathy for the poor found ready expression.

Canon John attended, as chaplain, Holy Family School, and attended regularly. He went round the classes and made sure that the instruction given to the children was sound and productive of devotion. He was somewhat sceptical of modern catechetics, preferring the traditional methods. I am sure he welcomed the new Catechism of the Catholic Church when it was published, though it was hardly the penny catechism of his own youth.

Like St. John Bosco he saw that the way to influence young people was to provide them with opportunities for games and holidays - for John the holidays were generally extended pilgrimages to Lourdes, taking in other shrines en route, including on an occasion the shrine of Our Lady of Good Success in Brussels. Our Lady of Good Success is of course the patroness of the Diocese of Aberdeen, whose mediaeval image found harbour in the Netherlands after the turmoil of the Reformation. It was ironic that in his latter years at Mastrick he should have been troubled by the antics of young people not of his congregation who left their graffiti over the walls of his house and church.

Talking of games, of sport, I have to mention that for Canon John there was only one real sport, one game, and one team. I don't need to mention what that team was - nor did he, since it was colour coded with the liturgical colour which seems to dominate the year - the colour of ordinary time. Whenever I made a pastoral visit to John there would be some allusion to that code, and I, who am no footballer, was expected to appreciate in tolerant manner what he alluded to. I occasionally feigned innocence, simply to tease him.

Within the church of the Holy Family all was beautiful and it was as if, as with the Stations of the Cross replicating places in Jerusalem connected with Our Lord's Passion, statues of Our Lady throughout the church reproduced many continental Marian shrines.

Journeying from the Old Testament to the New, brings us to that lovely passage in St. Matthew's Gospel where Jesus blesses his Father, "Lord of Heaven and Earth, for hiding these things (of the kingdom) from the learned and the clever and revealing them to mere children". There was a childlike simplicity about John himself - a faith which appeared untroubled; a devotion that appeared secure. He wanted young people to share what he had. Having "instructed many in virtue", he is promised star quality in heaven for all eternity.

Canon John's other abiding characteristic as a pastor was his attention to the sick. He visited daily the hospital attached to his parish bringing the sacraments and comfort to many. I sensed that he gave sure direction to many who were on their last journey. Again it was the pilgrim leader, and I imagine he echoed the words of St. Paul in his second letter to the Corinthians: "We know that when the tent that we live in on earth is folded up, there is a house built by God for us, an everlasting home not made by human hands, in the heavens".

I have already spoken about that self-assurance in the faith which he manifested, and once again we sense it as an echo of St. Paul: "We are always full of confidence, then, when we remember that to live in the body means to be exiled from the Lord going as we do by faith and not by sight". Canon John was visionary perhaps only in that sense, namely that he saw with the eyes of faith beyond the limitations of time and space. Perhaps it was that which gave him a certain affinity to St. Bernadette, and his abiding love for Lourdes. It was returning from Lourdes just over a week ago that he laid down his exile's pack. He did not have time even to fold his tent. On the train between Paris and London he fell asleep and woke to gaze upon the Lord. "Come to me", said the Lord, "all you who labour and are overburdened, and I will give you rest".

May his soul and the souls of the all the faithful departed, through the mercy of God, rest in peace. Amen.

Rev. Walter Patrick Crampton, M.A. — 30th August, 1999

Father Walter Crampton, retired parish priest of St. Mary of the Angels, Falkirk, died in the Strathcarron Hospice, Denny, on 30th August, 1999, in the 86th year of his age and the 60th of his priesthood. At the Funeral Mass in St. Francis Xavier's, Falkirk, on Friday, 3rd September following, the following homily was delivered by the Right Rev. Anthony Canon mcNally, V.G., parish priest of St. Columba's, Newington, Edinburgh:

Father Crampton made it clear in the instructions he left for his funeral that there was to be no panegyric. He said that he did not believe in "Instant canonisation" but he did believe in prayers for the dead. Perhaps that is why he chose the first reading from the Book of Maccabees where Judas took up a collection and sent the proceeds to Jerusalem to have a sacrifice for sin offered. And as the reading goes on to say this is "An altogether fine and noble action, in which he took full account of the resurrection. For if he had not expected the fallen to rise again it would have been superfluous and foolish to pray for the dead, whereas if he had in view the splendid recompense reserved for those who make a pious end, the thought was holy and devout." Father Crampton as we know was a humble and a very private person and so it was in character for him not to want a panegyric but instead to ask for our prayers.

I thought then that a few words on priesthood might be appropriate, as I remember a letter Fr. Crampton wrote to me just a few months ago, in which he spoke of his, and I quote, "modest priesthood - but so dear to me." A very beautiful feeling for priesthood. My priesthood which is so dear to me sums up the man.

Thomas Merton once said that " To fall in love with God was the greatest of all romances. To seek Him was the greatest of all adventures and to find him was the greatest human achievement." And I thought what a beautiful summary of a priest's life. To fall in love with God is the greatest of all romances. There are many reasons why a young man might want to be a priest: to help other people, to serve the Church, to imitate Christ and of course, sometimes there might be mixed motives. But surely underlying all the motives there must be this constant motivation of love for God. And God made that easier for us by giving us his Son, Jesus Christ, who taught us how to love - Jesus, is God's love in action. And just as the world did not understand Jesus and his single-minded love for his Father, equally the world does not understand priesthood and the love of God which motivates the priest. Underlying every priest's life is devotion to Christ, the Word of God made flesh. A priest's life is rooted in the person of Christ. He is the centre of the priest's life which becomes a life at the service of Christ and his church.

To seek him is the greatest of all adventures. How do we seek God? Is it not the other way round? Did he not seek us out first of all and give us Jesus to help our love. It is by getting to know Jesus. By being rooted in Jesus that we get to know God. As our second reading, chosen by Fr. Crampton, said, "through Jesus we have passed out of death into life". And "This has taught us love - that he gave up his life for us; and we, too, ought to give up our lives for our brothers. This is how we love God by loving one another and if we wish to embark on this greatest of all adventures of seeking God, we find him in Jesus and in each other. When a man becomes a priest he gives an unqualified "Yes" to Jesus. What someone called a "Forever Yes" and a "Yes forever."

Cardinal Newman once said, and I am very glad to quote him as he was a great favourite of Fr. Crampton's: "Blessed are those who in the flower of their youth gave themselves to Christ, heart and soul. To the Christ who gave his life for them." Looking around the sanctuary, there isn't much left of the flower of youth. And I speak for myself there is more of the autumn leaves than the flower of youth. But there is great beauty and dignity in the youthful profession that leads to lifelong commitment to Christ. And all of us, priests and religious, in the intervening years in our search for Christ in this greatest of all adventures have struggled, worked hard, faced difficulties, gone where we would rather not go. And we did it all for Him. Fidelity to one's commitment to Christ is difficult and demanding and costly, but it is something very beautiful and brings so many blessings when it is lived out day by day in the presence of Christ. This vision of priesthood was something I saw in Fr. Crampton when as a young boy in Blairs he was my spiritual director, and as a brother priest said to me very recently, it wasn't what he said, it wasn't what he did, it was what he was that influenced us as students. And thankfully through his years in Blairs and later in Drygrange a whole generation of priests were inspired by his example. And I am sure that those of you who were privileged to have him as your parish priest were equally inspired by his example.

Just a few weeks ago when he was quite ill he told me he had been praying to St. Teresa, the Little Flower, that he might die. But she isn't listening to my prayers, he said. He was ready to die. Ready to find and see the God he had loved and served all his priestly life. He could face death without fear because of his intimacy with Christ. An intimacy that came from the Eucharist and those words of Jesus in the gospel Fr. Crampton chose; "I am the living bread come down from heaven...anyone who eats this bread will live forever." He knew and believed in the death and resurrection of Jesus - the paschal death - the passing over that is a death which leads to new life.

I often say that our death and birth into eternal life must be seen just as our birth into this life. When we are born we are born into the care and arms of a loving mother. And God is our real Mother as well as being our Father; more tender, more loving and more understanding than any earthly mother. Just as here on earth our mother was tender and patient with us, in death God is even more so. Being born into God's arms will surely be as gentle and tender an experience as being born into our mother's arms.

But death inevitably brings sadness to those who are left behind. We are diminished, lessened, reduced by the loss of someone we loved and respected. And I would like to convey my deep sympathy and to give particular thanks to Mrs. Betty McGoff, the housekeeper, who for so many years has looked after and cared for Fr. Crampton. He was deeply grateful for all she did for him. And to us, his brother priests, it was our privilege to have known him, to have learned from him, and to have shared our priesthood with him. If he were here he would be asking us to pray for him, which is what we are about to do in this Mass. But we pray with confidence knowing that Fr. Crampton is now in better and infinitely more gentle hands than ours. He is with the God he loved and served all his life. And we pray that he will rest in peace.

Rev. Francis Kelly – 26th October, 1999

Father Francis Kelly, retired Parish Priest of St. Mary's, Whifflet, Coatbridge, died on 26th October, 1999, in the Victoria Infirmary, Glasgow, after a long illness. At the Funeral Mass on 30th October following in St. Augustine's, Langloan, Coatbridge, prior to interment in St. Patrick's Cemetery, New Stevenston, the principal celebrant was the Right Reverend Joseph Devine, Bishop of Motherwell, who delivered the following homily:

Today we gather for the funeral Mass for Fr. Francis Kelly, or Frank, to his circle of friends among the priests of the Diocese. He is the 5th of our retired priests to have died in 1999, along with priests such as Canon John Sheridan, Fr. Kelly's first parish priest for all practical purposes, Fr. James Keegan, who twice served in Frank's home parish of Shieldmuir, Fr. Denis Power and Canon George Fryer. I will be remembering all of them, Frank included, at the memorial Mass for our late Bishop, Francis Thomson, in the Cathedral in early December, the month of the death of Bishop Thomson. But that is in the future. Today we have the celebration of the life of a gifted priest of this Diocese, Fr. Francis Kelly.

He was born on 23rd of August, 1930, not the easiest time for any newborn of that era, so shortly after the Wall Street crash of the year before, leading to a recession in the world trade. Poverty was widespread. However, with the New Deal of 1934 under the remarkable Mr. Roosevelt, things became relatively easier by the middle of the 1930's when Frank began to attend school in St. Patrick's, Shieldmuir. He went to Our Lady's High School in 1942, at the mid point of the Second World War, where he gained distinction in his studies to such a degree that he proceeded to the Pontifical Scots College in Rome in 1948 to continue his chosen vocation in the priesthood. It must have been a wonderful experience to him to be there at that time, shortly after the college had been re-opened only a couple of years earlier. What he made of the formidable Rector of the time, Mgr. Clapperton, is not recorded, but I suspect that he greatly enjoyed the experience, for he retained a deep affection for the college, in the light of subsequent developments in his life.

He was ordained in Rome on 18th December, 1954. Shortly before then, when he was a deacon, Mgr. Thomas Taylor of Carfin, was in Rome for a meeting of the Pontifical Mission Society. As he was a contemporary of Mgr. Clapperton, he was welcome to stay at the Scots College in Rome on such occasions. If you are unaware of the history of Mgr. Taylor, the older he became, ever more difficult for him was to hold on to curates, who wanted to find pastures new, anywhere else than in Carfin. So in the post war years, when in Rome, he tended to try and recruit possible future curates from within the student body. In the autumn of 1954, when in Rome, he chanced upon Fr. Jim Foley, a classmate of Frank, and asked him where he came from. On learning that Jim was a senior student for the Diocese of Motherwell, he asked him his name. Without a moment's hesitation, Jim replied, Francis Kelly!

On returning home in the summer of 1955, Frank was spared that fate. He first spent an initial few months, a kind of summer and early autumn appointment in the parish of St. Barbara's, Muirhead, before going to St. Bridget's, in Baillieston for the next six years. He was very happy there and much liked by the parish community of that time.

Then in 1961, he was transferred to Larkhall, a remarkable change by any standard, going from Baillieston to a town that has a reputation for the kind of religious intolerance that one associates with the previous century. But it did not turn one hair of his head to another colour. He enjoyed his time there, not least as its Catholic community rates among the finest of any parish in the Diocese of Motherwell. In 1965 he transferred to St. Patrick's, Coatbridge which was to be a short term appointment.

In 1966, rather to his surprise, but much to his delight, he was off to Rome again, as Spiritual Director of the student body at the Scots College, but a very different kind of college from his student days. It was no longer in the city centre, but several miles from the centre on the Via Cassia. Nor was that the only change. The Second Vatican Council had concluded only a year before and change was everywhere, not least in seminaries. In a time of such innovation, it was not an easy role to fulfil, with its changed expectations, changed study priorities, changing liturgies, a much changed staff from only a couple of years earlier. In fact, all the staff of the time were new. But Frank gave of his best to his role, in a college and in a city for which he ever retained a great affection. While there, he gained a licentiate in the new discipline of Social Sciences, then being offered by the Gregorian University.

1969 saw him returning to Scotland, when he took up the post as assistant priest in St. Aloysius'. Chapelhall. Again, he felt very much at home there, at the centre of Lanarkshire, for in the very best sense, Fr. Kelly was very much a Lanarkshire man, doubtless, in great part due to his upbringing in Shieldmuir and his identification with the values instilled into him by his good parents and the parish community of the time, a time when many young people of his teenage years and later were to enter the priesthood and religious life from that parish.

Chapelhall would have been a quite similar kind of community. Therefore, he would have had no difficulty in settling back into the pastoral life and mission for which he had been ordained. During his time in Chapelhall he began a long record of service to the Diocese on the Education Committee of the old Lanark Council, followed by the Lanark Division of Strathclyde Regional Council, a role in which he served from 1972 until 1989.

But 1974 was to be a red letter year for him when he became parish priest of the old parish of St. Mary's in Cleland, a parish which celebrated less than a month ago its 125th Anniversary of foundation. He was to remain there for eight years and loved every day there. It was such a happy time for him, perhaps the place he enjoyed most in the 41 years in the active ministry. Had he been able to do so, I am certain that he would have loved to have gone back for the celebration there just a month or so ago.

In 1982 he moved to St. Mark's, Rutherglen, about as different from Cleland as any parish in the Diocese, a relatively new parish, much bigger in its population size than Cleland, with a congregation few of whom were natives of Rutherglen. Most had come there from the south side of Glasgow. Unemployment was widespread and the area was beginning to suffer from the kind of vandalism and crime that he would never have met before in any of the parishes where he had worked. I arrived in the Diocese the following year and it soon became clear that he was not very happy at being on the periphery of the Diocese, as the Archdiocese of Glasgow and the huge Castlemilk housing scheme was literally just across the road.

So when Fr. Foley moved to St. Augustine's to follow the beloved Canon John Moss in 1985, I offered him the vacant parish of St. Mary's in Whifflet. I did not need to ask him twice, as he was thrilled to return to much more familiar territory. He was to remain there for the following 11 years. For over much the greater part of that time, he continued to build up that fine community, enhancing the beauty of the church and proving to be such a good friend to those committed to his pastoral care.

However, by the end of this decade, it was clear that his health was declining and with increasing frequency he was in need of support, readily supplied for so long by Fr. John Givens. 1996 was really a kind of nightmare year for him, with recurring bouts of illness', culminating in a throat operation that was to rob him of his vocal cords. Ever a fighter, even then he did not want to retire, even although that was the only option. Providentially, the former chapel house in the parish of Holy Trinity and All Saints became vacant at that point. So with his devoted housekeeper, he moved into it in the September of 1996. Many a day in the past 3 years must have been a trial to him as his health declined, seemingly close to death on several occasions, but making a recovery except for his final illness.

I am sure that what kept him alive for as long as he did was the excellent care that he received, both medically and domestically. He died on the morning of last Tuesday, some 3 months after his 69th birthday.

Today, as we pray for his immortal repose, we do so in the context of readings that are full of hope for one who lived the christian life and exercised the ministerial priesthood. For such a one there is an eternally equivalent table and meal for all who celebrated the eucharist, that banquet on God's holy mountain where all the Lord's faithful servants will be housed, cared for and fed.

Surely among these are to be found those whose lives graced the lives of others, so many others. Few lives more grace the lives of others than that of a priest. Over his 45 years of ministry, think of the scores of weddings that Fr. Kelly conducted, the hundreds of children he baptised, the thousands of Masses that he offered and the many thousands of confessions he heard, to touch but only three of the sacraments. In all of these, he acted in *persona Christi* whose ordained minister he was, for Fr. Kelly never doubted his vocation to Christ's priesthood.

But the greatest challenge for all of us is the Gospel for today, the very heart of what it means to live the christian life. All of us struggle to meet its demands. In sickness and in health, so did Francis Kelly. He had few ambitions for himself. He was not a kind of person to be interested in power or wealth. Instead, he liked people. They were his wealth, along with a fine sense of humour and a generous heart. So it is with confidence that we entrust him to the generous judgement and welcome of the Lord, whom he sought to serve as best he knew how, to the end of his days. With no less confidence, therefore, we now pray:

"Eternal rest grant unto him, O Lord, and let perpetual light shine upon him. May he rest in peace". Amen.

LIST OF DECEASED CLERGY FROM 1986*

With Diocese, Place and Date of Death and Age.

Adamson, Charles Canon (Dunk.), Blairgowrie   25 Aug.   1994   56
Andrew, Ernest Provost (Dunk.), Perth   1 Aug.   1992   71

Bannon, James (Gall.), Ayr   22 Dec.   1986   71
Bergin, Malachy (Glasg.), Glasgow   8 Aug.   1993   68
Beveridge, John (Aberd.), Aberdeen   23 Apr.   1988   35
Boyle John Canon (Paisl.), Glasgow   17 May   1993   86
Boyle, John W. Canon (Moth.), Cardonald   31 Jan.   1998   75
Brady, Patrick J. Canon (Glasg.), Glasgow   7 Aug.   1977   83
Breen Joseph Canon (Glasg.), Glasgow   8 Sept.   1990   78
Brodie, Charles Canon (S.Andr.), Fauldhouse   15 Mar.   1999   79
Brosnan, Patrick (Moth.), Lanark   26 Mar.   1995   66
Burke Anthony J. (Glasg.), Glasgow   14 Apr.   1993   60
Burke Donal (Glasg.), Clydebank   12 July   1990   65
Burke, Patrick (Paisl.) Kilmacolm   11 Dec.   1991   65

Cahill, Hugh Canon (Moth.), Airdrie   11 Apr.   1990   84
Cahill, Thomas Canon (Glasg.), Glasgow   23 Sept.   1996   86
Campbell, Hugh (Dunk.) Dundee   25 Aug.   1993   66
Carney Matthew (Glasg.), Glasgow   3 Feb.   1991   75
Cawley John (Glasg.), Glasgow   24 Dec.   1987   78
Chandler, Albert (Paisl.), Dundee   8 Apr.   1992   83
Colbert, William (Glasg.), Cork   8 May   1997   77
Collins, Charles Canon (Aberd.), Aberdeen   31 Mar.   1986   73
Condon, Canon Christopher (Moth.), Cork   8 Apr.   1996   81
Connolly, John J. (Gall.), Galway   21 Jan.   2000   77
Connolly, Mgr. Peter Canon (S. Andr.),
  Musselburgh   28 Feb.   1992   88
Conroy, Mgr. John Canon (Moth.),
  Southampton   20 Apr.   1994   88
Cooper, Norman (S.Andr.), Isle of Skye   20 May   1996   40
Corcoran, Thomas Canon (S. Andr.), Lasswade   25 Sept.   1990   84
Corless, Thomas (Moth.), Uddingston   11 May   1990   62
Cosgrove, John (Moth.), Glasgow   28 Nov.   1990   83
Costello Edward G. (Pais), Greenock   28 June   1992   69
Coyle, Mgr. Francis (Glasg.), Glasgow   7 June   1998   73

---

* For list of priests deceased before 1800, see *Catholic Directory* for 1921; for those deceased after 1800 and before 1900, see *Catholic Directory* for 1942; for those deceased after 1900 and before 1925, see *Catholic Directory* for 1948: for those deceased between 1926 and 1950, see *Catholic Directory* for 1971; For those deceased between 1951 and 1965, see *Catholic Directory* for 1984; for those deceased between 1966 and 1975; see *Catholic Directory* for 1991; for those deceased between 1976 and 1985 see *Catholic Directory* for 1996.

Crampton, Walter P. (S.Andr.), Denny	30 Aug.	1999	85
Crawley, George (Glasg.) Glasgow	22 Aug.	1990	64
Davison, Laurence Canon (S.Andr.), Edinburgh	18 Sept.	1993	73
Deery, Hugh Canon (Glasg.), Glasgow	23 May	1989	74
Devane, Michael (S.Andr.), Methil	26 May	1999	81
Dineen, Patrick Canon (Glasg.), Castlewarren, Kilkenny	5 Sept.	1986	76
Doherty, Edward (Moth.), Blackpool	23 Aug.	1991	80
Doherty, Francis (S.Andr.), Bo'ness	25 Dec.	1999	72
Doherty, Martin Canon (Glasg.), Greenock	24 May	1991	84
Dooley, James (Moth.), Glasgow	21 Mar.	1988	73
Doonan, Bernard (S. Andr.), Denny	28 Sept.	1990	50
Douglas, Robert Canon (Moth.), Musselburgh	3 Nov.	1988	83
Duddy, William Canon (Moth.), Coatbridge	8 Oct.	1986	73
Duffin, Charles Canon (Glasg.), Glasgow	3 July	1989	80
Duffy, John Canon (Glasg.), Clydebank	21 Nov.	1998	78
Durcan, Patrick Provost (Paisl,), Greenock	14 Apr.	1998	74
Durkin, Edward (Dunk.), Dundee	23 Dec.	1987	57
Earley, John Canon (Paisl.), Johnstone	1 Jan.	1987	71
Engelen, Thomas (S.Andr.) Saltcoats	9 Mar.	1997	78
Fallon, Patrick (S.Andr.), Kirkcaldy	12 Aug.	1993	55
Farrell, Henry (Glasg.), Glasgow	10 July	1998	47
Farrelly, Mgr. Henry (Pais.), Coventry	25 Sept.	1995	69
Fehily, Mgr. Thomas Canon (Moth.), New Stevenston	16 Sept.	1987	69
Fitzgerald, James (Glasg.), Crieff	24 Feb.	1990	73
Fltzgibbon, John (Glasg.), Letterkenny	20 Nov.	1988	67
Frigerio, Thomas Edgar (Glasg.), Waterford	16 Dec.	1987	80
Fryer, George Canon (Moth.), Derry	20 Jan.	1999	80
Fusco, John (S. Andr.), Edinburgh	16 June	1994	86
Gahagan, Patrick (Glasg.), Glasgow	12 May	1993	62
Gallacher, Kieran Canon (Paisl.), Greenock	23 Aug.	1996	67
Gallagher, Daniel (Dunk.), Dundee	21 Apr.	1986	54
Gallagher, Daniel M. (Glasg.), Glasgow	2 July	1995	72
Gallagher, Edward (S.Andr.), Broxburn	19 Aug.	1998	58
Gallagher, Wm. James Canon (S. Andr.), Edinburgh	2 Nov.	1991	72
Garrity, Denis (Moth.), Airdrie	9 Mar.	1993	80
Gavagan, Michael (Glasg.), Kirkintilloch	5 Jan.	1987	68
Gilchrist, Edward (S. Andr.), Athlone	3 Apr.	1990	76
Gillen, Mgr. John Canon (Moth.), Moville	16 Apr.	1995	78

Gilmartin, Patrick Canon (Glasg.), Sligo	27 Nov.	1994	95
Glendinning, Joseph E. (Gall.), Newton Stewart	31 Dec.	1993	77
Gogarty, John (Glasg.), Waterford	30 Oct.	1986	74
Gorman, Peter (Moth.), Rutherglen	15 Sept.	1986	46
Gowans, John Canon (Aberd.), between Paris & London	15 July	1999	76
Gray, Cardinal Gordon Joseph, Archbishop Emeritus of St. Andrews and Edinburgh, Edinburgh	19 July	1993	82
Gunning, Desmond (Glasg.), Glasgow	2 Mar.	1996	78
Gunning, Patrick Canon (Gall.), Portencross	15 Nov.	1987	72
Hanlon, Mgr. John B. (Dunk.), Tayport	20 July	1990	59
Hanrahan, Mgr. John (Glasg.), Govan	1 June	1999	73
Haran, John Canon (Paisl.), Co. Sligo	6 June	1997	87
Harkin, John J. (Gall.), Stranraer	17 Aug.	1996	65
Hart, William Andrew, Bishop Emeritus of Dunkeld, Dundee	18 Oct.	1992	88
Healey, Robert (Moth.), Law	13 Mar.	1994	43
Hearty, Thomas Canon (Paisl.), Wemyss Bay	17 Mar.	1997	79
Henery, William (S.Andr.), Grangemouth	28 Apr.	1987	72
Henessy, Daniel Canon (Moth.), Glasgow	27 May	1995	71
Henry, James (S. Andr.), Edinburgh	16 Oct.	1987	42
Henry, Mgr. Patrick J., (Glasg.), Glasgow	6 Aug.	1995	68
Higgins, Peter Canon (S.Andr.), Lasswade	9 Feb.	1998	92
Hodgson, Reginald (S.Andr.), Uckfield	30 June	1996	80
Holden, Francis Canon (S.Andr.), Edinburgh	28 May	1993	77
Houlihan, Michael (Moth.), Glasgow	15 Oct.	1986	67
Hyland, Mgr. Thomas Canon (S.Andr.), Lasswade	11 May	1997	86
Jackson, Michael Canon (S.Andr.), Lasswade	2 Feb.	1999	71
Jamieson, Lawrence (Glasg.), Edinburgh	26 Mar.	1995	56
Johnston, Alexander (Glasg.), Youghal	13 Feb.	1990	66
Kane, Duncan (Glasg.), near Balfron	26 July	1995	72
Kane, John (Gall.), Galston	21 Dec.	1989	69
Keegan, Gerard T.D. Canon (Dunk.), Derrybeg, Co. Donegal	23 Aug.	1996	83
Keegan, James (Moth.), Lanark	3 Feb.	1999	71
Keenaghan, James (Paisl.), Glasgow	10 Mar.	1991	61
Keenan, Bernard Canon (Moth.), Dublin	2 Jan.	1992	85
Kelly, Patrick Canon (Moth.), Saltcoats	29 Mar.	1989	91
Kelly, Francis (Moth.), Glasgow	26 Oct.	1999	69
Kenny, Laurence (Moth.), Airdrie	13 Apr.	1992	61
Kiernan, Anthony Canon (S. Andr.), Brighton	15 Oct.	1991	70

Kiernan, Francis (Gall.), Saltcoats	20 Nov.	1988	64
Kilcoyne, Patrick (Moth.), East Kilbride	7 Mar.	1990	60
Kilpatrick, James Canon (Moth.), Burnside	4 Jan.	1989	76
Knight, Louis (Glasg./Orange, U.S.A.)			
Dana Point, U.S.A	14 Nov.	1994	70
Kruger, Karl-Heinz Canon (S. Andr.), Kilsyth .	24 May	1989	65
Lavery, Samuel J. Canon (Glasg.), Glasgow	6 Jan.	1996	83
Leen, John Canon (Gall.), Kilmarnock	9 Aug.	1995	77
Leverage, Thomas (Gall.), Ayr	16 June	1996	61
Lynch, Gerard (S. Andr.), Nunraw	29 July	1987	68
Lyne, Michael Canon (Glasg.), Lanark	24 Oct.	1994	79
Lyons, Peter Canon (S. Andr.), Banknock	15 May	1991	71
McAllister, Bernard (S.Andr.), Bannockburn	24 Mar.	1996	56
McAllister, Christopher Canon (S. Andr.),			
Bannockburn	29 Apr.	1990	80
McAteer, Mgr. Thomas Canon (Glasg.), Glasgow	11 May	1997	79
McCabe, Gerald Canon (S.Andr.), Dunfermline	9 Mar.	1993	70
McCabe, John J. (Glasgow), Moodiesburn	3 Dec.	1998	67
McCabe, Michael (Glasg.), Clydebank	22 Mar.	1996	63
McCann, Peter Canon (Moth.), Glasgow	1 Aug.	1994	79
McCluskey, Alexander (Paisl.), Greenock	23 June	1987	47
McCluskey, Martin (Gall.), Ayr	10 Sept.	1996	61
McColgan, Gerald B. (Moth.), Bellshill	25 Jan.	1987	58
McCurrach, George Canon (Aberd.),	15 Sept.	1995	79
McCready, John Canon (Glasg.), Glasgow	20 Mar.	1987	76
McDaid, Neil F. (Glasg.), Cardonald	25 Apr.	1999	78
Macdonald, John (Glasg.), Robroyston	8 Jan.	2000	81
McElholm, Joseph (Glasg.), Glasgow	24 June	1987	62
McEwen, Daniel (Glasg.), Hull	16 Sept.	1989	58
McEwan, Mgr. Hugh G. (Glasg.), Glasgow	23 Sept.	1989	64
McEwan, Hugh J. Canon (Glasg.), Glasgow	7 Feb.	1995	58
MacEwan, Sydney A. M. Canon (Argyll),			
Glasgow	25 Sept.	1991	83
McGarvey, Thomas Canon (S. Andr.), Kilsyth.	6 Oct.	1987	91
McGeown, John (S.Andr.), Gortin, Co. Tyrone	12 July	1986	72
McGill, James (Moth.), Cleland	12 Mar.	1986	70
McGinlay, John (Glasg.), Glasgow	19 Feb.	1986	69
McGlinchey, James (Moth.), Glasgow	26 June	1991	55
McGregor, Charles Canon (Aberd.), Aberdeen	29 July	1998	72
McGuinness, Daniel Canon (S.Andr.),	26 Jan.	1997	71
McGurk, Anthony Canon (Moth.), Kilrea,			
Co. Derry	29 Apr.	1997	80
McGurk, Thomas Canon (Moth.), Glasgow	17 May	1991	69
McHugo, Anthony (Glasgow), Dublin	10 Nov.	1995	74

Mackay, John (Glasg.), Clydebank	20 Dec.	1997	82
McKearney, Peter J. Canon (Dunk.), Keady	1 Apr.	1993	77
McKee, John (S.Andr.), Norwich	27 June	1986	75
McKee, John J. (Glas.), Glasgow	6 Dec.	1990	64
MacKellaig, Angus (Moth.), Law	11 Dec.	1992	78
MacKenzie, Kenneth Canon (Aberd.), Aberdeen	14 Sept.	1990	86
McKeon, Peter Canon (S.Andr.), Musselburgh	15 July	1996	87
MacKinnon, Mgr. Donald (Glasg.), Blackburn, Lancs	15 Aug.	1987	67
McLachlan, David (Glasg.), Clydebank	31 Mar.	1997	64
McLaren, John (Glasg.), Glasgow	1 Feb.	1989	59
McLaughlin, Charles (Gall.) Shrove, Co. Donegal	7 Mar.	1987	61
MacLean, Angus E. (Glasg.), Glasgow	12 Oct.	1994	50
McLean, John Canon (Argyll), Daliburgh	6 Dec.	1986	67
McMahon, Mgr. James Canon (Glasg.), Clydebank	14 Sept.	1998	76
MacNeil, Mgr. John A. Canon, V.G. (Argyll), Morar	4 Mar.	1993	59
MacPherson, Colin, Bishop of Argyll and The Isles, Oban	24 Mar.	1990	72
McQuade, John V. (Moth.), Glasgow	22 Sept.	1990	63
MacWilliam, Mgr. Alexander S. Canon (Aberd.), Aberdeen	20 Mar.	1988	86
McWilliam, John Lewis Provost (Aberd.), Huntly	10 Oct.	1995	90
Mackle, Gerard (Moth.), Edinburgh	6 Sept.	1996	73
Maguire, Thomas (Glasg.), Glasgow	27 May	1995	82
Mahoney, Bernard (Moth.), Robroyston	3 Apr.	1998	71
Malaney, James Canon (Dunk.), Cupar	27 July	1998	81
Mannion, Thomas P. Canon (Pais.), Wexford.	9 Aug.	1993	73
Marr, Peter (Glasgow.), Amendingen, Germany	12 July	1998	59
Martin, Joseph (Moth.) Cambuslang	28 Feb.	1991	73
Martin, Thomas Canon (S. Andr.), Lasswade	14 June	1988	76
Masterson, Michael (Aberd.), Fochabers	5 June	1997	57
Matthews, Charles Canon (Gall.), West Kilbride	15 Mar.	1996	68
Meechan, Denis Provost (Glasg.), Glasgow	19 Mar.	1989	83
Meehan, James Canon (Glasg.), Glasgow	29 July	1995	92
Meikleham, Thomas Canon (Glasg.), Glasgow	16 Jan.	1999	90
Mohan, Edward Canon (S. Andr.)., Lasswade.	14 Jan.	1991	83
Monaghan, James, Auxiliary Bishop Emeritus of St. Andrews and Edinburgh, Lasswade	3 June	1994	79
Mooney, Henry Canon (Paisl.), Cardonald	4 Feb.	1997	73
Morgan, William (Glasg.), Glasgow	30 Apr.	1996	82
Moriarty, Myles Canon (Gall.), Ayr	3 Sept.	1989	79
Morrison, John Canon (Argyll), Fort William	18 June	1992	79
Moss, John Canon (Moth.), Lanark	25 June	1992	73
Mullen, George Canon (Moth.), Airdrie	28 June	1990	78

Mulhall, Joseph (Glasg.), Glasgow	9 Jan.	1994 74
Murdoch, Mgr. William (Aberd.), Aberdeen	25 Sept.	1987 87
Murnin, Michael Canon (S. Andr.), Lasswade.	2 Mar.	1988 86
Murphy, Mgr. Brendan H. (Glasg.), Troon	4 July	1988 72
Murphy, Nicholas Canon (Gall.), Killaloe	1 June	1992 72
Murphy, Mgr. Peter (Paisl.), Linwood	15 Dec.	1999 76
Murphy, William (Glasg.), Waterville	26 July	1989 61
Nee, Joseph (Glasg.) Glasgow	21 Apr.	1987 70
Nicholson, James F. Canon (S. Andr.) Lasswade	23 Sept.	1998 67
Nolan, John (Dunk.), Alloa	6 June	1987 74
Oates, Bernard M. (Moth.), Glasgow	31 July	1988 61
O'Brien, John Canon (Glasg.), Glasgow	30 May	1999 74
O'Callaghan, Gerald (Moth.), Oysterhaven, Co. Cork	6 Nov.	1992 76
O'Callaghan, Richard, (Glasg.), Westport, Co. Mayo	3 Oct.	1998 84
O'Connell, Denis Canon (S.Andr.), Edinburgh	9 Oct.	1997 79
O'Connell, Michael (Glasg.), Bishopbriggs	10 Aug.	1995 80
O'Connor, Thomas B. (Pais.), Linwood	20 June	1993 69
O'Doherty, Daniel Canon (Moth.), Derry	7 Oct.	1992 77
O'Donnell, Mgr. John (Moth.), Wishaw	3 Mar.	1989 70
O'Donoghue, Patrick (Moth.), Bailieborough, Co. Cavan	19 Nov.	1995 69
O'Donohoe, Patrick G. Canon (Dunk.), Dundee	26 Aug.	1992 76
O'Dwyer, John Canon (Paisl.), Clydebank	4 Sept.	1996 69
O'Grady, Michael (Glasg.), Glasgow	25 Jan.	1987 74
O'Hanlon, James Canon (S. Andr.), Edinburgh	25 Jan.	1987 72
O'Hara, Edward (Glasg.), Granard	23 Apr.	1988 70
O'Kane, Jeremiah (Glasg.), Newbury	8 Mar.	1987 73
O'Leary, Daniel Canon (Glasg.), Robroyston	12 Mar.	1997 81
O'Regan, Bartholomew (Moth.), Caldercruix	22 Oct.	1997 66
O'Sullivan, John (Glasg.), Clydebank	15 July	1993 72
Phelan, James Canon (S. Andr.), Falkirk	29 Apr.	1990 77
Philips, George Canon (Aberd.), Aboyne	15 Mar.	1986 82
Power, Denis (Moth.),	28 Apr.	1999 72
Power, Thomas W. (S. Andr.), Clydebank	30 Apr.	1994 67
Purcell, Edmund (Dunk.), Dundee	7 Dec.	1991 80
Quigley, Edward (S. Andr.), Linlithgow	18 Dec.	1989 74
Quin, James (Moth.), Motherwell	10 Jan.	1994 70
Quinn, James (Glasg.), Glasgow	25 Dec.,	1990 75

Rafferty, Kevin, Auxiliary Bishop of St. Andrews
  and Edinburgh, Livingston   19 Apr   1996   62
Ramsay, John (S.Andr.), Livingston   22 Oct.   1997   70
Renfrew, Charles McDonald, Auxiliary Bishop
  of Glasgow, Glasgow   27 Feb.   1992   62
Renucci, Bruno (Glasg.), Glasgow   16 Feb.   1995   74
Robertson, John Canon (Dunk.), Edinburgh   17 Dec.   1995   62
Rogers, James Kevin (Moth.), East Kilbride   25 May   1986   57
Rooney, Andrew Canon (Dunk.), Dundee   27 Nov.   1991   68
Ross, John Canon (Dunk.), Glasgow   8 May   1995   80
Ryan, Thomas (Paisl.), Govan   5 Jan.   1997   71

Sheridan, John A. Canon (Moth.), Glasgow   16 Jan.   1999   92
Strain Desmond (Glasg.), Kilsyth   21 Nov.   1986   63
Strickland, William (Glasg.), Glasgow   15 Oct.   1990   70
Sullivan, Alexander Provost (Aberd.), Nairn   7 Jan.   1986   81

Tierney, Patrick (Glasg.), Glasgow   22 Oct.   1993   70
Tierney, Thomas (Glasg.), Cardonald   28 Feb.   1997   81
Traynor, James (Glasg.), Glasgow   2 Aug.   1996   85

Walker, Vincent Canon (Gall.), Prestwick   23 Oct.   1993   75
Ward, John Canon (S.Andr.), Edinburgh   11 May   1986   72
White, Daniel B. Canon (Moth.), Kilkee   I Sept.   1990   78
Wilkinson, James Joseph (Glasg.), Glasgow   11 Sept.   1994   69
Wilson, William Canon (S.Andr.), Kirkcaldy   10 Aug.   1995   87
Woods, Robert (Glasg.),Silsden, W. Yorks.   23 Mar   1993   81

CATHOLIC SOCIETIES AND INSTITUTIONS

(Secretaries of Associations, etc., are requested to send their information for this part of the *Directory* to the Rev. Editor, c/o the Publishers, **by the end of September each year.** The Editor cannot accept responsibility for inaccuracies resulting from non-compliance with this request. At the same time, he reserves the right to consider that a particular association or institution has ceased to exist)

A—General

ACROSS SCOTLAND.—A charity which organises groups of volunteer helpers and staff to take the seriously ill and severely handicapped on pilgrimages and holidays all over Europe. *Contact person:* Annie Stewart. *Official address::* 52 Westermains Avenue, Kirkintilloch GLASGOW G66 1EH. ☎/Fax: 0141-777 6931. (Across Scotland is affiliated to the Across Trust, Registered Charity No. 265540.)

ADOPTION SOCIETIES.—See under C—Social Care, No. 3.

AID FUND, SCOTTISH CATHOLIC INTERNATIONAL.—*President,* The Right Rev. John Mone, Bishop of Paisley, 107 Corsebar Road, Paisley PA2 9PY; *Executive Director,* Paul Chitnis. *Official address:* S.C.I.A.F., 19 Park Circus, GLASGOW G3 6BE. ☎ 0141-354 5555; Fax: 0141-354 5533. E-mail: sciaf@sciaf.org.uk

AID TO THE CHURCH IN NEED.—Meeting the needs of the church today in Eastern Europe and throughout the world. *Scottish Secretary::* Dr. John Watts, The Chapel House, 37 Blackburn Road, Addiewell, WEST CALDER EH55 8NF. ☎/Fax: 01501-762636.

APOSTLESHIP OF THE SEA.—*President,* His Eminence Cardinal Thomas J. Winning, Archbishop of Glasgow. *National Director and Chairman* Mr. Leo Gilbert. *Port Chaplain,* Rev. Oscar de la Torre, S.X. *Official address:* Stella Maris, 937 Dumbarton Road GLASGOW G14 9UF. ☎ 0141-339 6657; Fax: 0141-334 7463. (See also Travellers, Ministry to).

ARCHIVES, SCOTTISH CATHOLIC.—See Columba House.

BROADCASTING CENTRE, CATHOLIC.—*Director* Right Rev. Mgr. Thomas Connelly, ☎ 0141-221 1168 (Office hours), (Evenings ☎ 0141-641 2244) *Studio and Office,* 196 Clyde Street, GLASGOW G1 4JY. ☎ (Office hours); 0141-221 2955.

CALIX SOCIETY, THE—*Chairman,* James Ruthven; *Treasurer,* Christine Miller; *National Secretary,* Thomas S. Flannery, 153 Lethamhill Drive, GLASGOW G33. ☎ 0141-771 8780.

C.A.L.M. (Catholic Aids Link Ministry)—Offers pastoral support for anyone with or anyone related to another with the H.l.V. positive virus. Contact: Rev. Brian Donnelly, Co-ordinator, P.O. Box 852, Glasgow G20 0PW. ☎ 0141-945 5305.

CARFIN PILGRIMAGE CENTRE.—100 Newarthill Road, Carfin, MOTHERWELL ML1 5AL. ☎ 01698-268941; Fax: 01698-230988. *Chairman of Management Committee,* Mr. Frank Cassidy; *Centre Manager,* Ms. Anne Marie Cairns.

CATENIAN ASSOCIATION *(Province No.* 9) *Secretary:* J. Ritchie Greig, 120 Brackenbrae Avenue, Bishopbriggs, GLASGOW G64 2DU. ☎ 0141-563 6933.

CATENIAN ASSOCIATION *(Provincial Council No.* 16).—*President,* J.H. Turnbull, F.I.A.A.; *Director,* Michael G. Henderson, K.C.H.S., B.D.S.; *Treasurer,* Eddie O'Donnell; *Secretary:* George A. E. Brand, Dip.R.S.A., 8 Loanhead Terrace, ABERDEEN AB25 2SY. ☎/Fax: Aberdeen (01224) 630159. E-mail: geobra@msn.com

CATHOLIC MEDIA OFFICE (a media information centre established by the Scottish Hierarchy).—5 St. Vincent Place, GLASGOW Gl 2DH. ☎ 0141-221 1168; Fax: 0141-204 2458. *Director,* Right Rev. Mgr. Thomas Connelly. (Home ☎ 0141-641 2244); *Deputy Director:* Rev. Daniel McLoughlin (Home Tel./Fax: 01475-707033).
E-mail: scotbishopsconference@compuserve.com
Web site:www.scmo.org.uk

CATHOLIC UNION OF THE ARCHDIOCESE OF GLASGOW. —*President* His Eminence the Cardinal Archbishop of Glasgow-;*Treasurer,* Francis Cuilen, C.A., G.C.S.S., 196 Clyde Street, GLASGOW Gl 4JY.

CEARTAS AGUS SITH.—See Justice and Peace—Scotland.

COLUMBA HOUSE (SCOTTISH CATHOLIC. ARCHIVES).— *Keeper of the Scottish Catholic Archives and Administrator of Columba House:* Dr. Christine Johnson, M.A., Ph.D.; *Address:* Columba House, 16 Drummond Place, EDINBURGH EH3 6PL. ☎ 0131-556 3661.

CONVERTS' AID SOCIETY.—See ST. BARNABAS SOCIETY.

CRAIGHEAD INSTITUTE OF LIFE AND FAITH—*Contact:* Mrs. Esther McClure. *Address:* 26 Rose Street, GLASGOW G3 6RE. ☎ 0141-332 2733; Fax: 0141-353 1192.
E-mail: thecraigheadinstitute@compuserve.com

DEAF PEOPLE, ST. VINCENT'S CENTRE FOR.—*Manager,* Sister Barbara Sangster; *Chaplain,* Rev. Leonard Purcell. *Address:* St. Vincent's Centre for Deaf People, 51 Tobago Street, GLASGOW G40 2RH. ☎ 0141-554 8897 (Voice); 0141-550 1616 (Text); Fax: 0141-551 8904.

DUNKELD SICK AND RETIRED PRIESTS FUND—*Chairman,* Right Reverend Vincent Logan, Bishop of Dunkeld; *Treasurer,* Rev. Brian McLean, Ph.B., S.T.B., J.C.L.*Secretary:* Rev. Neil Dorward, M.A., B.D. St. James', 5 High Street, KINROSS KY13 7AW. ☎ 01577-863329.

EDUCATION COMMISSION, CATHOLIC.—*Secretary,* Mr. Leo Duffy, J.P., M.A., *Address:* Education Commission Office, University of Glasgow, St. Andrew's Campus, Duntocher Road, Bearsden, GLASGOW G61 4QA. ☎ 0141-943 0494; Fax: 0141-943 0106. E-mail: i.browne@educ.gla.ac.uk

ENGAGED ENCOUNTER (SCOTLAND)—*Executive Couple,* Michael and Jean Connelly, 2A Littledenny Road, DENNY FK6 5AS. ☎ Denny (01324) 822680.

EQUESTRIAN ORDER OF THE HOLY SEPULCHRE OF JERUSALEM (LIEUTENANCY OF SCOTLAND)—*Grand Prior:* His Eminence Cardinal Thomas J. Winning, K.C.+H.S., Archbishop of Glasgow; *Lieutenant:* Captain David O. Fairlie of Myres, M.B.E., J.P., D.L., K.C.H.S.; *Chancellor:* Donald MacLean, Esq., K.H.S.; *Secretary:* Brian J. Mallon, K.H.S., 40 Brackenbrae Avenue, Bishopbriggs, GLASGOW G64 2BP. ☎ 0141-772 3987; Fax: 0141-563 2530. *Official address:* Myres Castle, Auchtermuchty, Cupar KY14 7EW. ☎ 01337-828350.

EUCHARISTIC LEAGUE, PRIESTS'.—*Scottish Secretary and Diocesan Director for St. Andrews and Edinburgh:* Rev. Leo Glancy, Christ the King, Bowhouse Road, GRANGEMOUTH FK3 0HB. ☎ 01324-484974.Fax: 01324-665303. E-mail: leoctk@aol.com.
Aberdeen Diocesan Director: contact Scottish Secretary.
Argyll and The Isles Diocesan Director: Vacant.
Dunkeld Diocesan Contact: Bishop's House, 29 Roseangle, DUNDEE DD1 4LX
Galloway Diocesan Director: Very Rev. Thomas J. Provost Murphy, Our Lady and St. Patrick's 35 Sorn Road, Auchinleck, CUMNOCK KA18 2HR. ☎ Cumnock (01290) 421521.
Glasgow Diocesan Director: Vacant
Motherwell Diocesan Director: Rev. Brian Logue, St. Margaret's, 96 Hallcraig Street, AIRDRIE ML6 6AW. ☎ Airdrie (01236) 763370.
Paisley Diocesan Director: Vacant.

FERTILITY CARE SCOTLAND (Fertility/Infertility Awareness & Natural Family Planning). *Official address:* 196 Clyde Street, GLASGOW G1 4JY. ☎/Fax: 0141-221 0858. *Secretary:* Mrs. Rita Houston. For an information pack and details of Clinics throughout Scotland, including Aberdeen, Cumbernauld, Dumbarton, Dundee, Edinburgh, Falkirk, Glasgow, Hamilton, Inverness, Isle of Barra, Kirkintilloch, Livingston, Motherwell, Paisley, Penicuik and Wemyss Bay, contact the above number.

FOCOLARE (WORK OF MARY)—International, ecumenical movement seeking collective sanctity based on putting the Gospel into practice in everyday life. Specific aim: That all may be one. *Representative* and *Official address in Scotland,* Irene Jovaras, 152 Beechwood Drive, GLASGOW G11 7DX. ☎ 0141-339 2280; Fax: 0141-357 5243. E-mail: a.owsianka@vir.gla.ac.uk
FOCOLARE COMMUNITY,14 Summerside Plce, EDINBURGH EH6 4NZ. ☎ 0131-554 6976.

GARNETHILL CENTRE (a charitable organisation, sponsored by the Council of Religious of Scotland. Individual counselling and psychotherapy. Therapy groups. Training courses for individuals groups, communities and organisations).—*Director,* Rev. James Christie, S.J., M.Sc., C.Q.S.W., M.Inst. G.A. *Address:* 28 Rose Street, GLASGOW G3 6RE. ☎ 0141-333 0730; Fax: 0141-333 0737.

GERMAN-SPEAKING CATHOLICS, CENTRE FOR (Conducted by the Secular Institute of the Schoenstatt Sisters of Mary), Ardmory, 30 Langside Drive, GLASGOW G43 2QQ. ☎ 0141-637 3316.

GIRLS, INTERNATIONAL CATHOLIC SOCIETY FOR (Care and counselling service for all women away from home: accommodation, further education, training, contacts; also advice on *au pair* stays in European countries for language learning.) *Secretary:* Mrs. Brenda Gunn. *Official address:* 58 Aylward Road, Merton Park, LONDON SW20 9AF. ☎ 0181-241 7458. *Organising Secretary:* Sr. Sheelah Clarke, 55 Nightingale Road, Rickmansworth, Herts. WD3 2BU. ☎/Fax: 01293-778449.

GUIDERS' ADVISORY COMMITTEE, THE SCOTTISH CATHOLIC.— *Chairman,* awaiting appointment. *Secretary,* Mrs. Elizabeth Hill, c/o Scottish Guide Headquarters, 16 Coates Crescent, EDINBURGH EH3 7AH. ☎ 0131-226 4511; Fax: 0131-220 4828. *Chaplain,* Right Rev. John Mone Bishop of Paisley, 107 Corsebar Road, PAISLEY PA2 9PY. ☎ 0141-889 7200.

HANDICAPPED CHILDREN'S PILGRIMAGE TRUST (SCOTLAND).— *Patron:* His Eminence Thomas Joseph Cardinal Winning, Archbishop of Glasgow. *Secretary,* Mr. Robert C. Grant, 'Craigellachie', 28 Kennedy Drive, AIRDRIE ML8 9AN. ☎/Fax.: 01236-753933.
E-mail: bobbygrant@classic.fm.net

HISTORICAL ASSOCIATION, SCOTTISH CATHOLIC,—*Secretary,* Mrs. Wendy Doran 9 Laverockdale Loan, EDINBURGH EH13 0EZ. ☎ 0131-441 4816.

HOMES FOR THE AGED POOR AND INFIRM (Conducted by the Little Sisters of the Poor):
St. Joseph's Home, 43 Gilmore Place, EDINBURGH EH3 9NG. ☎ 0131-229 5672.
St. Joseph's Convent, Wellburn, Liff Road, Lochee, DUNDEE DD2 2QT. ☎ Dundee (01382) 622212.

St. Joseph's Home, 14 Cumnock Road Robroyston, GLASGOW G33 1QT. ☎ 0141-558 5114; Fax: 0141-558 7934.

Convent of Our Lady of the Holy Rosary, 44 Union Street GREENOCK PA16 8DP. ☎ Greenock (01475) 722465; Fax: 01475-722168.

HOSPICE, ST. ANDREW'S (For patients in the last stage of illness, conducted by the Religious Sisters of Charity). St. Andrew's Hospice, Henderson Street AIRDRIE ML6 6DJ. ☎ 01236-766951; Fax: 01236-748786..

HOSPICE, ST. MARGARET'S (For patients in the last stage of illness: conducted by the Religious Sisters of Charity). St. Margaret's Hospice East Barns Street, CLYDEBANK G81 IEG. ☎ 0141-952 1141; Fax: 0141-951 4206. E-mail: theresa@smh.org.uk

HOSPITAL, BON SECOURS Conducted by the Bon Secours Sisters), 36 Mansionhouse Road, GLASGOW G41 3DW. ☎ 0141-632 9231; Fax: 0141-636 5066.

HOSPITAL ST. MARY'S (Hospital and Convalescent Home- Conducted by the Sisters of Charity) Carstairs Road, LANARK ML11 7JU. ☎ Lanark (01555) 662393; Fax: 01555-664166.

HOSPITALITE DE NOTRE DAME DE LOURDES.—
Archdiocese of St. Andrews and Edinburgh:Secretary, Miss Norah Magennis, 59 Woodburn Terrace, DALKEITH EH22 2HT. ☎ 0131-683 6145.
Glasgow Archdiocese: Secretary, Miss Letitia Reilly, 31 Denmilne Path, GLASGOW G34 OAA. ☎ 0141-771 6807.
Motherwell Diocese: Secretary, Miss Mairi-Fiona MacKay, 112 Swinton Crescent, Baillieston, GLASGOW G69 6AT. ☎ 0141-771 2437.
Paisley Diocese:Secretary, Mrs Christine Smith, 8 Divert Walk, GOUROCK PA19 1DN. ☎ Gourock (01475) 634507.

INFERTILITY— See Fertility Care Scotland.

INNOCENTS, SOCIETY OF THE (SCOTTISH COUNCIL).—*National Secretary:* Mrs. Elizabeth Feeley, 5 Fife Crescent, Bothwell, GLASGOW G71 8DG. ☎ Bothwell (01698) 853115.

INNOCENTS, SOCIETY OF THE.—
Edinburgh: Acting Chairman: Mrs. Ann Curran- *Secretary:* Mr. Edward McGregor. *Official address:* 80 Constitution Street, Leith.
Glasgow: Chairman, Mrs. Elizabeth McAloon; *Secretary,* Sheila Maguire. *Official address,* 41 Merryland Street, Glasgow G51 2QG. ☎ 0141-221 3700.
Dundee: Chairman: Mrs. Margaret Sherriff; *Secretary:* Miss Gail Hodgson, *Official address:* 10 Panmure Street 2xl, Dundee DDI 2BW. ☎ Dundee (01382) 2Ni040.

Fort William: Chairman: Mrs. Marie McNeill; *Treasurer,* Mrs. Eileen MacKinnon; *Secretary,* Mrs. Josie McLeod. *Official address:* 72 Kilmallie Road, Caol, Fort William PH33 7EL. ☎ 013975645/3869/4586.

Kilmarnock: Chairman: Miss Bernadette McCrory: *Secretary:* Mrs. Elizabeth Lennon. *Official address:* 43 Titchfield Street, Kilmarnock KAI IPH. ☎ Kilmarnock (01563) 572233.

Motherwell: Chairman, Mrs. Denise McCully; *Treasurer,* Sr. Mary Rosaria, O.S.F.; *Secretary,* Mrs. Elizabeth Feeley. *Official address,* Innocents House, 17 Viewpark Road, Motherwell ML1 3ER. ☎ Motherwell (01698) 262699.

JERICHO HOUSES FOR THE 'SPECIAL NEEDS' HOMELESS
(Under the Jericho Benedictines, Monastery of Jesus, Harelaw Farm, Kilbarchan, JOHNSTONE PA10 2PY. ☎ Bridge of Weir (01505) 614669; Fax: 01505-613008.

Jericho House, 5-7 Bank Street, GREENOCK PA15 4PA. ☎ Greenock (01475) 783063.

Jericho House,1 Orangefield Place, GREENOCK PA15 1YX. ☎ Greenock (01475) 725425.

Jericho House, 14-16 Shankland Road, GREENOCK PA15 2NE. ☎ Greenock (0475) 741950.

Jericho House, 18-20 Shankland Road, GREENOCK PA15 2NE.☎ Gourock (0475) 645488.

Jericho House, 26 Oakshaw Street, PAISLEY PA1 2DD. ☎ 0141-887 9417.

Jericho House,36 Artillery Lane, DUNDEE DD1 1PE. ☎ Dundee (01382) 23627.

Jericho House, 53 Lothian Street, EDINBURGH EH1 1HB.☎ 0131-848 6068.

Jericho's Trochrague Guest House, GIRVAN KA26 9QB. ☎ Girvan (01465) 712074.

Jericho Distribution Centres for the Needy: 19 Broomlands Street, PAISLEY PA1 2LT. ☎ 0141-848 6088.

107 West Blackhall Street, GREENOCK PA15 1YD. ☎ Greenock (01475) 552580 PA15 1YD.

JERICHO (DISTRIBUTION) CENTRE FOR THE NEEDY, 19 Broomlands Street, PAISLEY PA1 2LT. ☎ 0141-848 6068.

JUSTICE AND PEACE—SCOTLAND (CEARTAS AGUS SITH).—
President, The Right Rev. John Mone, Bishop of Paisley, *Chairwoman,* Mrs. Jane Miezitis. *Secretary,* Mrs. Maryanne Ure. *Official address:* Justice and Peace (Scotland), 65 Bath Street, GLASGOW G2 2BX. ☎/Fax: 0141-333 0238. E-mail: justice_peace@virgin.net

KNIGHTS OF ST. COLUMBA.—*Supreme Secretary:* Mr. Francis J. Redmond, J.P., K.S.G. Head Office: 75 Hillington Road South, GLASGOW G52 2AE. ☎ 0141-883 5700; Fax: 0141-882 5703. E-mail: headoffice@K-S-C.freeserve.co.uk

Edinburgh Province: Secretary, Mr. Joseph Craigen. *Official address:* 107 Bowhouse Road, GRANGEMOUTH FK3 0EX. ☎ Grangemouth (01324) 48014.
Glasgow Province: Secretary, Mr. Edmund Byrne, 53 Clavens Road, GLASGOW G52 4EG. ☎ 0141-810 3781.
Lanarkshire Province: Secretary, Mr. J. T. Halferty, 22 Bullionslaw Drive, Rutherglen, GLASGOW G73 3NE. ☎ 0141-562 4233.
Paisley Province: Secretary Mr. Robert Burns, 4 Culloden Place, KILMARNOCK KA3 1UG. ☎ Kilmarnock (01563) 536153.

LAETARE INTERNATIONAL YOUTH HOLIDAY AND CONFERENCE CENTRE, Linlithgow. *Secretary,* Mrs. Ita Watts; *Official address:* Laetare Hostel, St. Michael's, Blackness Road, LINLITHGOW EH49 7JA. ☎/Fax: Linlithgow (01506) 842214.

LAY CARMELITES (Our Lady of the Assumption—British Province of Carmelites).— *Provincial Secretary,* Miss Sine Cameron-Mowat, 91 Bellwood Street, GLASGOW G41 3EY. ☎ 0141-649 1933.

LAY DOMINICANS, EDINBURGH—*Chaplain,* Rev. Fergus Kerr, O.P., 24 George Square, EDINBURGH EH8 9LD. ☎ 0131-668 1776.

LAY DOMINICANS, GLASGOW— *Secretary:* Mrs. Clare M. Fodey. *Official address.* c/o Blackfriars, 36 Queen's Drive, GLASGOW G42 8DD. ☎ 0141-423 2971; Fax: 0141-423 4575.

LEGION OF MARY.—*Senatus of Scotland: Secretary,* Margaret Casswell. *Official address:* Montfort House 38 Lansdowne Crescent, GLASGOW G20 6NH. ☎ 0141-339 3902.

MARRIAGE CARE LIMITED, SCOTTISH CATHOLIC—*President,* Right Rev. John Aloysius Mone Bishop of Paisley. *Chairman,* Mrs. Veronica Mullen *Comopany Secretary:* Mr. Jack Kerr; *Official address:* 50 Greenock Road, PAISLEY PA3 2LE. ☎/Fax: 0141-849 6183.

MARRIAGE CARE, SCOTTISH CATHOLIC (EDINBURGH CENTRE).— *Contact person* Dr. Margaret Addly. *Official Address,* Gillis Centre, 113 Whitehouse Loan, EDINBURGH EH9 IBD. ☎ 0131-452 8240. (Monday, Tuesday, 7 to 9 p.m.). *Appointments Secretary,* Miss Winifred Conlin (☎ Monday to Friday, 10 a.m. to 5 p.m.: 0131-440 2650).

MARRIAGE CARE, SCOTTISH CATHOLIC (GLASGOW CENTRE).— *Secretary,* Mr. Brian Murray, *Off icial address,* 196 Clyde Street, GLASGOW Gl 4JY. ☎ 0141-204 1239.

MARRIAGE CARE, SCOTTISH CATHOLIC (ABERDEEN CENTRE)— *Secretary,* Mrs. Kay Cooney. *Official address,* Margaret House, 132 Huntly Street, ABERDEEN AB10 1SU. ☎ Aberdeen (01224) 643174.
INVERNESS SUB CENTRE—☎ Inverness (01463) 831516.

MARRIAGE CARE, SCOTTISH CATHOLIC (AYRSHIRE CENTRE).—
Secretary : Mary McKay, 2 Osprey Drive, KILMARNOCK KA1 3LQ. ☎ 01563-
535248. *(Appointments:* 01294-551210)

MARRIAGE CARE, SCOTTISH CATHOLIC (DUNDEE CENTRE)—
Contact person: Pat Elsmie. *Official address,* 10 Panmure Street, DUNDEE
DDI 2BW. ☎ Dundee (01382)227551.

MARRIAGE CARE, SCOTTISH CATHOLIC (FALKIRK CENTRE).—
Secretary, Mrs. Fay McCahill. *Official address,* Hope Street, FALKIRK FKI
5AT. ☎ (Appointments) Falkirk (01324) 665700.

MARRIAGE CARE, SCOTTISH CATHOLIC (FIFE CENTRE).—*Chairman:*
Mr. Brian Robertson; *Treasurer:* Mr. Colin Heather; *Secretary,* Ms. Jo
O'Reilly, Address for correspondence: c/o 7 Cameron Street,
DUNFERMLINE KY12 8DP. ☎ 01383-727312.

MARRIAGE CARE, SCOTTISH (KILMARNOCK CENTRE)—*Chairman,*
Mr Paul Biagi; *Treasurer;* Mr. William Giffney;; *Sec;etary,* Mrs. Mary McKay.
Official address, 2 Osprey Drive, KILMARNOCK KA1 3LQ. ☎ 01563-535248.

MARRIAGE   CARE,   SCOTTISH   CATHOLIC   (MOTHERWELL
CENTRE)— *Secretary,* Mrs. Chris Kelly. *Official address,* Diocesan Centre,
Coursington Road, MOTHERWELL ML1 1PP. *Appointments Secretary,* Miss
Sadie McLusky (☎ Wishaw (01698) 376816).

MARRIAGE CARE, SCOTTISH CATHOLIC (PAISLEY CENTRE).—*Chief
Executive,* Mrs. Mary Tower. *Official address,* 50 Greenock Road, PAISLEY
PA3 2LE. ☎/Fax: 0141-849 6183.

MARRIAGE CARE, SCOTTISH CATHOLIC (STIRLING CENTRE)—.
Secretary, Mrs. Fay McCahill. *Official address,* Stirling Centre, c/o Hope
Street, FALKIRK FK! 5AT. ☎ 01324-665700.

MARY IMMACULATE QUEEN (SCOTLAND), THE FAMILY OF
MESSENGERS OF—*Coordinating Group:* Mr. James F. Murphy, William
McQuilter, Miss Margaret Watson. *Official address:* 10 Murroch Avenue,
DUMBARTON G82 3DP. ☎ 01389-731690.

MEN'S SOCIETY CATHOLIC (National Council).—*President,* George
McAleenan; *Treasurer,* Gerard Halloran; *Secretary,* John Neeson, 39 Ailsa
Avenue, Motherwell MLI 3LY. ☎ 01698-251093.

MENTALLY HANDICAPPED ADULTS, RESIDENTIAL AND TRAINING
CENTRE FOR (under the care of the Brothers of Charity), St. Aidan's,
Gattonside House, Gattonside, MELROSE TD6 9NN. ☎ Melrose (01896)
822226; Fax: 01896-822159.

MENTALLY HANDICAPPED, GLASGOW ARCHDIOCESAN COUNCIL FOR.— *Chairman,* Rev. Peter McCafferty; *Treasurer,* Mrs. Julia Johnston; *Secretary,* Mrs. Janet Smith, 11 Fernleigh Road, GLASGOW G43 2UD. ☎ 0141-637 3412. *Official address,* 196 Clyde Street, GLASGOW G1 4JY.

MENTALLY HANDICAPPED—*Assisi House,* 41 Easterhill Street, GLASGOW G32 8LN. ☎ 0141-778 6445 (long-term, for profoundly handicapped adults)
Mitre House, 14-21 Househillmuir Crescent, GLASGOW G53 6HW. ☎ 0141-881 0221 (short stay, for profoundly handicapped adults).

MISSIO SCOTLAND (Pontifical Mission Societies), National Council of Scotland established 25th June, 1923. *National President:* Right Rev. Mgr. Daniel Foley, St. Mary's, 6 Wilkieston Road, Ratho, NEWBRIDGE EH28 8RH. ☎/Fax: 0131-333 1051.
E-mail:@pws.scotland.demn.co.uk

1. *Society for the Propagation of the Faith: National Secretary/Treasurer:* Rev. Joseph Coyle, St. Joseph's, Faifley, CLYDEBANK G81 5EZ. ☎ Duntocher (01389) 872236.

2. *Society of St. Peter Apostle: National Secretary/Treasurer:* Rev. Deacon John Futers, Corpus Christi, 16 Dunvegan Avenue, Portlethen, ABERDEEN AB12 4NE. ☎ Aberdeen (01224) 780256.

3. *Society of Missionary Children: National Secretary/Treasurer;* Awaiting appointment. *Contact:* c/o Archdiocese of Glasgow, 196 Clyde Street, GLASGOW G1 4JY. ☎ 0141-226 5898.

4. *Society of Missionary Union: National Secretary/Treasurer:* Rev. Leo Glancy, Christ the King, Bowhouse Road, GRANGEMOUTH FK3 0HB. ☎/Fax: Grangemouth (01324) 484974.

MOTHERS, UNION OF CATHOLIC.—*Scottish National Council: President,* Mrs. Margaret Quinn; *Vice-President,* Mrs. Mary Finnigan; *Treasurer,* Mrs. Christine Gavin; *Secretary,* Mrs. Anne O'Dowd, 225 Balgreen Road, EDINBURGH EH11 2RZ. ☎ 0131-337 8118.

NATURAL FAMILY PLANNING — See Fertility Care Scotland.
NAZARETH HOUSE:
Nazareth House, 13 Hillhead, Lasswade, BONNYRIGG EH19 2JF. ☎ 0131-663 7191; Fax:0131-663 0979..
Nazareth House, 34 Claremont Street, ABERDEEN AB10 6RA. ☎ Aberdeen (01224) 582091.
Nazareth House, 23 Hill Street, KILMARNOCK KA3 IHG. ☎ Kilmarnock (01563) 522835; Fax: 01563-574980..
Nazareth House 1647 Paisley Road West, Cardonald, GLASGOW G52 3QT. ☎ 0141-882 1;41; Fax: 0141-882 8178.

NEWMAN ASSOCIATION.—*Scottish Council, Chairman,* Dr. Ian Thompson-*Secretary,* Dr. William Moyes, 34 Grange Road, Edinburgh EH9 IUL *Circles at Aberdeen, Tay, Edinburgh and Glasgow.*

NURSES', MIDWIYES' AND HEALTH VISITORS' GUILD OF SCOTLAND, CATHOLIC.— *National Secretary,* Mrs. Jane C. Harkin, The Whinnocks 11 Grieve Road, GREENOCK PA16 7LE. ☎ Greenock (01475) 725252.

NURSING HOME (under the Franciscan Sisters Minoresses). St. Francis' Nursing Home, Merryland Street, GLASGOW G51 2QD. ☎ 0141-445 1118; Fax: 0141-445 4336.

NURSING HOME FOR CHRONIC SICK.—St. Andrew's Hospice, Henderson Street, AIRDRIE ML6 6AS. ☎/Fax: Airdrie (01236) 766951.

NURSING HOME, ST. ANDREW'S for the treatment of psychiatric and geriatric patients. Under the care of the Augustinian Sisters. St. Andrew's, Stirches, HAWICK TD9 7NS. ☎ Hawick (01450) 372360; Fax: 01450-377801

PASTORAL AND SOCIAL CARE, NATIONAL COMMISSION FOR— *Co-ordinator:* David McCann. *Official address.* 1/2, 15c Hill Street, GLASGOW G3 6RN. ☎ 0141-572 0115; Fax: 0141-572 0025.

PASTORAL AND SOCIAL CARE, PAISLEY COMMISSION FOR— *President:* The Right Reverend John A. Mone, Bishop of Paisley. *Chairman:* Mrs. Jean Urquhart, 19 Thornly Park Avenue, PAISLEY PA2 7SD. ☎ 0141-884-2172.

PASTORAL CENTRE AND SOCIAL SERVICE OFFICE, DIOCESE OF DUNKELD.—
Diocesan Social Care Officer: Sr. Andrea, F.M.D.M.
Official address: Diocesan Centre, 24-28 Lawside Road, DUNDEE DD3 6XY. ☎ Dundee (01382) 25453.

PASTORAL CENTRE, DIOCESE OF MOTHERWELL.—50 Bonkle Road, Newmains, WISHAW ML2 9AP. ☎ Cambusnethan (01698) 385i97; Fax: (01698) 381924. *Director,* Rev. Henry O'Brien, S.T.D.

PASTORAL COORDINATION/PASTORAL DEVELOPMENT (ARCHDIOCESE OF ST. ANDREWS AND EDINBURGH)— *Pastoral Co-ordinator:* Rev. Charles Barclay; *Pastoral Development Officer:* Sr. Clare Wardhaugh. *Official address:* Gillis Centre, 113 Whitehouse Loan, EDINBURGH EH9 1BB. ☎ 0131-447 9943.

PILGRIMAGE COMMITTEE.—*Archdiocese of Clasgow: Secretary,* Rev. Peter Lennon, Immaculate Heart of Mary, 162 Broomfield Road, GLASGOW G21 3UE. ☎ 0141-558 5025. *Diocese of Motherwell: Director,* Rev. John Kelly, St. James', 232 Woodhall Avenue,COATBRIDGE ML5 5DF. ☎ Coatbridge (01236) 422233. *Diocese of Paisley: Secretary,* Vacant.

PIONEER ASSOCIATION, SCOTTISH REGIONAL COMMITTEE. *Secretary* Miss Susan McBride, 4 Myrtle Drive, WISHAW ML2 7TZ. ☎Wishaw (01698) 375950.

PLATER COLLEGE (Catholic Workers' College). *Principal,* Michael Blades M.A.(Oxon), M.B.A. *Vice-Principal:* Miss Patricia Edge, M.A.; *College Secretary:* David Bevan, D.M.S., F.I.Mgt. *Address:* Plater College, Pullens Lane, Oxford OX3 ODT. ☎ Oxford (01865) 740500; Fax: (01865) 740510. E-mail:samantha@plater.ac.uk

PLATERNIAN ASSOCIATION (Catholic Workers' College) (Scottish Area).— *Secretary,* Mr. Peter Allison, 9 Larchfield Gardens, WISHAW ML2 8TS. ☎ Cambusnethan (01698) 384367.
E-mail: peter.allison@talk21.com

POLICE GUILD, STRATHCLYDE CATHOLIC.—*Contact*—*Chaplsin:* *(Glasgow)* Right Rev. Mgr. Noel Woods, St. Joseph's, 14 Fullarton Avenue, GLASGOW G32 8NA. ☎ 0141-778 1054.

(Motherwell) Right Rev. Mgr. Alexander Devanny, V.G., St. Mary's, 120 Cadzow Street, HAMILTON ML3 6HX. ☎ Hamilton (01698) 423552.
(Paisley) Rev. Daniei McLoughlin, St. Francis', Auchenbothie Road, Port GLASGOW PA14 6JD. ☎ 01475-707033/704222.
(Greenock) Rev. John Doherty, St. Fillan's, 1b Main Street, Houston, JOHNSTONE PA6 7EL. ☎ 01505-612046.
(Galloway) Vacant.

PREGNANCY CARE.—See Innocents, Society of the, or St. Andrew's Children's Society; or St. Margaret of Scotland Adoption Society.

RELIGIOUS EDUCATION CENTRE (DIOCESE OF GALLOWAY)— Candida Casa, 8 Corsehill Road, AYR KA7 2ST. ☎/Fax: Ayr (01292) 266750.

RELIGIOUS EDUCATION CENTRE (ARCHDIOCESE OF GLASGOW).— 196 Clyde Street, GLASGOW Gl 4JY. ☎ 0141-226 5898; Fax: 0141-225 2600.

RELIGIOUS EDUCATION CENTRE (DIOCESE OF MOTHERWELL).— Diocesan Centre, Coursington Road, MOTHERWELL ML1 1PP. ☎ Motherwell (01698) 252447; Fax (01698) 275630.

RELIGIOUS ORDERS' INFORMATION OFFICE. A communications centre established by the Council of Religious of Scotland. *Secretary,* Sr. Winifred Connolly, F.M.M. C.R.S. Secretariat, Carmelite Monastery, 29 Mansionhouse Road,GLASGOW G41 3DN. ☎/Fax: 0141-649 6535.

ST. ANDREW'S CHILDREN'S SOCIETY Ltd., Registered Adoption Agency, Pregnancy Counselling, Adoption, Homefinding, Accommodation. *Official address:* Gillis Centre, 113 Whitehouse Loan, EDINBURGH EH9 1BB. ☎/Fax: 0131-452 8248.

ST. ANDREW'S HOSPICE (Under the Religious Sisters of Charity).—St. Andrew's Hospice, Henderson Street, AIRDRIE ML6 6DJ. ☎/Fax: 01236-766951.

ST. BARNABAS SOCIETY—for the assistance of non-Catholic clergy, religious and stipendiary layfolk received into full communion with the Church. *Honorary Scottish Representative:* Alan Grüber, 19 Yetholm Park, DUNFERMLINE KY12 7XR. ☎ Dunfermline (01383) 735663.

ST. BENEDICT, OBLATES OF (Pluscarden).—*Chairman,* Mr. E. Coyle; *Treasurer,* Mr. H. Bradley; *Secretary,* Miss A. W. McGarrity. *Officiai address,* Pluscarden Abbey, ELGIN IV30 3UA. ☎ 01343-890257; Fax: 01343-890258.

ST. MARGARET'S HOSPICE (under the Religious Sisters of Charity).—St; Margaret's Hospice East Barns Street, CLYDEBANK G81 IEG. ☎ 0141-951 1141; Fax: 0141-951 4206.

ST. VINCENT'S HOSPICE caring for the terminally ill—*Chairman,*Norris McGilloway. St. Vincent's Hospice, Midton Road, Howwood, JOHNSTONE PA9 1AF. ☎ Kilbarchan (01505) 705635; Fax: 01505-704568. E-mail: lynn@svh.sol.co.uk

ST. VINCENT DE PAUL SOCIETY.—*The Council of Scotland: National Secretary,* Miss Kathleen R. Gorman, 546 Sauchiehall Street, GLASGOW G2 3NG. ☎ 0141-332 7752; Fax: 0141-332 6775.

SANCTUARY ASSOCIATION (GLASGOW) LIMITED (for the rehabilitation of men with an alcohol problem).—*Chairman,* Mr. John Smith- *Managing Director,* Mr. Alan J. Smith- *Secretary,* Mrs. Caroline McRae. *Official address:* Sanctuary House, 8 Stanely Road, PAISLEY PA2 6HA. ☎ 0141-889 4624.

SCALAN ASSOCIATION, THE.—*Chairman,* Right Rev. Mgr. John F. Provost Copland; *Treasurer,* Mrs. Jane S. McEwan; *Secretary,* Rev. Michael Briody; *Official address:* Mrs. Jane S. McEwan, Ogilvie Cottage, Gallowhill, Glenlivet, BALLINDALLOCH AB37 9DL. ☎ 01807-590340,

SCOTTISH CATHOLIC INTERNATIONAL AID FUND.—*President* The Right Rev. John Mone, Bishop of Paisley, 107 Corsebar Road Paisley PA2 9PY. *Executive Director,* Paul Chitnis. *Official address:* S.C.I.A.F., 19 Park Circus, GLASGOW G3 6BE. ☎ 0141-354 5555; Fax: 0141-354 5533. E-mail: sciaf@sciaf.org.uk

SCOUT ADVISORY COUNCIL, SCOTTISH CATHOLIC.—*Chairman,* John Rafferty. *Secretary/Treasurer,* Mrs. Iris Canning 64 Cartsdyke Court, GREENOCK PA15 2TS. Td.: Greenock (0;475) 727241. *National Chaplain,* Rev. Brian Lamb, Ph.B., S.T.L., St. Parick's, 84 Station Road, SHOTTS ML7 4BJ. ☎ 01501-821838.

SECRETARIAT FOR THE LAITY—*President,* The Most Rev. Keith Patrick O'Brien, Archbishop of St. Andrews anEdinburgh; *Secretary/Treasurer,* Mr. John Coultas, J.P.,K.C.H.S., Dip.Hort., M.I.L.A.M., 72 Etive Crescent, Bishopbriggs, GLASGOW G64 IEY. ☎ 0141-772 2274.

SECRETARIAT FOR YOUNG PEOPLE—*President,* The Most Rev. Keith Patrick O'Brien, Archbishop of St. Andrews and Edinburgh; *Secretary,,* Mr. John Coultas, J.P.,K.C.H.S., Dip.Hort., M.I.L.A.M., 72 Etive Crescent, Bishopbriggs, GLASGOW G64 IEY. ☎ 0141-772 2274.

SECULAR FRANCISCAN ORDER—*Scottish Regional Council: Secretary,* Mrs. Eilis O'Neill, s.f.o., 5 Bolivar Terace, GLASGOW G42 9AT. ☎ 0141-569 7600.

SECULAR INSTITUTE OF OUR LADY OF MOUNT CARMEL (THE LEAVEN)—A Secular Institute for single women and widows who wish to consecrate themselves completely to God following the traditions and spiritual life of the Carmelite family. For information: The Secretary, The Leaven, Aylesford Friary, Aylesford, Kent ME20 7BX. *President:* Mrs. Dina McGhee; *Bursar:* Miss Althea Emery; *Scottish Contact.* Miss J. Macaskill, 5 Ainslie Terrace, Duns TDII 3HE.

SECULAR ORDER OF DISCALCED CARMELITES—*President:* Mr. Seamus O'Sullivan, *Treasurer:* Miss Fay McCubbin; *Secretary:* Mrs. Margaret Brett, 11 Madison Avenue, Glasgow G44 5AH. *Official address:* Mount Carmel Retreat Centre, 61 Hamilton Avenue, Glasgow G41 4HA. ☎ 0141-427 0794, Fax: 0141-427 9950.
DYSART (FIFE) group—*President,* Dr. Senga Greig; *Secretary,* Mr. John Harris, 1 Burnbank, Carnock, DUNFERMLINE KY12 9JF. ☎ 01383-850533.

SERRA INTERNATIONAL (For fostering Vocations).—*District Governor for Scotland,* Mr. Peter Connor, 30 Ben Nevis Road, PAISLEY PA2 7LF. ☎ 0141-563 8084.

SERRA CLUB OF DUNKELD—*Secretary:* Norah Sloan. *Official address:* c/o St. Joseph's Convent of Mercy, Lawside Road, DUNDEE DD3 6BJ.

SERRA CLUB OF GLASGOW.— *Secretary,* Mr. Charles Campbell, 9 Braefoot Avenue, Milngavie, GLASGOW G62 6JS. ☎ 0141-956 6109.

SERRA CLUB OF PAISLEY.— *Secretary,* Mr. William Robertson. *Official address:* Montfort House, Darnley Road, Barrhead, GLASGOW G78 IJA. ☎ 01505-321005.

SICK, CATHOLIC UNION OF THE.—*Organiser,* Miss Rose Kelly, 90 The Paddockholm, Station Wynd, Corstorphine EDINBURGH EH12 7XR. ☎ 0131-334 4709. *Chaplain,* Very Rev. Stephen Canon Judge, B.D.

SOCIAL CARE, NATIONAL COMMISSION FOR.—National Co-ordinator: Mr. David McCann. Official address: 1/2, 15c Hill Street, GLASGOW G3 6RN. ☎ 0141-572 0115; Fax: 0141-572 0025.

SOCIAL SERVICE CENTRE, GLASGOW ARCHDIOCESAN—*Director:* Mr. David Ramsay; *Secretary:* Mrs Annette Moran. *Official address:* Archdiocesan Social Services Centre, 196 Clyde Street, GLASGOW Gl 4JY. ☎ 0141-226 5898; Fax: 0141-225 2600.

SURVIVE-MIVA (**M**issionary **V**ehicle **A**ssociation) (a Catholic lay organisation to provide transport for Missionaries in areas of urgent need in developing countries).—*Secretary:* Lynn Blackmore. *Official address,* Survive-Miva, Catholic Chaplaincy to the University, Mount Pleasant, Liverpool L3 5TQ. ☎ 0151-708 7250; Fax: 0151-708 9253. E-mail: info@survive_miva.org.

TALBOT ASSOCIATION. *Chairman,* Mr. Daniel Burns; *Director,* Mrs. Margaret Stevenson; *Assistant Director:* Ms. Anne O'Neill; *Treasurer,* Mr. James Young; *Administrator,* Mr. John McGilly; *Official address,* Talbot Centre, 344 Paisley Road, GLASGOW G5 8RD. ☎ 0141-429 4541. *(Temporary address:* 13th Floor Fleming House, 134 Renfrew Street GLASGOW G3 6ST. ☎ 0141 -331 1108.
Talbot House, Good Shepherd, 1920 London Road, GLASGOW G32 8XG. ☎ 0141-778 1184.
Talbot House, 1 Belmont Street, GLASGOW G12 8EP. ☎ 0141-339 1556.
Talbot House, Muirhead Road, Baillieston, GLASGOW G69. ☎ 0141-771 1071.
Talbot House, 122 Hill Street, GLASGOW G3 6UA. ☎ 0141-332 7717.
Talbot House London Road School, 1920 London Road, GLASGOW G32. ☎ 0141-778 4400.

TEAMS OF OUR LADY (International Catholic movement for married spirituality)— *Sector Couple:* Maureen and Dennis Macnamara, 63 Viewforth Terrace, KIRKCALDY KY1 3BW. ☎ 01592-652725.

TRANSPORT GUILD, CATHOLIC.—*Motherwell Diocese: Secretary,* Mr. James Donnelly, 142 Baird Hill, Murray, East Kilbride, GLASGOW G75 0EF. ☎/Fax: East Kilbride (01355) 223720.

TRANSPORT GUILDS, FEDERATION OF CATHOLIC.—*Secretary,* Mr. James Donnelly, 142 Baird Hill, Murray, East Kilbride, GLASGOW G75 0EF. ☎/Fax: East Kilbride (013552) 223720.

TRAVELLERS, MINISTRY TO—Mission to travelling people confided to the Apostleship of the Sea. *Official address:* c/o Apostleship of the Sea, Stla Maris, 937 Dumbarton Road, GLASGOW G14 9UF. Td.: 0141-339 6657. *Chaplain to Travellers,* Rev. Oscar de la Torre, S.X. ☎ 0141-339 6657; Fax: 0141-334 7463. *Senior Catechist,* Sr. Breda Byrne.

TRIBUNAL, THE SCOTTISH CATHOLIC.—*Judicial Vicar (Officialis)*, Rev. Gerard Tartaglia, Ph.B.,S.T.B.J.C.L. *Address:* R.C. Scottish National Tribunal,22 Woodrow Road, GLASGOW G41 5PN. ☎ 0141-427 3036. Fax: 0141-427 7715.
E-mail: g-tag@hotmail.com

TURNBULL HALL CATHOLIC SOCIETY, UNIVERSITY OF GLASGOW.—c/o Turnbull Hall, 13-15 Southpark Terrace, GLASGOW G12 8LG. ☎ (Chaplains only) 0141-339 4315/ 0141-330 5567.(Students) 0141-334 2942. Fax: (Chaplains only) 0141-330 5567.
E-mail (chaplains only): RCChaplaincy@gla.ac.uk

UNA VOCE (SCOTLAND)—*Secretary:* Miss Mary Neilson, 6 Belford Park, EDINBURGH EH4 3DP. ☎ 0131-332 1804.

UNDA-SCOTLAND—*President,* Right Rev. Joseph Devine, Bishop of Motherwell; *Chairman,* Mr. Dermot McQuarrie; *Treasurer,* Mr. Hugh Kelly; *Secretary,* Rev. Daniel J. McLoughlin, Catholic Media Office, 5 St. Vincent Place, Glasgow Gl 2DH. ☎ 0141221 1168; Fax: 0141-204 2458. (Home: ☎/Fax: 01475-707033).

UNIVERSITY CATHOLIC SOCIETIES.—*St. Andrews University Canmore Society:* The Secretary, Canmore Society, Canmore, 24 The Scores, ST. ANDREWS KYl6 9AS. ☎ St. Andrews (01334) 472179.
Edinburgh University Catholic Students' Union: The Secretary, 23 George Square, EDINBURGH EH8 9LD. ☎ 0131-650 0904.
E-mail: cathsoc@holyrood.ed.ac.uk.
Web:http://www.ed.ac.uk/ cathsoc/
Aberdeen University Catholic Society: The Secretary, Elphinstone House, 7 High Street, Old Aberdeen, ABERDEEN AB24 3EE. ☎ Aberdeen (01224) 482444.
Dundee University Catholic Society: The Secretary, c/o Chaplaincy Centre, 42 Wilkie's Lane Dundee DUNDEE DDI 5HR. ☎ Dundee (01382) 23755.
Stirling University Catholic Society:: The Secretary c/o Chaplaincy Centre, University of Stirling, STIRLING FK9 4LA. ☎ 01786-467164.

UNIVERSITY STUDENTS, CATHOLIC CHAPLAINCY FOR ABERDEEN.— Elphinstone House, 7 High Street, Old Aberdeen, ABERDEEN AB24 3EE. ☎ Aberdeen (01224) 482444. E-mails: rcopsey@carmelnet.org; dwaite@carmel.net.org

UNIVERSITY STUDENTS, CATHOLIC CHAPLAINCY FOR ST. ANDREWS.— Canmore, 24 The Scores, ST. ANDREWS KYl6 9AS. ☎ St. Andrews (01334) 472179.

UNIVERSITY STUDENTS CATHOLIC CHAPLAINCY FOR DUNDEE.— Chaplaincy Centre, 42 Wilkie's Lane, DUNDEE DDI 5HR. ☎ Dundee (01382) 23755.

UNIVERSITY STUDENTS, CATHOLIC CHAPLAINCY FOR EDINBURGH.—24 George Square, EDINBURGH EH8 9LD. ☎ 0131-650 0900.

UNIVERSITY STUDENTS, CATHOLIC CHAPLAINCY FOR GLASGOW.— 15 Southpark Terrace, GLASGOW G12 8LG. ☎ 0141-339 4315; Fax: 0141-330 5567. Students, ☎ 0141-334 2942.

UNIVERSITY STUDENTS, CATHOLIC CHAPLAINCY FOR STIRLING, Chaplaincy Centre, University of Stirling, STIRLING FK9 4LA. ☎ Stirling (01786) 467164). *Chaplain's Residence:* Catholic Presbytery, 52 Quakerfield Bannockburn, STIRLING FK7 8HZ. ☎ 01786-812249. E-mail: chapl@stir.ac.uk

UNIVERSITY STUDENTS, CATHOLIC CHAPLAINCY FOR STRATHCLYDE, *Chaplain's Residence:* Blackfriars, 36 Queen's Drive, GLASGOW G42 8DD. Td.: 0141423 2971. *Chaplaincy (Ecumenical):* St. Paul's Building, 90 John Street, GLASGOW Gl IJH. ☎ 0141-553 4144.

VOCATIONS—SCOTLAND.—*Directors:* Rev. Stephen Connolly, Rev. Michael Bagan, National Vocations Of fice, 2 Chesters Road, Bearsden, GLASGOW G61 4AG ☎/Fax:: 0141-943 1995.

VOCATIONS GROUP, INVERCLYDE.— *Secretary,* Miss Sheila Murphy, 62 Battery Park Drive, GREENOCK PA16 7UB. ☎ Greenock (01475) 727003.

VOLUNTEER MISSIONARY MOVEMENT.—*Regional Officer:* Mrs. Clare M. Fodey. *Official address:* V.M.M., P.O.Box 2225, GLASGOW G33 2YB. ☎/Fax: 0141-770 5090.

WAYSIDE CLUB FOR LODGING HOUSE AND DESTITUTE MEN (Conducted by the Legion of Mary). *Chairman,* Lawrence McGarry; *Treasurer,* James White; *Secretary,* Patrick Toal. *Official Address:* P.O. Box 140, 32 Midland Street, Glasgow Gl 4PP. ☎ 0141-221 0169.

B—Retreat Centres in Scotland

BENEDICTINE ADORERS OF THE SACRED HEART (Tyburn Nuns): Benedictine Priory, Mackerston Place, LARGS KA30 8BY. ☎ 01475-67027.

CRAIG LODGE: Craig Lodge, DALMALLY PA33 IAR. ☎01838-200216.

DISCALCED CARMELITE FRIARS: Mount Carmel Retreat Centre, 61 Hamilton Avenue, GLASGOW G41 4HA. ☎ 0141-427 0794.

FAITHFUL COMPANIONS OF JESUS:
Craighead Institute of Life and Faith, 26 Rose Street, Glasgow G3 6RE. ☎ 0141-332 2733.

JERICHO BENEDICTINES: Trochrague Guest House, GIRVAN KA26 9QB. ☎ 01465-2074.

JESUIT FATHERS: Ignatian Spirituality Centre, 7 Woodside Place, GLASGOW G3 7QF. ☎ 0141-354 9977; Fax: 0141-354 0099.

KINHARVIE HOUSE: Marist Centre, New Abbey, DUMFRIES DG2 8DZ. ☎ 01387-85433.

KINNOULL (Redemptorist Fathers): St. Mary's Mission and Renewal Centre Kinnoull, PERTH PH2 7BP. ☎ 01738-624075. Fax: 01736442071.

LAETARE: Laetare Youth International Holiday Hostel, 53 Blackness Road, LINLITHGOW EH49 7JA. ☎ 01506-842214.

MONTFORT HOUSE RETREAT CENTRE: Montfort House, Darnley Road Barrhead, GLASGOW G78 ITA. ☎ 0141-881 1440.

NUNRAW (Cistercians): Sancta Maria Abbey, Nunraw, HADDINGTON EH41 4LW. ☎ (Abbey) 01620-830233; (Guests) 01620-830228.

PLUSCARDEN (Benedictines): Pluscarden Abbey, ELGIN IV30 3UA. ☎ 01343-890257. Fax: 01343-890258.

SCHOENSTATT SISTERS OF MARY: Schoenstatt, Clachan of Campsie, Lennoxtown, GLASGOW G65 7AG. ☎ 01360-3127i8; Fax: 01360-312291.

SMITHSTONE HOUSE (Sacred Heart Fathers): Smithstone House, Dalry Road, KILWINNING KA13 5PL. ☎ 01294-552515.

C—Social Care Services

1. HOMES FOR PEOPLE WITH LEARNING DISABILITIES
St. Aidan's, Gattonside, MELROSE TD6 9NW. ☎ Melrose (01896) 822226; Fax: 01896-822159. (residential and training services for adults.)
St. Mary's Nursing Home, Aurs Road, Barrhead, GLASGOW G78 2SL. ☎ 0141-881 1544; Fax: 0141-876 1566.

2A. RESIDENTIAL SCHOOLS
CORA Foundation, CORA House, Greenock Road, BISHOPTON PA7 5PW. ☎ 01505-863697; Fax: 01505-863691. E-mail: hqcora@aol.com

Chief Executive: Brian Steele.

Good Shepherd Centre, BISHOPTON PA7 5PF.

☎ Bishopton (01505) 862814; Fax: 01505-864167. (girls only).

St. Mary's, Kenmure, Bishopbriggs, GLASGOW G64 2EH. ☎ 0141-563 0220; Fax: 0141-563 0023. (girls and boys).

St. Philip's, Plains, AIRDRIE ML6 7SF. Td.: Airdrie (01236) 765407; Fax: 01236-755637. (boys only).

Springboig St. John's, 1190 Edinburgh Road, GLASGOW G33 4EH. ☎ 0141-774 9791; Fax: 0141-774 4613. (boys only).

2B. DAY UNITS

St. Francis, 1190 Edinburgh Road, GLASGOW G33 4EH. ☎ 0141-774 4499.

St. Francis, Greenock Road, BISHOPTON PA7 5PF. ☎ 01505-862899.

St. Francis, Beechwood House, Plains, AIRDRIE ML6 7SF. ☎ 01236-750888.

3. ADOPTION AND FOSTERING SERVICES
St. Andrew's Children's Society Ltd.:
Chairperson: Mrs. Maureen McEvoy; *Treasurer:* Mrs. Joan Saywood, C.A. *Director of Adoption Services:* Stephen Small. *Official address:* Gillis Centre 113 Whitehouse Loan, EDINBURGH EH9 IBB. ☎ 0131-452 8248; Fax. 0131452 8248.
St. Margaret's Children and Family Care Centre:
Executive Chairman: Very Rev. Mgr. Thomas J. Monaghan; *Director;* Margaret Campbell; *Official address:* 274 Bath Street, GLASGOW G2 4JR ☎ 0141-332 8371; Fax. 0141-332 8398.

4. MISCELLANEOUS
Notre Dame Centre. *Clinical Director,* Sister Mary Ross, S.N.D.; *Executive Officer:* Miss Catherine M. McGhie.
(a) Notre Dame Clinic, 20 Athole Gardens, GLASGOW G12 9BA. ☎ 0141-339 2366; Fax: 0141-357 1443.
(b) Fern Tower Adolescent Unit, 1 Dundonald Road, GLASGOW G12 9LJ. (Registered Office). ☎ 0141-334 6131; Fax: 0141-334 6260.

5. GLASGOW ARCHDIOCESAN SOCIAL SERVICES AGENCIES

(1) Service Manager: Mrs. Elizabeth McPake.
    SERVICES TO PEOPLE WITH LEARNING DISABILITIES:

Auldhouse Project
18 Stoneside Drive, GLASGOW G43 1JF
☎ 0141-649 3393
Barrhead Community
19 Lyoncross Avenue, Barrhead, GLASGOW G78 2TG
☎ 0141-880 6694.

Broomloan Court Project
Flat 13/5, Block 5, Broomloan Court, Ibrox, GLASGOW G51 3XJ
☎ 0141-427 4461.

Elderslie Project
1 Cherrywood Bungalows, 14 Cherrywood Road,
Elderslie, JOHNSTONE PA5 9EE
☎ 01505-879092.

Mitre House
14-21 Househillmuir Crescent, GLASGOW G53 6HW
☎ 0141-881 0221.

Rosewood Day Centre
1 Ludovic Square, JOHNSTONE PA5 8EE.
☎ 01505 324065.

Southside Project
664 Pollokshaws Road, GLASGOW G41 2QE
☎ 0141-423 9279.

St. Andrews Drive Project
52 St. Andrews Drive,GLASGOW G41 5HF
☎ 0141-427 1100.

(2) Service Manager: Miss Sheena Gault
     RESIDENTIAL SERVICES TO PEOPLE WITH LEARNING DISABILITIES

Causewayside Street Project
133 Causewayside Street, Tollcross, GLASGOW G32 8LP
☎ 0141-763 2262.

Lanark Project
10 St. Mungo's, LANARK ML11 9AD
☎ 01555-663283

Assisi House
41 Easterhill Street, Tollcross, GLASGOW G32 8LN
☎ 0141-778 6445

Firhill Project
197 Firhill Road, Maryhill, GLASGOW G20 7SD.
☎ 0141-945 6153.

(3) Service Manager: Mrs. Sheena Gault
     SERVICES TO PEOPLE WITH SENSORY IMPAIRMENT

St. Vincent's Centre
51 Tobago Street, GLASGOW G40 2RH
☎ 0141-554 8897 (Voice).
0141-550 1616 (Text)
Barrowfield Deaf/Blind Complex
15 Dalserf Street, Barrowfield, GLASGOW G31 4AR.
☎ 0141-554 2593.

(4) Manager: Mrs. Sheena Gault
     HOME CARE SERVICES TO PEOPLE WITH LEARNING DISABILITIES

SCOPE
Unit 2, Mansfield Park, Partick, GLASGOW G11 5QP
☎ 0141-337 6191.

(5) Service Manager: Mr. Michael Mesarowicz
     RESPITE SERVICES FOR PEOPLE WITH LEARNING DISABILITIES

Breakaway Project
99 Hawkwood, Whitehills, East Kilbride, GLASGOW G75 0SP
☎ 01355-227581.

Duffy House
2/4 Wandilla Avenue, Drumry, CLYDEBANK G81 2PN
☎ 0141-941 2068.

Ferrie House
101/103 Lochend Road, Gartcosh, GLASGOW G69 8AQ
☎ 01236-879092.

Glenlora Cottages
217/227 Glenlora Drive, GLASGOW G53 6JS
☎ 0141-881 2077.

Kelso House
287 Kelso Street, Yoker, GLASGOW G13 4PA
☎ 0141-951 1821.

Langness Road
20 Langness Road, Cranhill, GLASGOW G33 8XG
☎ 0141-774 4544.

Muirfield Place
61 Muirfield Place, Woodside, KILWINNING KA13 6NZ
☎ 01294-557164.

(6) Service Manager: Mr. Michael Lynch
     YOUNG HOMELESS PEOLPLE

De Paul House
27 Cruden Street, Govan, GLASGOW G51 3RP.
☎ 0141-445 2800.

Glengowan House
196 Nithsdale Road, Pollokshields, GLASGOW G41 5EU
☎ 0141-423 4765.

Rachel House, 505 Baltic Street, Dalmarnock, GLASGOW G40 4SG
☎ 0141-556 5465.

London Road Project
1920 London Road, GLASGOW G32 8XG
☎ 0141-778 1184.

(7) Service Manager: Mr. Michael Lynch
     PEOPLE WITH A DRUGS PROBLEM

Red Tower 4 Douglas Drive West, HELENSBURGH G84 9AL
☎ 01436-679137.

(8) Service Manager: Mr. Charles Dickson
     SERVICES TO ELDERLY PEOPLE

Annandale Street Project
8 Annandale Street, Govanhill, GLASGOW G42 7AH
☎ 0141-424 3235.

Govanhill Street Project
380 Govanhill Street, Govanhill, GLASGOW G42 7HT
☎ 0141-423 0755.

McNeil Street Project
57 McNeil Street, GLASGOW G5 0NQ
☎ 0141-420 6712.

Moffat Street Project
256 Moffat Street, GLASGOW G5 0ND
☎ 0141-429 2523.

Springbank Street Project
21 Springbank Street, Queen's Cross, GLASGOW G20 7EF
☎ 0141-945 4181.

West End Project
37 Napier Crescent, Brucehill, DUMBARTON G82 4ED
☎ 01389-730466

(9) Service Manager: Mr. Charles Dickson
     SERVICES TO PEOPLE WITH MENTAL ILLNESS

Arden Project
Flat 1/2, 17 Kilmuir Road, Arden, GLASGOW G46 8BG
☎ 0141-621 0236.

Batson Street Project
74 Batson Street, GLASGOW G42 7HG
☎ 0141-423 1413.

Carbeth Street
83 Carbeth Street, Possilpark, GLASGOW G22 5QF
☎0141-336 5174.

Fullers Gate Project
30 Fullers Gate, Faifley, CLYDEBANK G81 5AN
☎ 01389-879630.

DIOCESAN STATISTICS
BAPTISMS, CONFIRMATIONS and MARRIAGES IN 1998
ARCHDIOCESE OF ST. ANDREWS AND EDINBURGH

CITY OF EDINBURGH:	1	2	3	4	5
St. Mary's Cathedral & St. Anne's	31	13	25	30	1294
St. Albert the Great	4	2	16	6	398
St. Andrew	12	-	5	2	200
St. Catherine	6	2	-	2	311
St. Columba	17	1	4	13	370
St. Cuthbert	20	2	15	9	482
St. Gregory the Great	6	-	-	1	253
Holy Cross	16	-	-	2	285
St. John the Baptist	10	4	8	3	390
St. John the Evangelist	27	2	37	10	617
St. John Ogilvie	11	-	17	4	184
St. John Vianney	13	-	-	4	232
St. Joseph	12	9	34	1	246
St. Kentigern	15	-	12	5	504
St. Margaret	4	1	-	3	161
St. Margaret Mary	26	2	12	4	200
St. Mark	22	3	24	4	521
St. Mary Magdalene	4	-	3	2	120
St. Mary Star of the Sea	41	3	23	6	413
SS. Ninian & Triduana	9	1	21	6	330
St. Patrick	6	1	-	10	719
St. Paul	8	-	25	-	223
St. Peter	17	1	2	10	513
Sacred Heart	29	4	16	10	967
St. Teresa of Lisieux	11	9	13	2	168
OUTSIDE THE CITY OF EDINBURGH:					
Addiewell	1	-	15	1	117
Armadale	14	-	32	3	256
Ballingry cf. Lochore					
Banknock	9	-	16	2	254
Bannockburn	21	1	1	10	447
Bathgate	38	11	45	19	999
Blackburn	14	2	25	3	428
Blanefield	6	-	22	4	240
Bo'ness	18	2	22	5	344
Bonnybridge	9	2	-	3	326

Columns: 1. Infant Baptisms; 2. Adult Receptions, whether with or without absolute Baptism; 3. Confirmations, including adults confirmed whether on the occasion of reception or later; 4. Marriages; 5. Mass attendance, all Sunday Masses first weekend of November, 1998.

	1	2	3	4	5
Bowhill	2	-	-	2	118
Broxburn	24	8	50	12	555
Burntisland	7	4	20	3	270
Cowdenbeath	4	1	15	2	318
Cowie	10	-	-	1	121
Currie	17	1	-	4	410
Dalkeith: St. David	14	2	38	9	499
St. Luke & St. Anne	5	-	2	3	397
Denny	46	2	50	14	1012
Dunbar	-	-	9	4	174
Dunfermline: St. Margaret	29	7	-	14	793
Our Lady of Lourdes	10	-	34	4	486
Duns & Eyemouth	7	-	1	2	147
East Calder	14	4	-	4	228
Falkirk: St. Francis Xavier	59	9	-	16	1583
St. Mary of the Angels	12	-	6	1	
Falkland					93
Fauldhouse	31	-	37	7	553
Galashiels	15	-	48	4	301
Glenrothes: St. Mary (Leslie)	16	10	35	6	336
St. Paul	14	4	18	9	435
Gorebridge, cf. Dalkeith St. Luke & St. Anne					
Grangemouth: Christ the King	19	6	18	8	305
Sacred Heart	5	-	15	5	143
Haddington	9	-	21	2	298
Hawick	9	2	20	4	227
Innerleithen, cf. Peebles					70
Inverkeithing	12	-	11	4	382
Jedburgh	3	-	7	2	116
Kelso	5	1	-	-	108
Kelty	6	-	18	1	167
Kennoway	-	-	-	-	111
Kilsyth	38	1	52	5	865
Kirkcaldy: St. Marie's	16	1	30	4	478
St. Pius X	14	1	25	5	317
Larbert	9	1	17	-	247
Lennoxtown	29	-	33	5	472
Leven	6	-	-	-	235
Linlithgow	26	1	-	6	640
Livingston: St. Andrew	25	12	-	7	484
St. Peter	37	5	36	2	554
St. Philip	27	3	30	-	250
Loanhead	4	2	-	1	219
Lochgelly	7	-	-	4	224
Lochore & Ballingry	3	2	27	4	149
Melrose, cf. Galashiels					72
Methil	6	-	-	1	164
Milton of Campsie	17	-	9	3	391

	1	2	3	4	5
Musselburgh	40	5	29	8	691
North Berwick	11	-	6	4	
Nunraw					119
Oakley	10	1	-	2	393
Pathhead	13	-	-		85
Peebles	7	-	-	4	174
Penicuik	11	-	35	2	275
Pittenweem & Crail	6	1	1	-	144
Polmont	14	-	16	1	320
Prestonpans	28	-	25	8	530
Rosewell & Bonnyrigg	19	-	24	9	554
Rosyth	20	-	21	2	270
St. Andrews	13	8	6	11	400
Selkirk & Melrose & Earlston	5	-	17	1	137
South Queensferry	14	1	32	2	453
Stirling: Holy Spirit	6	-	17	-	378
St. Margaret of Scotland	4	-	18	2	399
St. Mary	34	5	103	18	645
University cf. Cowie	1	-	-	-	39
Stoneyburn	4	-	15	-	80
Torrance	3	-	3	-	131
Tranent	11	3	-	5	369
West Calder	12	1	12	9	660
Whitburn	13	1	-	3	356
Winchburgh	6	-	14	-	333
TOTALS	**1,480**	**194**	**1,615**	**482**	**38,117**

DIOCESE OF ABERDEEN

CITY OF ABERDEEN:	1	2	3	4	5
St. Mary's Cathedral	34	9	55	15	1002
St. Columba	3	2	13	1	123
St. Francis & Westhill	26	3	40	2	569
Holy Family	7	-	15	-	133
St. Joseph	5	2	2	-	182
Our Lady of Aberdeen & Portlethen	6	-	-	1	110
St. Peter	10	2	1	-	220
Sacred Heart	6	-	3	-	47
University	-	1	-	8	94

Columns: 1. Infant Baptisms; 2. Adult Receptions, whether with or without absolute Baptism; 3. Confirmations, including adults confirmed whether on the occasion of reception or later; 4. Marriages; 5. Mass attendance, all Sunday Masses first weekend of November, 1998.

OUTSIDE THE CITY OF ABERDEEN:

	1	2	3	4	5
Aviemore	-	-	3	1	113
Ballater, Braemar & Aboyne	1	2	4	1	90
Banchory	4	-	-	5	215
Banff	-	-	-	-	65
Beauly	2	1	12	1	176
Blairs	5	-	-	8	111
Brora	1	-	6	3	57
Buckie	3	-	-	1	197
Culloden	4	-	5	5	297
Dingwall	14	1	2	6	150
Dornie	8	-	-	5	111
Dufftown & Aberlour	-	-	-	-	59
Elgin & Lossiemouth	20	-	38	2	421
Ellon	6	1	19	1	248
Fochabers	-	-	-	1	87
Forres	4	-	6	-	106
Fort Augustus, Stratherrick	-	-	-	1	114
Fraserburgh	2	1	5	1	93
Huntly	2	-	2	-	75
Inverness: St. Mary	31	1	23	10	473
St. Ninian	4	-	9	-	308
Inverurie	10	-	17	5	210
Keith	15	-	-	5	145
Kirkwall	-	1	1	3	86
Lerwick	1	-	-	-	103
Marydale	1	-	-	1	15
Nairn	10	-	11	-	131
Peterhead	8	3	14	4	136
Pluscarden	-	-	-	-	49
Stonehaven	11	-	19	2	223
Tain, Alness & Invergordon	5	-	-	1	172
Thurso	5	-	-	3	111
Tomintoul	1	-	1	2	62
Wick	1	1	1	-	74
TOTALS	**276**	**31**	**327**	**102**	**7,693**

DIOCESE OF ARGYLL AND THE ISLES

CITY OF OBAN:	1	2	3	4	5
St. Columba's Cathedral	17	1	26	8	613

OUTSIDE THE CITY OF OBAN:

Ardkenneth	2	-	11	4	217
Arisaig	3	-	-	1	170
Benbecula	12	1	-	5	218
Bornish	7	-	-	1	148

	1	2	3	4	5
Campbeltown	4	2	2	4	136
Castlebay	13	-	18	5	266
Corpach	10	-	-	2	280
Daliburgh	12	-	25	2	450
Dunoon	-	-	-	-	420
Eriskay	1	-	-	3	82
Fort William	25	1	1	8	489
Glencoe	2	-	-	-	80
Glenfinnan	2	-	-	2	35
Kingussie	2	5	-	-	46
Knoydart	-	-	-	-	49
Lochgilphead	7	-	-	1	160
Mingarry	1	-	-	-	52
Morar	9	-	-	5	205
Northbay	1	-	10	-	139
Rothesay	19	-	-	10	355
Roy Bridge	2	-	15	5	180
Stornoway	2	-	11	2	110
Taynuilt	-	-	-	2	58
Arran	2	-	3	1	42
TOTALS	**155**	**10**	**122**	**71**	**5,000**

DIOCESE OF DUNKELD

CITY OF DUNDEE:	1	2	3	4	5
St. Andrew's Cathedral	7	1	4	6	588
St. Clement	12	-	15	3	416
St. Columba	10	-	13	2	175
St. Francis	46	-	5	5	655
Immaculate Conception	33	-	31	11	658
St. Joseph	6	-	19	2	339
St. Leonard & St. Fergus	32	3	45	8	717
Our Lady of Victories	15	1	16	2	250
St. Matthew	2	-	4	-	128
St. Ninian	25	-	-	-	410
Our Lady of Good Counsel	7	-	-	-	155
Our Lady of Sorrows	10	-	10	1	259
St. Patrick	12	-	-	6	422
SS. Peter & Paul	24	5	21	5	389
St. Pius X	21	-	25	12	323
St. Teresa of Avila	2	-	-	1	103
St. Vincent De Paul	9	1	9	3	367

Columns: 1. Infant Baptisms; 2. Adult Receptions, whether with or without absolute Baptism; 3. Confirmations, including adults confirmed whether on the occasion of reception or later; 4. Marriages; 5. Mass attendance, all Sunday Masses first weekend of November, 1998.

OUTSIDE THE CITY OF DUNDEE:

	1	2	3	4	5
Alloa	18	3	-	5	513
Alva	6	-	-	1	357
Arbroath	15	1	21	4	337
Auchterarder	2	-	10	3	134
Blairgowrie	8	-	-	2	295
Callander	6	-	-	-	168
Carnoustie	4	1	10	-	247
Crieff	6	-	21	13	261
Cupar	13	1	16	3	380
Dunblane	8	1	-	2	320
Forfar	10	-	6	6	300
Highvalleyfield	1	-	13	-	145
Kinross	6	-	18	1	268
Monifieth	13	-	27	4	434
Montrose	14	2	-	3	232
Newport-on-Tay	16	-	-	2	260
Perth: St. John, with St. Mary Magdalene					
and Dunkeld (Birnam)	41	2	23	16	1170
Our Lady of Lourdes	6	-	34	1	236
Pitlochry	2	-	-	3	226
Tullibody	9	2	35	3	226
TOTALS	**477**	**24**	**451**	**139**	**12,963**

DIOCESE OF GALLOWAY

CITY OF AYR:	1	2	3	4	5
Good Shepherd Cathedral	6	-	-	-	207
St. Margaret	21	-	38	3	697
St. Paul	11	-	27	5	442

OUTSIDE THE CITY OF AYR:

Annan & Langholm	9	1	10	5	185
Ardrossan	29	5	38	11	936
Auchinleck	4	-	15	-	100
Beith	3	-	7	2	98
Castle Douglas	3	1	1	1	66
Catrine	1	-	6	-	86
Cumnock & New Cumnock	11	3	24	6	294
Dalbeattie	4	-	-	-	132
Dalry	2	2	-	2	157
Drongan	-	-	2	-	40

	1	2	3	4	5
Dumfries: St. Andrew	27	4	36	12	549
St. Teresa	14	-	20	2	342
Galston	12	-	12	-	297
Girvan	13	-	12	2	291
Gretna	2	-	-	3	20
Hurlford	5	-	9	3	166
Irvine: St. John Ogilvie	13	2	39	6	392
St. Margaret	8	-	7	1	163
St. Mary	12	-	13	14	491
Kilbirnie	5	-	26	3	257
Kilmarnock: St. Joseph	35	3	24	5	871
St. Matthew	26	-	17	4	371
St. Michael	4	-	10	-	197
Mount Carmel	26	-	39	6	284
Kilwinning	40	4	4	8	572
Kirkconnel	-	-	-	1	11
Kirkcudbright	3	-	-	3	137
Langholm, cf. Annan	-	-	-	-	32
Largs	19	2	25	9	618
Lockerbie	6	-	-	3	164
Maybole	10	-	16	3	159
Millport	1	-	-	1	55
Mossblown	7	2	16	3	134
Muirkirk	4	-	3	2	55
Newton Stewart & Whithorn	5	-	9	3	212
Prestwick	14	-	27	4	470
Saltcoats: St. Brendan	13	-	26	2	428
Our Lady, Star of the Sea	21	1	12	7	676
Stevenston	22	1	41	7	497
Stewarton	9	1	8	1	148
Stranraer	12	1	16	3	227
Troon	18	1	26	11	576
Waterside	6	-	19	-	63
West Kilbride	2	-	-	2	167
TOTALS	**518**	**34**	**680**	**169**	**13,532**

ARCHDIOCESE OF GLASGOW

CITY OF GLASGOW:	1	2	3	4	5
St. Andrew's Cathedral	18	2	29	19	607
St. Agnes	23	3	3	3	334

Columns: 1. Infant Baptisms; 2. Adult Receptions, whether with or without absolute Baptism; 3. Confirmations, including adults confirmed whether on the occasion of reception or later; 4. Marriages; 5. Mass attendance, all Sunday Masses first weekend of November, 1998.

	1	2	3	4	5
St. Albert	18	-	-	3	506
All Saints	34	-	-	2	361
St. Aloysius, Garnethill	5	2	90	13	789
St. Aloysius, Springburn	13	-	-	3	405
St. Alphonsus	8	2	2	2	1178
St. Anne	17	-	69	5	220
St. Anthony	20	-	-	9	382
St. Augustine	27	-	2	9	476
St. Barnabas	26	-	-	3	511
St Bartholomew	48	-	58	3	418
St Benedict	17	-	27	-	343
St. Bernadette	4	1	1	1	394
St. Bernard	19	-	57	-	147
St. Brendan	41	2	49	6	662
St. Brigid	54	-	98	6	672
St. Catherine Laboure	32	1	1	8	471
St. Charles	15	-	-	5	275
Christ the King	74	3	123	17	1636
St. Columba	17	1	30	2	282
St. Constantine	63	1	1	7	930
St. Conval	34	2	2	11	520
Corpus Christi	34	3	3	5	704
St. Gabriel	62	-	40	13	1683
St. Gregory	27	-	41	5	525
St. Helen	65	1	1	8	1730
Holy Cross	82	4	4	24	1622
Holy Name	27	-	-	7	850
Immaculate Conception	55	6	123	15	953
Immaculate Heart of Mary	29	-	-	4	431
St. James	27	-	-	11	550
St. Joachim	15	-	-	1	247
Bl. John Duns Scotus	32	1	61	8	732
St. John Ogilvie	N/A	N/A	N/A	N/A	N/A
St Joseph	38	-	-	9	819
St Jude	14	1	56	1	271
St. Laurence	18	-	39	1	279
St. Leo the Great	9	2	2	2	437
St. Louise	20	-	-	2	189
St. Margaret Mary	46	3	3	7	874
St. Maria Goretti	17	-	43	7	329
St. Mark	28	-	43	2	231
St. Martin	25	1	40	4	152
St. Mary	27	-	17	1	308
St. Mary Immaculate	41	1	1	14	641
St. Michael	39	-	130	3	540
St. Monica	12	-	-	-	223
St. Mungo	30	3	3	9	578

	1	2	3	4	5
St. Ninian	32	6	89	13	1778
Our Lady of the Assumption	22	-	-	8	181
Our Lady of Consolation	19	-	-	1	550
Our Lady of Fatima	16	-	13	-	166
Our Lady of Good Counsel	29	-	21	5	1071
Our Lady of Lourdes	78	3	3	15	1905
Our Lady of Perpetual Succour	9	1	13	3	332
Our Lady and St. George	34	1	1	4	1166
Our Lady and St. Margaret	13	-	-	2	122
St. Patrick	16	3	30	9	447
St Paul, Shettleston	59	5	5	12	1165
St Paul, Whiteinch	29	-	78	6	511
St. Peter	65	3	39	19	1065
St. Philip	23	-	-	3	187
St. Philomena	38	1	90	8	835
St. Pius X	27	1	59	2	108
St. Robert Bellarmine	27	1	1	5	675
St. Roch	44	-	74	3	365
Sacred Heart	26	-	-	3	295
St. Saviour	5	-	-	5	222
St. Simon	14	1	6	7	501
St. Stephen	-	-	-	-	130
St. Teresa	66	1	37	10	362
St. Thomas	26	-	-	12	773
St. Vincent de Paul	49	-	35	10	569
Glasgow University Chaplaincy	7	1	1	4	245
Strathclyde University Chaplaincy	2	1	-	1	79

PARISHES OUTSIDE THE CITY OF GLASGOW:

	1	2	3	4	5
Alexandria	26	-	80	2	545
Balloch	38	-	-	7	629
Bearsden	48	4	64	15	1238
Bishopbriggs—St. Dominic	43	1	78	10	1470
St. Matthew	46	-	-	19	1356
Bonhill	22	-	-	2	339
Cardross	-	-	-	-	122
Clydebank—St. Eunan	49	-	-	7	688
St. Margaret	31	-	-	7	893
Our Holy Redeemer	22	-	-	6	501

Columns: 1. Infant Baptisms; 2. Adult Receptions, whether with or without absolute Baptism; 3. Confirmations, including adults confirmed whether on the occasion of reception or later; 4. Marriages; 5. Mass attendance, all Sunday Masses first weekend of November, 1998.

	1	2	3	4	5
Condorrat	32	2	41	15	919
Croy	36	3	57	10	809
Cumbernauld—St. Joseph	28	2	85	7	754
St Lucy	28	-	31	7	511
Sacred Heart	55	2	51	12	899
Dalmuir—Our Lady of Loreto	32	-	-	-	490
St. Stephen	9	-	-	7	470
Dumbarton—St. Michael	41	9	49	8	828
St. Patrick	52	5	66	15	1401
St. Peter	20	-	34	1	408
Duntocher	56	-	-	21	1355
Faifley	31	-	42	7	489
Garelochhead	1	-	-	-	49
Helensburgh	37	-	-	14	500
Kirkintilloch—St. Flannan	39	-	64	13	852
Holy Family & St. Ninian	51	4	4	26	1180
Milngavie	19	2	27	3	823
Old Kilpatrick	21	1	-	6	457
Renton	4	-	-	1	358
Rosneath	2	-	-	-	99
Twechar	4	-	4	1	138
TOTALS	**3,144**	**109**	**2,664**	**720**	**65,802**

DIOCESE OF MOTHERWELL

	1	2	3	4	5
CITY OF MOTHERWELL:					
Our Lady of Good Aid Cathedral.	56	7	7	15	1348
St. Bernadette	35	-	-	9	900
St Brendan	24	-	-	4	527
St Luke	10	-	-	4	360
OUTSIDE THE CITY OF MOTHERWELL:					
Airdrie—St. Andrew	39	-	72	8	480
St. Edward	53	4	48	23	683
St. Margaret	30	-	32	13	1034
St. Serf	28	1	-	38	495
Baillieston—St. Bridget	42	5	5	11	1139
St. Francis	19	-	-	5	666
Bargeddie	11	1	37	6	275
Bellshill—St Gerard	22	2	64	9	661
Sacred Heart	46	-	90	11	1120
Biggar	3	-	-	1	125
Blackwood	6	-	21	4	207

	1	2	3	4	5
Blantyre—St. John Ogilvie	37	8	8	7	752
St. Joseph	67	-	-	27	1634
Bothwell	25	1	89	5	1083
Burnbank	9	-	-	6	800
Calderbank	14	-	-	6	437
Caldercruix	17	-	-	2	360
Cambuslang	32	-	19	12	889
Carfin	34	1	1	15	867
Carluke	30	1	1	4	710
Chapelhall	22	1	57	11	886
Cleland	19	-	-	7	505
Coatbridge—St. Augustine	56	1	120	22	915
St. Bartholomew	30	-	90	9	609
St. Bernard	11	-	70	1	415
Holy Trinity & All Saints	28	-	26	6	1101
St. James	28	-	153	10	1016
St. Mary	31	-	57	9	1240
St. Monica	55	-	162	15	1291
St. Patrick	86	3	95	22	1666
St. Stephen	31	-	56	7	753
Craigend	41	3	3	4	400
Easterhouse—St. Benedict	27	14	54	2	177
St. Clare	19	1	62	2	204
East Kilbride—St. Bride	37	2	77	4	1509
St. Leonard	106	9	123	31	1750
Our Lady of Lourdes	53	-	53	12	1395
St. Vincent de Paul	30	-	-	6	741
Forth	-	-	-	1	45
Glenboig	14	-	47	4	518
Halfway	13	-	-	4	577
Hamilton—St. Mary	29	2	2	16	995
St. Ninian	25	-	-	12	764
Our Lady & St. Anne	67	1	89	14	1541
St. Paul	3	-	24	-	125
St. Peter	35	-	76	17	901
Harthill	17	-	-	3	272
Holytown	23	-	68	5	502
Lanark	22	1	1	8	612
Larkhall	7	1	29	2	563
Moodiesburn	25	-	1	54	631
Mossend	27	-	1	4	982
Muirhead	21	1	1	5	600
Newarthill	25	-	89	12	947

Columns: 1. Infant Baptisms; 2. Adult Receptions, whether with or without absolute Baptism; 3. Confirmations, including adults confirmed whether on the occasion of reception or later; 4. Marriages; 5. Mass attendance, all Sunday Masses first weekend of November, 1998.

	1	2	3	4	5
Newmains	31	11	60	8	758
New Stevenston	13	-	50	5	436
Plains	26	-	-	8	815
Rutherglen—St. Anthony	42	-	-	10	912
St. Columbkille	85	2	2	16	1708
St. Mark	18	-	-	2	368
Shotts	30	-	-	18	1027
Stepps	18	-	-	4	491
Strathaven	18	-	-	6	342
Uddingston	58	-	57	15	1681
Viewpark—St. Columba	54	-	97	20	1538
St. Gabriel	36	-	45	8	484
Wishaw—St. Aidan	35	-	98	9	1083
St. Ignatius	25	3	67	10	1257
St. Patrick	30	-	57	13	619
St. Thomas	32	-	70	9	650
TOTALS	**2,303**	**87**	**2,862**	**652**	**58,869**

DIOCESE OF PAISLEY

	1	2	3	4	5
CITY OF PAISLEY:					
St. Mirin's Cathedral	63	1	124	14	1351
St. Charles	72	1	65	17	1213
St. Fergus	26	2	70	-	287
St. James	15	-	18	1	172
St. Mary	41	1	1	6	963
St. Paul	9	1	61	3	487
St. Peter	36	-	-	10	457
OUTSIDE THE CITY OF PAISLEY:					
Barrhead	98	7	64	14	1357
Bishopton	3	-	-	2	368
Clarkston	86	-	-	13	1779
Eaglesham	4	-	6	4	163
Elderslie	2	-	9	-	97
Erskine—St. Bernadette	34	-	64	6	511
St. John Bosco	19	-	-	4	561
Gourock	28	-	52	10	851
Greenock—St. Andrew	62	2	78	20	1205
St. Joseph	53	2	60	8	782
St. Laurence	31	1	116	6	743
St. Mary	35	1	53	12	900
St. Mungo	21	-	-	6	622
St. Patrick	64	1	1	15	1873
Houston	23	1	16	12	504
Howwood	12	1	3	4	235

	1	2	3	4	5
Johnstone—St. Aidan	5	-	8	4	286
St. Anthony	8	-	26	-	341
St. Margaret	77	3	3	17	1073
Kilmacolm	1	-	-	-	127
Linwood	37	-	62	16	792
Neilston	18	2	27	5	347
Newton Mearns	40	2	80	5	1110
Port Glasgow—St. Francis	26	-	-	12	837
Holy Family	56	7	95	10	905
St. John the Baptist	16	-	-	6	654
Renfrew—St. Columba	17	4	57	2	820
St. James	43	1	74	8	535
Wemyss Bay	20	2	10	5	370
TOTALS	1,218	43	1,323	287	25,678

Columns: 1. Infant Baptisms; 2. Adult Receptions, whether with or without absolute Baptism; 3. Confirmations, including adults confirmed whether on the occasion of reception or later; 4. Marriages; 5. Mass attendance, all Sunday Masses first weekend of November, 1998.

GENERAL SUMMARY OF STATISTICS
FOR SCOTLAND FOR 1999
(As at 1st October, 1999)

ARCHDIOCESE OF ST. ANDREWS AND EDINBURGH

Secular priests (including 40 retired or working outwith the Diocese)	135
Regular Priests	52
Total Number of Priests in the Archdiocese	187
Permanent Deacon	1
Students in Major Seminaries	6
Aspirant in Vocations Scotland Scheme	1
Parishes	95
Religious Communities of Men	13
Brothers	12
Religious Communities of Women	38
Sisters	180
*Baptisms for 1998	1,674
Marriages for 1998	482
Mass attendance, first Sunday of November, 1998	38,117
Estimated Catholic population in the Archdiocese	112,652

DIOCESE OF ABERDEEN

Secular priests (including 5 retired or working outwith the Diocese)	27
Regular Priests	19
Total Number of Priests in the Diocese	46
Permanent Deacons	8
Students in Major Seminaries	4
Parishes	39
Religious Communities of Men	1
Religious Communities of Women	9
Sisters	32
*Baptisms for 1998	307
Marriages for 1998	102
Mass attendance, first Sunday of November, 1998	7,693
Estimated Catholic population in the Diocese	17,000

•The figures for Baptisms include adults received into the Church whether already baptized or not.

DIOCESE OF ARGYLL AND THE ISLES

Secular priests (including 10 retired or working outwith the Diocese)	30
Regular Priests	3
Total Number of Priests in the Diocese	33
Students in Major Seminaries	3
Parishes	24
Religious Communities of Women	4
Sisters	12
*Baptisms for 1998	165
Marriages for 1998	71
Mass attendance, first Sunday in November, 1998	5,000
Estimated Catholic population in the Diocese	11,200

DIOCESE OF DUNKELD

Secular priests (including 3 retired or working outwith the Diocese)	37
Regular Priests	14
Total Number of Priests in the Diocese	51
Permanent Deacons	11
Students in Major Seminaries	8
Aspirant in Vocations Scotland Scheme	1
Parishes	39
Religious Communities of Men	5
Brothers	2
Religious Communities of Women	9
Sisters	44
*Baptisms for 1998	501
Marriages for 1998	139
Mass attendance, first Sunday of November, 1998	12,963
Estimated Catholic population in the Diocese	43,000

DIOCESE OF GALLOWAY

Secular priests (including 15 retired or working outwith the Diocese and 1 Chaplain to the Forces)	57
Regular Priests	2
Total Number of Priests in the Diocese	59
Students in Major Seminaries	4
Aspirant in Vocations Scotland Scheme	1
Parishes :	47
Religious Communities of Men	4
Brothers	8
Religious Communities of Women	15
Sisters	40
Religious Communities of Men and Women	1
*Baptisms for 1998	552
Marriages for 1998	169
Mass attendance, first Sunday of November, 1998	13,532
Estimated Catholic population in the Diocese	47,150

*The figures for Baptisms include adults received into the Church, whether already baptized or not.

ARCHDIOCESE OF GLASGOW

Secular Priests (*including 64 retired or working outwith the diocese, 2 belonging to a Personal Prelature and 3 Chaplains to the Forces*)	217
Regular Priests	40
Total Number of Priests in the Archdiocese	257
Students in Major Seminaries	12
Aspirants in Vocations Scotland Scheme	3
Parishes	107
Religious Communities of Men	14
Brothers	24
Religious Communities of Women	47
Sisters	220
*Baptisms for 1998	3,253
Marriages for 1998	720
Mass attendance, first Sunday of November, 1998	65,802
Estimated Catholic population in the Archdiocese	227,599

DIOCESE OF MOTHERWELL

Secular Priests (*including 34 retired or working outwith the diocese and 1 Chaplain to the Forces*)	137
Regular Priests	24
Total Number of Priests in the Diocese	161
Permanent Deacons (*including any belonging to the Regular Clergy*)	2
Students in Major Seminaries	5
Aspirants in Vocations Scotland Scheme	5
Parishes	74
Religious Communities of Men	6
Brothers	6
Religious Communities of Women	22
Sisters	104
*Baptisms for 1998	2,390
Marriages for 1998	652
Mass attendance, first Sunday of November, 1998	58,869
Estimated Catholic population in the Diocese	163,221

*The figure for Baptisms includes adults received into the Church whether already baptized or not.

DIOCESE OF PAISLEY

Secular Priests *(including 27 retired or working outwith the diocese, and 1 Chaplain to the Forces)*	84
Regular Priests	3
Total Number of Priests in the Diocese	87
Students in Major Seminaries	9
Parishes	36
Religious Communities of Men	3
Brothers	9
Religious Communities of Women	15
Sisters	61
*Baptisms for 1998	1,261
Marriages for 1998	287
Mass attendance, first Sunday of November 1998	25,678
Estimated Catholic population in the Diocese	79,429

GENERAL SUMMARY OF STATISTICS FOR SCOTLAND
AS AT 1st OCTOBER, 1999

Secular priests	724	
Regular Priests	157	
Total Number of Priests in Scotland		881
Permanent Deacons		22
Students in Major Seminaries		51
Aspirants in Vocations Scotland Scheme		11
Parishes		460
Religious Communities of Men		46
Brothers		61
Religious Communities of Women		159
Sisters		693
Religious Communities of Men and Women		1
*Baptisms for 1998		10,103
Marriages for 1998		2,622
Mass attendance, first Sunday in November, 1998		227,654
Estimated Catholic population in Scotland in 1999		701,851
Estimated population of Scotland (30th June, 1998)		**5,120,000

*The figure for Baptisms includes adults received into the Church whether already baptized or not.

**Source, General Register Office (Scotland). Crown Copyright, 1999

LISTED BUILDINGS
OF THE CATHOLIC CHURCH
IN SCOTLAND

The Listing of Buildings of Special Architectural or Historic Interest and the Scheduling of Ancient Monuments is a duty which was imposed on the Secretary of State for Scotland by various Acts of Parliament, and is now imposed on the Scottish Ministers.. This is carried out on their behalf by the Historic Buildings Council for Scotland, Historic Scotland and the Ancient Monuments Board for Scotland.

LISTED BUILDING AND CONSERVATION AREA CONTROL FOR ETERIORS OF CHURCHES IN ECCLESIASTICAL USE

Agreed by the Scottish Catholic Heritage Commission with Historic Scotland for a trial period of three years.

Historic Scotland, acting on behalf of the Secretary of State has been in consultation with the Churches with a view to explaining a change in procedures with regard to ecclesiastical exemption from listed building control.

For many years, the Catholic Church in Scotland, together with other denominations, hs enjoyed the privilege known as "ecclesiastical exemption" from listed building control.

Amendments have been made to "ecclesiastical exemption", and these amendments are being tested in a pilot scheme which runs from 1st January 1999 for a three-year period.

The most important change to "ecclesiastical exemption" is the introduction of a 'decision-making body'. For the Catholic Church in Scotland, the 'decision-making body' operates under the umbrella of the Scottish Catholic Heritage Commission.

Where a parish and/or diocese proposes to undertake work to the exterior of its building(s), but no agreement can be reached between the applicant and the statutory authorities, the application will be referred to the Scottish Catholic Heritage Commission. The Commission will determine, in effect, whether listed building/ conservation area consent should be given. You should note that an applicant is expected to accept the decision of the Commission, and deemed consent to the application will be in terms of that decision.

COMPOSITION OF THE COMMISSION

The usual membership of the Commission will be supplemented by advisers nominated by the dioceses.

PROCEDURES

Applications can be referred to the Commission either by Historic Scotland and/or by the parish or diocese.

Applications received will be acknowledged to the parish and/or diocese concerned; and to Historic Scotland.

Applications referred to the Commission will be allocated a reference number which should be quoted on all future correspondence.

The application will then be referred to a panel comprising at least three members appointed by the Scottish Catholic Heritage Commission. A list of those approved by the dioceses to serve on a panel will be maintained by the Commission.

The panel may request further information from any agency, and/or may seek to arrange a meeting with the various parties to the application.

The Commision will seek to determine an application within one calendar month of receipt. If it appears that consideration of an application will take longer the applicant will be informed.

The decision of the Commission will be communicated to the applicant in writing, together with an acknowledgement slip to be completed and returned by the applicant.

Note. The ascription of ownership is intended merely to reflect how the title to the property may be taken in civil law and is entirely without prejudice to the rights of individual parishes, etc., in Canon Law. Cf. Canons 515§3, 1256 and 1284§2n2 of the Code of Canon Law.

This list, introduced in the issue of 1988 as a preliminary list, has been expanded and amplified by the Scottish Catholic Heritage Commision, through its secretary and researcher, Dr. Mary McHugh. It has not been possible to identify the architects of some buildings. Individual architects or firms are designed as shown in the offical list provided by the Scottish Development Department.

ARCHDIOCESE OF ST. ANDREWS AND EDINBURGH

(a) Archdiocesan Property.
i. Edinburgh:

St. Mary's Cathedral. James (Gillespie) Graham, 1813; Buchanan &
Bennett, 1894; Reginald Fairlie, 1932; Reid & Forbes, 1932, 1970. **B**
Cathedral Halls. 1800, 1828, 1858-61, c.1980. **B**

St.Columba, Newington. Church and boundary walls.
R.M.Cameron,1888. **B**

St. Francis of Assisi, Lothian Street, former Church (Jericho
Benedictines). Style of James Gillespie Graham, 1834. **B**

St. John the Evangelist, Portobello. J.T. Walford, 1904-6. **A**

St. Margaret Mary, Granton. Reginald Fairlie, 1938. **B**. Church **C(S)**.
Presbytery **B group with Church.**

St. Mary, Star of the Sea, Leith. Edward Welby Pugin & Joseph
Hansom, 1852-4. **B**

SS. Ninian & Triduana, Restalrig. Sir Giles Gilbert Scott, 1932-3; James
Dunbar Naismith, 1977. **B**

St.Patrick,Cowgate. 1771-4. **B**

St. Peter, Morningside. Sir Robert Lorimer,1906-8. School, 1928-9. **A**

Sacred Heart Lauriston. Fr. Richard Vaughan, 1960. **B.**

Halls & Presbytery, Archibald Macpherson, 1909. **B**

Gillis Centre. c 1670, 1835, James Murray, 1973. **B**

St. Bennet's (Archbishop's House). John Henderson, c. 1859. **B**

26 George Square. 1772. **A**

ii. Outside Edinburgh:

Bannockburn, Our Lady & St. Ninian. Archibald Macpherson, 1927.
C(S)

Broxburn, SS. John Cantius & Nicholas. **B**

Dalkeith, St. David. Joseph Aloysius Hansom, 1854; Reginald Fairlie &
Partners, 1971. **A**

Dunfermline, St. Margaret. Sir R. Rowland Anderson, 1894-6. **B**

Falkirk, St. Mary of the Angels, Church & Presbytery. Gillespie, Kidd &
Coia, 1960-61. **A**

Galashiels, Our Lady & St. Andrew. William Wardell, 1856-8, 1870. **B**

Glenrothes, St. Mary's, Leslie. Church, with boundary walls, steps and
piers. R. Thornton Shiells, 187679. **B**

Glenrothes, St. Paul. Gillespie, Kidd & Coia, 1964. **B**

Grangemouth, Sacred Heart. Archibald Macpherson, 1927. **C(S)**
Haddington, St. Mary's. Church, Edward Welby Pugin, 1862. **B**
Innerleithen, St. James. Church, Biggar of Edinburgh, 1881;
Presbytery & School, Biggar of Edinburgh. **B**
Jedburgh, Immaculate Conception. Reginald Fairlie, 1937. **B**
Kelso, Immaculate Conception. W.W. Wardell, 1857-8; Archibald
Macpherson, 1916, 1935. **C(S)**
Kilsyth, St. Patrick, Church & Presbytery. Gillespie, Kidd & Coia, 1964.
A
Kirkcaldy, St. Marie's, Church & boundary walls. John Bennie Wilson,
1899- 1901. **B**
Linlithgow, St. Michael's. Pugin, 1887. **B**
Melrose, High Cross. John Smith, 1866; Peddie & Kinnear. **B**
Musselburgh, Our Lady of Loretto and St. Michael. Archibald
Macpherson, A.E. Purdie, 1903-5. **B**
North Berwick, Our Lady Star of the Sea. John Kinross, 1889; Lady
Chapel, Sir Robert Lorimer, 1901. **B**
Oakley, The Holy Name Church. Charles W. Gray, 1958. Windows,
Gabriel Loire of Chartres. **B**
Peebles, St. Joseph. Church & Presbytery: **B (B group with school and
schoolhouse);** Halls (with Boundary walls): **C(S)**
Pittenweem, Christ the King (including enclosing walls and entrance
gatepiers): Early l9th Century, 1935, 1954. **B (for group)**
Rosewell, St. Matthew. Archibald Macpherson, c. 1925. **B**
St. Andrews, St. James. Reginald Fairlie,1910. **B**
Selkirk, Our Lady and St. Joseph. Church and Boundary walls, George
Goldie, 1866. C(S)
Stirling, St. Mary. Church, Peter Paul Pugin, 1883, **B**; Parish Hall, 1838,
C(S); Presbytery, 18thCenhlry, **B**

(b) Property of Religious Institutes.
Edinburgh, Convent of the Good Shepherd, Chapel. W.J. Devlin, 1928.
B
St. Mary, Star of the Sea, Leith. Edward Welby Pugin & Joseph Hansom,
1852-4; Reginald Fairlie, 1938. **B**
Dysart, Carmelite Monastery. 16th Century (?), 1726. **B**
Musselburgh, St. Anne's Convent. c.1880. **B (as part of group).**
North Berwick, Servite Convent. Later 18th century, 19th century. **A**
Nunraw, Sancta Maria Abbey, Gatehouse. **A**
Rosewell. William Burns & David Bryce, 1839-44. **B**

(c) Private Property.
Edinburgh, Columba House, 16 Drummond Place. Robert Reid;
Thomas Bonnar, 1819. **A**
Traquair House, Domestic Oratory. **B**

DIOCESE OF ABERDEEN

(a) Diocesan Property
i. Aberdeen.
St. Mary's Cathedral: Alexander Ellis, 1860; Spire, R.G. Wilson (Ellis & Wilson), 1877; Bells, Taylor of Loughborough. **B**
Halls & Rooms, 14-16 Huntly Street. **B**
St. Peter: Church, James Massie, 1803-04; Gallery, Harry Leith, 1815; Façade to Court & No. 1 Chapel Court, Harry Leith, 1817; House, 1774. **B**
Sacred Heart: Church & Presbytery, C.J. Menart, 1911. **B**

ii. Outside Aberdeen.
Ballater: St. Nathalan, Archibald Macpherson, 1905.
Banff: Our Lady of Mount Carmel, Alexander Ellis, 1870. **B**
Beauly: Church, Presbytery & Bunal Ground, 1843; 1864 (probably Joseph Hansom). **B**.
Blairs: Chapel, Robert Curran of Warrington, 1899; interior, C.J. Menart, 1910 11. **A**
Old Chapel and Menzies Apartments, early 19th C, John Gall of Aberdeen from 1827. **B**
Braemar: St. Andrew's, church, entrance gates and lamp standard, 1839. **B**.
Buckie: St. Peter: Bishop Kyle & Alexander Ellis, 1851-7; A.& W. Aird, 1907. **A**
Cannich: Marydale: Church, Presbytery & Former School, Joseph Hansom, 1866. **B**
Chapeltown: Our Lady of Perpetual Succour: John Kinross, 1896-7. **A**
House & Burial ground, former School & former Schoolhouse, 1869. **C(S) (B group)**
Dornie: St. Duthac, J.A. Hansom, 1860. **B**
Dufftown: St. Mary of the Assumption, Church, Hall & Gatepiers, Bishop Kyle & Rev. Walter Lovi 1824-S; enlarged, Patrick Devlin, 1925. **B**
Elgin: St. Sylvester, Church & Presbytery, Thomas MacKenzie, 1843-4; Church, alterations, William J. Devlin, 1932; School frontage, Mr. George Melvin, 1872. **B**
Eskadale: St. Mary, Church & Burial ground, 1826; alterations & additions, Peter Paul Pugin, 1881. **B**.
Stables, 1826. **B**
House **C(S) (B group with Church & stable)**
Fetternear: St. John, Church & House, George Goldie, 1859. **B**
Fochabers: St. Mary, 1828. **C**
Huntly: St. Margaret, Bishop Kyle, 1834. **A**
Inverness: St. Mary: Church, Wm. Robertson, 1836-7, W.J. Carruthers, 1888. **A** Presbytery. **B**

Inverurie: Immaculate Conception; Church, House & outhouse, Bishop Kyle(?), 1852. **B**

Keith: St. Thomas: Church & Presbytery, Rev. Walter Lovi, 1831; Hall, 1915, C.J. Menart, 1916. **A**

Lerwick: St. Margaret: Church, James Malcolm Baikie of Lerwick, 1910-11; Presbytery, Boundary walls, gate, gatepiers. **C(S)**

Nairn: St. Mary; 1864, John Robertson, 1901. **C(S).**

Old Deer: Abbey of Deer. **B, Ancient Monument.**

Peterhead; St. Mary, Church & Presbytery, Bishop Kyle(?), 1850-1. **B**

Portsoy: Church of the Annunciation, Mr. Dawson of Banff, 1829. **B**

Preshome: St. Gregory, 1789-91, Peter Paul Pugin, 1896. **A**

Stonehaven: Immaculate Conception, 1877. **B**

Tombae: Church of the Incarnation, John Gall, 1927-9, Bishop Kyle & (?)Rev. Walter Lovi, 1843-4 **A**

Tomintoul; our Lady and St. Michael's (incorporating presbytery and Burial ground), George Mathewson, 1837. **B**

Tynet: St. Ninian, 1755, 1787. **A**

Wick: St. Joachim: Church & House, Mr. Dawson of Banff, 1835-7 **B**
Convent. **C(S) (B group with Church)**

(b) Property of Religious Institutes.

Elgin: Convent of Mercy, Late-l58th Century core. **A**
Convent Church; John Kinross, 1896. **A**

Pluscarden: Monastery: 1290; John Kinross, 1897-1900, restoration of Lady Chapel, etc., Ian Lindsay, 1945-66; Wm. Murray Jack, from 1967. **A**
Priory Lodge: c.1821, Wm. Anderson. **B**

(c) Private Property.

Scalan: Seminary, 1717, 1767. **A**.
South steading, with mill-wheel, late 18th century. **(A group)**

DIOCESE OF ARGYLL AND THE ISLES

Diocesan Property

Oban: St. Columba's Cathedral: Sir Giles Gilbert Scott, 1932-53. **A**

Achluachrach: St. Cyril: Church & Burial ground: Late l9th Century; Restored and rebuilt Reginald Fairlie. **B**

Ardkenneth: St. Michael: Local people, supervised By Rev. James McGregory, 1829. **B**

Arisaig: St. Mary: Church & Presbytery, William Burn, 1849; 1900. **C(S)(B group with old Church.**
Old Church and Burial ground. Probably late medieval. **B**

Bornish: St. Mary: 1837. **B**

Brodick: R.C. Church (Holy Cross); mid-19th century. **C(S)**

Campbeltown: St. Kieran: Church, 1849-50; Presbytery, 1880; Boundary walls, gates and gatepiers. **C(S)**

Canna: R.C. Church; William Frame, 1885-9. **B**
Castlebay: Our Lady, Star of the Sea: Woulfe Brennan, Oban, 1888. **B**.
    Presbytery. **B Group with Church.**
Craigston, Barra: St. Brendan: c.1858. **C(S)**
Daliburgh: St. Peter: 1907. **C(S)**
Drimnin: St. Columba. x1835. **B**
Eigg: R,C. Church & presbytery: 1910. **C(S)**
Eriskay: St. Michael. 1903. **C(S)**
Fort William: Immaculate Conception: Reginald Fairley, 1936-8. **A**
Glendaruel: St. Sophia. **B**
Glenfinnan: St. Mary & St. Finnan: Church & Belfry: Edward Welby
    Pugin, 1872-4. **B**
Invergarry: St. Finnan: Ian Lindsay, c.1935. **B**
Kingussie: Our Lady of the Rosary & St. Columba: Church & Presbytery:
    Norman Dick, 1931-2. **B**
Mallaig: St. Patrick: Reginald Fairlie, 1935. **C(S)**
Morar: St. Cumin: Church & Presbytery, 1888. **C(S)**
    Polnish: Our Lady of the Braes: c.1872. **B**
Rothesay; St. Andrew: Church & Presbytery; Reginald Fairlie, 1925. **A**
Roy Bridge: St. Margaret: Reginald Fairlie, 1929. **B**
    Presbytery. **C(S) (B group with Church)**

DIOCESE OF DUNKELD

(a) Diocesan Property.
i. Dundee:
St. Andrew's Cathedral: George Mathewson, 1836; C.G. Menart, 1920-1.
    B
St. Francis (excluding chapel): Reginald Fairlie, 1933. **B**
Imrnaculate Conception, Lochee: Joseph Aloysius Hansom, 1886; A.B.
    Wall, 1897. **B**
    Hall. **A**
St. Joseph: Alexander Ellis and Robert G. Wilson, 1872. **B**
Our Lady of Good Counsel, Broughty Ferry: Thomas M. Cappon, 1904.
    C(S)
St. Patrick (Church, presbytery and hall): T.M. Cappon, Harry East,
    W.G. Lamond, 1897; Reginald Fairlie,1927. **B**
SS. Peter and Paul: Reginald Fairlie, 1928. **B**

ii. Outside Dundee:
Arbroath, St. Thomas of Canterbury: George Mathewson, 1848. **B**
Brechin, St. Ninian: William Leiper, 1875-6. **B**
Doune, SS. Fillan and Alphonsus: John Laurie Fogo, 1875. **C(S)**
Dunblane, Holy Family: Reginald Fairlie, 1935. **C(S)**
Perth, St. John: 1832, 1848,, 1856; Andrew Heiton, 1892. **C(S)**
Strathttay, Holy Cross: **B**
Tayport, St. Mary, Star of the Sea: Reginald Fairlie, 1939. **B**

(b) Property of Religious Institutes.
Dundee:
St. Colette's Convent, Roseangle. **C**
St. Joseph's Convent, Lawside: Archibald McPherson, 1892; Chapel, Reginald Fairlie 1921, 1925. **B**
Kilgraston, Convent of the Sacred Heart:
  House. **A**
  Gates. **B**
  Lodge. **B**
  Former Stable Block. **B**
  Walled Garden. **C(S)**
Kinnoull, St. Mary's Monastery: Andrew Heiton, 1869-70. **B**

(c) Private Property
Murthly Castle: St. Antony's Chapel. **B**

DIOCESE OF GALLOWAY

(a) Diocesan Property,
Ayr, St. Margaret: 1826-7. **B**
Annan, St. Columba: x1838. **B**
Ardrossan, St. Peter-in-Chains: Gillespie, Kidd & Coia, 1938. **A**
Beith, Our Lady of Perpetual Succour: 1816. **C(S)**
Castle Douglas, St. John the Evangelist (Church, Presbytery and retaining walls): George Goldie, 1867. **C(S)**
Cumnock, St. John: William Burgess, 1881-2. **B**
Dalbeattie, St. Peter, church, boundary railings and gatepiers: 1814; tower, 1854. **B**
Dalry, St. Palladius; 1851. **B**
Dumfries, St. Andrew's: Marmaduke Maxwell of Terregles, 1843; Towers of old Cathedral: John H. Bell & Alexander Fraser, 1858. **B**
Galston, St. Sophia: 1886. **B**
Gretna, St. Ninian: C.E. Simmons, C.M. Crickner, 1917. **B**
Lockerbie, Holy Trinity: c.1874-5. **B**
Maybole, Our Lady and St. Cuthbert: 1876-8 **B**
New Abbey, St. Mary (Church & Presbytery): Walter Newall, c.1824. **B**
Newton Stewart, Our Lady and St. Ninian (Church, Presbytery, churchyard, includes Boundary walls, gatepiers and railings): Messrs. Goldie & Childe (London), 1876; Charles Gray, 1973. **B**
Troon, Our Lady and St. Meddan: Church, includes passage and Boundary wall. **A**;
  Presbytery, Reginald Fairlie, 1914. **B**
Wigtown, Sacred Heart: **C(S)**

ARCHDIOCESE OF GLASGOW

(a) Archdioocesan Property.
i. Glasgow:

St. Andrew's Cathedral: James Gillespie-Graham, 1816; Pugin & Pugin, 1892. **A**

St. Agnes: Peter Paul Pugin, 1894. **B**

St. Albert: John B. Wilson, 1887. **B**

St. Aloysius, Garnethill: Charles Menart, 1910. **A**

St. Aloysius, Springburn, Church and Presbytery: J.L. Bruce, 1883. **B**

St. Alphonsus, Church and Presbytery: Peter Paul Pugin, 1905. **B**

St. Anne: Gillespie, Kidd & Coia, 1933. **A**

St. Anthony: Church, John Honeyman, 1877-9. **B**
Presbytery, Peter Paul Pugin, 1892. **C**

St. Augustine, Milton: Church and Presbytery, R. Fairlie & Partners, 1956. **B**

St. Charles: Gillespie, Kidd & Coia, 1959-60. **B**

St. Columba: Church and Presbytery, retaining wall and gates, G.A. Coia, 1948-41. **A**

Corpus Christi, Scotstounhill: Peter Whiston, 1969-72. **C(S)**

St. Helen, Langside: Church and Hall, John Bennie Wilson. **C(S)**

Holy Cross: Church & Presbytery, Pugin & Pugin. **B**

Immaculate Heart of Mary: Thomas Cordiner, 1951. **B**

St. Joachim: Church and Presbytery, Gillespie, Kidd & Coia, 1957. **C(S)**

St. Laurence, Drumchapel: Church and Presbytery, boundary wall, gates, gate-piers and railings, Reginald Fairlie & Partners, 1954-7. **B**

St. Margaret Mary: Church and presbytery, Thomas Cordiner, 1959. **B**

St. Martin: Church and Presbytery, Gillespie, Kidd & Coia, 1961. **B**

St. Mary, Abercromby Street: Goldie & Childe, 1841, 1877. **A**

St. Mary Immaculate: Church and Presbytery, W. Nicholson (Manchester), 1865; War Memorial. **B**

St. Mungo: Church, George Goldie, 1869. **B**

St. Ninian, Knightswood: Church and Church Hall, Boundary walls, gates and gate piers, C.H. Purcell, 1956-9. **B**

Our Lady of Good Counsel: Church. **A**

Presbytery (including gate-piers). **B**

St. Patrick: Peter Paul Pugin, 1898. **B**

St. Paul, Shettleston: Church, Gillespie, Kidd & Coia, 1959. **B**

St. Peter: Church & Presbytery, Peter Paul Pugin, 1903. **B**

St. Pius X, Drumchapel: Church and Presbytery, Boundary walls, gates and railings, Alexander McAnally, 1954-7. **B**

Sacred Heart: Church, Charles Menart, 1910; Presbytery. **A**

St. Thomas: Thomas Cordiner. **B**

St. Kentigern's Hostel (original house)(formerly St. Peter's College): c.1874. **B**

Turnbull Hall: 1955. **B**

The Oaks, 40 Newlands Road (House, garden walls and gatepiers). **B**

118-126 Howard Street: **B**

12 Renfield Street: **B**

ii. **Outside Glasgow.**
Bishopbriggs, St. Matthew: Church, Gillespie, Kidd & Coia, 1950. **C(S)**
Clydebank, St. Margaret: Church and Presbytery, Gillespie, Kidd & Coia, 1972. **B**
Clydebank, Our Holy Redeemer: including Presbytery, boundary walls and gate-piers, Peter Paul Pugin, 1903. **B**
Cardross, St. Mahew (Kirkton Chapel & Graveyard): Anon, 6th Century; 1467; Ian G. Lindsay and Partners, 1955. **A**
Cardross, St. Peter's College: I. Metztein, J. Cowell, A. Macmillan, J. Coia, of Gillespie Kidd & Coia, 1966. **A**
Burnett of Glasgow, c.1870. **B (A group with College)**
Kilmahew Castle (remains of). **B**
Cumbernauld, Sacred Heart: Church and Presbytery, Gillespie, Kidd & Coia, 1964. **A**
Dumbarton, St. Michael: Gillespie, Kidd & Coia, 1965. **B**
Dumbarton, St. Patrick: Dunn & Hanson, 1903 (Belfry, 1927). **B**
Helensburgh, St. Joseph: Church, gate-piers and Gates, C.J. Menart. **B**
Helensburgh, Red Tower: William Leiper, 1898. **A**
Kirkintilloch, Holy Family and St. Ninian: Pugin & Pugin, 1893. **B**

(b) Property of Religious Institutes.
Glasgow, Carmelite Monastery, Langside. Adapted By Bruce & Hay, 1918; Wylie & Shanks, 1987. **B**
Glasgow, St. Aloysius College: Archibald Macpherson,1883,1892. **B**
Mount Building: James Sellars. **C**
Glasgow, St. Benet's, Nithsdale Road: c.1880. **C(S)**
Glasgow, St. Mungo's: Retreat, Osmund Cooke, 1890-2. **B**
Glasgow, Nazareth House, Cardonald: **C(S)**
Dumbarton, Carmelite Monastery: 'Garmoyle', Burnet, Son & Campbell, 1890. **B**
Dumbarton, Notre Dame Convent Chapel, Craigend: Reginald Fairlie, 1935. **B**

(c) Private Property with Church Connection.
Glasgow, Glengowan House, 196 Nithsdale Road: 1880-90. **C(S)**
Glasgow, 231 Nithsdale Road: W.F. McGibbon(?), 1880-90. **B**
Glasgow, 19 Park Circus (S.C.I.A.F.): Charles Wilson, 185S-6, Built, 1861-3. **A**

(d) Scheduled Ancient Monuments.
Cardross: Kilmahew Castle (remains of)
Kirkintilloch: Antonine Wall (behind St. Flannan's)

DIOCESE OF MOTHERWELL

Diocesan Property.
Airdrie, St. Margaret: 1839. **B**
Baillieston, St. Bridget: Pugin & Pugin. **B**
Coatbridge, Holy Trinity and All Saints: Bruce & Hay, 1904. **C(S)**
Coatbridge, St. Patrick: Church, halls, piers, gates, fencing, Peter Paul
    Pugin, Cuthbert Welby Pugin, 1896. **B**
Easterhouse, St. Benedict: Gillespie, Kidd & Coia. **A**
East Kilbride, St. Bride: Church and presbytery, Gillespie, Kidd & Coia.
    A
Hamilton, St. Mary: church and former presbytery, 1846. **B**
    presbytery and hall. **C**
Lanark, St. Mary: Church, George Goldie & Matthew Hadfield, 1859;
    Ashlin & Coleman, 1910. **B**
    Hall, Goldie & Hadfield, 1859, 1889. **B**
    Presbytery, Goldie & Madfield, 1859.
    Gates. **C(S)**
Larkhall, St. Mary: 1905. **C(S)**

DIOCESE OF PAISLEY

(a) Diocesan Property.
Paisley, St. Mary: Peter Paul Pugin, 1894, 1905. **B**
Eaglesham, St. Bridget: 1850. **C(S)**
Greenock, St. Laurence (church and presbytery): Gillespie, Kidd &
    Coia. **A**
Greenock, St. Mary: George Goldie, 1862. **B**
Greenock, St. Patrick (church and presbytery): Gillespie, Kidd & Coia,
    1959. **A**
Houston, St. Fillan (Church, Presbytery & former School): Church,
    1840; Presbytery, c.1840, 1872, 1901. **B**
Port Glasgow, Holy Family (church and presbytery): Gillespie, Kidd &
    Coia, 1959. **A**
Wemyss Bay St. Joseph & St. Patrick: Peter Paul Pugin, 1901. **C(S).**

(b) Property of other Church Organisations.
Bishopton, Old Bishopton House (in former Convent): early 17th
    Century(?), 1916-20. **B**
Gate Lodge to former Convent: Wm. Leiper, 1890; Cook & Hamilton, c.
    1916-20. **C(S)**

ARCHIVES AND RECORDS MANAGEMENT

The following Information Sheet has been issued by the Scottish Catholic Heritage Commission as a summary of what is required in the maintenance of ecclesiastical records:

Canon Law requires the keeping of parochial registers, of baptisms and marriages, confirmations, and any other registers prescribed by the Episcopal Conference and the Diocesan Bishop.

The registers, and any associated documentation, such as pre-nuptial enquiries, must be carefully preserved.

Each parish should have an archive, which may be a room and/or lockable cabinets and cupboards, where parochial registers, printed books, and other documents and items may safely be stored.

Try to avoid basements and attics, which may be particularly prone eg., to damp; and ensure the archive store is secure.

As well as the registers, a parochial archive should usefully contain episcopal letters, parish notice/announcement books, correspondence (particularly outgoing correspondence) etc. Bills, receipts, bank statements, cheque counterfoils, should also be kept safely. Computer discs, particularly if parochial registers are being kept on disc, should also be kept securely within the archive. Other disc-based information must also be stored securely.

Organisations operating within parishes,eg., the UCM, St.Vincent de Paul, etc., should be encouraged to preserve their records. The archivist will be happy to meet with the various societies at either parochial or diocesan level, to advise on the safekeeping and maintenance of their records.

Some documents, though not necessarily all, will be of historical significance. Before disposing of any item or document please seek the advice of your diocesan archivist who will be able to offer advice on appropriate arrangements.

If a list does not already exist, draw up a list of the material contained in the parish archive, and keep this handy within the archive room itself.

Access to parochial documents and items is at the discretion of the parish priest. Before admitting anyone to the parish archive, you have the right to ask them to produce identification eg., in the form of a reference from their parish priest, or from their university or college supervisor. Bear in mind also, that there are already specific restrictions on the type of information which can be provided from computer databases, and that within the next five to ten years, these provisions will be broadened to increasingly include manual records.

If any records are to be used over a period of time, you may wish to come to an arrangement with your diocesan archivist (where there is one, otherwise your diocesan chancellor) that the records be deposited within the diocesan archive and consulted there rather than in the presbytery.

APPENDIX
CHRONICLE OF EVENTS
1998-1999
Contributed by
The Catholic Press and Media Office

Monday 1 June 1998
LIMEX Graduations, Gillis Centre, Edinburgh

For some 10 years priests, religious and people, have benefited from the LIMEX course of studies at Gillis Centre, enabling them to graduate with diploma or degree from the Loyola Institute for Ministry Extension Course.

Another group has finished the LIMEX course this year and on Monday 1 June 1998 eight students graduated - one with a Masters Degree in Religious Education; two with a Masters Degree in Pastoral Studies; one with a Certificate in Religious Education; and four with a Certificate in Pastoral Studies.

The programme continues to grow within our Archdiocese and indeed has now been embraced by the Archdiocese of Glasgow as part of its formation programme for Lay Ministry.

The present LIMEX course now has been further developed by Loyola to meet some of the current needs within the Church and so LIMEX II has introduced several tracts allowing students to study, for instance, parish administration, small group dynamics, ministry in the workplace, spirituality of the laity etc.

At present, many of those who have graduated through LIMEX are holding positions at both diocesan and parish level.

Wednesday 3rd of June 1998
New Member of Cathedral Chapter

Bishop Logan formally installed the Very Reverend John Canon O'Farrell, parish priest of The Immaculate Conception (St. Mary's), Lochee as a member of the Cathedral Chapter on Wednesday 3rd of June .

M.J.M.

4th June 1998
Motherwell Diocesan Golden Jubilee - Schools Mass

All eighty of the Primary Schools and thirteen Secondary Schools were represented at a Mass in the Motherwell Cathedral, to celebrate the Golden Jubilee of the Diocese. It also recognised the very valuable contribution made by the Catholic Schools over fifty years in the Diocese.

Bishop Joseph Devine concelebrated Mass with his Vicars General and the Chaplains to the Secondary Schools.

F.C.

Friday 5th June 1998
Dedication of Fox Covert Primary School, Edinburgh

Along with the local clergy, whose parishioners attend Fox Covert Primary School, namely Fathers Tom McNulty, Stephen Judge and Charles Barclay, Archbishop O'Brien dedicated Fox Covert Primary School.

Although opened for some years, Fox Covert which is on a shared site with a nondenominational school, had never had a 'dedication' to a particular saint. The Headteacher, Miss Barbara Service, conducted a survey among pupils, teachers and parents and the most popular dedication was to St Bernadette. At the end of the Mass, the Archbishop presented all of the pupils with souvenir medals of the occasion.

Saturday 6th June 1998
125th Anniversary of St Mary's Church, Pathhead

The small church of St Mary's, Pathhead, celebrated its 125th anniversary with a concelebrated Mass and reception.

Archbishop O'Brien led the celebrations in Pathhead, with the parish priest, Father Ben Robinson and retired parish priest, Canon Michael McCullagh, now living in St Anne's, Musselburgh.

The church in Pathhead had been erected and opened on 2 June 1872 - at the expense of the Marchioness-Dowager of Lothian. The then parish priest, Father Sharp of Dalkeith, was assisted by Father Fanning of St Joseph's, Glasgow and Father Lomax of the Sacred Heart Church, Edinburgh.

Despite the small numbers at present in the parish, the congregation are more than happy to have a resident parish priest at this present time in the person of Father Ben Robinson.

Sunday 7th June 1998
125th Anniversary of Opening of St Mary's Church, Pathhead

Along with Canon Michael McCullagh, former parish priest and Father Ben Robinson, present parish priest, Archbishop O'Brien led the celebrations marking the 125th anniversary of St Mary's Church, Pathhead on Trinity Sunday.

In his homily, the Archbishop initially quoted from the Catholic Directory for Scotland for 1873, reminding the parishioners that: "A new chapel - erected at the expense of the Marchioness Dowager of Lothian - was opened on 2 June 1872". With regard to parishioners, there is a description of a large Catholic population in the area extending over a wide track of country bounded on the East by Haddingtonshire, on the West by Peeblesshire and on the South by Roxburghshire. Even before the building of the Catholic Church dedicated to St Mary, Mass had occasionally been celebrated by Father Mantica SJ, who was based in Portobello.

While thanking previous parish priests, the Archbishop singled out the much-loved and revered Canon Michael Cassidy, who conducted an outstanding apostolate, not only for the parishioners of Pathhead, but for the much wider travelling community, mainly again Irish immigrants who served on the farms in the area.

Tuesday 9th June 1998
Gourock Memorial

On the feast of St Columba Bishop John Mone dedicated a Celtic Cross in St Columba's High School Gourock, in memory of the head teacher Gerry McKenna who died suddenly

B.J.C.

Friday 12'h June 1998
Indian Bishop visits Galloway

Bishop Denzil D'Souza arrived in Scotland today to spend a few weeks in the diocese of Galloway. He is bishop of Aizawl, a tribal area in the extreme north east of India. During his time in Scotland, Bishop D'Souza was able to visit a number of parishes in the Galloway diocese, to meet priests and people and to participate in several liturgies and meetings. He was also able to describe conditions in his diocese in India where the people are what is known as Tribals, the non-Christians being neither Hindu nor Moslem. His diocese is very widespread, communications are extremely difficult but the bishop painted a picture of a local Church that is confident and alive.

+M.T.

14th June 1998
Motherwell Diocesan Assembly

As part of the Diocese's Golden Jubilee celebrations a Diocesan Assembly was held in St Aidan's High School, Wishaw. Over four hundred delegates from parishes and societies spent the day discussing the question of the lapsed.

Monsignor John Burns, Vicar General, gave the keynote address and thereafter the assembly met in groups to deliberate on what could be done to make contact with the lapsed and to make them feel welcome back into the Church.

Mrs Anne Marie Fagan presided at the Assembly which also heard the testimony of some lapsed Catholics who had returned to the Church.

F.C.

Sunday 14th June 1998
Pastoral Ministry Course, Galloway Diocese

In beautiful weather those members of Galloway diocese who had participated in the two-year course in Pastoral Ministry (St. Margaret's Institute) came together in Candida Casa, the bishop's house, to receive certificates. About twenty people from various parishes had successfully completed the course and were present for the event, held in the bishop's chapel and garden.

+M.T.

Sunday 14th June 1998
Lourdes Banners on Display

A special exhibition marking 50 years of the Glasgow Lourdes Hospitalité opened today in the St Mungo Museum of Religion. It chronicled the growth of the association from its early beginning in post-war Europe to the present day. The highlight was a colourful collection of banners which have been used down the years to lead Scots pilgrims in the daily Blessed Sacrament processions at the Shrine to Our Lady in Lourdes. It included the original 1948 banner with the image of St Mungo in the centre. The Hospitalité was set up to help promote pilgrimages to Lourdes, and to aid the sick and disabled on their visit to the shrine.

Wednesday 17th June 1998
Scots Lobby Parliament on Euthanasia

Fears at the threat of new legislation allowing euthanasia to be practised in Britain were highlighted when Cardinal Thomas Winning and Bishop Mario Conti led a lobby of 500 Scots to the Palace of Westminster. In a meeting with the Lord Chancellor, Lord Irvine of Lairg, in his offices at the House of Lords, they expressed their concern over measures contained in the green paper 'Who Decides?' on the issue of people with mental incapacity. They warned against introducing legally binding advance directives (living wills), sanctioning the withdrawal of food and drink from unconscious patients, and allowing medical experimentation on nonconsenting adults. After the meeting, Cardinal Winning said: "The Lord Chancellor assured us that the Government was involved in a genuine consultation - that they had no shadow legislation ready to implement. He said they would work through the 4000 plus responses they have had to the green paper before arriving at any firm view. I believe that the vast majority of the responses echoed our concerns, and so I would hope that Government will heed the warnings." At a meeting in the Palace of Westminster's Jubilee Room, the Cardinal also met with a cross-party group of Scottish MPs where he again voiced his concerns at the threat of allowing euthanasia through the back door. "The Government say they are opposed to euthanasia. But they seem to be opposed to euthanasia in the way a householder is opposed to burglary - a householder who carefully locks his front door every night, but leaves the back entrance wide open," he said. Around 500 people from all over Scotland joined the lobby which arrived in London aboard a special train chartered by the Society for the Protection of the Unborn Child.

Wednesday 17th June 1998
Tyburn Centenary Celebrated in Largs

The only contemplative community in the Diocese of Galloway is the Tyburn Benedictine Adorers of the Sacred Heart of Jesus, Montmartre, known as the Tyburn Nuns. They have houses in Australia, New Zealand, Ireland and Peru as well as in Scotland. Their Mother House is at Tyburn in London. This order of Benedictine Nuns are celebrating the centenary of their establishment in England and a triduum of Masses was celebrated in Largs, beginning today. Bishop Taylor was the principal celebrant at a Mass that brought together the Largs community, the Mother General and others from London and many friends from all over Scotland.

+M.T.

Friday 19th June 1998
Golden Jubilee of Sister Raphael de St Madeleine

Sister Raphael, whose family name is Lemetti, a Little Sister of the Poor, celebrated her Golden Jubilee at St Joseph's, Gilmore Place, Edinburgh. Born in Camelon in 1925, Sister made her final vows at the Mother House in Brittany on 15 October 1952 and the rest of her religious life was spent in France, mostly in the home at La Tronche near Grenoble, moving to Valence, North of Marseille in 1996 - a total of 45 years. Archbishop O'Brien congratulated her, reminding the congregation that while we do often hear of the outstanding work of missionaries, we so rarely think of religious sisters like Sister Raphael, spending most of her life in a country so near to us.

Friday 19th June 1998
Golden Jubilee of Sister Raphael de Ste Madeleine LSP

Sister Raphael de Ste Madeleine joined with her religious community and her own family in thanking God for the Golden Jubilee of her profession, with Mass at St Joseph's, Gilmore Place, Edinburgh on Friday 19 June 1998, concelebrated with Archbishop O'Brien, Canon Hugh Gordon, Chaplain and other priest friends.

Born in Camelon in 1925, Sister received the habit of the Little Sisters of the Poor in Sheffield on 28 May 1946, shortly afterwards going to the novitiate in Dublin where she was professed on 28 June 1948. It was in France that Sister made her final vows in the Mother House in Brittany on 15 October 1952, with the rest of her religious life being spent in France, mostly in the home at La Tronche near Grenoble, moving to Valence, north of Marseille in 1996, a total of approximately 45 years of apostolate with the poor.

Friday 19th June 1998
Honorary Degree for Dr John Durkan

The University of Glasgow awarded an honorary degree - Doctor of Divinity - to Dr John Durkan, the distinguished Catholic historian who is acknowledged as a leading authority on the Renaissance and Reformation in sixteenth century Scotland. A research fellow with Glasgow University's department of Scottish History, he achieved a Master of Arts degree in History from the University's faculty of Arts in 1938. He also holds a PhD from Edinburgh University and was awarded an Honorary Doctorate in Literature from Edinburgh in 1982. Before embarking full-time on historical research, he taught history in a number of Glasgow schools from 1939 to 1976. He is a founder member of the Scottish Catholic Historical Association and a frequent contributor to The Innes Review. His 80th birthday in 1994 was commemorated with a Festschrift volume of essays covering his interests in bibliography, learning, literature, music, philosophy and religious history.

Monday 22 June 1998
Thanksgiving Mass with St Thomas of Aquin's High School, Edinburgh

The Cathedral in Edinburgh hosted a Thanksgiving Mass on the closure of St Thomas of Aquin's High School on its present site. In his homily, the Archbishop gave an indication of the fascinating history of the development of the use of buildings on the present site in Chalmers Street. This was paralleled with the development of education in the City of Edinburgh at St Thomas of Aquin's; and at a more deep level, was paralleled with the development of the meaning of what constitutes a Catholic School.

Initially, the head teachers and staff of the school were Sisters of Mercy, highly trained, educated and dedicated women, who saw a need for education and set about fulfiling that need. Sister Mary Agnes Snow was the founding sister in 1886 and she was followed by a succession of outstanding women until Sister Mary St Jerome was appointed head of the school. On the retiral of Sister Mary St Jerome in 1961, a lay teacher, Miss Patricia Bird, was appointed as the head teacher of the school.

The central aim of St Thomas of Aquin's is still that of the Sisters of Mercy, who were its founders. This is to provide a Christian and caring environment in which young people can grow into Christian and caring adults, shaping the society in which they live and playing a crucial role in the formation of future generations.

Monday 22 June 1998
Thanksgiving Mass with St Thomas of Aquin's High School, Edinburgh

With the present buildings of St Thomas of Aquin's High School being inadequate, the City of Edinburgh Council had decided to move the school to two temporary sites at Darroch and North Merchiston, both nearby in Edinburgh until a new school can be completed.

At a Thanksgiving Mass in Sacred Heart Church, Lauriston, Edinburgh on Monday 22 June 1998, Archbishop O'Brien outlined something of the development of the buildings of the present St Thomas of Aquin's, with the Sisters of Mercy at nearby St Catherine's Convent initially providing both the buildings and the teaching staff.

He further outlined something of the development of education in the City of Edinburgh - with St Thomas of Aquin's initially being founded to educate and train girls and young women for a career in teaching. St Thomas's is at present a fully comprehensive and co-educational school, with its own catchment area.

After the summer holidays, the Archbishop visited the two new campuses of St Thomas's at Darroch and North Merchiston and led services of dedication, along with the present school chaplain, Father Alex Davie of St Mary's Cathedral, Edinburgh, Head Teacher, staff and pupils.

Wednesday 24 June 1998
Celebrations in Fauldhouse - School and Parish

The Feast of St John the Baptist saw celebrations taking place in St John the Baptist Primary School and in St John the Baptist Church, Fauldhouse.

The Primary School was celebrating the 30th anniversary of its establishment in its present buildings on a new site. Mass was celebrated with Archbishop Keith Patrick O'Brien congratulating all present, especially the head teacher and staff, who had set such high standards for their pupils.

In the evening, Canon Michael McCullagh preached at the 125th anniversary celebrations in St John the Baptist church, tracing the history of the parish and church.

The first priest to say Mass in Fauldhouse was Father John Black of the Western District. He was born in 1824 and ordained in Rome in 1848; in that year he came to live in Lanark and his parish stretched from Biggar to Fauldhouse. It was in 1865 that Fauldhouse became an independent parish and welcomed its first resident priest, Father William Farrell. The present church was opened on 24 June 1873, the Feast of St John the Baptist, with Solemn Pontifical High Mass being celebrated by Archbishop Strain and the choir coming from St Mary's Cathedral, Edinburgh, singing a Mass by Weber.

Wednesday 24 June 1998
125th Anniversary of St John the Baptist Church, Fauldhouse

A large congregation gathered at St John the Baptist Church, Fauldhouse, to celebrate the 125th anniversary of the opening of the church.

Joining with Archbishop O'Brien were Canon Charles Brodie, the present parish priest, Canon Michael McCullagh, a son of the parish, who was the special preacher, and priests of the Deanery, as well as other priests from the parish, including Father Charles Barclay, Father John Creanor and Father Tom Flynn.

Canon Michael McCullagh outlined something of the history of the church and the great influence which the parish had had on himself and so many others.

Earlier in the day, Archbishop O'Brien had joined in celebrations in St John the Baptist Primary School, Fauldhouse following on the 30th anniversary of the opening of the school on its present site, being welcomed by the new Head Teacher, Mrs Margaret McShane.

27th June - 6th July. 1998
Dunkeld Youth Head for Taizé

This summer a number of members of the Dunkeld Youth Service linked with young people from the Diocese of Aberdeen for a trip to Taizé between 27th June - 6th July. Taizé is a small village in France, half-way between Paris and Lyon. Fifty years ago a man called Brother Roger wanted to find a place for himself to live out his Christian faith. At his house in Taizé in the 1940s he began to welcome Jewish refugees in a spirit of openness and reconciliation. Gradually more and more people heard about Taizé and were attracted to the simple community way of life being lived there. Today, it is not uncommon for 6000 people, of different denominations and degrees of church going, to be at Taizé sharing this simple community lifestyle of prayer, faith sharing and friendship.

M.J.M.

Sunday 28 June 1998
Blessing of Stained Glass Window, Tobermory

On a weekend visit to Oban, Archbishop O'Brien, Apostolic Administrator, travelled to the Island of Mull on Sunday and Monday, 28 and 29 June 1998.

Celebrating the midday Mass in Our Lady, Star of the Sea, Tobermory, Archbishop O'Brien dedicated a recently-presented stained glass window in the beautifully decorated church in the midst of a crowded congregation. Afterwards, a reception followed in a local hotel.

Monday 29th. June 1998
Silver Jubilee of Fr. Aldo Angelosanto

A large number of priests from throughout the diocese as well as a packed congregation joined Fr. Aldo Angelosanto and members of his family in a Mass of Thanksgiving to celebrate the Silver Jubilee of his Ordination to the Priesthood in the Church of St. Pius X on

Fr. Aldo was ordained by Bishop William Andrew Hart in St. Andrew's Cathedral on 3rd. July 1973 having completed his ecclesiastical studies at St. Mary's College, Blairs, and the Scots College, Rome. His first appointment was as assistant priest in St. Mary's Lochee where he remained until 1977 when he was appointed assistant priest in St. John's Perth. In 1981 he was appointed parish priest of St. Fillan's, Newport on Tay. Then in 1988 he returned to the City of Dundee where he was appointed parish priest of St. Columba's. After two years at St. Columba's he was appointed to St. Pius X his present charge. Since his ordination Fr. Aldo has also held a number of diocesan appointments: in 1975 he was appointed chaplain to the deaf. From 1980 - 1985 he was the diocesan representative on Radio Tay and editor of the diocesan newspaper, The Dunkeld News, from 1986 - 1990. In 1991 he was appointed Diocesan Spiritual Director of the Union of Catholic Mothers within the diocese.

M.J.M.

Monday 29th. June 1998
Golden Jubilee of the Augustians in the Diocese of Dunkeld.

Bishop Logan was the principal concelebrant at a Mass of Thanksgiving to mark the Golden Jubilee of the presence of the Augustinians in the Diocese of Dunkeld in SS Peter & Paul on Monday 29th. June .

The Augustinians came to the Diocese of Dunkeld in 1948 at the invitation of Bishop Scanlan, then Bishop of the Diocese, who had written to the Augustinian Provincial in 1946 inviting them to the Diocese.

The first community was led by Fr. Tom Daly, the first Augustinian Prior in Scotland since the Reformation. The breaking of historical records was continued with the ordination of the present Prior, Fr. Ian Wilson O.S.A, who became the first Augustinian to be ordained in Scotland since the Reformation.

In its fifty years under the leadership of the Augustinians the parish has produced four members of the order, Fr. Ian Wilson, ordained in 1984; Fr. George Stibbles, who was one of the first postulants to go to Clare Priory in Suffolk after its re-establishment, and was ordained in Rome in the year 1956; Brother Peter Quinn, who was professed in 1965,but sadly died in 1991; and Fr. Derek McGuire who was the first parishioner to be ordained an Augustinian.

M.T.M.

Monday 29th June 1998
Priestly Golden and Diamond Jubilees

The Feast of St John the Baptist saw the 60th anniversary celebration of the ordination of Canon John McNay, retired parish priest of Holy Name Parish, Oakley in Oakley. A crowded congregation listened to Canon Boyle, another retired parish priest, speaking of the priesthood and outlining something of the priestly history and service of Canon McNay.

In the evening, in the church of St Anthony's, Polmont, Canon William Anthony's celebrations took place with Archbishop O'Brien, who had known Canon Anthony when he was an assistant priest in St Columba's, Edinburgh, speaking of the priesthood of Canon Willie, who had been a convert to the faith and initially prepared for the priesthood at Campion House, Osterley.

Monday 29th June 1998
Jubilees of Canons

On the Feast of Ss Peter and Paul, Monday 29 June 1998, two senior priests of the Archdiocese of St Andrews and Edinburgh celebrated jubilees of ordination - Canon William Anthony celebrating the Golden Jubilee of his Ordination to the priesthood in St Anthony's Church, Polmont and Canon John McNay celebrating the Diamond Jubilee of his Ordination to the priesthood in Holy Name Parish, Oakley.

Archbishop O'Brien paid tribute to the years of dedicated service of these two priests, now living in retirement, with Canon Daniel Boyle, a close friend of Canon John McNay and from the same hometown and parish in Sacred Heart, Grangemouth, preaching the homily at the Jubilee Mass of Canon McNay.

Sunday 5th July 1998
Pastoral Visit to St Kieran's, Campbeltown

Archbishop O'Brien conducted a pastoral visit to St Kieran's, Campbeltown, celebrating Masses in St Kieran's on Saturday 4 and Sunday 5 July 1998. On a previous visit, along with parish priest, Father Roddy MacAuley, the Archbishop had joined the first public service ferry from Campbeltown to Ballycastle, his hometown, in the North of Ireland.

On this visit, the Archbishop stayed overnight on the Island of Islay, celebrating Mass there at 4.00 pm and meeting the people of the island afterwards.

Sunday 5th July 1998
Cardinal Winning at Kilwinning

Fifty years ago the Archdiocese of Glasgow was divided and the parishes of the northern part of Ayrshire were transferred to the Diocese of Galloway. To commemorate this enlargement of the diocese Cardinal Winning was invited to be principal celebrant of a Mass in St. Winin's, Kilwinning. In his words of welcome the parish priest, Fr. Matthew McManus, addressed the Cardinal: "This town rejoices in the name of the church of Winning so we hope you have a sense of belonging here among us. ...Over the years more and more Glasgow people have come to our area. The life of the Church as well as the wider community has been enriched by them" .

+M.T.

Sunday, 5th July,1998
National Health Service Anniversary

A service in St Giles Cathedral, Edinburgh, marking the 50th anniversary of the National Health Service was attended by Bishop John Mone of Paisley.

B.J.C.

Monday 6th Monday 13th July 1998
Galloway Lourdes Pilgrimage

Galloway has a diocesan pilgrimage to Lourdes every second year. This year's pilgrimage was very successful, a departure from custom being the fact that the sick and disabled resided not in one of the hospitals but in the Sue Ryder Home. As usual the Galloway youth provided invaluable help and gave an outstanding witness of their faith and their willing commitment to the needs of the sick. This year's pilgrimage coincided with the finals of the World Cup and we were treated to the added attraction of thousands of excited French people celebrating their country's victory.

+ M.T.

Monday 13th July 1998
Sister Loyola chosen as Superior General

The Franciscan Sister of the Immaculate Conception - the only religious congregation to have been founded in Glasgow - have elected Sister Mary Loyola Kelly as their new Superior General, in succession to Sister Mary Martina Morgan. The community which was founded in 1847 has houses in Glasgow, as well as the dioceses of St Andrews & Edinburgh, Paisley and Motherwell, and missions in Kenya, Nigeria and the United States At their six-yearly General Chapter, held in the Carmelite Retreat House, Pollokshields, the Sisters also elected a new Council, forming a leadership team with Sister Loyola at the helm. The new Council is made up of Assistant General Sister Bernard McAtamney, and Sisters Dolores Cochrane, Anthony Coyle and Gemma McMahon, all natives of the west of Scotland.

24th July 1998
Motherwell Golden Jubilee Pilgrimage to Lourdes

To mark the Golden Jubilee year for the Motherwell Diocese the bi-annual pilgrimage to Lourdes took on a greater significance with about four hundred pilgrims participating.

Led by Bishop Joseph Devine and priests of the Diocese, a big contingent of pilgrims went to the Shrine of Our Lady. Many parishes, in addition to sending sick pilgrims, also sponsored young people to participate, This swelled the normal numbers of youth from the Association of to Lourdes Motherwell Aid (ALMA).

Parish groups joined up with the main pilgrimage to celebrate the Diocese's Golden Jubilee.

F.C.

3rd-7th August 1998
Dunkeld Youth Service - Discovery Week

Dunkeld Youth Service organised a week of events at Birchwood House, Birnam, from 3rd to the 7th of August to provide an opportunity for other young people (16 years+) to learn about the work of the Youth Service and become involved in the future. To help foster these two main objectives, a number of activities were planned including prayer, outdoor Mass, new skills workshops e.g. dancing, graffiti art, drama, creative writing, talent show, calligraphy, and art amongst many others.

M.J.M.

Friday 7th August 1998
Pastoral Visit to Morar, Mallaig and Canna

Father Michael Hutson invited local clergy to Morar and Mallaig for a weekend celebration marking the pastoral visit of Archbishop O'Brien, Apostolic Administrator.

Clergy gathered in Our Lady of Perpetual Succour and St Cumin on Friday 7 August - and on Saturday 8 August, the Feast of St Dominic, Father Tom Kearns OP, Chaplain to the University of Edinburgh, preached on St Dominic and on the links of the Dominicans with that area of Scotland.

The Archbishop celebrated Mass in St Patrick's, Mallaig and then led a pilgrimage to Canna, with parishioners travelling from various other islands, not only for the celebration of Mass, but also to share in a fundraising sale for the restoration of the ancient church.

Saturday 15th August 1998
Aberdeen Priest Professed at Pluscarden

The first secular priest from Aberdeen to be professed as a monk in modern times, made his vows during a Solemn Mass celebrated by the Abbot Dom Hugh Gilbert, OSB, in the presence of the Bishop of the Diocese, Bishop Conti. Fr. James Birrell received in religion the name Martin, which was a dedication of one of the churches he served, at Ullapool, during his time as a secular priest of the diocese. The Bishop saw this as a further strengthening of the bond between the diocese and the Benedictine community at Pluscarden, at the heart of the diocese.

Saturday 22nd August 1998
Thanksgiving Mass for Servite Sisters at Leuchie House, North Berwick

In September 1996, the Servite Sisters thanked God for the Silver Jubilee of their service at Leuchie House since it was opened as a Servite Convent and the Richard Cave Multiple Sclerosis Home; two years later, they gathered for a 'Farewell and Thanksgiving' Mass with residents, staff and friends. At this Mass, Archbishop O'Brien gave a history of the links of the Multiple Sclerosis Society with Leuchie House, the home of the Hamilton Dalrymple family.

Sir Richard Cave, whose wife suffered from multiple sclerosis, founded the Multiple Sclerosis Society in England and Society was looking for a holiday home; Sir Hew and Lady Anne Louise Hamilton Dalrymple and their family, found that their own home was too large for their purposes; the Servite Sisters wished to expand their particular apostolate to help those in any sort of need. Leuchie House was the answer to prayer from the Sisters, the Dalrymple Family and the Multiple Sclerosis Society. Over the past 27 years since its foundation, perhaps 10,000 guests were received there for comfort and care, love and happiness, rest and recuperation - for all those incapacitated by multiple sclerosis and other disabilities.

Although the Servite Sisters have now left Leuchie House because of shortage of vocations, their apostolate would continue under the direction of the Multiple Sclerosis Society.

Friday 28th August 1998
Memorial Service for Victims of Omagh Bombing

At an ecumenical service to remember the victims of the bomb explosion which claimed 30 lives in the town of Omagh, County Tyrone, on 15 August, Cardinal Winning called on terrorists to turn away from violence and to submit information on the whereabouts of some 20 bodies lying in unmarked graves across Ireland. He said: "Many families in the last three decades have lost loved ones, but are unable to give them a proper burial because they lie hidden in unmarked graves, in unknown, lonely, unvisited places. Decency and compassion demand that those families are now afforded the consolation of knowing where their relatives lie so that they can give them a decent Christian burial. Representatives from the major churches - the Church of Scotland, the Episcopal Church, the Salvation Army, the Methodist and Congregational - took part in the service at St Andrew's Cathedral, Glasgow. As people entered, they signed a book of condolences for the people of Omagh, expressing their sorrow at the tragedy and their desire that peace would reign.

Sunday 30th August 1998
Whithorn Pilgrimage in honour of St. Ninian

The weather this year was brilliant. Plenty of sun, a warm day, a very gentle breeze and a great sense of wellbeing among the groups taking part, plus the path through the glen was dry and the walk over the stones seemed easier than usual. Bishop Taylor was principal celebrant at the Mass and Canon John Walls gave a very impressive homily. "We come to Whithorn to this cradle of Christianity, to celebrate our roots not just in the sense of remembering St. Ninian and asking him to pray for us, but in a more profound sense of recognising the common roots of faith we share; we are conscious in a more explicit way of our unity, that *communio* that the Spirit gives us: one Lord, one faith, one baptism.

+M.T.

Sunday 30th August 1998
40th Anniversary of the Erection of the Statue of Our Lady of the Isles, South Uist

Many priests and people from the Islands gathered with Archbishop O'Brien for the 40th anniversary celebrations of the erection of the statue of Our Lady of the Isles.

Preaching on the occasion, the Archbishop paid tribute to those who had been responsible for the erection of the statue in 1958, particularly the late Canon John Morrison. The statue was also a tribute to the skills of the sculpture Hew Lorimer, responsible for carving the statue and who wrote: "I believe that in the humblest way were are collaborators on earth in God's continuing act of creation and that this is the role of the artist in society".

The Archbishop went on to add that we should be making those words our own and applying them to ourselves when we state that we too in the humblest way are collaborators on earth in God's continuing act of creation. This is our role in society in the Church and in the world in which we live.

Monday 31st August - Friday 4th September
Galloway Clergy on Retreat

The annual retreat for Galloway priests took place this year at Minsteracres Pastoral Centre in Co. Durham. It was a very successful week in which the priests reflected on our ministry in today's world and Church. The week was led by Fr. Eugene Duffy from Ireland who introduced each session, after which we were free to discuss what had been said. In the afternoons we took advantage of the opportunity to visit places of note in the area, particularly the beautiful city of Durham with its magnificent Cathedral.

+M.T.

Friday 4th September 1998
Fifty Years of Care in Clydebank

The Religious Sisters of Charity celebrated 50 years of service to the people of Clydebank with a Mass of Thanksgiving in St Margaret's church, led by Cardinal Winning. Special guests included the Congregation's Superior General Sister Una O'Neill and the Provincial Sister Mary Benton. Founded in Dublin by Mary Aikenhead in 1815, the Sisters of Charity opened their first Scottish convent at Millbrae Crescent, Clydebank, on 8th September 1948. Two years later, they opened St Margaret's Hospice as the first care provision of its kind in Scotland for terminally ill people.

Tuesday 8th September 1998
Golden Jubilee of Pluscarden

On the feast of the birthday of Our Lady 1998 the Benedictine community at Pluscarden celebrated the Golden Jubilee of the resumption of monastic life, after some 400 years, in what remained of the 13th century monastic buildings.

These buildings, partly restored by the fourth Marquess of Bute, were given by his son Lord Colum Crichton Stuart to the Benedictines of Prinknash in Gloucestershire. The pioneering community which recommenced the monastic life in 1948 had to live in primitive conditions. Improvements over the years include most notably the restoration of the roofs of what remained of the abbey church, namely the transepts and chancel, the partial restoration of the cloister, and the building of the Hospice Wing.

Since that date also there has been an increase of vocations to the Benedictine community which now comprises 25 monks.

The Mass of thanksgiving was celebrated by the Abbot of Pluscarden, Dom Hugh Gilbert, assisted by the Bishop of the Diocese, the Right Reverend Mario Conti, and the Abbot President Dom Francis Rossiter. Other concelebrants included the former and first Abbot of the restored abbey, the Right Reverend Alfred Spencer, OSB.

At the end of the Mass the Bishop congratulated the community, giving them a banner representing the arms of the abbey which had been made by Patrick Barden, and which on this occasion was proudly flying from the monastic flagpole.

After the Mass a reception was held in a marquee erected in the Abbey grounds.

Tuesday 8th September
Centenary of St. Ann's, Mossblown

St. Ann's parish, founded in 1898, and serving Mossblown, Annbank and Tarbolton, has been in multi-celebratory activity this year, the highlights being two Masses. The parish Mass took place today, a local chronicler recording that "With the bishop was the present parish priest, Fr. John Murphy, past priests and priests from the diocese... with people coming from all over the world". The school centenary Mass on 16th November "was also a huge success; the children each received a mug with the school logo on it"

+M.T.

Wednesday 9th September 1998
Southern Comfort at Kirkcudbright

All the teachers of the Catholic primary schools in Dumfries & Galloway (the southern part of the diocese of Galloway) gathered in Kirkcudbright this evening for their annual Mass. Ayrshire (the northern part of the diocese) sent a few representatives to the Mass at which Bishop Taylor was the principal celebrant. After the Mass the company went to a local hotel and partook of an enjoyable meal.

+M.T.

Wednesday 9th September 1998
St Aloysius College Junior School Opened

The new St Aloysius College Junior School at Garnethill, Glasgow, was officially opened with a blessing from Cardinal Winning. Standing opposite the main College building on Hill Street, the £3million purpose-built school is dedicated to St John Ogilvie. A specially commissioned painting of the Jesuit martyr, by the College's head of Art, George Burns, was unveiled to mark the occasion. Designed by architects Elder and Cannon, the building has been nominated for a number of awards.

Thursday 10th September 1998
150th Aniversary of St. Palladius' parish, Dalry

The second oldest parish in Ayrshire, St. Palladius, was founded in 1848 by Fr. William Burke. The present church (which unfortunately was seriously damaged by the gales of 26th December 1998 but has since been repaired) was built in 1851. At the Mass today, which Bishop Taylor concelebrated with Canon Thomas McGread, the parish priest, we remembered with gratitude all the priests and laity who kept the flame of Catholic Christianity alive in the north of Ayrshire.

+M.T.

Friday 11th September 1998
Centenary of Our Lady and St Ninian's Parish, Bannockburn

On 11 September 1898, the first Catholic place of worship in the Bannockburn area since the Reformation was opened at Greenyards on the Cowie Road. In preceding years the number of Catholics in the area, south-east of Stirling, was greatly increasing due to the development of coalmining. As a result of the generosity of Mrs Murray of Polmaise, who also made generous donations to St Mary's, Stirling, a chapel school was opened. At first, Masses were celebrated by the clergy of St Mary's, but in 1900 the first resident parish priest was appointed, Father Francis McManus.

Archbishop O'Brien celebrated a special Centenary Mass, solemnly dedicating the church and new altar. Father Godfrey Tortolano OFM, a native of the parish, gave the homily with about 400 people participating in the solemn liturgy and enjoying a social together afterwards in the local community centre.

Friday 11th September 1998
Bene Merenti for Lochee Parishioner.

A double celebration took place on Friday 11th. September 1998 in the parish of St. Mary's Lochee. The first was a Mass of Thanksgiving to mark the election of parish priest Canon John O'Farrell as a member of the Cathedral Chapter. Canon O'Farrell was principal concelebrant of the Mass and was joined by Canon Connolly, Provost of the Cathedral Chapter and parish priest of St. Teresa's Dundee; Fr. Ian Mullen, parish priest of St. Clement's, Dundee; Fr. Michael Milton, parish priest of St. Ninian's; Fr Padraig Gallagher C.Ss.R, Rector of St. Mary's Kinnoull; Fr. Chaplain to the Little Sisters of the Poor at Wellburn, and Mgr. Joseph Creegan, parish priest of St. Joseph's Dundee, who also gave the homily. After the Mass everyone present was invited to the C.hurch hall for a Buffet Supper and Social, during which Canon O'Farrell was presented with a cheque by John Duffy. Canon O'Farrell was also presented with his Canon's robes by Barry Mulligan.

n his address following the presentation Canon O'Farrell introduced Bishop Logan who had joined the celebrations and invited him to present Mr. Con Dolan with the *Bene Merenti* in recognition of Mr. Dolan's lifelong service of the Church and community of St. Mary's Lochee.

M.J.M.

Saturday 12 September 1998
Aid to the Church in Need

On the commemoration of the feast of the Exaltation of the Cross, office bearers, representatives and parishioners gathered in St Mary's Cathedral, Edinburgh acknowledging with thanksgiving the work of the organisation 'Aid to the Church in Need'. The work of the organisation is described as 'meeting the needs of the Church today in Eastern Europe and throughout the world'. Archbishop O'Brien outlined something of the work of the Archdiocese of St Andrews and Edinburgh abroad, initially in Bauchi, Northern Nigeria and now in three parishes in El Salvador and in Chiapas in Mexico. He then spoke from his own knowledge of the needs of Eastern Europe, following on his participation in the Synod of Bishops on Europe in Rome called by Pope John Paul II in 1991, just two years after the so-called 'Velvet Revolution' of 1989.

At the conclusion of Mass, the congregation moved to the Cathedral Hall to view an exhibition and display of the work of the organisation.

National Conference on International Debt

A National Conference on International Debt attended by representatives from parishes throughout Scotland as well as members of the Scottish Hierarchy and representatives from the other Churches in Scotland was hailed as a major success by Bishop Vincent Logan who had spearheaded the organisation of the event in his role as President of the Jubilee 2000 National Committee. Bishop Logan stated that the Conference was organised in response to Pope John Paul's call for a substantial reduction in the debt burden of the poor throughout the world.

In a keynote address, Mgr Diarmuid Martin of the Vatican's Council for Justice and Peace spoke on the Church's efforts world-wide to respond to the Pope's call. Mgr Martin called on Scotland and the rest of the rich world to act against the appalling human suffering imposed by the debt crisis. Mgr Martin pointed out that debt relief was only part of a wider issue. He said: "The significance of the cancellation of debt can only be understood within the overall Jubilee vision of the restoration of equitable relations among people." He urged the Church to look beyond its regional boundaries in order to balance out the inequalities in the global economy.

He attacked the consumerist society of the developed world and stated that it was up to people in richer nations to turn away from the "superficial aspects of consumer life" in order to re-establish equity amongst people. "This," he said, "would free funds to resolve the debt situation in developing nations."

The Conference focused especially on the impact of the repayment of debt on women and children. Two women from Africa, Margaret Mwaniki from Kenya and Elizabeth Atiemo from Ghana, made the journey to Scotland to share their experiences. Mrs Atiemo, who is a

Pastoral Assistant in the Diocese of Koforidua, Ghana, told the conference how her country's own debt repayments were crippling women and children. She said that 80% of women and children in Ghana were illiterate and that 75% of all health care was provided by mission and religious organisations, as the government struggled to pay off debts, instead of attending to health and education. She concluded her presentation by pleading with delegates to do everything in their power to stop a system that is strangling her country to death.

Mr. Michael Richardson from HM. Treasury and the World Bank's British Chief, Mr Andrew Rogerson also made keynote speeches during the Conference. Mr Rogerson spoke of the successes, particularly in Uganda, of the Heavily Indebted Poor Countries (HIPC) debt initiative which was an attempt to reduce debt to a sustainable level. He informed delegates that writing off the debts was not as simple as it sounded. The ultimate goal must be poverty reduction thereby reducing the burden placed on the poor.

Delegates were given an outline of the events which resulted in the present day crisis going back to the early 1980s when Mexico announced that it could not pay its foreign debt and the shock waves that this announcement sent throughout the commercial world. This along with the Oil Crisis of the 1970s and the growing financial crises, which saw other countries in Latin America and Africa facing problems repaying their national debts, resulted in a threat to the international financial system. Faced with this threat the major creditors of the world agreed to reduce some debt of the most impoverished countries through the Heavily Indebted Poor Countries (HIPC) Initiative, which was endorsed by the IMF and the World Bank. This initiative provided exceptional assistance to eligible countries, following sound economic policies, to help them reduce their external debt burden. Such assistance aimed to help provide the incentive for investment and broaden domestic support for policy reforms.

Delegates were also informed that the forthcoming Great Jubilee of the Year 2000, combined with devastating poverty of the least developed countries, the widening gap between rich and poor world-wide, the relative failure of past efforts at debt reduction, and a new opportunity for debt relief, present a challenge which the Church believes the world community cannot ignore.

As the conference closed, Bishop Logan stated that "Delegates were left enlightened by Elizabeth Atiemo and Margaret Mwaniki's accounts and got a real feel for what it must be like to live in a country which has been blighted by debt. He added: "All the speakers were very informative and inspiring and the delegates left with a renewed vigour and commitment to eradicating the debt burden. "It was very encouraging to see so many people from all walks of life, both young and old, who clearly have had their imagination sparked by this issue".

Monday 14th September, 1998
Paisley Diocese's 50 Years

Bishop John Mone formally ended the celebrations marking the 50th year of Paisley diocese with a concelebrated Mass of Thanksgiving in St Mirin's Cathedral before a full congregation of the diocese's 36 parishes with virtually all the priests of the diocese including representatives of religious orders. The Papal Colours and St Andrew's Cross seemed to be flying proudly over the Cathedral as the clergy entered the Mother Church of Paisley. It was near the site where the first church in the West of Scotland was opened in 1808 after the Reformation.

Before Mass itself small plays were produced on the sanctuary by schools of the see. They showed the development of the Church in Paisley itself from St Mirin (7th century) to the creation of Paisley diocese by Pius Xll in 1947 and his Apostolic Constitution *Maxime Interest.*

Paisley Abbey and its aftermath were well portrayed, the martyrdom of the Scottish Martyr for the Papacy, St John Ogilvie who had such strong association with Renfrewshire, was well recalled. The series ended with a display by the present seminarians and a massive Paisley diocesan arms and its motto which reflects that of the diocese: For the good of souls (the opening words of Pius Xll in his Apostolic Constitution creating the see).

The pillars of the Cathedral had posters drawn by pupils of the schools covering the same historical development. There was an excellent floral display.

The music was most challenging and elevating as the Bishop and priests entered the Cathedral. Bishop Mone thanked God for the fifty years of grace given to Paisley as a new diocese, for the work of his predecessors Bishop James Black and Bishop Stephen McGill for the 20 years each gave covering the first forty years, the clergy of the fifty years in helping to form the diocese and for their loyalty, to the religious for their example and help in so many ways, the People of God for their on-going support and fidelity in making the diocese what it became, the children gave hope for they are the Catholic adults of tomorrow.

B.J.C.

Tuesday 29 September 1998
Clergy Meetings and Vocations Mass in Oban

A meeting of the Diocesan Fabric and Finance Committee took place in Cathedral Hall, Oban, on Tuesday 29 September 1998, following on meetings of the various Clergy Funds. In the evening priests, religious and people of the Diocese gathered with Archbishop O'Brien for the celebration of a Vocations Mass in St Columba's Cathedral, Oban.

On the following morning, 30 September 1998, Archbishop O'Brien celebrated Mass with the Carmelite Sisters in Oban; and a General Meeting of the Clergy took place in the afternoon.

Tuesday, 29th September, 1998
St Laurence's New Hall Greenock

Bishop John Mone blessed a new St Laurence's Hall, Greenock. He and Provost Cathy Allan of Inverclyde District Council, jointly unveiled a commemorative plaque. Replacing what was popularly called the "Boiler House" the new hall was designed by architect John McManus, Lochwinnoch. It gives the parish its first centre since the present church was built 44 years ago. Fr James Byers revealed that a Lottery grant of over £2,000 had been awarded to the parish for the new hall which will cost £50,000. The past was also linked with the present with a portrait being unveiled at the entrance to the hall of Canon Michael Condon who founded the parish in 1855

B.J.C.

Wednesday 30th September 1998
Launch of One Bread, One Body

The first ever joint teaching document, 'One Bread, One Body', produced by the Bishops' Conferences of Scotland, England and Wales and Ireland was launched at simultaneous news conferences in Glasgow, London and Dublin. The new document encourages renewed devotion to the Blessed Sacrament and lays out clear rules governing the admission of non-Catholics to the sacraments. The document is very clear that widespread invitations to non-Catholics to take communion are not permitted. It outlines the strict conditions which must be fulfilled before any non-Catholic may receive the Sacrament: when no minister of the reformed tradition is available, the person demonstrates belief in the Catholic doctrine of the real presence of Christ in the Eucharist, and the person is properly disposed. Cardinal Basil Hume of Westminster said the teaching document was an expression of Catholic faith. "It is written primarily for Catholics, encouraging us to renew and refresh our understanding of Catholic teaching and our reverence for this great mystery of faith."

Wednesday 30th September 1998
40th Anniversary of St. Teresa's, Dumfries

A large congregation, with Bishop Taylor and many of the priests who had served the parish since 1958, commemorated the anniversary with Mass in the beautiful church. The homily was given by Mgr. Francis Duffy, the first parish priest of St. Teresa's, who, to the great amusement of the congregation, recalled the trials and tribulations that led up to the solemn opening of the church and indeed accompanied that memorable occasion. In addition to many other mini-disasters even the bus bringing the musicians and singers from St. Andrew's parish, Dumfries, was involved in an accident en route and, as a result of the delay and police involvement, Mgr. Duffy experienced an understandable panic that he still vividly remembers.

+M.T.

Friday, 2nd October 1998
Linwood Centenary

About thirty priests joined Bishop John Mone and Bishop Stephen McGill in concelebrated Mass of the centenary of the parish of St Conval's, Linwood. In its one hundred years the parish has had 17 parish priests and 17 assistants. Present pastor Canon Brendan Healy had the privilege of consecrating the church as coconsecrator with Bishop Mone.

In his message to the People of God Bishop Mone said: I have a special place in my heart for all of you and always look forward to any visits I make to St Conval's...The young are indeed the Church of both today and the new Millennium... I thank you for the warmth of your welcome... I have felt so much at home and very much one of the family. I love coming among you...The warmth of that community spirit has been the result of a great effort from you the priests and people. You have built on the past and achieved much that is precious to hand on to those who will take over from you. . .Thank you for keeping the faith but don't keep it to yourself— pass it on! That is just about your most important task as we prepare to usher in the Great Jubilee of the year 2000. . . give thanks to God for all the blessings He has bestowed on St Conval's these past hundred years.

B.J.C.

Saturday October 3rd 1998
Centenary of Greyfriars, Elgin

The Sisters of Mercy in Elgin celebrated the centenary of the Convent with a Solemn Mass in the Convent Chapel at which Bishop Conti was the chief celebrant.

At the end of the last century the ruins of the former 15th century Franciscan Friary were acquired by the Fourth Marquess of Bute who set about its restoration. It is a perfect example of a late mediaeval convent and the only one of its kind surviving in Scotland. The barrel-vaulted church contains a magnificent rood screen which is surmounted by a copy of the famous crucifix at San Damiano in Assisi, before which St. Francis received instruction from Christ to rebuild his Church. This rood screen contains two altars, one of which is dedicated to St. Francis and other saints of the Franciscan Order, and the other to Our Lady of Mercy and saints connected with the mediaeval orders devoted to the ransoming of prisoners. The great east window adorning the sanctuary portrays Christ leading a procession of women saints, virgins and martyrs. The Blessed Sacrament is once again reserved in what was the mediaeval Sacrament House on the north wall of the church. A very beautiful cloister surrounds what remains of the mediaeval well, while the Sisters' refectory retains some of the mediaeval ceiling beams and the great fireplace.

When the restoration work was completed the Sisters were invited to move from their convent on adjacent ground to the former friary, and they have continued to live there ever since. Their works of mercy included the staffing of St. Sylvester's school, as well as the establishment of St. Marie's private school, of which the Bishop was himself at one time a pupil. Other former pupils joined friends of the community to celebrate the event, which was also marked by a concert in the nave of the convent chapel the same evening.

Greyfriars became the venue for the Bishop's celebration of the 40th anniversary of his ordination to the priesthood when on Saturday 24th he celebrated Mass with the religious of the diocese, and on Monday 26th October with the clergy of the diocese whom he entertained to lunch thereafter at the Mansefield Hotel. A week later there was a similar gathering with the permanent deacons of the diocese and their wives.

Sunday 4 October 1998
Annual Red Mass in St Mary's Cathedral, Edinburgh

Members of the legal profession were led by Lord Gill as they asked God's blessing on the new legal term.

The homily was preached by Archbishop O'Brien. He held up as an example the recently beatified Blessed Joseph Tovini as an example of faith in action. At his beatification, the Pope had stated that Tovini "had the courage to translate the inspiration of the Gospel into works, initiatives and institutions"; he had accomplished all this at a time when Catholics were being pressured to 'confine their faith within church walls'.

What is called for at this present time, said the Archbishop, is an increase in vocations, not only to the priesthood and the religious life, but to the vocation of being 'lay confessors in the Church'. These are people who, formed by the Gospel and by the teaching and love of Jesus Christ, are ready to confess their faith in their chosen professions and live true to the standards and the example given by Jesus Christ himself.

Monday 5th October 1998
A New Scotland in the New Europe

In a speech at the Brussels headquarters of COMECE - the office of the Bishops Conferences of the European Union, Cardinal Winning spoke of the hopes and challenges confronting Scotland as it rediscovers its national identity within a rapidly changing Europe. In a widely reported address, he said: "Democrats can be reassured that the emerging sense of nationhood and political nationalism in Scotland is unique in European terms. It is mature, respectful of democracy and international in outlook. What we are seeing is the re-birth of ancient nationhood in a cradle of modern democracy. An old-yet-new nation is taking its place once more on the world stage with its legal system, democratic institutions, respect for human rights, educational facilities already in place." He added: "However we decide to govern our land and our continent, what matters in the future is that national borders would be seen as gateways to new sights, sounds and experiences, gateways to treasure troves of culture, of tradition and of faith."

Tuesday 6th October 1998
National Conference of Priests and Deacons in Fort William

The National Conference of Priests and Deacons of Scotland took place in Milton Hotel, Fort William from Tuesday 6 October until Thursday 8 October 1998.

There was a priest representative from each deanery in Scotland - and the Chairperson of the gathering was Father Michael MacDonald, parish priest of St John the Evangelist, Caol.

9th October 1998
Centenary of St. Patrick's, Shieldmuir Church

His Eminence Thomas Cardinal Winning, Archbishop of Glasgow was the principal concelebrant at Mass in his home parish to mark the Centenary of the opening of the Church in 1898.

The Cardinal was joined by Bishop Joseph Devine and his Vicars General together with parish priest Fr Gerard Chromy and priests who were born in the parish or had served there.

The Provost of North Lanarkshire Council, Councillor Vincent Mathieson and local Church leaders were present at the Mass and the reception thereafter in the Church hall.

F.C.

Sunday 11th October 1998
Catholic Deaf Association

On Sunday afternoon, 11 October 1998, along with Father Leo Glancy, the Archdiocesan Chaplain to the Deaf, Archbishop O'Brien celebrated Mass with the Catholic Deaf Association. Following on the Mass, Archbishop O'Brien shared something of the plans of the Catholic Deaf Association for their 'way forward' as we looked to the new millennium. Following on the Mass, the Catholic Deaf Association Choir took part in an annual Choir Festival, with various groups of deaf people presenting music from various parts of the country.

Monday 12th October 1998
Visit to Eastern Asia

As president and treasurer of the Scottish Catholic International Aid Fund Bishop John Mone left for visit to Eastern Asia calling on Vietnam, Cambodia and Laos. On his return his report in the Scottish Catholic Observer, Paisley Daily Express and Greenock Telegraph gives gruesome details of war in such areas, hunger, murder and despair but there is also hope. The hope comes from the generosity of Scottish Catholics through SCIAF giving vast help to those in great need.

B.J.C.

Friday 16th October 1998
10th Anniversary of Archdiocesan Ecumenical Core Group

A Thanksgiving Mass was celebrated in St Catherine's Convent, Edinburgh with Archbishop O'Brien and Father Philip Kerr, Vicar Episcopal for Ecumenism.

The celebration marked the 10th anniversary celebrations of the establishment of the Ecumenical Core Group of the Archdiocese and Bishop Conti, President of the Commission for Christian Doctrine and Unity, preached the sermon, speaking specifically on recent Vatican documentation on Ecumenism and encouraging the members of the Ecumenical Core Group in their endeavours.

Mr Paddy Ferry presented a report on the ten years life of the Ecumenical Core Group established almost at the beginning of Archbishop O'Brien's episcopacy, following on the first Archdiocesan Assembly. Thanks were paid to the initial Resource Team, led by Monsignor Tony McNally and the late Canon Karl Kruger - and to all who had helped over the years, particularly Father Johnny Doherty CSsR.

It is hoped that an Archdiocesan Ecumenical Commission will be established following on the outstanding work of the Archdiocesan Ecumenical Core Group and the priests, religious and people who have helped over the years, particularly the Sisters of St Catherine's Convent, who have been unstinting in their hospitality.

Saturday 24th October 1998
Day for Religious

The various Religious Congregations in the diocese of Galloway gathered today for one of their regular meetings. The invited speakers were David Mackey and Frank Ward who are the Galloway Diocesan Co-ordinators for Marriage and Family Life. Though unlikely to be married or to have families, the religious showed a keen interest in the work that was being done by the two co-ordinators and appreciated the efforts being made by the diocese to help those who are preparing for marriage or are already married and to give support to families.

+M.T.

Sunday 25th October 1998
Bon Secours Glasgow Golden Jubilee

A Mass of Thanksgiving was celebrated at St Helen's Church, Langside, to mark the 50th anniversary of the arrival of the Sisters of Bon Secours in Glasgow. Their arrival from Paris in 1948 coincided with the creation of the National Health Service in Britain, and they founded a nursing home on Mansionhouse Road. In 1960 Bon Secours opened as the first independent hospital in the west of Scotland. Since their foundation in 1824, the Sisters of Bon Secours have lived up to their title of 'good care', offering love and compassion after the example of Christ, the healer of mind and body.

Tuesday 27th October 1998
Renewal in Maybole

The Life in the Spirit seminars are being conducted ecumenically in Maybole at present. This evening Bishop Taylor was invited to be the speaker. The hall was full and an appreciative audience listened to a talk on "New Life"; this was followed by a lively discussion and questions.

+M.T.

30th October 1998
Motherwell Diocese - Civic Reception

North and South Lanarkshire Councils combined to honour the Diocese of Motherwell on the occasion of the Golden Jubilee of its foundation.

The Civic Reception was held in the Civic Centre, Motherwell and the principal guest was Bishop Joseph Devine and his Vicars General who were joined by representatives from all of the parishes in the Diocese.

Provost Vincent Mathieson, North Lanarkshire Council, presided at the dinner in the company of Provost Sam Casserley, South Lanarkshire Council, and Councillors and officials from both Councils.

A presentation of a commemorative plaque was made on behalf of the Councils.

F.C.

Friday 6th November 1998
Centenary of the Daughters of Charity in Dunfermline

A crowded church, with many priests, who had served in Dunfermline and in Fife, gathered in St Margaret's Church, Dunfermline, along with the Daughters of Charity, led by Sister Zoe, the Provincial, to thank God for the work of the Daughters of Charity over the past 100 years in the town and parishes.

From 1888 the Sisters initially engaged in the apostolate of teaching where a sister held the post of headmistress until Sister Mary retired in 1944. Following on the increase in the numbers of Catholic teachers, the apostolate of the Sisters changed - and they engaged in a very important and specific parochial apostolate. In more recent years, they have also engaged in hospital apostolates in the town, particularly in Queen Margaret Hospital, working not only in St Margaret's Parish, but also in the more-recently established parish of Our Lady of Lourdes. In his words of thanks to the Sisters, Archbishop O'Brien stated: "If there has been any hallmark of the Daughters of Charity in this part of our Archdiocese, it has indeed been the hallmark of service - service of God, service of the parish, schools and hospitals and service of individual people. The Sisters have indeed followed in the footsteps of Queen Margaret, Saint, Queen and Patroness of Scotland whose 900th anniversary of her death was recently celebrated".

Thursday 12th November 1998
Reception of the Moderator of the General Assembly at Aberdeen Cathedral

The Very Reverend Alan Main, Professor of practical theology at King's College, University of Aberdeen, and Dean of Christ's College, Moderator of the General Assembly of the Church of Scotland 1998/9 was formally welcomed to St. Mary's Cathedral along with his wife and colleagues by Bishop Mario Conti, a long-standing friend. The Bishop was joined by Abbot Hugh Gilbert, OSB of Pluscarden, and the clergy of the City. Representatives of other Churches took part in the service during which the Moderator delivered an address.

The congregation included formal representatives from each of the parishes of the city who were subsequently entertained along with the Moderator and his party at Bishop's House, 3 Queen's Cross.

Friday 13th November 1998
20th Anniversary of Scottish Marriage Care, Falkirk

A Thanksgiving Mass and celebration of the 20th anniversary of the establishment of Scottish Marriage Care in Falkirk took place on Friday 13 November 1998.

Father Leo Glancy, the present chaplain, preached on the occasion at Mass concelebrated by Archbishop O'Brien and priests who have served in the parish and assisted the work of the centre.

Particular thanks were paid by Father Glancy to one of the founding fathers of the Falkirk Branch, namely Father Karl Kruger, the first parish priest of Christ the King, Grangemouth.

Tuesday 17th November 1998
Visit to Cornton Vale Women's Prison

Along with the chaplains, Father Loreto Tabone and Sister Monica Neilson, Archbishop O'Brien paid a formal visit to Cornton Vale Prison in Stirling. Accompanying him also was Father Brian Gowans, Chaplaincy Adviser to the Scottish Prison Service. As well as meeting the Governor, Mrs Kate Donegan and various officials, the Archbishop met various prisoners, both in their cells and at recreation.

Just over one week later the Governor of the prison, Mrs Donegan, delivered the annual Archdiocesan Social Care Lecture entitled: 'Reality of Women in Prison - a Christian Response?'.

Thursday 19th November 1998

Annual Mass for Galloway Dead Bishop Taylor led priests and people from all over the diocese in the annual celebration of Mass for the deceased of the diocese and, in particular, for those who have departed this life in the last twelve months.

+M.T.

Sunday 22nd November 1998
Bishop Attacks 'Value for Money' Fixation

Bishop Vincent Logan of Dunkeld hit out at what he called society's obsession with 'value for money' and called for a radical change of heart which would bring about a better world. Bishop Logan was speaking at the annual Civic and Academic Mass, the Feast of Christ the King (Sunday 22nd November) in St. Andrew's Cathedral, Dundee. Among the guests were Lord Provost Mervyn Rolfe of Dundee, City Council members and officials, Lord Provost of Perth John Culliven and council representatives, councillors from Angus, Principal Ian Graham-Bryce of Dundee University, Vice Principal James McGoldrick of Abertay University and academic staff from the universities colleges and schools. Bishop Logan said "So often now in our society value equals value for money. I am convinced that our society places far too much emphasis on productivity and physical efficiency. It is also my conviction that a society is civilised in proportion to the protection it affords its weakest members. Personally, I think the weakest of all are children in the womb. Who speaks for them? What protection does our society offer them? And what of our frail elderly? How do we regard them? As valued members of our community, who are given genuine choices? Again, who speaks for them? Then there are the terminally ill and their families who fear proposed legislation may well usher in euthanasia. Who speaks for them? I believe that our society needs to hear again the goods news of Christ the King, whose kingship is based, not on position, privilege or power, but on service, compassion and love".

M.J.M.

Sunday, 22nd November, 1998
Catholic Education Pastoral

The scope and work of Catholic Education today was expressed in pastoral letter by Bishop John Mone of Paisley. He praised the high standards of Catholic schools and all that is employed in the training of youth and the efforts of school boards. The present Catholic education system was set up in the aftermath of the Education Act (Scotland) of 1918

B.J.C.

Monday 23rd. November 1998
Centenary of St. Patrick's Dundee.

Past and present members of the congregation of St. Patrick's Church, Dundee, packed into the church on the evening of Monday 23. November 1998 to celebrate a Thanksgiving Mass to celebrate the parish's centenary. Bishop Logan was principal concelebrant of the Mass, while Cardinal Thomas Winning was the preacher. In his homily, Cardinal Winning, spoke about his affinity with the local community. He said, "Even though I am a visitor here tonight I feel very much part of this community because what unites us is deeper than a friendship or acquaintance or blood tie". He also looked back over the 100 years of St. Patrick's and paid tribute to some of the people who made the church what it is today particularly Canon Luigi Butti who was entrusted with the task of founding the parish in the 1890s. Parish priest of St. Patrick's, Monsignor Hugh McInally, said, "We are delighted the Cardinal agreed to be with us to mark such a milestone in the history of our parish. We have inherited a rich past from our forebears, not only in the fabric of our building, but in the faith which has been handed on to us. Much work has been done in St. Patrick's in recent years to ensure the building is here for future generations. In preparing for our Centenary celebrations, we have looked back to all that has gone before us, but as the Great Jubilee of the year 2000 approaches, it is essential too that we look forward and prepare to leave a spiritual heritage as rich as that we inherited for those who will worship here in the next 100 years". At the end of Mass Mgr. McInally invited all those invited to the celebrations to a reception in the parish hall .

M.J.M.

Friday, 27th November, 1998
Re-opening of St Luke's, Motherwell

Bishop Joseph Devine concelebrated Mass with parish priest Fr Daniel mooney and other priests of the Diocese on the occasion of the official re-opening of St Luke's Church, Motherwell following substantial renovations.

Provost Vincent Mathieson, North Lanarkshire Council attended the Mass and presented the parish with a commemorative plaque.

F.C.

Saturday 28th November 1998
Annual Mass of the Knights of the Holy Sepulchre

The Knights of the Holy Sepulchre gathered for their Annual Mass in the Chapel Royal at Falkland Palace.

Speaking to them, Archbishop O'Brien reminded them of the high standards of service to which the Knights were called, thanking them for their own work as individuals and as a group for the Arab peoples in the Holy Land so many evicted from their ancient homelands.

As well as engaging in practical work, the Archbishop suggested that the Knights engage in the practice of the 'Stations of the Cross' particularly when pilgrimage groups from Scotland were in the Holy Land.

Saturday 28th November 1998
Diocesan Pastoral Council

The Galloway Diocesan Pastoral Council meets each November and May. The subject of this meeting was The role of priest and of lay person in today's Church. Thirty-three parishes were represented, as well as the diocesan religious and youth. Each of the deaneries made a presentation. There was a similarity among them, especially in recognising that there are fewer priests than before and calling for more lay involvement. However there emerged a wide variety of proposals and suggestions; several pleading for radical solutions and for action instead of words.

+M.T.

Saturday 28th November 1998
Auchinleck St. Vincent de Paul Society

The 50th anniversary of the foundation of the Auchinleck Conference of the St. Vincent de Paul Society was celebrated with Mass in Our Lady of Lourdes & St. Patrick's church, followed by a social evening in the parish hall. The Conference had in fact been inaugurated in Birnie Knowe, a village which no longer exists. The present church in Auchinleck was opened in 1964.

+M.T.

Saturday, 28th November 1998
St Andrew's Hall Larkfield

A refurbished St Andrew's Hall, Larkfield, Greenock, was dedicated by Bishop John Mone. The original hall was part of the first St Andrew's Church built by Fr James A O'Neill shortly after the formation of St Andrew's Parish in 1951. Because of restrictions following World War II the church was of a temporary nature and was scarcely able to cope with the growing Catholic population in the then developing Larkfield housing estate. The present St Andrew's Church was built by Mgr Matthew Kinsella and opening in 1968.

B.J.C.

Sunday 29 November 1998
Solemn Dedication and Opening of the New Museum of Scotland

Archbishop O'Brien gathered with other Church Leaders in St Giles Cathedral, Edinburgh for the Solemn Dedication of the new Museum of Scotland. On the following day, he assisted at the opening of the new museum, performed by Her Majesty the Queen on St Andrew's Day.

Tuesday December 1st - Thursday December 17th 1998
Scots Bishop attends the Assembly of the World Council of Churches

Bishop Conti, co-Moderator of the Joint Working Group between the World Council of Churches and the Roman Catholic Church, attended the WCC Assembly in Harare as head of the Catholic delegation of twenty-four members representing the Church world-wide. During the course of the Assembly the Bishop had the privilege of reading the Pope's letter to the gathered Church representatives who received it with sustained applause.

Apart from plenary sessions of the Council there were other meetings, some of them described as padares, an African word describing a market place. One set of padares was led by a Catholic priest, Father Michael McMahon of Scotus College, along with the Reverend Tom McIntyre, Convenor of the Church of Scotland's Committee on Church unity.

At the presentation of the seventh report of the Joint Working Group, detailing the work that had been undertaken by the group since the last Assembly of the World Council of Churches, and proposing the items for a future agenda, the Bishop advised the Assembly of the welcome which the report had already received from the Pontifical Council for the promotion of Christian unity and expressed the hope that it would be received by the Assembly and the agenda adopted. The report was unanimously accepted and the agenda endorsed.

The Bishop chaired a couple of meetings at which the members of the Catholic Delegation presented to a wide audience an assessment of the relations between the Catholic Church and other Churches with special reference to the relationship of the Catholic Church to the World Council of Churches. He also chaired a meeting to which were invited other Catholic participants and observers at the Assembly. These included, as well as lay people, members of the local clergy including a number of African Bishops.

Both the Moderator of the General Assembly of the Church of Scotland and the Archbishop of Canterbury, who were present at the Assembly with their wives, were invited along with Bishop Conti and several members of the delegation to dinner by the Apostolic Nuncio, Archbishop Peter Prabhu.

Thursday 3rd December 1998
Galloway Head Teachers' Mass

The annual Mass for head teachers of the Catholic primary schools in the diocese of Galloway took place this evening in the chapel of the bishop's house. There was a good attendance and, after Mass, the head teachers enjoyed a social evening together.

+M.T.

Friday 4th December 1998
Cardinal's Charity Ball Jackpot

A record sum of £85,000 was raised at the 22nd annual Charity Ball hosted by Cardinal Winning in the Glasgow Thistle Hotel. The beneficiaries of the fundraising evening were the newly renamed St Margaret's Children and Family Care Society, formerly known as St Margaret's Adoption Society. Helping achieve the record figure was a bid of £25,000 for an auction prize of a silver handcrafted crib gifted by the Cardinal.

Tuesday 8th December 1998
Retirement of Fr. Tom Mulligan MHM

Fr. Tom Mulligan is a native of Hamilton and a Mill Hill Father who, after many years of missionary work in Africa, has spent the last few years as chaplain to the Benedictine Priory at Largs. A Mass this evening, attended by Bishop Taylor and a large crowd of priests and lay people, friends of Fr. Mulligan, marked the formal end of Fr. Mulligan's association with the Priory. He is succeeded as chaplain by Canon John J. Crowley, retired parish priest of St. Mary's, Star of the Sea, Largs.

+M.T.

Friday 11th December 1998
The Extending of St. Quivox

St. Quivox church, Prestwick, was opened in 1933 and extended in 1969. However its social facilities have been inadequate so the new extension, comprising hall, ancillary rooms and church access improvements provides a much needed resource for a lively and growing parish community. We congratulate the parish community of St. Quivox on this fine new resource for which they have been saving for many years.

+M.T.

Friday 11th December 1998
Protest to Sudanese Embassy

As President of Justice and Peace Scotland Bishop John Mone joined in a desperate fight to save two priests in Sudan from an agonising death by crucifixion. He asked every Scot to write vehemently a protest to the Sudanise Embassy, London at the barbaric sentence of the two priests— Fr Hilary Boma and Fr Lina Tujana— and eighteen others.

B.J.C.

14th December 1998
New Canons Installed

Bishop Joseph Devine presided at the installation of two new Canons to the Motherwell Cathedral Chapter.

The new Canons welcome Canon Michael McCarthy of St Athanasius, Carluke and Canon Patrick O'Hare of St Thomas, Wishaw.

A crowded Cathedral included parishioners from both parishes.

F.C.

Thursday 17th December 1998
Mgr. Duffy's Diamond Jubilee

To mark Mgr. Duffy's long and outstanding years of service in the priesthood a Mass was celebrated in Our Lady & St. Meddan's, Troon, today, the exact anniversary of his ordination in Rome sixty years ago. Cardinal Winning preached the homily; Bishop Taylor, more than twenty priests and hundreds of people from near and far participated. There were many references to Mgr. Duffy's qualities both human and priestly and to the outstanding success that has always attended his work, whether in Blairs College, in radio and television, in inter-church relations, as parish priest or as vicar general. Mgr. Duffy has graced Galloway diocese, and indeed the Catholic Church in Scotland, for sixty years. May he continue to do so, this man so much admired and loved.

+M.T.

December 1998
Storm Damage

Damage was experienced by several churches in the Motherwell Diocese due to severe storms on Boxing Day 1998. The worst damage was sustained by St Clare's Church, Easterhouse and St Bartholomew's Church, Coatbridge. St Clare's Church was out of use for a full year.

F.C.

Tuesday December 29th 1998
Solemn Mass on the Closure of Fort Augustus Abbey

Bishop Mario Conti of Aberdeen presided at a Mass of Thanksgiving to mark the closure of Fort Augustus Abbey on the feast of St. Thomas à Becket, in the presence of the Abbot President of the English Congregation of the Benedictine Order, Abbot Francis Rossiter, the Prior and community of Fort Augustus, members of the parish, and friends.

In his homily, after briefly sketching the history of the Abbey, the Bishop reminded the congregation that it had fallen to him to consecrate the Abbey Church during his time as Bishop. He described this as "the last act in the drama of the Abbey's making", and added: "I find it painful removing the keystone in this great final liturgy".

The Bishop concluded his address: "For one hundred and twenty years several generations of monks here have daily celebrated the Mass, and sung the round of Offices which make up the pattern of prayer which is the Church's spousal reply to the greatness of God's love uttered in Christ.

For one hundred and twenty years men have sought the paths of holiness in these cloisters, and studied the Gospels, the writings of the Fathers, the lessons of the schoolmen, and the literature of mankind. They have educated those who came to them, and led by word and the example of their lives those who were searching for God. They have lent their help to the pastors in the field and looked after those closest to hand.

How can one adequately describe the benefits which this place has brought to the Church and the community?

Our Mass is a tribute which goes, as every Mass does, beyond a merely human capacity to give thanks.

'And what now? not a loss of vision, surely, but the expression of a deeper hope? rooted in the paschal reality of death and resurrection: 'Unless a grain of wheat falls into the earth and dies, it remains alone; but if it dies, it bears much fruit' (John, 12,24)

'A time to plant and a time to uproot'. It is our prayer that the sower overtake the reaper. As always the harvest is God's."

Within days the few remaining members of the community scattered to their new abodes, whether Abbeys in England or parishes in the Diocese of Aberdeen. The Prior the Very Reverend Dom Francis Davidson, OSB remained thereafter for several months at Fort Augustus, arranging for the disposal of the community's assets, and the transfer of his own accommodation and some church furnishings to the Lodge which has been generously placed at the disposal of the Diocese of Aberdeen by the Lovat Estates as the residence of a priest, and a chapel for the congregation. Several items of historic interest have been donated to the Blairs Museum, and papers deposited at Columba House in the archives of the Catholic Church in Scotland.

Thursday 7th January 1999- Thursday 4th February 1999
Pastoral Visit to four priests on loan to dioceses in
El Salvador and Mexico

Archbishop O'Brien spent four weeks in Central America at the beginning of 1999. There are three priests from the Archdiocese on loan to three different dioceses in El Salvador, namely Father Basil Postlethwaite in the parish of Dulce Nombre de Maria in the Diocese of Chalatenango; Father Tommy Greenan in the parish of La Canoa in the Diocese of Santiago de Maria, Usulutan; and Father Tim McConville in the parish of Christ the King, in the Archdiocese of San Salvador. Father Henry McLaughlin is in the Huixtan parish in the Diocese of San Cristobal de las Casas, Chiapas in Southern Mexico.

Archbishop O'Brien celebrated Masses each day in different communities in the different parishes in which the Edinburgh priests are serving - meeting formally with each of the four bishops and receiving their thanks for the dedicated service of the priests from the Archdiocese of St Andrews and Edinburgh.

Sunday 10th. January 1999.
Blessing of The Site of The New Church of
St. Anne's Carnoustie.

On the afternoon of Sunday 10th. January 1999 Bishop Logan, assisted by Fr. Mark Cassidy parish priest of St. Anne's, Carnoustie, blessed the site of the proposed new Church at Carnoustie. Among those present were Provost Frances Duncan of Angus District Council, members of the Diocesan Fabric and Planning Board, and representatives from Milton Studios, the Glamis based firm of architects who have designed the new building.

M.J.M.

Monday, 11th January 1999
Hurricane Mitch

The pupils and staff of Notre Dame High School, Greenock, presented a cheque to value of £1,500 to Bishop John Mone of Paisley for the victims of Hurricane Mitch. He received the cheque on behalf of SCIAF. The same pupils also provided funds for Imperial Cancer Research.

B.J.C.

Tuesday 12th January 1999
Bishop Taylor and the Ladies' Guild

Bishop Taylor was invited to address the Ladies Guild of Old Cumnock Parish Church. The subject he was given was "Ecumenism - The Way Ahead". There was a lively audience and their interest was shown in the discussion and a series of challenging, though not unfriendly, questions. In the best tradition of Cumnock meetings the evening ended with tea and home baking.

+M.T.

Tuesday 19th January 1999
St. Joseph's Academy, Cumnock Campus

One of the casualties of school rationalisation has been the end of St. Conval's High School, Cumnock. It is now the Cumnock Campus of St. Joseph's Academy (whose other Campus is in Kilmarnock) and the facility has been reduced from six to four years. Today Bishop Taylor visited the Cumnock Campus, meeting the head teacher, management team, staff and pupils and expressing the commitment of the diocese to do all that it could to support the school in its new form.

+M.T.

17th January 1999
City Hall Mass for Cardinal's Golden Jubilee of Priesthood

A great Cardinal. A great Scot and a great friend ... that was how the Papal Ambassador. Archbishop Pablo Puente described Cardinal Winning at the end of a special celebration Mass in the City Halls.

Hundreds of bishops and priests surrounded the Cardinal on the stage of the hall in a moving Mass attended by representatives from the world of national politics, local government and other churches.

The Cardinal used his homily to defend the traditional family. He said: "Currently the family is undergoing a traumatic period, and there can be little doubt that there are well organised and resourced forces at work in our society which are hell-bent - and I use those words advisedly on destroying the Christian family."

The Cardinal also took the opportunity to thank his co-workers, the priests, who, he said, had been role models for him for over half a century.

Saturday 23rd January 1999
Extension to Historic Aberdeen School

St. Peter's is one of the oldest Catholic Schools in Scotland, having been founded about 1832 by the Reverend Charles Gordon better known as Priest Gordon (1772-1855). The original buildings, designed by the distinguished Aberdeen Architect, John Smith, have recently been converted into a home for the mentally frail. Within the last two decades the school has been relocated from its second location in Nelson Street, to a site on King Street within a short distance from St. Machar's Cathedral and the University of Aberdeen. Since its relocation the school has increased in numbers, and it became necessary for the education authorities to provide an annex. This was blessed by Bishop Conti on Saturday 23rd January, when a plaque recording the school's history was unveiled by the retiring Headmistress, Mrs Sally Reid.

A granite statue of Priest Gordon in Mass vestments stands in the forecourt of the school. Sculpted by Alexander Brodie it was paid for by public subscription and originally stood in Constitution Street. The plaster model was a notable feature in the library of Blairs College. A painting from the life of Priest Gordon, by the President of the Scottish Academy and pupil of Raeburn, Sir John Watson Gordon, now hangs in the stairwell of Bishop's House. It was formerly in the Constitution Street School.

Sunday 7th February 1999
Mass and Dedication of Memorial Windows in
Holy Family Church, Dunblane

The dedication of three new stained glass windows in the Church of the Holy Family, Dunblane took place during the celebration of Mass on the afternoon of Sunday 7th February 1999. The ceremony was performed by Bishop Logan, assisted by the parish priest Canon Basil O'Sullivan. The windows were erected as a memorial to the children and their teacher killed on the morning of the 13th March 1996 in the Dunblane School massacre. The theme of the windows is "From darkness into light" re-echoing not only the journey from the darkness of Calvary to the light of the Resurrection, but also the struggle to find an answer to the terrible event that struck those families who lost loved ones on that fateful morning. Addressing those present at the Mass Bishop Logan stated "If we are to find consolation and hope then it is in him, Jesus Christ, the Light of the World. He can lead us through darkness to light. That is our Christian faith. He has already led the children and their teacher who died on the Calvary of 13 March 1996 to the resurrection of life with him in heaven. And we wait to be reunited with them one day. That too is our faith. That faith is expressed beautifully in these memorial windows which will be dedicated today. May they be an inspiration to all who see them. May they renew our faith, increase our hope and deepen our love - through Jesus Christ our Lord, the Light of the World, who has the power to lead us from darkness to light".

M.J.M.

Sunday 7th February 1999
Annual Galloway Lourdes Day

One of the problems of Galloway diocese is its geography; most of the people live in Ayrshire, a minority lives in Dumfries & Galloway and between the two there is a large area of sparsely populated Southern Uplands. The result is that the Dumfries & Galloway section sometimes feels neglected, with diocesan events usually being held in Ayrshire so that the southerners, if they wish to take part, are faced with a long round-trip. Today however, for the first time in many years, the annual Lourdes Day was held in St. Teresa's, Dumfries. The event consisted of the Lourdes Hospitalité Mass (with anointing of the sick) followed by the AGM. The previous year's pilgrimage was reviewed and preparations were put in hand for the next diocesan pilgrimage which will take place in July 2000. St. Teresa's parish community gave a warm and sociable welcome in the usual way to all participants.

+M.T.

Wednesday 10th February 1999
125th. Anniversary Mass, St. Joseph's Dundee.

The Parishioners of St. Joseph's Dundee welcomed Bishop Logan and a number of priests to a Mass of Thanksgiving to mark the 125th Anniversary of the opening of their church. Before the opening of the present church in 1872 the parishioners gathered in what was termed "an old low, ruinous shed, damp and ill ventilated". The church was built at the cost of £5,000 at a time when the weekly wage was around £1. Commenting on the celebrations Mgr. Joseph Creegan V.G., parish priest of St. Joseph's, stated that the parish had been blessed with a rich heritage both in the building itself and in the faith that had been handed down to the parishioners of today. He also stated that while the celebration marked 125 years of the history of the parish it was not only an occasion for looking backwards, but also one for looking forward for the new millennium offering the challenge to parishioners to consider their legacy for future generations. Bishop Logan concelebrated the Mass with parish priest, Mgr. Joseph Creegan V.G., Mgrs Hugh McInally V.G. and Benjamin Donachie, Canon John Connolly (a former assistant priest of the parish), Canon Charles Hendry, Fr. Ian Wilson, Fr. Stephen Mulholland, Fr. Anthony McCarthy, Fr. Kevin Golden and Fr. Michael Milton (both former assistant priests at St. Joseph's.

M.J.M.

February 14th 1999
St Valentine in the Gorbals

TV crews, journalists and photographers from all over Europe descended on the parish of Blessed John Duns Scotus to mark the enshrining of the relics of St Valentine in the atrium of the Church.
In a homily to accompany the ceremony, Fr Peter Hall stressed that St Valentine had little in common with the sickly sweet representations of love to be found on Valentine cards, but was really a heroic witness to Christ who offered his life for the faith.

Sunday 15th February 1999
200th Anniversary of Death of Bishop John Geddes
Commemorated in Aberdeen

On the Sunday following the actual 200th Anniversary of the death of Bishop John Geddes, (11th February 1799) Bishop Conti joined Fr. Andrew Mann in celebrating the 11 am Mass at St. Peter's, Aberdeen. It was in the Chapel House there that Bishop John Geddes died in the arms of his nephew the Reverend Charles Gordon, better known in Aberdeen as "Priest Gordon".
Bishop John Geddes was born in the Enzie in 1735, and trained for the priesthood at the Scots College in Rome. He was in turn Superior at Scalan, while still in his 20s, and Rector of the Royal Scots College at

Madrid, which he transferred to Valladolid. While he was in Spain he was appointed coadjutor to Bishop George Hay. On his return to Scotland in 1781 he took up residence in Edinburgh then the heart of the Scottish Enlightenment, "The Athens of the North". His popularity was a contributing factor to the eventual emancipation of Scots Catholics. He continued to undertake numerous pastoral visitations, the most notable being the 600 mile journey on foot from Glasgow to the Island of Sanday in Orkney. Due to ill health he retired to Aberdeen in 1793 and died six years later in the Chapel House adjacent to St. Peter's, historically the Mother Church of the post-Reformation Catholic community in Aberdeen and the Northeast.

In his sermon to mark the occasion Bishop Conti referred to Bishop Geddes' motto "Ambula Coram Deo" - to walk in the presence of the Lord, adding that both the Bishop's motto and his example remained an inspiration not only to pastors, but to all who journey in faith.

Following the Mass a small group of people accompanied the Bishop and Fr. Andrew Mann on foot to the "Snow Kirkyard" where John Geddes is buried along with his nephews the Reverend John Gordon, and his brother Charles. Adjacent is the tomb of the Menzies of Pitfodels on whose estate the two nephews laboured in turn for the establishment of the Seminary of Blairs.

+M.C.

Sunday 21st February 1999
Galloway Mass of Election

The First Sunday of Lent and therefore the annual Mass for those adults in the diocese preparing for baptism or for entry into full communion in the Catholic Church. Those involved, together with their RCIA teams and their families and friends were welcomed by Bishop Taylor to Good Shepherd Cathedral. After the homily, in which Bishop Taylor stressed particularly the theme for this year, viz. God The Merciful Father, the Rite of Election took place, the candidates inscribed their names in the Book of the Elect and were greeted informally by the bishop before they left the church for the parish hall where they continued, under the guidance of some catechists, their reflection on what they had heard during the Liturgy of the Word. At the end of Mass they were joined by their families and friends for tea/coffee etc. before setting off home.

+M.T.

28th February 1999
Canon Anthony Kilcoyne's 90th Birthday

With the death of Canon John Sheridan in January 1999, Canon Anthony Kilcoyne became the oldest priest in the Diocese of Motherwell and he celebrated his 90th Birthday with a Mass and lunch in St Joseph's Home, Robroyston where he is resident.

Bishop Joseph Devine and priests of the Diocese joined the Canon in celebrating this milestone together with members of the Canon's family from Ireland.

F.C.

Wednesday 3rd March 1999
Installation of Aberdeen Rector

As one of the oldest Universities in Scotland - founded by Papal Bull of Alexander Vl, Aberdeen University maintains the custom of the students electing their Rector. For the first time ever, a woman was chosen, and for the first time since the Reformation a Catholic, in the person of Clarissa Dixon-Wright sometime Barrister, and better known as one of "the two fat ladies" of television fame. In a witty speech in the Mitchell Hall of the University of Aberdeen, the new Rector revealed her credentials to sustained applause.

Saturday 6th March 1999
Pastoral Visit to St James', Innerleithen and St Joseph's, Peebles

Archbishop O'Brien paid a pastoral visit to the parishes of St James', Innerleithen and St Joseph's, Peebles over this weekend.
On Saturday 6 March, the Solemn Dedication of the Church of St Joseph, Peebles took place, with the assistance of Father John Robinson, parish priest, a crowded congregation and with the local ministers as guests.
Archbishop O'Brien outlined something of the history of the parish, as well as reminding the people not to forget all that was owed to parishioners and priests in the past and the apostolate which would be expected of the lay faithful in the years which lay ahead.

March 9th 1999
New Catholic Families Movement formed

Cardinal Winning has announce the formation of a new Catholic Families Movement to offer support to young families trying to bring up children according to the teachings of the Church.
To set the ball rolling Fr Frank Pavone from the USA and Fr John Fleming from the Pontifical Academy for Life spoke to a packed gathering at St Aloysius, Garnethill on the intrinsic link between being pro-life and pro-family.
The new group aims to offer two events a year at which families can come together for education and solidarity.

Saturday 13th March 1999
Visit of Members of Pontifical Council for the Laity to Edinburgh

Monsignor Renato Boccardo, the Secretary of the Youth Section of the Pontifical Council for the Laity in Rome, and one of his advisers, Father Etien, visited the Archdiocese on Saturday 13 March 1999, speaking to a gathering there of the National Commission for the Lay Faithful - Secretariat for Young People. The members of the Secretariat outlined the work which they will accomplish in their various dioceses, as well as nationally - and received a report from Monsignor Boccardo of the preparations being made in Rome for the next World Youth Day to be celebrated in Rome in the Holy Year 2000.

On the next day, Monsignor Boccardo and his party visited some of the youth projects in Edinburgh, particularly spending time in St Teresa's Parish, Craigmillar - before moving on to other dioceses in Scotland.

Saturday 13th March 1999
Homelessness in Scotland

Bishop Conti of Aberdeen was invited to chair a meeting at which representatives of the City of Aberdeen and of the churches and other voluntary agencies came together, under the auspices of Scottish Churches Housing Agency, to address the problem of homelessness. This took place at Beechgrove Church Centre and led to the formation of an ecumenical group to consider ways in which the Churches might give practical help to those in need.

Monday 15th March 1999
Friends of the Scottish Churches Scheme Meeting in Aberdeen

The Trust which exists to promote the opening of churches to the general public, and which advertises those churches which are members of the Scheme in an annual directory, has a general meeting annually in one of the Scottish cities. In 1999 this meeting took place in Aberdeen where Bishop Conti, a member of the Scheme's Board of Trustees, shared in welcoming the visitors. Following a Civic Reception given at the Town House by the Lord Provost, Councillor Mrs Margaret Farquhar, participants were able to visit some of the central churches of the city, including St. Peter's in the Castlegate, and St. Mary's Cathedral.

Tuesday 16th March 1999.
Thanksgiving Mass to Mark The End of
Centenary Year.

Archbishop Keith Patrick O'Brien, Archbishop of St. Andrews & Edinburgh, was the guest of honour at a Thanksgiving Mass on the evening of Tuesday 16th. March 1999 to mark the end of a year of celebrations to mark the centenary of St. Patrick's Dundee. Bishop Logan was principal celebrant of the Mass, which was concelebrated by Mgr. Hugh McInally, V.G. and a number of priests from throughout the diocese.

M.J.M.

Friday 19th March 1999
A Reward for his Labours

Over a great many years Mr. Charlie Brennan, a parishioner of St. Mary's in Irvine, has been a kenspeckle figure in the church and a great help to successive parish priests. This evening, St. Joseph's Day, he had been persuaded reluctantly to purchase a ticket for a St. Patrick's Night Concert in the parish hall which, to his astonishment, turned out to be in his honour. Charlie was the recipient of a number of gifts as well as several pre-funeral eulogies from Canon Sam McGinness, the present parish priest, Canon Tom Murphy, his predecessor, and Bishop Taylor. Charlie himself recovered his composure sufficiently to reply in his usual, not entirely flattering manner.

+M.T.

Sunday 21st March 1999
Opening of Scottish Churches Parliamentary Office

Archbishop O'Brien took part in the dedication of the Scottish Churches Parliamentary Office situated in St Columba's by the Castle, Edinburgh.

Reverend Graham Blount is the Parliamentary Officer for the Churches - and sharing in the Act of Dedication were other Church Leaders.

Mr John Deighan has been appointed as the Parliamentary Officer for the Catholic Church in Scotland, having offices both in Edinburgh and in Glasgow.

25th March 1999
Permanent Diaconate Ordination

Rev Joseph Dowds was ordained to the Permanent Diaconate by Bishop Joseph Devine, Bishop of Motherwell in the Cathedral,

Deacon Dowds was only the second permanent deacon to be ordained for the Diocese. He was appointed to St Mary's Parish, Hamilton.

F.C.

Thursday 25th March 1999
St Stephen's High School Oratory Dedicated

St Stephen's High School Port Glasgow which serves the three parishes of Port Glasgow and elsewhere had its oratory dedicated by Bishop John Mone before a large congregation. The pupils and staff provided most of the building in a very ornate fashion and colourful setting. The Bishop expressed his thanks for what they had achieved and said he was in favour of schools having such an oratory not simply as a place to meet but where the Lord can be found and spoken to in silent prayer and devotion.

B.J.C.

March 28th 1999
Pray for Peace Plea to Parishes

As Europe endures its first Easter at war in 54 years, Cardinal Winning has made an urgent appeal for prayers for peace.

In a Holy Week letter to parishes, the Cardinal urged churchgoers to offer special prayers for peace in the Balkans - and for progress towards peace in Northern Ireland as a stand-off threatens the peace process on the anniversary of the historic Good Friday Agreement.

Besides offering specially composed bidding prayers on Easter Sunday, parishioners will be provided with a prayer for peace, composed by the Cardinal, for use throughout the Easter octave.

The Cardinal's move follows appeals by Pope John Paul for a negotiated settlement in Kosovo with a specific "invitation" to the Yugoslav government to "immediately return to the path of dialogue".

Cardinal Winning said: "It is tragic that we should pass the final Easter of this century of bloodshed with war once more raging on mainland Europe. No-one who remembers the wartime blitz at Clydebank, or any of the other areas hit, can feel anything but intense sympathy for the peoples of Kosovo currently living through a nightmare.

"But I would also ask people to remember the Good Friday agreement in Northern Ireland. Last Easter saw a historic advance made there. I'm asking people to pray that the last few pieces of the jigsaw might be put in place to ensure a peaceful future for all the peoples of Northern Ireland."

Tuesday 30th March 1999
Galloway Chrism Mass

Perhaps the greatest diocesan event of the year is the Chrism Mass. Good Shepherd Cathedral is packed, people come in buses and cars from the farthest ends of the diocese and there is a great sense of community and worship as Mass is celebrated with the participation of the bishop and most of the priests and the sacred oils are blessed for the forthcoming year. In his homily Bishop Taylor spoke of the mercy of God, mediated especially to us through the paschal mystery and urged us to respond to that mercy through repentance and through our own witness of compassion to those in need. The Chrism Mass is always an excellent and impressive doorway into the celebration of the Sacred Triduum.

+M.T.

Thursday, 8th April 1999
Centenary of Venerable Etienne Pernet

Bishop John Mone joined with the Little Sisters of the Assumption for a Mass of thanksgiving for the centenary of the death of their founder, the Venerable Etienne (Stephen) Pernet. The Mass was in St Fergus' Church, Paisley, where the Little Sisters made their foundation in November 1968.

They were founded in France in 1865 to care for families in need and to keep the family together especially if the mother was ill. In the poor parts of Paris there was no social security or healthcare, the Little Sisters flourished. They spread throughout the world into five continents. They arrived in Scotland in 1946 opening a house in Edinburgh. In his first year as Bishop of Paisley, Bishop Stephen McGill invited them to Ferguslie where they remain to this day.

On the first stage to canonisation Father Pernet was declared Venerable by John Paul II.

B.J.C.

12th April 1999
St Andrew's Hospice, Airdrie

Bishop Joseph Devine, priests of the Motherwell Diocese together with representatives of the local Health Board and civic leaders, assembled to mark the completion of an extension to St Andrew's Hospice in Airdrie, The new facilities will cater for expanded out-patient care and has been made possible by the building of a new convent for the Sisters of Charity who had previously been housed in the Hospice.

F.C.

Saturday 17th April 1999
Establishment of Archdiocesan Pastoral Council

With a firm sub-structure of parish pastoral councils and deanery pastoral councils, the inaugural meeting of the Archdiocesan Pastoral Council took place in Gillis Centre on Saturday 17 April 1999.

Archbishop O'Brien opened the gathering with prayer and Mr George McLafferty chaired the gathering.

The meeting established various working parties and will be liaising closely with the newly established Assembly of Priests which was to have its first meeting at the beginning of May 1999.

Saturday 24th April 1999
Day for Religious

The Religious of Galloway gathered in St. Paul's Hall in Ayr, the principal speaker being Sister Kathleen Hogg DC. Sister Kathleen is the director of SPRED for the diocese and has recently succeeded in setting up the first centre, in Queen Margaret Academy, Ayr, with six disabled people and their six friends-catechists. Sister Kathleen spoke of the purpose of SPRED, its motivation and its methods; she asked those present to do what they could to make it better known in the diocese and to encourage people to make as much use of it as possible.

+M.T.

April 25th 1999
Archdiocese Honours Unsung Heroes

The sterling work of more than two hundred parishioners the length and breadth of Glasgow was recognised at the biggest single awards ceremony staged in the Archdiocese.

With thousands of years of devoted service between them, the recipients of the specially commissioned Glasgow Archdiocesan Medal were praised for their work to ensure the ordinary pastoral, spiritual and social life of parishes runs smoothly.

The unprecedented ceremony in St Andrew's Cathedral on Sunday 25 April marked 50 years of the re-establishment of the Province of Glasgow with the creation of the new Dioceses of Motherwell and Paisley.

Such were the number of recipients, that another awards round of awards will be presented at the end of this month.

For Cardinal Winning, who handed out the gongs, the celebration also marked the 25th anniversary of his appointment as Archbishop of Glasgow.

Sunday 25th April 1999
Dedication of St Finnan's Church, Invergarry

Archbishop O'Brien celebrated Mass over the weekend in St Margaret's, Roy Bridge and St Joseph's, Spean Bridge.

On Sunday 25 April at the invitation of the parish priest, Monsignor Thomas Wynne, the Archbishop conducted a solemn dedication of the church of St Finnan in Invergarry. Since its establishment, the Benedictine monks at Fort Augustus Abbey had cared for the people in the area - consequently, it was only fitting that Father Francis Davidson OSB, last Prior of Fort Augustus Abbey, shared in the concelebrated Mass. Shortly before the closure of Fort Augustus Abbey, Monsignor Wynne undertook the pastoral care of the people of Invergarry, initiating a programme of renovation and redecoration of the church. During the celebration, some young parishioners made their First Holy Communion and the solemn liturgy was carried out with great dignity. A social followed in a local hotel.

27th April 1999
School Celebrates Canonisation of
St. Marcellin Champagnat.

Past pupils, parents, members of staff and pupils of St. John's High School, Dundee gathered in the school hall to celebrate a special thanksgiving Mass on Tuesday 27th. April to mark the canonisation of St. Marcellin Champagnat, the founder of the Marist Order. The Principal Concelebrant was Fr. Michael Milton, co-ordinating Chaplain at St. John's. In his homily, Fr. Milton recalled the life of St. Marcellin Charnpagnat, his influence on the charism of the Marist Order, and the influence that the Marist Order had on the development of Catholic education within the City of Dundee. Also concelebrating the Mass were Canon John O'Farrell, Fr. Ian Wilson O.S.A., Fr. Sean Quinlan O.S.A, and Fr. Colin Golden, a former pupil of the School. The Deacon of the Mass was Rev. Tony Cousins.

M.J.M.

Friday 30th April 3rd May 1999
Cursillo in Aberdeen Diocese

Organised by Deacon John Woodside, the first Cursillo meeting took place at Pluscarden and was attended by members of the diocese and those, already members of the movement, who had driven north to join them.

Bishop Conti met the members at St. Scholastica's, and, on his return from a pastoral visit to Caithness, the participants again to hear a report of the success of the weekend which will act as a launch of the Cursillo movement in the diocese, dedicated to the spiritual enrichment of the Sacrament of Marriage.

Sunday, 2nd May 1999
Beatification of Ven Padre Pio

Marking the day of Beatification that day by John Paul II of the Venerable Padre Pio there was a Mass in St Mirin's Cathedral, Paisley offered by Bishop John Mone. There was a large congregation composed of people of various Padre Pio Groups from different parishes.

B.J.C.

May 3rd 1999
Cardinal Appeals for Release of Scots Prisoner

Cardinal Winning has appealed to the Home Secretary to get involved in the case of Scottish teacher Sandra Gregory. She was sentenced to 22 years in prison in Thailand in 1993 after being found carrying drugs. The Cardinal said: "To grant early release on parole, in agreement with the Thai authorities, would not be a sign of weakness. Indeed a liberated Sandra Gregory would probably be an eloquent witness to the inadvisability of becoming involved in the drugs scene."

Sunday 9th May 1999
Galloway Mass for People with Special Needs

Each year in May Galloway diocese has a Mass for people with special needs. This year it took place in St. Paul's, Ayr. Many disabled people along with their families and friends and helpers were present and a number of them were responsible for the readings, the general intercessions and the gifts. During the Mass the first six people who have been trained as friends-catechists were gathered and blessed by Bishop Taylor. He commended their commitment to the work and hoped that in it they would find happiness and fulfilment.

+M.T.

Monday 10th May 1999
Bishop Attends Community Celebrations at Fordyce

The attractive village of Fordyce in Banffshire, once famous for its Academy, marked the Quincentenary of its being made a Burgh of Barony, by obtaining a coat of arms.

Bishop Conti had been invited to join a small group of dignitaries which walked in procession from the former Academy to the open space opposite the former Parish Church, close by the Castle which is a central feature of the village. Apart from the Bishop the group comprised the Chairman of the Community Association, the Lord Lieutenant of

Banffshire, Ross Herald, and the Earls of Caithness and Seafield, whose families had long associations with the Burgh. The inclusion of the Bishop of Aberdeen was prompted by the fact that the original Charter was sought by and awarded to Bishop William Elphinstone, who, as Bishop of Aberdeen, had a residence in the village, which, at the late mediaeval period, was the centre of social and religious activity in the area.

In splendid spring weather, Ross Herald read the Grant of Arms and presented it to the Chairman of the Community Association. The Bishop was asked to say a prayer for the community which he did, prefixing it with a few remarks about the connection of the Burgh with William Elphinstone, Bishop of Aberdeen, and founder of its University. In his prayer, Bishop Conti alluded to the reputation of the village for learning throughout the years, by praying that the present and future generations of villagers would build on the ground of a common faith, and on the values of the Gospel in which they had been schooled for many centuries.

A flag was blessed and hoisted on the flagpost of the castle. The villagers and guests were then treated to a buffet in the school premises.

+M.C.

Tuesday 12th May 1999
Appointment of Lay Curator for the Blairs Museum

The Blairs Museum Trust, with the support of the Bishops as Trustees of John Menzies of Pitfodels, appointed its first full-time professional lay curator in the person of Miss Jacky Miller, until her appointment to the Blairs Museum, Assistant Keeper of Applied Art at Aberdeen Art Gallery and Museums.

There was considerable interest in the post reflecting the high regard which the collection has among museum specialists, and the appointment was made from an excellent short leet. Deacon John Woodside continues as a representative of the Trustees with the title of Keeper.

Thursday 13th May 1999
Bishop Taylor in Prison

Today, Ascension Thursday, Bishop Taylor paid his first visit to the new prison outside Kilmarnock. In fact he was there twice, once to meet the director and his senior staff and to make a tour of the buildings, later he returned to celebrate Mass in the prison chapel, accompanied by Fr. Joseph Boland (the chaplain) and his team. The bishop was happy to discuss with the director the philosophy and methods of this first private prison in Scotland. He was also delighted to have the opportunity of spending time with some of the men and of chatting informally with them.

+M.T.

Saturday 22nd May 1999
850th. Anniversary of the Diocese of Brechin.

At the invitation of Bishop Neville Chamberlain, Bishop of the Episcopal Diocese of Brechin, Bishop Logan was the guest preacher at the celebration to mark the 850th. Anniversary of the foundation of the Diocese of Brechin.

The central event of the day was the celebration of the Eucharist in the grounds of Brechin Castle during which Bishop Logan delivered his homily.

Recalling the historical background to the celebrations Bishop Logan stated that the Church at Brechin was founded during the reign of Kenneth II in the 10th. Century and was dedicated to the Holy Trinity. However archeological clues from the round tower point to an even earlier foundation of a church dedicated to the apostles Peter and Paul during the reign of the Pictish king Nechtan. The distinct Irish influences in the architecture lead historians to believe that a Columban-style monastic settlement was established some 1400 years ago.

Recalling the establishment of the medieval diocese of Brechin by King David of Scotland in 1150 Bishop Logan also recalled the different cultural and economic background of the people ministered to by those who were part of the Diocese of Brechin. He also stated that the Church of today had much to learn for those of past years, especially in the task facing the Christian Churches of today in working together to establish a collaboration which would help to build a Church of communion to tackle the challenges facing Christians as they prepare to enter into a new Millennium.

M.J.M.

Saturday 22nd May 1999
Galloway Diocesan Pastoral Council
on 'The Father of Mercy'

Material on this subject, the Pope's theme for 1999, had previously been sent to each parish with a request for a written response from the parish pastoral council. The responses were compiled and the morning session of today's Diocesan Pastoral Council was devoted to hearing what the parishes had said. These included: better inter-acting with each person we meet; taking the beatitudes as a guide to follow; being willing to give of oneself, being sensitive to others' needs; talking and listening to people; taking the Church to where people are, visiting the lapsed with an invitation; building up communications and trust. Others felt that we should also be talking about such matters as celibacy, homosexuality, ordination of women, contraception, appointments of bishops and priests, decision making and taking. It was evident from the day that we are called to a better understanding of how we ourselves are merciful. Equally important was the realisation that each one of us is in need. The

Church should be seen to be showing mercy especially in the forthcoming Jubilee - to the lapsed, the divorced, the remarried, the priests who have left the active ministry. Bishop Taylor has asked the deans to convene deanery meetings using the DPC findings, and to send a report of the deanery meeting to the Diocesan Pastoral Office.

+M.T.

Sunday 23rd May 1999
Galloway Neophytes Pentecost Mass

The annual cycle of RCIA came to an end on Pentecost Sunday when, at a Mass in Good Shepherd Cathedral, Ayr, Bishop Taylor welcomed all those who had been received into full communion with the Church in their parishes at the Easter Vigil. He thanked them for their courage and generosity and expressed his delight in being able to share their happiness. When he had met them at the Rite of Election, they were still in process of being initiated into membership of the Catholic Church. Now they were full members, gifted for active service. He rejoiced with them and with those who had helped them on their journey of faith and asked them to use their gifts in order to witness to their faith commitment and to extend God's kingdom.

+M.T.

May 23rd 1999
Archdiocese's Accounts in the Black

For the first time in decades the finances of the Archdiocese of Glasgow are in the black.

Newly published figures for the end of 1998 show the Archdiocese with net assets of £36,622 - confirming last year's achievement when the debt burden, which peaked at £9.7m in 1992, was wiped out.

"The new figures afford great satisfaction," a delighted Cardinal Winning said.

"Between February 1993 and May 1998, £4,856,403 was donated by the Catholic community to the special Diocesan Appeal. Without such commitment from the people, the debt eradication would simply not have been possible.

SUNDAY AND HOLY DAY VIGIL AND EVENING MASSES

in the four Cities

(including the adjacent areas forming part of the respective City Districts during their existence from 1975 to 1996)

1. CITY OF EDINBURGH*

A. Sunday Vigil-Masses.

5.00 p.m.— SS. Ninian and Triduana(Restalrig); St. Patrick (Cowgate);
St. Margaret (South Queensferry)**

5.30 p.m.— St. Margaret Mary (Granton).

6.00 p.m.— Cathedral; St. Cuthbert (Slateford); Heriot-Watt UniversityChaplaincy (Riccarton)** (in University Term); St. John the Baptist (Corstorphine); St. Joseph (Balerno) **; St. Mary, Star of the Sea (Leith); St. Philomena (Winchburgh)**; St. Teresa (Craigmillar).

6.15 p.m.— St. Margaret (Davidson's Mains).

6.30 p.m.— St. Catherine (Gracemount); Holy Cross (Trinity): St. John the Evangelist (Portobello); St. John Ogilvie (Wester Hailes); Sacred Heart (Lauriston).

B. Sunday Evening Masses.

4.30 p.m.— St. Patrick (Cowgate).

5.30 p.m.— St. Peter (Morningside).

6.00 p.m.— St. Mark (Oxgangs).

6.30 p.m.— St. Columba (Newington); St. John the Evangelist (Portobello).

7.15 p.m.— St. Albert,the Great (George Square) (in University Term only).

7.30 p.m.— Cathedral.

8.00 p.m.— Sacred Heart (Lauriston).

C. Holy Day Vigil-Masses.

5.45 p.m.— Sacred Heart (Lauriston).

6.00 p.m.— Cathedral; St. Patrick (Cowgate).

7.00 p.m.— St. Margaret (Davidson's Mains); St. Mary (Ratho)**.

7.30 p.m.— St. Catherine (Gracemount); St. Kentigern (Barnton); St. Margaret Mary (Granton); St. Mary, Star of the Sea (Leith); SS. Ninian and Triduana (Restalrig).

*For the exact location of each church, please refer to the main body of this Directory. All are in the pre-1975 County of the Chy of Edinburgh, except those marked (**), which are listed alphabetically under the place-name

D. Holy Day Evening Masses.

5.15 p.m.— St. Albert the Great (George Square).
5.30 p.m.— St. Patrick (Cowgate).
5.45 p.m.— Sacred Heart (Lauriston).
6.00 p.m.— St. Gregory (The Inch).
6.30 p.m.— St. Peter (Morningside).
7.00 p.m.— Holy Cross (Trinity); St. John the Evangelist (Portobello); St. Joseph (Balerno)**; St. Joseph (Sighthill); St. Mary Magdalene (Bingham and Magdalene, Portobello); St. Paul (Muirhouse); St. Teresa (Craigmillar).
7.30 p.m.— Cathedral; St. Andrew (Ravelston), St. Catherine (Gracemount) St. Columba (Newington); St. Cuthbert (Slateford); St. John the Baptist (Corstorphine); St. John Ogilvie (Wester Hailes); St. John Vianney (Gilmerton); St. Margaret Mary (Granton); St. Mark (Oxgangs).

2. CITY OF ABERDEEN

A. Sunday Vigil-Masses.

5.00 p.m.— St. Peter (Castlegate) (in Winter); Dyce Mass Centre.*
6.00 p.m.— St. Peter (Castlegate) (except Winter).
6.30 p.m.— Elphinstone House (Old Aberdeen) (during University Term).
7.00 p.m.— Cathedral

B. Sunday Evening Masses.

5.00 p.m.— Holy Family (Mastrick).
6.00p.m.— Cathedral; St. Francis (Mannofield); St. Joseph (Woodside).
6.30 p.m.— Elphinstone House (Oid Aberdeen) (during University Term).

C. Holy Day Evening Masses.

5.15 p.m.— Elphinstone House (Old Aberdeen) (during University Term).
7.00p.m.— Sacred Heart (Torry).
7.30 p.m.— Cathedral; Holy Family (Mastrick); St. Joseph (Woodside); Our Lady of Aberdeen (Kincorth).
7.45 p.m.— St. Francis (Mannofield).

*For the exacz location of each church, please refer to the main body of the Directory. All are in the pre-1975 County of the City of Aberdeen except Dyce Mass Centre.

3. CITY OF DUNDEE

A. Sunday Vigil-Masses.

5.00 p.m.— St. Vincent de Paul (Kingsway East)*.
6.00 p.m.— St. Bride (Monifieth); St. Cement (Charleston); St.
Columba (Kirkton); Immaculate Conception (Lochee);
St. Leonard and St. Fergus (Ardler); St. Ninian
(Menzieshill); St.Patrick (Stobswell);
SS. Peter and Paul(Coldside); St. Pius X
(Douglas).
6.30 p.m.— Our Lady of Sorrows (Fintry).

B. Sunday Evening Masses.

4.45 p.m.— University Chaplaincy (42 Wilkie's Lane)
(in University Chapel, Cross Row).
6.00 p.m.— St. Leonard and St. Fergus (Ardler).
6.15 p.m.— St. Bride (Monifieth).
6.30 p.m.— St. Francis.
7.00 p.m.— Cathedral.

C. Holy Day Vigil-Masses.

6.30 p.m.— SS. Peter and Paul (Coldside).
7.00 p.m.— St. Leonard and St. Fergus (Ardler); St. Matthew
(Whitfield); St. Patrick (Stobswell); St. Pius X (Douglas);
St. Vincent de Paul (Kingsway East).

D. Holy Day Evening Masses.

4.00 p.m.— St. Bride (Monifieth).
6.00 p.m.— St. Joseph (Wilkie's Lane); Our Lady of Good Counsel
(Broughty Ferry).
6.30 p.m.— St. Francis; St. Matthew (Whitfield); St. Ninian
(Menzieshill); SS. Peter and Paul (Coldside).
7.00 p.m.— Cathedral; St. Bride (Monifieth); St. Clement
(Charleston); St. Columba (Kirkton); St. Leonard and
St. Fergus (Ardler); St. Mary (Forebank); St. Pius X
(Douglas); St. Teresa of Avila; St. Vincent de Paul
(Kingsway East).
7.30 p.m.— Immaculate Conception (Lochee); Our Lady of Sorrows

(Fintry).

*For the exact location of each church, please refer to the main body of this Directory. All are in the
pre-1975 County of the City of Dundee, except St. Bride, Monifieth.

4. CITY OF GLASGOW

A. Sunday Vigil-Masses.

5.00 p.m.—St. Alphonsus (Calton); Sacred Heart (Bridgeton).*

5.15 p.m.—Our Lady of Fatima (Dalmarnock).

5.30 p.m.—All Saints (Barmulloch); St. Anthony (Govan); St. Bernard (South Nitshill); St. Brendan (Yoker); St. Cadoc (Halfway, Cambuslang)**; St. Columbkille (Rutherglen)**; St. Dominic (Craigend)**, St. Helen (Langside); St. James (Crookston); Bl. John Duns Scotus (Gorbals); St. Joseph (Tollcross); St. Mark (Shettleston); St. Michael (Parkhead); Our Lady of the Assumption (Ruchill); Our Lady of Good Counsel (Dennistoun); St. Pius X (Drumchapel).

5.45 p.m.— St. Aloysius (Garnethill).

6.00 p.m.—St. Agnes (Lambhill); St. Aloysius (Springburn); St. Anne (Dennistoun); St. Barnabas (Shettleston); St. Benedict (Drumchapel); St. Benedict (Easterhouse)**; St. Bride (Cambuslang);*, St. Charles (North Kelvinside); St. Clare (Easterhouse)**, St. Columba (Woodside); St. Constantine (Govan); St, Conval (Pollok); Corpus Christi (Scotstounhill); St. Francis (Baillieston)**; St. Gabriel (Merrylee), St. Gregory (Wyndford); Holy Cross (Crosshill); Holy Name (Mansewood); Immaculate Heart of Mary (Balornock); St. John Ogilvie (Easterhouse), St. Jude (Barlanark); St. Laurence (Drumchapel); St. Leo (Dumbreck), St. Margaret Mary (Castlemilk); St. Maria Goretti (Cranhill); St. Martin (Castlemilk); St. Mary (Abercromby Street); St. Mary Immaculate (Pollokshaws); St. Monica (Milton); St. Mungo (Townhead); Our Lady of Perpetual Succour (Broomhill), Our Lady and St. Margaret (Kinning Park); St. Patrick (Anderston); St. Peter (Partick) St. Philomena (Provanmill); St. Robert Bellarmine (Househillwood); St. Roch (Garngad);St. Saviour (Govan); St. Stephen (Sighthill); St. Teresa (Possilpark); St. Vincent de Paul (Thornliebank).

6.15 p.m.—Glasgow University Chaplaincy (October to June).

6.30 p.m.—Cathedral; St. Albert (Pollokshields); St. Anthony (Rutherglen)**; St. Bartholomew (Castlemilk); St. Bernadette (Carntyne); St. Bridget (Baillieston)**; St. Catherine (North Balornock); Christ the King (King's Park); Immaculate Conception (Maryhill); St. Joachim (Carmyle); St. Louise (Deaconsbank); St. Mark (Rutherglen)**; Our Lady of Consolation (Govanhill); Our Lady and St. George (Penilee); St. Paul (Shettleston); St. Paul (Whiteinch); St. Thomas (Riddrie).

7.00 p.m.—St. Augustine (Milton); St. Ninian (Knightswood); Our Lady of Lourdes (Cardonald).

*For the exact location of each church, please refer to the main body of the Directory. All are in the Archdiocese of Glasgow except those marked (**), which are in the Diocese of Motherwell.

B. Sunday Evening Masses.

4.45 p.m.——St. Alphonsus (Calton).

5.00 p.m.—Cathedral; St. Anne (Dennistoun); St. Brigid (Toryglen); St.Columba (Woodside); St. Helen (Langside); St. Mark (Shettleston); St. Mary Immaculate (Pollokshaws); St. Ninian (Knightswood); St. Philomena (Provanmill).

5.15 p.m.—Holy Name (Mansewood).

5.30p.m.—Corpus Christi (Scotstounhill); St. Jude (Barlanark); St. Michael (Parkhead); Our Lady of Good Counsel (Dennistoun); Our Lady and St. George (Penilee); St. Philip (Ruchazie); St. Teresa (Possilpark).

6.00p.m.—St. Albert (Pollokshields); St. Anthony Rutherglen)**; St. Benedict (Drumchapel); St. Brendan (Yoker); St. Bride (Cambuslang)**; St. Bridget (Bailieston)**:St. Charles (North Kelvinside); St. Clare (Easterhouse)**;   St.   Columbkille   (Rutherglen)**;   St. Constantine (Govan); St. Francis (Baillieston)**; St. Gabriel (Merrylee); Immaculate Heart of Mary (Balornock); Bl. John Duns Scotus (Gorbals); St. Joseph (Tollcross); St. Louise (Deaconsbank); St. Margaret Mary (Castlemilk); St. Mary (Abercromby Street);   Our Lady of Lourdes (Cardonald); St. Peter (Partick); St. Robert Bellarmine (Househillwood).

6.15 p.m.—Glasgow University Chaplaincy.

6.30 p.m.—St. Bartholomew (Castlemilk); St. Catherine (North Balornock); Christ the King (King's Park); Immaculate Conception (Maryhill); St. Paul (Shettleston)(Youth Mass); St. Paul (Whiteinch); St. Simon (Partick).

7.00 p.m.—St. Mungo (Townhead); Our Lady of Consolation (Govanhill).

8.00 p.m.—Holy Cross (Crosshill).

9.00 p.m.—St. Aloysius (Garnethill).

C. Holy Day Vigil-Masses.

5.15 p.m.—Cathedral.

5.30 p.m.—St. Alphonsus (Calton); St. Bernard (South Nitshill); St. Helen (Langside); St. Michael (Parkhead).

5.45 p.m.— St. Aloysius (Garnethill).

6.00 p.m.— St. Aloysius (Springburn); Corpus Christi (Scotstounhill);St. Francis (Baillieston)**; Holy Cross (Crosshill); St. Mary (Abercromby Street); St. Mungo (Townhead); St. Ninian (Knightswood); St. Patrick (Anderston); St. Peter (Partick).

6.30 p.m.— St. Bernadette (Carntyne); St. Brigid (Toryglen); Christ the King (King's Park); St. Paul (Whiteinch).

7.00 p.m.— St. Anne (Dennistoun); St. Augustine (Milton); St. Barnabas (Shettleston);St. Benedict (Drumchapel);St. Columbkille (Rutherglen)**;   St. Constantine (Govan);   St. Dominic (Craigend)**, St. Gregory (Wyndford); Immaculate Heart of

Mary (Balornock); St. James (Crookston); St. Joachim (Carmyle); Bl. John Duns Scotus (Gorbals); St. Martin (Castlemilk); St. Monica (Milton); Our Lady of Lourdes (Cardonald); Our Lady of Perpetual Succour (Broomhill); St. Robert Bellarmine (Househillwood); St. Roch (Garngad); St. Saviour (Govan); St. Teresa (Possilpark); St. Thomas (Riddrie).

7.30 p.m.—All Saints (Barmulloch); St. Anthony (Rutherglen)**; St. Bartholomew (Castlemilk); St. Brendan (Yoker); St. Bride (Cambuslang)**; St. Bridget (Baillieston)**; St. Maria Goretti (Cranhill); St. Paul (Shettleston).

D. Holy Day Evening Masses.

5.00 p.m.— St. Bride (Cambuslang)**.

5.05 p.m.— Glasgow University Chaplaincy.

5.10 p.m.— Strathclyde University (Jordanhill College of Education) (in University term only).

5.15 p.m.— Cathedral.

5.30 p.m.— St. Alphonsus (Calton); St. Anthony (Govan); St. Conval (Pollok); St. Michael (Parkhead).

5.45 p.m.— St. Aloysius (Garnethill).

6.00 p.m.—St. Aloysius (Springburn); St. Barnabas (Shettleston); Corpus Christi (Scotstounhill); Holy Cross (Crosshill); St. Mary (Abercromby Street); Our Lady of Good Counsel (Dennistoun); Our Lady of Consolation (Govanhill); St. Peter (Partick); St. Philomena (Provanmill); Sacred Heart (Bridgeton).

6.30 p.m.—St. Brigid (Toryglen); St. Charles (North Kelvinside); Holy Name (Mansewood); St. John Ogilvie (Easterhouse); St. Louise (Deaconsbank); St. Paul (Whiteinch).

7.00 p.m.—St. Agnes (Lambhill); St. Anne (Dennistoun);St. Benedict (Drumchapel), St. Columba (Woodside); St. Columbkille (Rutherglen)**; St. Constantine (Govan); St. Conval (Pollok); St. Francis (Baillieston)**; St. Gregory (Wyndford); Immaculate Heart of Mary (Balornock), St. James (Crookston); Bl. John Duns Scotus (Gorbals); St. Jude (Barlanark); St. Laurence (Drumchapel); St. Leo (Dumbreck); St. Margaret Mary (Castlemilk); St. Mark (Rutherglen)**; St. Mark (Shettleston); St. Mungo (Garthamlock)**; 'St. Mungo (Townhead); St. Ninian (Knightswood); Our Lady of the Assumption (Ruchill), Our Lady of Fatima (Dalmarnock); Our Lady of Lourdes (Cardonald); Our Lady and St. George (Penilee); Our Lady and St. Margaret (Kinning Park); St. Pius X (Drumchapel); St. Robert Bellarmine (Househillwood); St. Roch (Garngad); St. Thomas (Riddrie); St. Vincent de Paul (Thornliebank).

7.15 p.m.— St. Cadoc (Halfway, Cambuslang)**.

7.30 p.m.— St. Albert (Pollokshields); St. Anthony (Rutherglen)**; St. Bartholomew (Castlemilk); St. Benedict (Easterhouse)**; St. Brendan (Yoker); St. Bridget (Baillieston)**; Christ the King (King's Park); St. Clare (Easterhouse)**; St. Helen (Langside); St. Joachim (Carmyle); St. Joseph (Tollcross); St. Maria Goretti (Cranhill); St. Mary Immaculate (Pollokshaws); Our Lady of the Assumption (Ruchill); St. Paul (Shettleston); St. Philip (Ruchazie); St. Simon (Partick).

8.00 p.m.— St. Gabriel (Merrylee).

INDEX TO ADVERTISERS